PEARSON CUSTOM LIBRARY

NUTRITION

ESSENTIALS OF NUTRITION
BIO 112
Oakton Community College
Urbi Ghosh

PEARSON

PEARSON   ISBN 10: 1-256-21126-5
ISBN 13: 978-1-256-21126-6

Table of Contents

The Role of Nutrition in Our Health

The Role of Nutrition in Our Health

CHAPTER OBJECTIVES

After reading this chapter you will be able to:

1. Define the term *nutrition*.
2. Discuss why nutrition is important to health.
3. Identify the six classes of nutrients essential for health.
4. Identify the Dietary Reference Intakes for nutrients.
5. Describe the four steps of the scientific method.
6. List at least four sources of reliable and accurate nutrition information.

M

iguel hadn't expected that college life would make him feel so tired. After classes, he just wanted to go back to his dorm and sleep. Plus, he had been having difficulty concentrating and was worried that his first-semester grades would be far below those he'd achieved in high school. Scott, his roommate, had little sympathy. "It's all that junk food you eat!" he insisted. "Let's go down to the organic market for some real food." Miguel dragged himself to the market with Scott but rested at the juice counter while his roommate went shopping. A middle-aged woman wearing a white lab coat approached him and introduced herself as the market's staff nutritionist. "You're looking a little pale," she said. "Anything wrong?" Miguel explained that he had been feeling tired lately. "I don't doubt it," the woman answered. "I can see from your skin tone that you're anemic. You need to start taking an iron supplement." She took a bottle of pills from a shelf and handed it to him. "This one is the easiest for you to absorb, and it's on special this week. Take it twice a day, and you should start feeling better in a day or two." Miguel purchased the supplement and began taking it that night with the meal his roommate had prepared. He took it twice the next day as well, just as the nutritionist had recommended, but didn't feel any better. After 2 more days, he visited the university health clinic, where a nurse drew some blood for testing. When the results of the blood tests came in, the physician told him that his thyroid gland wasn't making enough of the hormone that he needed to keep his body functioning properly. She prescribed a medication and congratulated Miguel for catching the problem early. "If you had waited," she said, "it would only have gotten worse, and you could have become seriously ill." Miguel asked if he should continue taking his iron supplements. The physician looked puzzled. "Where did you get the idea that you needed iron supplements?"

Like Miguel, you've probably been offered nutrition-related advice from well-meaning friends and self-professed "experts." Perhaps you found the advice helpful, or maybe, as in Miguel's case, it turned out to be all wrong. Where can you go for reliable advice about nutrition? What exactly *is* nutrition, anyway, and why does what we eat have such an influence on our health? In this chapter, we'll begin to answer these questions, and you'll gain a deeper understanding as you work through the rest of this book. Our goal is that, by the time you finish this course, you'll be the expert on your own nutritional needs!

What Is Nutrition?

If you think that the word *nutrition* means pretty much the same thing as *food*, you're right—partially. But the word has a broader meaning, which will gradually become clear as you make your way in this course. Specifically, **nutrition** is the science that studies food and how food nourishes our body and influences our health. It encompasses how we consume, digest, metabolize, and store nutrients and how these nutrients affect our body. Nutrition also involves studying the factors that influence our eating patterns, making recommendations about the amount we should eat of each type of food, attempting to maintain food safety, and addressing issues related to the global food supply. You can think of nutrition, then, as the discipline that encompasses everything about food.

Nutrition is a relatively new scientific discipline. Although food has played a defining role in the lives of humans since the evolution of our species, the importance of nutrition to our health has been formally recognized and studied over only the past 100 years or so. Early research in nutrition focused on making the link between nutrient deficiencies and illness. For instance, the cause of scurvy, which is a vitamin C deficiency, was discovered in the mid-1700s. At that time, however, vitamin C had not been identified—what was known was that some ingredient found in citrus fruits could prevent scurvy. Another example of early discoveries in nutrition is presented in the accompanying Nutrition Myth or Fact? box about a disease called pellagra.

Nutrition research continued to focus on identifying and preventing deficiency diseases through the first half of the 20th century. Then, as the higher standard of living after World War II led to an improvement in the American diet, nutrition research began pursuing a new objective: supporting wellness and preventing and treating **chronic diseases**—that is, diseases that come on slowly and can persist for years, often despite treatment. Chronic diseases of particular interest to nutrition researchers include obesity, heart disease, type 2 diabetes, and various cancers. This new research has raised as many questions as it has answered, and we still have a great deal to learn about the relationship between nutrition and chronic disease.

In the closing decades of the 20th century, an exciting new area of nutrition research began to emerge. Reflecting our growing understanding of genetics, *nutrigenomics* seeks to uncover links between our genes, our environment, and our diet. The Nutrition Debate later in this chapter describes this new field of research in detail.

How Does Nutrition Contribute to Health?

Think about it: if you eat three meals a day, by this time next year, you'll have had more than a thousand chances to influence your body's makeup! As you'll learn in this text, you are what you eat: the substances you take into your body are broken

Brian Chase/Bvdc/Dreamstime

🍎 Nutrition is the science that studies all aspects of food.

nutrition The science that studies food and how food nourishes our body and influences our health.

chronic diseases Diseases that come on slowly and can persist for years, often despite treatment.

NUTRITION MYTH OR FACT?
Is Pellagra an Infectious Disease?

In the first few years of the 20th century, Dr. Joseph Goldberger successfully controlled outbreaks of several fatal infectious diseases, from yellow fever in Louisiana to typhus in Mexico. So it wasn't surprising that, in 1914, the Surgeon General of the United States chose him to tackle another disease, thought to be infectious, that was raging throughout the South. Called *pellagra,* the disease was characterized by a skin rash, diarrhea, and mental impairment. At the time, it afflicted more than 50,000 people each year, and in about 10% of cases it resulted in death.[1]

Goldberger began studying the disease by carefully observing its occurrence in groups of people. He asked, if it is infectious, then why would it strike children in orphanages and prison inmates yet leave their nurses and guards unaffected? Why did it overwhelmingly affect impoverished millworkers and sharecroppers while leaving their affluent (and well-fed) neighbors healthy? Could a dietary deficiency cause pellagra?

To confirm his hunch, he conducted a series of trials in which he fed afflicted orphans and prisoners, who had been consuming a

Lester V. Bergman/Corbis

Pellagra is often characterized by a scaly skin rash.

limited, corn-based diet, a variety of nutrient-rich foods, including meats. They recovered. Moreover, orphans and inmates who did not have pellagra and ate the new diet did not develop the disease. Finally, Goldberger recruited eleven healthy prison inmates, who, in return for a pardon of their sentence, agreed to consume a corn-based diet. After 5 months, six of the eleven developed pellagra.

Still, many skeptics were unable to give up the idea that pellagra was an infectious disease. To prove that pellagra was not spread by germs, Goldberger and his colleagues deliberately injected themselves with and ingested patients' scabs, nasal secretions, and other bodily fluids. He and his team remained healthy.

Although Goldberger could not identify the precise component in the new diet that cured pellagra, he eventually found an inexpensive and widely available substance, brewer's yeast, that when added to the diet prevented or reversed the disease. Shortly after Goldberger's death in 1937, scientists identified the nutrient that is deficient in the diet of pellagra patients: niacin, one of the B-vitamins, which is plentiful in brewer's yeast.[1]

down and reassembled into your brain cells, bones, muscles—all of your tissues and organs. The foods you eat also provide your body with the energy it needs to function properly. In addition, we know that proper nutrition can help us improve our health, prevent certain diseases, achieve and maintain a desirable weight, and maintain our energy and vitality. Let's take a closer look at how nutrition supports health and wellness.

Nutrition Is One of Several Factors Supporting Wellness

Wellness can be defined in many ways. Traditionally considered simply the absence of disease, wellness has been redefined as we have learned more about our body and what it means to live a healthful lifestyle. Wellness is now considered to be a multidimensional process, one that includes physical, emotional, social, occupational, and spiritual health (**Figure 1**). Wellness is not an endpoint in our lives, but is an active process we work on every day.

In this book, we focus on two critical aspects of physical health: nutrition and physical activity. The two are so closely related that you can think of them as two sides of the same coin: our overall state of nutrition is influenced by how much energy we expend doing daily activities, and our level of physical activity has a major impact on how we use the nutrients in our food. We can perform more strenuous activities for longer periods of time when we eat a nutritious diet, whereas an inadequate or excessive food intake can make us lethargic. A poor diet, inadequate or

wellness A multidimensional, lifelong process that includes physical, emotional, social, occupational, and spiritual health.

Wrangel/Dreamstime

Physical health includes nutrition and physical activity

Spiritual health includes spiritual values and beliefs

Emotional health includes positive feelings about oneself and life

Social health includes family, community, and social environment

Occupational health includes meaningful work or vocation

◆ **Figure 1** Many factors contribute to wellness. Primary among these are a nutritious diet and regular physical activity.

excessive physical activity, or a combination of these also can lead to serious health problems. Finally, several studies have suggested that healthful nutrition and regular physical activity can increase feelings of well-being and reduce feelings of anxiety and depression. In other words, wholesome food and physical activity just plain feel good!

A Healthful Diet Can Prevent Some Diseases and Reduce Your Risk for Others

Nutrition appears to play a role—from a direct cause to a mild influence—in the development of many diseases (Figure 2). As we noted earlier, poor nutrition is a direct cause of deficiency diseases, such as scurvy and pellagra. Early nutrition research focused on identifying the missing nutrient behind such diseases and on developing guidelines for nutrient intakes that are high enough to prevent them. Over the years, nutrition scientists successfully lobbied for the fortification of foods with the nutrients of greatest concern. These measures, along with a more abundant and reliable food supply, have almost completely wiped out the majority of nutrient-deficiency diseases in developed countries. However, they are still major problems in many developing nations.

In addition to causing disease directly, poor nutrition can have a more subtle influence on our health. For instance, it can contribute to the development of brittle bones (a disease called *osteoporosis*), as well as to the progression of some forms of cancer. These associations are considered mild; however, poor nutrition is also strongly associated with three chronic diseases—heart disease, stroke, and diabetes—which are among the top ten causes of death in the United States (Figure 3).

It probably won't surprise you to learn that the primary link between poor nutrition and mortality is obesity. That is, obesity is fundamentally a consequence of eating more calories than are expended. At the same time, obesity is a well-

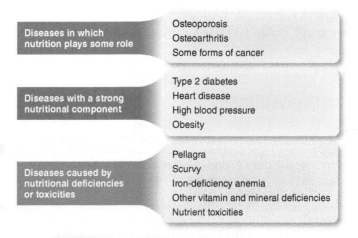

Diseases in which nutrition plays some role	Osteoporosis Osteoarthritis Some forms of cancer
Diseases with a strong nutritional component	Type 2 diabetes Heart disease High blood pressure Obesity
Diseases caused by nutritional deficiencies or toxicities	Pellagra Scurvy Iron-deficiency anemia Other vitamin and mineral deficiencies Nutrient toxicities

◆ **Figure 2** The relationship between nutrition and human disease. Notice that whereas nutritional factors are only marginally implicated in the diseases of the top row, they are strongly linked to the development of the diseases in the middle row and truly causative of those in the bottom row.

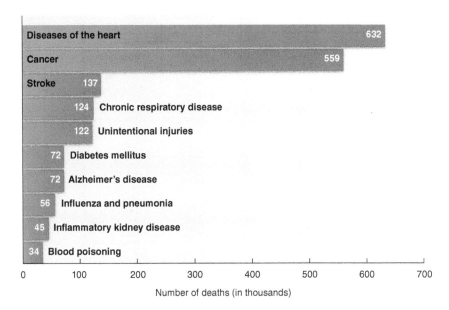

Figure 3 Of the ten leading causes of death in the United States in 2005, three—heart disease, stroke, and diabetes—are strongly associated with poor nutrition. In addition, nutrition plays a more limited role in the development of some forms of cancer.
Data from U.S. Dept. of Health and Human Services, CDC, NCHS, National Vital Statistics Reports, Vol. 57. No. 14, April 17, 2009.

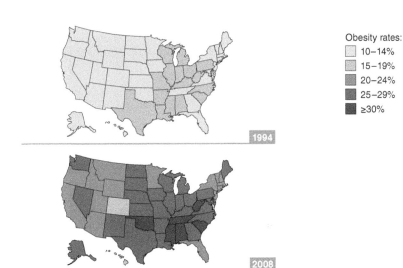

Obesity rates:
- 10–14%
- 15–19%
- 20–24%
- 25–29%
- ≥30%

Figure 4 These diagrams illustrate the increase in obesity rates across the United States from 1994 to 2008 as documented in the Behavioral Risk Factor Surveillance System. Obesity is defined as a body mass index greater than or equal to 30, or approximately 30 lb overweight for a 5'4" woman.
Graphics from Centers for Disease Control and Prevention, U.S. Obesity Trends 1985 to 2008. Available at www.cdc.gov/obesity/data/trends.html#State.

established risk factor for heart disease, stroke, type 2 diabetes, and some forms of cancer. Unfortunately, the prevalence of obesity has dramatically increased throughout the United States during the past 20 years (Figure 4). Throughout this text, we will discuss in detail how nutrition and physical activity affect the development of obesity.

RECAP Nutrition is the science that studies food and how food affects our body and our health. Nutrition is an important component of wellness and is strongly associated with physical activity. One goal of a healthful diet is to prevent nutrient-deficiency diseases, such as scurvy and pellagra; a second goal is to lower the risk for chronic diseases, such as type 2 diabetes and heart disease.

What Are Nutrients?

A glass of milk or a spoonful of peanut butter may seem to be made up of only one substance, but in reality most foods are a combination of many different chemicals. Some of these chemicals are not useful to the body, whereas others are critical to human growth and function. These latter chemicals are referred to as **nutrients.** The following are the six groups of nutrients found in the foods we eat (**Figure 5**):

- carbohydrates
- fats and oils (two types of lipids)
- proteins
- vitamins
- minerals
- water

The term *organic* is commonly used to describe foods that are grown without the use of synthetic pesticides. When scientists describe individual nutrients as **organic,** however, they mean that these nutrients contain both carbon and hydrogen, fundamental units of matter that are common to all living organisms. Carbohydrates, lipids, proteins, and vitamins are organic. Minerals and water are not. Organic and inorganic

nutrients Chemicals found in foods that are critical to human growth and function.

organic A substance or nutrient that contains the elements carbon and hydrogen.

▶ **Figure 5** The six groups of essential nutrients found in the foods we consume.

SIX GROUPS OF ESSENTIAL NUTRIENTS

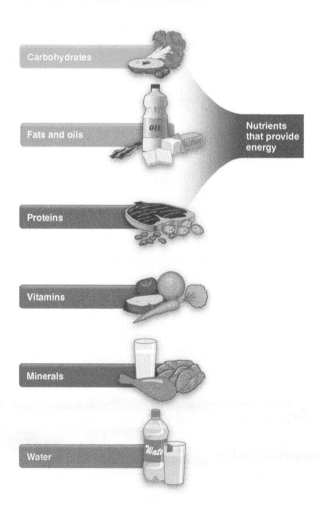

nutrients are equally important for sustaining life but differ in their structures, functions, and basic chemistry.

Alcohol is a chemical commonly consumed in beverages and which may also be added to some foods as a flavoring or preservative. But it is not considered a nutrient because it is not critical for body functioning or the building or repairing of tissues. In fact, alcohol is considered to be both a drug and a toxin. We discuss alcohol *In Depth* later in this chapter.

Macronutrients Provide Energy

Carbohydrates, fats, and proteins are the only nutrients that provide energy. By this we mean that our body breaks down these nutrients and reassemble their components into a fuel that supports physical activity and basic functioning. Although taking a multivitamin might be beneficial in other ways, it will not provide you with the energy for a 20-minute session on the stair-climber! The energy nutrients are also referred to as **macronutrients.** *Macro* means "large," and our body needs relatively large amounts of these nutrients to support normal function and health.

Energy Is Measured in Kilocalories

The energy in foods is measured in units called *kilocalories (kcal)*. A kilocalorie is the amount of heat required to raise the temperature of 1 kilogram (about 2.2 pounds) of water by 1 degree Celsius. We can say that the energy found in 1 gram of carbohydrate is equal to 4 kcal.

You've certainly also seen the term *Calorie*. What's the difference? Well, technically, 1 kilocalorie is equal to 1,000 Calories. *Kilo-* is a prefix used in the metric system to indicate 1,000 (think of *kilometer*). For the sake of simplicity, nutrition labels use the term *Calories* to indicate kilocalories. Thus, if the wrapper on an ice cream bar states that it contains 150 Calories, it actually contains 150 kilocalories.

In this textbook, we use the term *energy* when referring to the general concept of energy intake or energy expenditure. We use the term *kilocalories (kcal)* when discussing units of energy. We use the term *Calories* only when presenting information about foods.

Both carbohydrates and proteins provide 4 kcal per gram, alcohol provides 7 kcal per gram, and fats provide 9 kcal per gram. Thus, for every gram of fat we consume, we obtain more than twice the energy derived from a gram of carbohydrate or protein. Refer to the You Do the Math box on the next page to learn how to calculate the energy contribution of carbohydrates, fats, and proteins in a given food.

Carbohydrates Are a Primary Fuel Source

Carbohydrates are the primary source of fuel for our body, particularly for our brain and during physical exercise **(Figure 6)**. *Carbo-* refers to carbon, and *-hydrate* refers to water. You may remember that water is made up of hydrogen and oxygen. Thus, carbohydrates are composed of chains of carbon, hydrogen, and oxygen.

Carbohydrates encompass a wide variety of foods; rice, wheat, and other grains as well as vegetables are carbohydrates, and fruits contain natural sugars that are

Carbohydrates are the primary source of fuel for our body, particularly for our brain.

macronutrients Nutrients that our body needs in relatively large amounts to support normal function and health. Carbohydrates, fats, and proteins are macronutrients.

carbohydrates The primary fuel source for our body, particularly for our brain and for physical exercise.

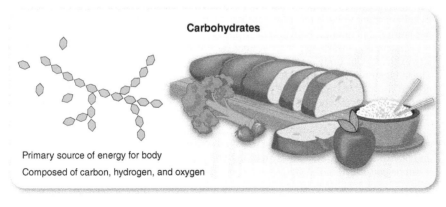

Carbohydrates

Primary source of energy for body

Composed of carbon, hydrogen, and oxygen

◀ **Figure 6** Carbohydrates are a primary source of energy for our body and are found in a wide variety of foods.

YOU DO THE MATH
Calculating the Energy Contribution of Carbohydrates, Fats, and Proteins

The energy in food is used for everything from maintaining normal body functions—such as breathing, digesting food, and repairing damaged tissues and organs—to enabling you to perform physical activity and even to read this text. So how much energy is produced from the foods you eat?

Carbohydrates are the main energy source for your body and should make up the largest percentage of your nutrient intake, about 45–65%; they provide 4 kcal of energy per gram of carbohydrate consumed. Proteins also provide 4 kcal of energy per gram, but they should be limited to no more than 10–35% of your daily energy intake. Fats provide the most energy, 9 kcal per gram. Fats should make up approximately 20–35% of your total energy intake per day. In order to figure out whether you're taking in the appropriate percentages of carbohydrates, fats, and proteins, you will need to use a little math.

1. Let's say you have completed a personal diet analysis, and you consume 2,500 kcal per day. From your diet analysis, you also find that you consume 300 g of carbohydrates, 90 g of fat, and 123 g of protein.

2. To calculate your percentage of total energy that comes from carbohydrate, you must do two things:

   a. Take your total grams of carbohydrate and multiply by the energy value for carbohydrate to give you how many kcal of carbohydrate you have consumed.

   $$300 \text{ g of carbohydrate} \times 4 \text{ kcal/g}$$
   $$= 1,200 \text{ kcal of carbohydrate}$$

   b. Take the number of kcal of carbohydrate you have consumed, divide this number by the total number of kcal you consumed, and multiply by 100. This will give you the percentage of the total energy you consume that comes from carbohydrate.

   $$(1,200 \text{ kcal}/2,500 \text{ kcal}) \times 100 \times = 48\%$$
   $$\text{of total energy comes from carbohydrate}$$

3. To calculate your percentage of total energy that comes from fat, you follow the same steps but incorporate the energy value for fat:

   a. Take your total grams of fat and multiply by the energy value for fat to find the kcal of fat you consumed.

   $$90 \text{ g of fat} \times 9 \text{ kcal/g} = 810 \text{ kcal of fat}$$

   b. Take the number of kcal of fat you have consumed, divide this number by the total number of kcal you consumed, and multiply by 100 to get the percentage of total energy you consume that comes from fat.

   $$(810 \text{ kcal}/2,500 \text{ kcal}) \times 100 = 32.4\%$$
   $$\text{of total energy comes from fat}$$

Now try these steps to calculate the percentage of the total energy you consume that comes from protein.

Also, have you ever heard that alcohol provides "empty calories"? Alcohol contributes 7 kcal per gram. You can calculate the percentage of kcal from alcohol in your daily diet, but remember that it is not considered an energy nutrient.

These calculations will be very useful throughout this course as you learn more about how to design a healthful diet and how to read labels to assist you in meeting your nutritional goals. Later in this book you will learn how to estimate your unique energy needs.

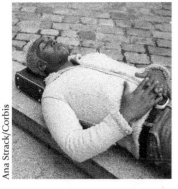

Ana Strack/Corbis

🔺 Fats are an important source of energy for our body, especially when we are at rest.

fats An important energy source for our body at rest and during low-intensity exercise.

carbohydrates. Carbohydrates are also found in legumes (including lentils, dry beans, and peas), milk and other dairy products, seeds, and nuts.

Fats Provide Energy and Other Essential Nutrients

Fats are another important source of energy for our body **(Figure 7)**. They are a type of *lipids*, a diverse group of organic substances that are insoluble in water. Like carbohydrates, fats are composed of carbon, hydrogen, and oxygen; however, they contain proportionally much less oxygen and water than carbohydrates do. This quality allows them to pack together tightly, which explains why they yield more energy per gram than either carbohydrates or proteins.

Fats are an important energy source for our body at rest and during low-intensity exercise. Our body is capable of storing large amounts of fat as adipose tissue. These fat stores can then be broken down for energy during periods when we are not eating—for example, while we are asleep. Foods that contain fats are also essential for the transportation into our body of certain vitamins that are soluble only in fat.

Dietary fats come in a variety of forms. Solid fats include such things as butter, lard, and margarine. Liquid fats, referred to as *oils,* include vegetable oils, such as canola and olive oils. Cholesterol is a form of lipid that our body can make independently, and it can be consumed in the diet.

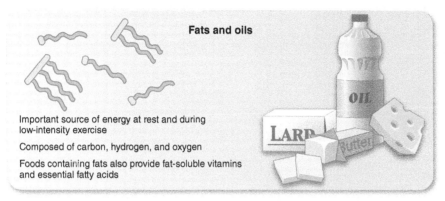

Figure 7 Fats are an important energy source during rest and low-intensity exercise. Foods containing fats also provide other important nutrients.

Proteins Support Tissue Growth, Repair, and Maintenance

Proteins also contain carbon, hydrogen, and oxygen, but they are different from carbohydrates and fats in that they contain the element *nitrogen* (Figure 8). Within proteins, these four elements assemble into small building blocks known as amino acids. We break down dietary proteins into amino acids and reassemble them to build our own body proteins—for instance, the proteins in our muscles and blood.

Although proteins can provide energy, they are not a primary source of energy for our body. Instead, the main role of proteins is in building new cells and tissues. Proteins are also important in regulating the breakdown of foods and our fluid balance.

Proteins are found primarily in meats and dairy products, but seeds, nuts, and legumes are also good sources, and we obtain small amounts from vegetables and whole grains.

Micronutrients Assist in the Regulation of Body Functions

Vitamins and minerals are referred to as **micronutrients.** That's because we need relatively small amounts of these nutrients to support normal health and body functions.

Vitamins are organic compounds that help regulate our body's functions. Contrary to popular belief, vitamins do not contain energy (kilocalories); however, they are essential to energy **metabolism,** the process by which the macronutrients are

proteins The only macronutrient that contains nitrogen; the basic building blocks of proteins are amino acids.

micronutrients Nutrients needed in relatively small amounts to support normal health and body functions. Vitamins and minerals are micronutrients.

vitamins Organic compounds that assist us in regulating our body's processes.

metabolism The process by which large molecules, such as carbohydrates, fats, and proteins, are broken down via chemical reactions into smaller molecules that can be used as fuel, stored, or assembled into new compounds the body needs.

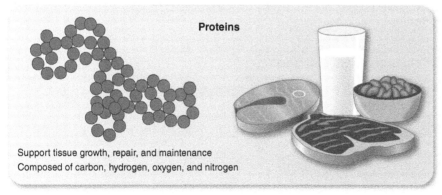

Figure 8 Proteins contain nitrogen in addition to carbon, hydrogen, and oxygen. Proteins support the growth, repair, and maintenance of body tissues.

TABLE 1	Overview of Vitamins	
Type	**Names**	**Distinguishing Features**
Fat-soluble	A, D, E, and K	Soluble in fat
		Stored in the human body
		Toxicity can occur from consuming excess amounts, which accumulate in the body
Water-soluble	C, B-vitamins (thiamin, riboflavin, niacin, vitamin B_6, vitamin B_{12}, pantothenic acid, biotin, and folate)	Soluble in water
		Not stored to any extent in the human body
		Excess excreted in urine
		Toxicity generally only occurs as a result of vitamin supplementation

Fat-soluble vitamins are found in a variety of fat-containing foods, including dairy products.

fat-soluble vitamins Vitamins that are not soluble in water but are soluble in fat. These include vitamins A, D, E, and K.

water-soluble vitamins Vitamins that are soluble in water. These include vitamin C and the B-vitamins.

minerals Inorganic substances that are not broken down during digestion and absorption and are not destroyed by heat or light. Minerals assist in the regulation of many body processes and are classified as major minerals or trace minerals.

major minerals Minerals we need to consume in amounts of at least 100 mg per day and of which the total amount in our body is at least 5 g.

trace minerals Minerals we need to consume in amounts less than 100 mg per day and of which the total amount in our body is less than 5 g.

broken down into the smaller molecules that our body can absorb and use. So vitamins assist with releasing and using the energy in carbohydrates, fats, and proteins. They are also critical in building and maintaining healthy bone, muscle, and blood; supporting our immune system, so that we can fight infection and disease; and ensuring healthy vision.

Vitamins are classified as two types: **fat-soluble vitamins** and **water-soluble vitamins (Table 1)**. This classification affects how vitamins are absorbed, transported, and stored in our body. Both types of vitamins are essential for our health and are found in a variety of foods.

Minerals are inorganic substances because they do not contain carbon and hydrogen. In fact, minerals are not compounds made up of smaller components; instead, they are fundamental units of matter themselves. Some important dietary minerals are sodium, potassium, calcium, magnesium, and iron. Since minerals are already in the most fundamental form possible, they cannot be broken down during digestion or when our body uses them to promote normal function; they are also not destroyed by heat or light. Thus, all minerals maintain their structure, no matter what environment they are in. This means that the calcium in our bones is the same as the calcium in the milk we drink, and the sodium in our cells is the same as the sodium in our table salt.

Minerals have many important functions in our body. They assist in fluid regulation and energy production, are essential to the health of our bones and blood, and help rid our body of the harmful by-products of metabolism.

Minerals are classified according to the amounts we need in our diet and according to how much of the mineral is found in our body. The two categories of minerals in our diet and body are the **major minerals** and the **trace minerals (Table 2)**.

TABLE 2	Overview of Minerals	
Type	**Names**	**Distinguishing Features**
Major minerals	Calcium, phosphorus, sodium, potassium, chloride, magnesium, sulfur	Needed in amounts greater than 100 mg/day in our diets
		Amount present in the human body is greater than 5 g (or 5,000 mg)
Trace minerals	Iron, zinc, copper, manganese, fluoride, chromium, molybdenum, selenium, iodine	Needed in amounts less than 100 mg/day in our diets
		Amount present in the human body is less than 5 g (or 5,000 mg)

Water Supports All Body Functions

Water is an inorganic nutrient (it contains oxygen and hydrogen, but not carbon) that is vital for our survival. We consume water in its pure form; in juices, soups, and other liquids; and in solid foods, such as fruits and vegetables. Adequate water intake ensures the proper balance of fluid both inside and outside our cells, and it assists in the regulation of nerve impulses, muscle contractions, nutrient transport, and the excretion of waste products. Because of the key role that water plays in our health.

RECAP The six essential nutrient groups found in foods are carbohydrates, fats, proteins, vitamins, minerals, and water. Carbohydrates, fats, and proteins are macronutrients. Often referred to as energy nutrients, they provide our body with energy. Carbohydrates and fats are our main energy sources; proteins primarily support tissue growth, repair, and maintenance. Vitamins and minerals are micronutrients. Vitamins are organic compounds that assist in breaking down the macronutrients for energy and in maintaining many other functions. Minerals are inorganic units of matter that play critical roles in virtually all aspects of human health and function. Water is critical for our survival and is important for regulating nervous impulses, muscle contractions, nutrient transport, and the excretion of waste products.

Scott Rothstein/Webking/Dreamstime

⬥ Peanuts are a good source of magnesium and phosphorus, which play important roles in the formation and maintenance of our skeleton.

How Much of Each Nutrient Do Most People Need?

Now that you know what the six classes of nutrients are, you're probably wondering how much of each you need each day. That depends on your gender, your age, your activity level, and many other factors. You'll learn how to plan a healthful diet that's just right for you. To get ready, you need to become familiar with the current standard intake recommendations that apply to most healthy people.

Use the Dietary Reference Intakes to Check Your Nutrient Intake

The United States and Canada share a set of standards defining the recommended intake values for various nutrients. These are called the **Dietary Reference Intakes (DRIs)(Figure 9)**. The DRIs are dietary standards for healthy people only; they do not apply to people with diseases or to those who are suffering from nutrient deficiencies. For each nutrient (such as vitamin C or iron), the DRIs identify the amount

Dietary Reference Intakes (DRIs) A set of nutritional reference values for the United States and Canada that applies to healthy people.

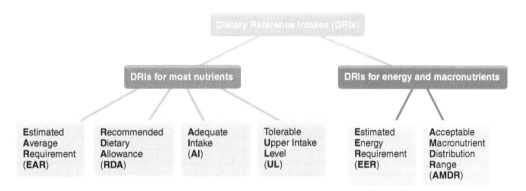

⬥ **Figure 9** The Dietary Reference Intakes (DRIs) for all nutrients. Note that the Estimated Energy Requirement (EER) applies only to energy, and the Acceptable Macronutrient Distribution Range (AMDR) applies only to the macronutrients and alcohol.

needed to prevent deficiency diseases in healthy individuals, as well as the amount that may reduce the risk for chronic diseases in healthy people. The DRIs also establish an upper level of safety for nutrient intake.

The DRIs for most nutrients consist of four values:

- Estimated Average Requirement (EAR)
- Recommended Dietary Allowance (RDA)
- Adequate Intake (AI)
- Tolerable Upper Intake Level (UL)

For total energy and the macronutrients, different standards are used. We'll identify those shortly.

The Estimated Average Requirement Guides the Recommended Dietary Allowance

The **Estimated Average Requirement (EAR)** represents the average daily intake level estimated to meet the requirement of half the healthy individuals in a particular life stage and gender group.[2] Figure 10 is a graph representing this value. As an example, the EAR for phosphorus for women between the ages of 19 and 30 years represents the average daily intake of phosphorus that meets the requirement of half the women in this age group. Scientists use the EAR to define the Recommended Dietary Allowance (RDA) for a given nutrient. Obviously, if the EAR meets the needs of only half the people in a group, then the recommended intake will be higher.

The Recommended Dietary Allowance Meets the Needs of Nearly All Healthy People

The **Recommended Dietary Allowance (RDA)** represents the average daily nutrient intake level that meets the requirements of 97–98% of healthy individuals in a particular life stage and gender group (Figure 11).[2] For example, the RDA for phosphorus is 700 mg per day for women between the ages of 19 and 30 years. This amount of phosphorus will meet the nutrient requirements of almost all women in this age category.

Again, scientists use the EAR to establish the RDA. In fact, if an EAR cannot be determined for a nutrient, then this nutrient cannot have an RDA. When this occurs, an Adequate Intake value is determined for the nutrient.

The Adequate Intake Is Based on Estimates of Nutrient Intakes

The **Adequate Intake (AI)** value is a recommended average daily nutrient intake level assumed to be adequate. It is based on observations or experiments involving healthy

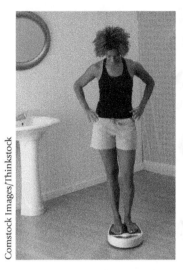

Knowing your daily Estimated Energy Requirement (EER) is a helpful way to maintain a healthy body weight.

Estimated Average Requirement (EAR) The average daily nutrient intake level estimated to meet the requirement of half the healthy individuals in a particular life stage or gender group.

Recommended Dietary Allowance (RDA) The average daily nutrient intake level that meets the nutrient requirements of 97–98% of healthy individuals in a particular life stage and gender group.

Adequate Intake (AI) A recommended average daily nutrient intake level based on observed or experimentally determined estimates of nutrient intake by a group of healthy people.

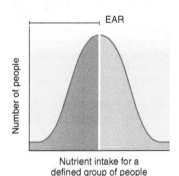

Figure 10 The Estimated Average Requirement (EAR) represents the average daily nutrient intake level that meets the requirements of half the healthy individuals in a given group.

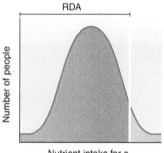

Figure 11 The Recommended Dietary Allowance (RDA) represents the average daily nutrient intake level that meets the requirements of almost all (97–98%) healthy individuals in a given life stage or gender group.

people, and it is used when an RDA cannot be determined.[2] For nutrients having an AI value, including calcium, vitamin D, vitamin K, fluoride, and others, more research needs to be done, so that an EAR, and subsequently an RDA, can be established.

In addition to RDA and AI values for nutrients, an upper level of safety for nutrients, or Tolerable Upper Intake Level, has also been established.

The Tolerable Upper Intake Level Is the Highest Level That Poses No Health Risk

The **Tolerable Upper Intake Level (UL)** is the highest average daily nutrient intake level likely to pose no risk of adverse health effects to almost all individuals in a particular life stage and gender group.[2] This does not mean that we should consume this intake level or that we will receive more benefits from a nutrient by meeting it. Rather, as our intake of a nutrient increases in amounts above the UL, the potential for toxic effects and health problems increases. Use the UL value to help you determine the highest average intake level that is deemed safe to consume.

The Estimated Energy Requirement Is the Intake Predicted to Maintain a Healthy Weight

The **Estimated Energy Requirement (EER)** is defined as the average dietary energy intake that is predicted to maintain energy balance in a healthy adult. The EER can be individualized according to a person's level of activity, age, gender, weight, and height, along with other factors.[3] The EER for an active person is higher than the EER for an inactive person, even if all the other factors (age, gender, and so on) are the same.

The Acceptable Macronutrient Distribution Range Is Associated with Reduced Risk for Chronic Diseases

The **Acceptable Macronutrient Distribution Range (AMDR)** defines a range of macronutrient intakes that provides adequate levels of essential nutrients and is associated with a reduced risk for chronic disease.[3] The AMDR is expressed as a percentage of total energy, or total kilocalories. The AMDR also has a lower and an upper boundary; if we consume nutrients below or above this range, we increase our risk of either a deficiency or chronic disease. The AMDRs for carbohydrate, fat, and protein are listed in Table 3.

Diets Based on the DRIs Promote Wellness

The primary goal of dietary planning is to develop an eating plan that is nutritionally adequate, meaning that the chances of consuming too little or too much of any nutrient are very low. By eating foods that give you nutrient intakes that meet the DRI values, you help your body maintain a healthful weight, support your daily physical activity, prevent nutrient deficiencies and toxicities, and reduce your risk for chronic disease.

Throughout this text, the DRI values are reviewed with each nutrient as it is introduced. They are also listed together in tables on the inside cover and pages at the back of this book. Find your life stage group and gender in the left-hand column; then simply look across to see each nutrient's value for you. Using the DRI values in conjunction with diet-planning tools, such as the USDA Food Guide or the Dietary Guidelines for Americans, will ensure that you have a healthful and adequate diet.

Tolerable Upper Intake Level (UL) The highest average daily nutrient intake level likely to pose no risk of adverse health effects to almost all individuals in a particular life stage and gender group.

Estimated Energy Requirement (EER) The average dietary energy intake that is predicted to maintain energy balance in a healthy adult.

Acceptable Macronutrient Distribution Range (AMDR) The range of macronutrient intakes that provides adequate levels of essential nutrients and is associated with a reduced risk for chronic disease.

TABLE 3	Acceptable Macronutrient Distribution Ranges (AMDRs) for Healthful Diets
Nutrient	**AMDR***
Carbohydrate	45–65%
Fat	20–35%
Protein	10–35%

Data from Institute of Medicine, Food and Nutrition Board. 2005. *Dietary Reference Intakes for Energy Carbohydrates, Fiber, Fat, Fatty Acids, Cholesterol, Protein, and Amino Acids (Macronutrients)*. Washington, DC: National Academies Press. Reprinted by permission.
*AMDR values are expressed as percentages of total energy or as percentage of total calories.

RECAP The Dietary Reference Intakes (DRIs) are nutrient standards established for healthy people in a particular life stage and gender group. The Estimated Average Requirement (EAR) identifies the level of intake that meets the requirements of half the healthy individuals in a group. The Recommended Dietary Allowance (RDA) identifies the intake level that meets the requirements of 97–98% of healthy individuals in a group. The Adequate Intake (AI) is used when there is not enough information to set an RDA. The Tolerable Upper Intake Level (UL) is the highest daily nutrient intake level that likely poses no risk for adverse health effects. The Estimated Energy Requirement (EER) is the average daily energy intake that is predicted to maintain energy balance in a healthy adult. The Acceptable Macronutrient Distribution Range (AMDR) defines ranges of macronutrient intake that provide adequate levels of essential nutrients and are associated with reduced risk for chronic disease.

Research Study Results: Who Can We Believe?

"Eat more carbohydrates! Fats cause obesity!"

"Eat more protein and fat! Carbohydrates cause obesity!"

Do you ever feel overwhelmed by the abundant and often conflicting advice in media reports related to nutrition? If so, you are not alone. In addition to the "high-carb, low-carb" controversy, we've been told that calcium supplements are essential to prevent bone loss and that calcium supplements have no effect on bone loss; that high fluid intake prevents constipation and that high fluid intake has no effect on constipation; that coffee and tea can be harmful and that both can be beneficial! How can you navigate this sea of changing information? What constitutes valid, reliable evidence, and how can you determine whether research findings apply to you?

To become a more informed critic of product claims and nutrition news, you need to understand the research process and how to interpret the results of different types of studies. Let's have a look.

Research Involves Applying the Scientific Method

When confronted with a claim about any aspect of our world, from "The Earth is flat" to "Carbohydrates cause obesity," scientists, including nutritionists, must first consider whether the claim can be tested. In other words, can evidence be presented to substantiate the claim and, if so, what data would qualify as evidence? Scientists worldwide use a standardized method of looking at evidence, called the *scientific method*. This method usually includes the following steps, which are described in more detail below and summarized in **Figure 12**:

- The researcher makes an *observation* and a description of a phenomenon.
- The researcher proposes a *hypothesis*, or an educated guess, to explain why the phenomenon occurs.
- The researcher develops an *experimental design* that will test the hypothesis.
- The researcher *collects and analyzes data* that will either support or reject the hypothesis.
- If the data do not support the original hypothesis, then the researcher proposes and tests an *alternative hypothesis*.
- If the data support the original hypothesis, then the researcher draws a *conclusion*.
- The experiment must be *repeatable*, so that other researchers can obtain similar results.
- Finally, the researcher proposes a *theory* offering a conclusion drawn from repeated experiments that have supported the hypothesis time and time again.

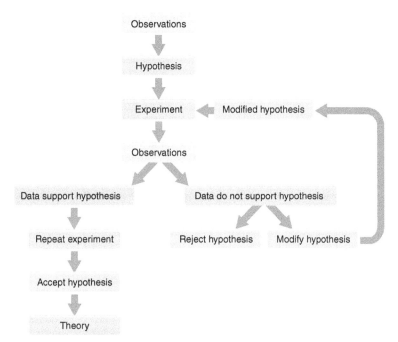

Figure 12 The scientific method, which forms the framework for scientific research. The researcher makes an observation regarding a phenomenon. This leads the researcher to ask a question. A hypothesis is generated to explain the observations. The researcher conducts an experiment to test the hypothesis. Observations are made during the experiment, and data are generated and documented. The data may either support or refute the hypothesis. If the data support the hypothesis, more experiments are conducted to test and confirm support for the hypothesis. A hypothesis that is supported after repeated testing may be called a theory. If the data do not support the hypothesis, the hypothesis is either rejected or modified and then retested.

Observation of a Phenomenon Initiates the Research Process

The first step in the scientific method is to observe and describe a phenomenon. Let's say you are working in a healthcare office that caters to older clients. You have observed that many of them have high blood pressure, but some have normal blood pressure. After talking with a large number of clients, you notice a pattern in that those who report being more physically active are also those with lower blood pressure readings. This observation leads you to question a possible relationship between physical activity and blood pressure. Your next step would be to develop a *hypothesis*, a possible explanation for your observation.

A Hypothesis Is a Possible Explanation for an Observation

A **hypothesis** is sometimes referred to as a research question. In our example, your hypothesis could be "Adults over age 65 with high blood pressure who begin and maintain a program of 45 minutes of aerobic exercise daily will experience a decrease in blood pressure." Your hypothesis must be written so that it can be supported or rejected. In other words, it must be testable.

An Experiment Is Designed to Test the Hypothesis

An *experiment* is a scientific study that is conducted to test a hypothesis. A well-designed experiment should have several key elements:

- The *sample size,* or the number of people being studied, should be adequate to ensure that the results obtained are not due to chance alone. For example, would you be more likely to believe a study that tested 5 people or 500?

hypothesis An educated guess as to why a phenomenon occurs.

- Having a *control group* is essential for comparing treated to untreated individuals. A control group consists of people who are as much like the treated group as possible, except with respect to the *variable* being tested. For instance, in your study, 45 minutes of daily aerobic exercise would be the variable; the experimental group would consist of people over age 65 with high blood pressure who exercise; and the control group would consist of similar people who do not exercise. Using a control group helps a researcher judge whether a particular treatment has worked.
- A good experimental design also attempts to control for other variables that may coincidentally influence the results. For example, what if someone in your study was on a diet, smoked, or took blood pressure–lowering medication? Since any of these factors could affect the results, researchers try to design experiments that have as many *constants* as possible. In doing so, they increase the chance that their results will be valid. To use an old saying, you can think of validity as "comparing apples to apples."

Data Are Collected and Analyzed to Determine Whether They Support or Reject the Hypothesis

As part of the design of the experiment, the researcher must determine what kind of data is to be collected and how they will be collected. For example, in your study the data being collected are blood pressure readings. These values could be collected by people or a machine, but machine measurements would be more reliable and consistent than measurements taken by research assistants.

Once the data have been collected, they must be interpreted or analyzed. Often, the data will begin to make sense only after they have been organized and put into different forms, such as tables or graphs, that reveal patterns that at first were not obvious. In your study, you could create a graph comparing blood pressure readings from both your experimental group and your control group to see if there was a significant difference between the blood pressure readings of those who exercised and those who did not.

Most Hypotheses Need to Be Refined

Remember that a hypothesis is basically a guess as to what causes a particular phenomenon. Rarely do scientists get it right the first time. The original hypothesis is often refined after the initial results are obtained, usually because the answer to the question is not clear and leads to more questions. When this happens, an alternative hypothesis is proposed, a new experiment is designed, and the new hypothesis is tested.

An Experiment Must Be Repeatable

One research study does not prove or disprove a hypothesis. Ideally, multiple experiments are conducted over many years to thoroughly test a hypothesis. Indeed, repeatability is a cornerstone of scientific investigation. Supporters and skeptics alike must be able to replicate an experiment and arrive at similar conclusions, or the hypothesis becomes invalid. Have you ever wondered why the measurements used in scientific textbooks are always in the metric system? The answer is repeatability. Scientists use the metric system because it is universal, thus allowing repeatability in any research facility worldwide.

Unfortunately, media reports on the findings of a research study that has just been published rarely include a thorough review of the other studies conducted on that topic. Thus, you should never accept one report in a newspaper or magazine as absolute fact on any topic.

A Theory May Be Developed Following Extensive Research

theory A conclusion drawn from repeated experiments.

If the results of multiple experiments consistently support a hypothesis, then scientists may advance a **theory.** A theory represents a scientific consensus (agreement) as to why a particular phenomenon occurs. Although theories are based on data drawn from repeated experiments, they can still be challenged and changed as the knowledge within a scientific discipline evolves. For example, at the beginning of this chapter, we said that the prevailing theory held that pellagra was an infectious disease. Many different types of experiments were conducted before their results finally confirmed that the disease is due to niacin deficiency. We continue to apply the scientific method to test hypotheses and challenge theories today.

RECAP The scientific method begins with observation of a phenomenon. The researcher then proposes a hypothesis, and designs and conducts an experiment, collecting and analyzing data that support or refute the hypothesis. If the data are rejected, then an alternative hypothesis is proposed and tested. If the data support the original hypothesis, then a conclusion is drawn. A hypothesis that is supported after repeated experiments may be called a theory.

Various Types of Research Studies Tell Us Different Stories

You have just learned how the scientific method is applied to test a hypothesis. Depending on how the research study is designed, we can gather information that tells us different stories. Let's take a look at the types of research conducted and see what they tell us.

Epidemiological Studies Inform Us of Existing Relationships

Epidemiological studies are also referred to as observational studies. They involve assessing nutritional habits, disease trends, or other health phenomena of large populations and determining the factors that may influence these phenomena. However, these studies can indicate only relationships between factors, not specifically a cause-and-effect relationship. Let's say that an epidemiological study finds that the blood pressure values of physically active older adults are lower than those of inactive older adults. These results do not indicate that regular physical activity reduces blood pressure or that inactivity causes high blood pressure. All these results can tell us is that there is a relationship between higher physical activity and lower blood pressure in older people.

▲ Epidemiological studies indicate relationships between factors, such as between exercise and blood pressure in older adults, but cannot prove cause and effect.

Model Systems

Humans are not very good experimental models because it is difficult to control for all of the variables that affect our lives. Humans also have long life spans, so it would take a long time to determine the results of certain nutritional interventions. For this reason, laboratory studies generally involve experiments with animals. Animals with short reproduction times can be studied when researchers need to look at the effects of specific treatments over many generations. Animal studies also are used to conduct research that is not acceptable to conduct with humans. For instance, it is possible to study nutritional deficiencies in animals by causing a deficiency and studying its adverse health effects over the life span of the animal. In many cases, animal studies provide preliminary information that can assist us in designing and implementing human studies.

One drawback to animal studies is that the results may not apply directly to humans. Another drawback is the ethical implications of these studies, especially when the research reduces the animals' quality of life.

Human Studies

The two primary types of studies conducted with humans are case control studies and clinical trials. *Case control studies* are epidemiological studies done on a smaller scale. They involve comparing a group of individuals with a particular condition (for instance, adults over age 65 with high blood pressure) to a similar group without this condition. This comparison allows the researcher to identify factors other than the defined condition that differ between the two groups. By identifying these factors, researchers can gain a better understanding of things that may cause or help prevent the condition. For instance, in your experiment, you may find that older adults with low blood pressure not only are more physically active but also eat more fruits and vegetables and less sodium.

Clinical trials are tightly controlled experiments in which an intervention is made to determine its effect on a certain condition. Interventions may include medications, nutritional supplements, controlled diets, and exercise programs. The experimental group is given the intervention, but the control group is not. The responses are then compared. In your experiment, you could assign the experimental group to an exercise program and the control group to a program in which no exercise is done. After the intervention phase, you could compare the blood pressures of the people who exercised and those who did not. If the blood pressure of the experimental group decreased and the blood pressure of the control group did not, and if the amount of the decrease was statistically significant, then you could propose that the exercise program caused a decrease in blood pressure.

Among clinical trials, the type considered most likely to produce valid, reliable data is the *double-blind, placebo-controlled study*. In a double-blind study, neither the researchers nor the participants know which group is really getting the treatment. Blinding helps prevent the researchers from seeing only the results they want to see. A *placebo* is an imitation treatment that has no scientifically recognized therapeutic value—for instance, a sugar pill that looks, feels, smells, and tastes identical to the medication being tested. In a double-blind, placebo-controlled study, neither the researchers providing the treatment nor the study participants receiving it know whether the treatment being administered is the one being tested or a placebo.

Another important variable that cannot be overlooked in clinical trials is the effect of participation in the study on the participants' state of mind. This is known as the *psychosomatic effect* or *placebo effect*. Sometimes, just knowing they're in a study causes participants to experience physiologic changes, which they may interpret as therapeutic. For example, the older people in your blood pressure study may subconsciously be more relaxed and content because they feel validated and important. They may therefore show a decrease in blood pressure. Similarly, someone who takes an "herbal supplement," believing that it will help relieve insomnia, may fall asleep more easily because of that belief, even if the pill is actually a placebo.

Use Your Knowledge of Research to Help You Evaluate Media Reports

How can all of this research information assist you in becoming a better consumer and critic of media reports? By having a better understanding of the research process and types of research conducted, you are more capable of discerning the truth or fallacy within media reports. Keep the Quick Tips points shown on the next page in mind when examining any media report.

Throughout this text, we provide you with information to assist you in becoming a more educated consumer regarding nutrition. You will learn about labeling guidelines, the proper use of supplements, and whether various nutrition topics are myths or facts. We'll also test your knowledge at the end of every chapter with a feature called Find the Quack. As you may know, *quackery* is the misrepresentation of a product, program, or service for financial gain. For example, a high-priced supplement may be marketed as uniquely therapeutic, when, in fact, it is only as effective as much less expensive remedies commonly available. Many manufacturers of such products describe them as "patented," but this means only that the product has been registered with the United States Patent Office, for a fee. It provides no guarantee of the product's effectiveness or its safety. After considering the information presented in each Find the Quack feature, you'll have a chance to decide for yourself: Is this a

QUICK TIPS

Detecting Media Hype

✓ Consider the source of the information. Who is reporting it? Is it an article in a newspaper, in a magazine, or on the Internet? Who wrote it? If the report is made by a person or group who may financially benefit from your buying the products, you should be skeptical of the reported results. Also, many people who write for popular magazines and newspapers are not trained in science and are capable of misinterpreting research results.

✓ Find out who conducted the research and who paid for it. Was the study funded by a company that stands to profit from certain results? Are the researchers receiving goods, personal travel funds, speaking fees, or other perks from the research sponsor, or do they have investments in companies or products related to their study? If the answer to these questions is yes, there exists a conflict of interest between the researchers and the funding agency. This conflict of interest may seriously compromise the researchers' ability to conduct unbiased research and report the results in an accurate and responsible manner.

✓ Evaluate the content. Is the report based on reputable research studies? Did the research follow the scientific method, and were the results reported in a reputable scientific journal? Ideally, the journal is peer-reviewed; that is, the articles are critiqued by other specialists working in the same scientific field. A reputable report should include the reference, or source of the information, and should identify researchers by name. This allows the reader to investigate the original study and determine its merit. Some reputable nutrition journals are identified later in this chapter.

✓ Watch for red flags. Is the report based on testimonials about personal experiences? These should make you suspicious, as testimonials are fraught with bias. Are sweeping conclusions made from only one study? Remember that one study cannot answer all of our questions or prove any hypothesis. View the findings from individual studies in their proper perspective. Are the claims made in the report too good to be true? For instance, does the report say the treatment can quickly cure a chronic disease or improve a multitude of conditions? If something sounds too good to be true, it probably is. In short, testimonials, sweeping conclusions, and claims about curing diseases or treating many conditions are red flags that should prompt you to question the validity of the report.

legitimate product or service, or is it quackery? Armed with the information in this book, plus plenty of opportunities to test your knowledge, you will become more confident when trying to evaluate nutrition claims.

RECAP Epidemiological studies involve large populations, model studies involve animals, and human studies include case control studies and clinical trials. Each type of study can be used to gather a different kind of data. When evaluating media reports, consider who is reporting the information, who conducted and paid for the research, whether the research was published in a reputable journal, and whether it involves testimonials or makes claims that sound too good to be true. Quackery is the misrepresentation of a product, program, or service for financial gain.

Kristin Piljay

⬆ To become a more educated consumer and informed critic of nutrition reports in the media, you need to understand the research process and how to interpret study results.

Nutrition Advice: Who Can You Trust?

Earlier in this chapter, you learned that one of the major nutritional concerns in the United States is our high risk for certain chronic diseases. One result of this concern has been the publication of an almost overwhelming quantity of nutritional information on television shows, websites, newspapers, magazines, journals, and many other forums. In addition to this information overload, we continually discover that the nutritional messages from these supposedly "expert" sources are confusing, dissimilar, or even contradictory. On certain issues, even nutrition scientists and physicians cannot seem to agree! If you are wondering how to determine whether an "expert" is trustworthy, the following discussion should help.

Trustworthy Experts Are Educated and Credentialed

The number of health professionals who provide reliable nutrition information is considerable, so it's not possible to identify them all in this chapter. The following are the most important professionals providing reputable nutrition information:

- Registered Dietitian (RD): A registered dietitian is an individual who possesses at least a baccalaureate (bachelor's) degree and has completed a defined content of course work and experience in nutrition and dietetics. This individual has also successfully completed the Registration Exam for Dietitians. For a list of individuals who are registered dietitians in your community, you can look in the yellow pages of your phone book or contact the American Dietetic Association at www.eatright.org.
- Licensed Nutritionist (LN): A licensed nutritionist is an individual who is educated, is trained, and holds a professional license in nutrition. This individual may also be a registered dietitian, but a person can be a licensed nutritionist independent of being an RD. Each state in the United States has its own licensing laws. Individuals who practice nutrition and dietetics without the required license or registration can be prosecuted for breaking the law.
- Nutritionist: This term generally has no definition or laws regulating it. It may refer to anyone who thinks he or she is knowledgeable about nutrition. To make sure the person is a legitimate nutrition professional, ask whether he or she is registered with the American Dietetic Association (ADA). The ADA will certify only those individuals who have at least a bachelor's degree with training in the field of nutrition.
- Professional with an advanced degree (a master's degree [MA or MS] or doctoral degree [PhD]) in nutrition: Many individuals, including many registered dietitians, hold an advanced degree in nutrition. Some teach at community colleges and universities, and others work in fitness and healthcare settings. Professionals with advanced degrees who are not licensed nutritionists or registered dietitians are not certified to provide clinical dietary counseling or treatment for individuals with diseases or illnesses; however, they are still very knowledgeable about nutrition and health.
- Medical Doctor (MD): A medical doctor, also called a physician, is educated, trained, and licensed to practice medicine in the United States. This individual typically has limited experience and training in the area of nutrition. However, if you become ill, the medical doctor is usually one of the first health professionals to see for an accurate medical diagnosis. If you require a dietary plan to treat an illness or a disease, most medical doctors will refer you to an RD or a licensed nutritionist to assist you in meeting your dietary needs.

Remember that, as an educated consumer, it is important to seek out individuals who can provide you with reliable nutrition information. Even highly educated and

 Your medical doctor may have limited experience and training in the area of nutrition but can refer you to a registered dietitian (RD) or licensed nutritionist to assist you in meeting your dietary needs.

HOT
T O P I C
Do You Respond to Spam?

If you have an e-mail account, you're probably familiar with spam ads that promise weight-loss miracles for "only $19.99!" Do you delete them unread? A study from Brooklyn College of the City University of New York found that, in the course of one year, 42% of students with weight problems had opened spam e-mails touting weight-loss products, and almost 19% had placed an order! Lead researchers were shocked by the findings and advised physicians to discuss with patients the potential risks of using weight-loss products marketed via spam e-mails.[4]

credentialed people have limits on their knowledge and can make mistakes. Seeking a second opinion about nutrition information that affects your health is strongly advised.

Government Sources of Information Are Usually Trustworthy

Many government health agencies have come together in the last 20 years to address the growing problem of nutrition-related disease in the United States. These agencies are funded with taxpayer dollars, and many provide financial support for research in the areas of nutrition and health. Thus, these agencies have the resources to organize and disseminate the most recent and reliable information related to nutrition and other areas of health and wellness. A few of the most recognized and respected of these government agencies are discussed here.

The Centers for Disease Control and Prevention Protects the Health and Safety of Americans

The **Centers for Disease Control and Prevention (CDC)** is considered to be the leading federal agency in the United States that protects human health and safety. Located in Atlanta, Georgia, the CDC works to promote health and quality of life by preventing and controlling disease, injury, and disability. To learn more about the CDC follow the link listed in Web Resources at the end of this chapter.

Among its many activities, the CDC supports the following two large national surveys, which provide important nutrition and health information:

- The National Health and Nutrition Examination Survey (NHANES) is conducted by the National Center for Health Statistics and the CDC; it tracks the nutrient consumption of Americans. Nutrition and other health information is gathered during an interview conducted in a person's household and during an examination in a mobile unit. The nutritional data are gathered using a tool called the **24-hour recall** interview, which is a data collection tool that assesses everything a person has consumed over the past 24 hours. The database for the NHANES survey is extremely large, and an abundance of research papers have been generated from it.
- The Behavioral Risk Factor Surveillance System (BRFSS) was established by the CDC. The world's largest telephone survey, it tracks lifestyle behaviors that increase our risk for chronic disease, including a lack of adequate physical activity, a diet that is low in fiber and high in fat, the use of tobacco and alcohol, and a lack of preventive medical care. These behaviors have garnered significant interest because it is estimated that four out of ten deaths (40%) in the United States can be attributed to smoking, alcohol misuse, lack of physical activity, and an unhealthful diet.[5]

The National Institutes of Health Is the Leading Medical Research Agency in the World

The **National Institutes of Health (NIH)** is the world's leading medical research center and the focal point for medical research in the United States. It is part of the U.S. Department of Health and Human Services. The mission of the NIH is to uncover knowledge that leads to better health for everyone. This mission is accomplished by supporting medical research throughout the world and by fostering the communication of medical information. The NIH has many institutes and centers, which focus on a broad array of nutrition-related health issues. The following are some of these institutes:

- National Cancer Institute (NCI)
- National Heart, Lung, and Blood Institute (NHLBI)
- National Institute of Diabetes and Digestive and Kidney Diseases (NIDDK)
- National Center for Complementary and Alternative Medicine (NCCAM)

NIH headquarters are located in Bethesda, Maryland. To find out more about the NIH follow the link listed in Web Resources at the end of this chapter.

Michael Donne/Photo Researchers

▲ Lifestyle behaviors, such as eating an unhealthful diet, can increase your risk for chronic disease.

Centers for Disease Control and Prevention (CDC) The leading federal agency in the United States that protects the health and safety of people. Its mission is to promote health and quality of life by preventing and controlling disease, injury, and disability.

24-hour recall A data collection tool that assesses everything a person has consumed over the past 24 hours.

National Institutes of Health (NIH) The world's leading medical research center and the focal point for medical research in the United States.

Professional Organizations Provide Reliable Nutrition Information

A number of professional organizations publish cutting-edge nutrition research studies and educational information in journals that are accessible in most university and medical libraries. These organizations include the following:

- American Dietetic Association (ADA): This is the largest organization of food and nutrition professionals in the United States. The mission of this organization is to promote nutrition, health, and well-being. The ADA publishes a professional journal, called the *Journal of the American Dietetic Association*.
- American Society for Nutrition (ASN): The ASN is a research society whose goal is to improve quality of life through the science of nutrition. The ASN publishes a professional journal, called the *American Journal of Clinical Nutrition*.
- Society for Nutrition Education (SNE): The SNE is dedicated to promoting healthy, sustainable food choices in communities through nutrition research and education. The primary goals of the SNE are to educate individuals, communities, and professionals about nutrition education and to influence policy makers about nutrition, food, and health. The professional journal of the SNE is the *Journal of Nutrition Education and Behavior*.
- American College of Sports Medicine (ACSM): The ACSM is the leading sports medicine and exercise science organization in the world. Many members are nutrition professionals who combine their nutrition and exercise expertise to promote health and athletic performance. *Medicine and Science in Sports and Exercise* is the professional journal of the ACSM.

Information about all these groups can be found in the links listed in Web Resources at the end of this chapter.

RECAP The Centers for Disease Control and Prevention is the leading federal agency in the United States that protects the health and safety of people. The CDC supports two large national surveys, which provide important nutrition and health information: the National Health and Nutrition Examination Survey (NHANES) and the Behavioral Risk Factor Surveillance System (BRFSS). The National Institutes of Health is the leading medical research agency in the world. The American Dietetic Association, the American Society for Clinical Nutrition, the Society for Nutrition Education, and the American College of Sports Medicine are examples of professional organizations that provide reliable nutrition information.

NUTRI-CASE LIZ

"Am I ever sorry I caught the news last night right before going to bed! They reported on this study that had just come out, saying that ballet dancers are at some super-abnormally high risk for fractures! I couldn't sleep, thinking about it, and then today in dance class every move I made I was freaking out about breaking my ankle! I can't go on being afraid like this!"

What information should Liz find out about the fracture study to evaluate its merits? Identify *at least two factors* she should evaluate. Let's say that her investigation of these factors leads her to conclude that the study is trustworthy: what else should she bear in mind about the research process that might help her take a more healthy perspective when thinking about this single study?

Rubberball/Getty Images

Nutrition DEBATE

Nutrigenomics: Personalized Nutrition or Pie in the Sky?

Agouti mice are normally yellow, obese, and prone to cancer and diabetes. When agouti mice breed, these traits are passed on to their offspring. Look at the picture of the agouti mice on this page; do you see a difference? The mouse on the right is obviously brown and of normal weight, but what you can't see is that it did not inherit its parents' susceptibility to disease. What caused this dramatic difference?

In 2000, researchers found that, when they changed the mother's diet just before conception, they could "turn off" the agouti gene, and any offspring born to that mother would appear normal.[6] As you might know, a *gene* is a segment of DNA, a substance in cells that is responsible for passing on traits from parents to offspring. The diet that the researchers fed the mother was high in a chemical that attached to the agouti gene and disabled it.[6] This study was one of the first to link a change in diet to a genetic modification, and it led to the emerging science of *nutrigenomics*.

What Is Nutrigenomics

Nutrigenomics is a scientific discipline studying the interactions between genes, the environment, and nutrition.[7,8] A key theory behind nutrigenomics is that our genes may respond to factors in our diet.

Nutrigenomics proposes that foods can act as a switch in body cells, turning on some genes and turning off others. When a gene is activated, it instructs the cell to create a protein that will show up as a characteristic or an ability, such as yellow fur or a tendency to store fat. When a gene is switched off, the cell will not create that protein, and the organism's form or function will differ. In addition, scientists are discovering that diet can affect gene expression not only in the exposed organism but also in his or her offspring.[6–8] It's an intriguing

Randy Jirtle

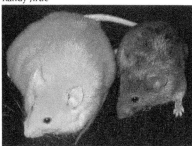

With only a change in diet, inbred agouti mice (left) gave birth to young mice (right) that differed not only in their appearance but also in their susceptibility to disease.

theory—but is there any evidence to support it?

Evidence for Nutrigenomics

Several observations support the theory. For example, nutrition researchers have long noted that some people will lose weight on a specific diet and exercise program, whereas others following the same program will not.[8,9] The varying results are now thought to depend to a certain extent on how the foods in that diet affect the study participants' genes. Evidence from population studies also supports nutrigenomics. For example, when different ethnic groups are exposed to a Western diet, the percentage of type 2 diabetes increases in some populations significantly more than in others.[7]

Evidence of nutrigenomics' influencing future generations includes the breakthrough study of agouti mice, as well as data that suggest a link between the availability of food and diabetes. Researchers have found that, when one generation experiences a food surplus during critical periods of reproductive development, their offspring are more likely to develop diabetes.[6]

Promises and Challenges of Nutrigenomics

One promise of nutrigenomics is that it can help people improve their health

through diet alone.[8] For example, some researchers are studying how leafy green vegetables may turn on an important gene that suppresses cancerous tumors.[10]

Another promise of nutrigenomics is personalized nutrition. In the world of nutrigenomics, you would provide a tissue sample for genetic analysis. Then, your healthcare provider would tailor a diet to your genetic makeup. This "personalized diet" would identify foods you should eat and foods you should avoid in order to turn on beneficial genes and turn off genes that may be detrimental.

One challenge in making nutrigenomic therapies a reality is determining what foods turn on or off specific genes in specific people. Genetic pathways are extremely complicated, and turning on a gene may have a beneficial effect on one body function but a harmful effect on another. Individual factors, such as age, gender, and lifestyle, also may affect how different foods interact with these different genes. Even emotional and social factors may play a role.[11] In addition, dietary intervention to prevent or treat chronic diseases would be challenging because multiple genes may be involved: for instance, scientists have determined that hundreds of genes are linked to type 2 diabetes.

Even by themselves, food interactions are extremely complicated because, in any one meal, we consume hundreds of compounds. Think about all the ingredients in just one food item, such as pancakes. Each one of these ingredients may directly or indirectly affect the expression of many different genes in many different ways.[11] Which of the ingredients consumed affect what gene and how? It will be years before researchers are capable of mapping out these complex interactions.

Chapter Review

Test Yourself ANSWERS

1. False. Calories are a measure of the energy in foods, not their fat content exclusively. More precisely, a kilocalorie is the amount of heat required to raise the temperature of 1 kilogram of water by 1 degree Celsius.

2. True. Carbohydrates and fats are the primary energy sources for our body.

3. True. The RDA does meet the needs of almost all healthy people of a given age and gender.

Find the Quack

Since she was a little girl, LaVeeta has imagined her wedding day with the same essential detail: walking down the aisle in her mother's wedding dress. Now her wedding is just 6 months away and, to fit into that dress, she'll need to lose a whole dress size. It's not surprising, then, that when she sees a weight-loss booth at a bridal show, LaVeeta stops in. A slender young woman introduces herself as Amy and listens closely as LaVeeta explains why she simply must lose 30 pounds in the next 6 months. Amy smiles reassuringly: "You've come to the right place! Your goal of losing 30 pounds in 6 months is closer than you ever imagined with Mini Mix, my patented minimizer-formula weight-loss powder. Mixed with 8 ounces of skim milk, it's a complete low-calorie breakfast, and it curbs your appetite for the rest of the day! It's full of vitamins and minerals, so you won't need to worry when you just don't feel like eating anything else all day—Mini Mix meets your nutritional needs for up to 24 hours!"

LaVeeta notices the price on the stack of cans of the powder: $49 for a can that says it's "a 30-day supply." She quickly calculates: $300 seems like a lot of money for 6 months' worth of powdered vitamins. How can she tell whether the product is legit? While she is trying to decide, another customer approaches the booth, and Amy begins to chat with her. LaVeeta uses the opportunity to look around the booth. She notices on the wall a framed certificate. Beneath Amy's name is the title Certified Nutrition Consultant, and beneath that is the name of a professional-sounding association of "Nutrition Consultants." LaVeeta then picks up a can of Mini Mix. On the label, she reads the following:

- Consumed as recommended with 8 ounces of skim milk, Mini Mix provides 100% of the recommended intake of 1 day's micronutrient needs for just 150 calories.

- One scoop of Mini Mix powder also contains a precise blend of natural appetite suppressants from around the world, including willow bark from Germany and guarana from Brazil. Mini Mix also contains all-natural vanilla or chocolate flavoring.

- Drinking one Mini Mix shake per day will curb your appetite for the rest of the day. Because you won't feel hungry, you won't be tempted to overeat. You'll lose weight quickly and keep it off for life!

1. The certificate on the wall of the Mini Mix booth states that Amy is a certified nutrition consultant. Does this mean that Amy has graduated from an educational institution with a degree in nutrition? If not, what does it mean?

2. The Mini Mix label says that the product "provides 100% of the recommended intake of 1 day's micronutrient needs for just 150 calories." Amy claims, "It's full of vitamins and minerals, so you won't need to worry when you just don't feel like eating anything else all day—Mini Mix meets your nutritional needs for up to 24 hours!" Are these claims essentially identical? Could they be true? Why or why not?

3. Mini Mix contains "willow bark from Germany and guarana from Brazil." Look up these plants on a reputable online encyclopedia, such as *Britannica*. What substances do they contain?

4. Mini Mix costs $49 for a 30-day supply. Should LaVeeta purchase a can? Why or why not?

Answers can be found on the companion website at www.pearsonhighered.com/thompsonmanore.

Review Questions

1. Vitamins A and C, thiamin, calcium, and magnesium are considered
   a. water-soluble vitamins.
   b. fat-soluble vitamins.
   c. energy nutrients.
   d. micronutrients.

2. The world's leading medical research center is the
   a. Centers for Disease Control and Prevention.
   b. National Institutes of Health.
   c. American Medical Association.
   d. National Health and Nutrition Examination Survey.

3. Ten grams of fat
   a. contain 40 kcal of energy.
   b. constitute the Dietary Reference Intake for an average adult male.
   c. contain 90 kcal of energy.
   d. constitute the Tolerable Upper Intake Level for an average adult male.

4. Which of the following statements about hypotheses is true?
   a. Hypotheses can be proven by clinical trials.
   b. "Many inactive people have high blood pressure" is an example of a hypothesis.
   c. If the results of multiple experiments consistently support a hypothesis, it is confirmed as fact.
   d. "A high-protein diet increases the risk for porous bones" is an example of a hypothesis.

5. Which of the following foods contains all six nutrient groups?
   a. strawberry ice cream
   b. an egg-salad sandwich
   c. creamy tomato soup
   d. all of the above

6. True or false? Fat-soluble vitamins provide energy.

7. True or false? The Recommended Dietary Allowance represents the average daily intake level that meets the requirements of almost all healthy individuals in a given life stage and gender group.

8. True or false? Nutrition significantly affects a person's risk for heart disease.

9. True or false? Nutrition-related reports in the *American Journal of Clinical Nutrition* are usually trustworthy.

10. True or false? Carbohydrates, fats, and proteins all contain carbon, hydrogen, and oxygen.

Answers to Review Questions can be found at the back of this text, and additional essay questions and answers are located on the companion website, at www.pearsonhighered.com/thompsonmanore.

Web Resources

www.eatright.org
American Dietetic Association (ADA)

Obtain a list of registered dietitians in your community from the largest organization of food and nutrition professionals in the United States.

www.cdc.gov
Centers for Disease Control and Prevention (CDC)

Visit this site for additional information about the leading federal agency in the United States that protects the health and safety of people.

www.cdc.gov/nchs
National Center for Health Statistics

Go to this site to learn more about the National Health and Nutrition Examination Survey (also referred to as NHANES) and other national health surveys.

www.nih.gov
National Institutes of Health (NIH)

Find out more about the National Institutes of Health, an agency under the U.S. Department of Health and Human Services.

www.nutrition.org
The American Society for Nutrition (ASN)

Learn more about the American Society for Nutrition and its goal to improve quality of life through the science of nutrition.

www.sne.org
Society for Nutrition Education (SNE)

Go to this site for further information about the Society for Nutritional Education and its goals to educate individuals, communities, and professionals about nutrition education and influence policy makers about nutrition, food, and health.

www.acsm.org
American College of Sports Medicine (ACSM)

Obtain information about the leading sports medicine and exercise science organization in the world.

References

1. Kraut, A. Dr. Joseph Goldberger & the War on Pellagra. National Institutes of Health, Office of NIH History. Available at http://www.history.nih.gov/exhibits/goldberger and H. Markel. 2003. The New Yorker who changed the diet of the South. *New York Times* 12 August, 2003:D5.

2. Institute of Medicine, Food and Nutrition Board. 2003. *Dietary Reference Intakes: Applications in Dietary Planning.* Washington, DC: National Academies Press.

3. Institute of Medicine, Food and Nutrition Board. 2002. *Dietary Reference Intakes for Energy, Carbohydrates, Fiber, Fat, Protein and Amino Acids (Macronutrients).* Washington, DC: National Academies Press.

4. Fogel, J., and SBS Shlivko. 2010. Weight Problems and Spam E-mail for Weight Loss Products. *Southern Medical Journal.* January 2010. Vol. 103. Issue 1. pp. 31–36.

5. U.S. Department of Health and Human Services. Centers for Disease Control and Prevention. 2009. Health Risks in the United States. Behavioral Risk Factor Surveillance System: At a Glance, 2009. Available at http://www.cdc.gov/chronicdisease/resources/publications/AAG/brfss.htm.

6. Watters, E. 2006. DNA is not destiny. *Discover* 27(11):32–75.

7. The NCMHD Center of Excellence for Nutritional Genomics. Retrieved April 2007, from http://nutrigenomics.ucdavis.edu.

8. Johnson, N., and J. Kaput. 2003. Nutrigenomics: an emerging scientific discipline. *Food Technology* 57(4):60–67.

9. Grierson, B. 2003. What your genes want you to eat. *New York Times,* May 4.

10. Wallace, K. 2007. Diet, exercise may lower colon cancer risk [television broadcast]. CBS News, March 15.

11. Kaput, J., and R. Rodriguez. 2004. Nutritional genomics: the next frontier in the postgenomic era. *Physiological Genomics* 16:166–177.

Answers to Review Questions

Answers to Review Questions 11-15 (essay questions) for this chapter are located on the Companion Website at **www.pearsonhighered.com/thompsonmanore**

1. **d.** micronutrients.
2. **b.** National Institutes of Health.
3. **c.** contain 90 kcal of energy.
4. **d.** "A high-protein diet increases the risk for porous bones" is an example of a hypothesis.
5. **d.** all of the above
6. False. Vitamins do not provide any energy, although many vitamins are critical to the metabolic processes that assist us in generating energy from carbohydrates, fats, and proteins.
7. True.
8. True.
9. True.
10. True.

Designing a Healthful Diet

From Chapter 2 of *Nutrition: An Applied Approach*, Third Edition. Janice Thompson, Melinda Manore. Copyright © 2012 by Pearson Education, Inc. Published by Pearson Benjamin Cummings. All rights reserved.

Designing a Healthful Diet

After reading this chapter you will be able to:

1. Identify the characteristics of a healthful diet.

2. Name five components that must be included on food labels and use the Nutrition Facts Panel to determine the nutritional adequacy of a given food.

3. Describe the Dietary Guidelines for Americans and discuss how these Guidelines can be used to design a healthful diet.

4. Identify the food groups, number of servings, and serving sizes included in MyPyramid.

5. Explain how MyPyramid can be used to design a healthful ethnic diet.

6. List at least four ways to practice moderation and apply healthful dietary guidelines when eating out.

Dan Kenyon/Taxi/Getty Images

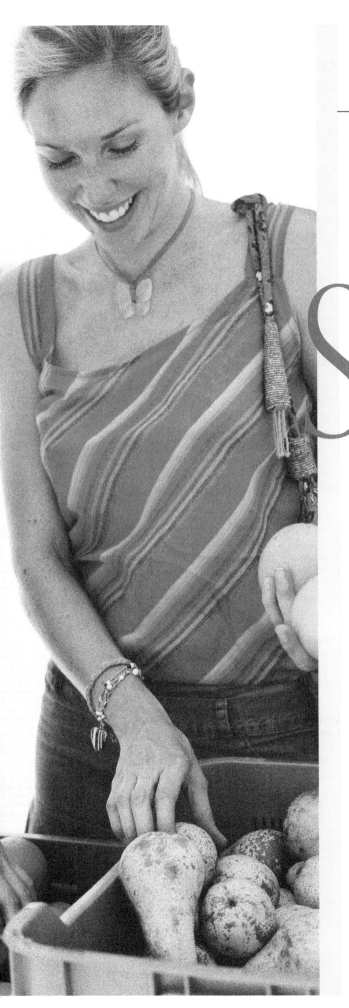

S hivani and her parents moved to the United States from India when she was 6 years old. Although she was delicate in comparison to her American peers, Shivani was healthy and energetic, excelling in school and riding her new bike in her suburban neighborhood. By the time Shivani entered high school, her weight had caught up to that of her American classmates. Now a college freshman, she has joined the more than 16% of U.S. teens who are overweight.[1] Shivani explains, "In India, the diet is mostly rice, lentils, and vegetables. Many people are vegetarians, and many others eat meat only once or twice a week, and very small portions. Desserts are only for special occasions. When we moved to America, I wanted to eat like all the other kids: hamburgers, french fries, sodas, and sweets. I gained a lot of weight on that diet, and now my doctor says my cholesterol level, my blood pressure, and my blood sugar level are all too high. I wish I could start eating like my relatives back in India again, but they don't serve rice and lentils at the dorm cafeteria."

What influence does diet have on health? What exactly qualifies as a "poor diet," and what makes a diet healthful? Is it more important to watch how much we eat or what kinds of foods we choose? Is low-carb better, or low-fat? What do the national Dietary Guidelines advise, and do they apply to real people (like you)?

The truth is, there's no one way to eat that's right for everyone. We're individuals with unique preferences, needs, and cultural influences. You may love broccoli, whereas your roommate can't stand it. A person with diabetes may need to eat less added sugar and more protein than a person without diabetes.

A healthful diet can help prevent disease.

People following certain religious practices may avoid specific meats and dairy products. Thus, there are literally millions of ways to design a healthful diet to fit individual needs.

Given all this potential confusion, it's a good thing there are nutritional tools to guide us in designing our own healthful diet. In this chapter, we'll discover these tools, including the Dietary Guidelines for Americans, the USDA Food Guide, and others. Before we explore the question of how to design a healthful diet, however, we should first make sure we understand what a healthful diet *is*.

What Is a Healthful Diet?

A **healthful diet** provides the proper combination of energy and nutrients. It has four characteristics: it is adequate, moderate, balanced, and varied. No matter if you are young or old, overweight or underweight, healthy or ill, if you keep these characteristics in mind, you will be able to select foods that provide you with the optimal combination of nutrients and energy each day.

A Healthful Diet Is Adequate

An **adequate diet** provides enough of the energy, nutrients, and fiber to maintain a person's health. A diet may be inadequate in only one area, or many areas. For example, many people in the United States do not eat enough vegetables and therefore are not consuming enough of the fiber and micronutrients vegetables provide. However, their intake of protein, fat, and carbohydrate may be adequate. In fact, some people who eat too few vegetables are overweight or obese, which means that they are eating a diet that, although inadequate in one area, exceeds their energy needs. On the other hand, a generalized state of undernutrition can occur if an individual's diet contains an inadequate level of several nutrients for a long period of time.

A diet that is adequate for one person may not be adequate for another. For example, the energy needs of a small woman who is lightly active are approximately 1,700 to 2,000 kilocalories (kcal) each day, whereas a highly active male athlete may require more than 4,000 kcal each day to support his body's demands. These two individuals differ greatly in their activity level and in their quantity of body fat and muscle mass, which means they require very different levels of fat, carbohydrate, protein, and other nutrients to support their daily needs.

healthful diet A diet that provides the proper combination of energy and nutrients and is adequate, moderate, balanced, and varied.

adequate diet A diet that provides enough of the energy, nutrients, and fiber needed to maintain a person's health.

moderation Eating any foods in moderate amounts—not too much and not too little.

A diet that is adequate for one person may not be adequate for another. A woman who is lightly active may require fewer kilocalories of energy per day than a highly active male.

A Healthful Diet Is Moderate

Moderation is one of the keys to a healthful diet. **Moderation** refers to eating any foods in moderate amounts—not too much and not too little. If we eat too much or too little of certain foods, we cannot reach our health goals. For example, some people drink as much as 60 fluid ounces (three 20-oz bottles) of soft drinks on some days. Drinking this much contributes an extra 765 kcal of energy to a person's diet. In order to allow for these extra kcal and avoid weight gain, most people would need to reduce their food intake significantly. This could mean eliminating many healthful food choices. In contrast, people who drink mostly water or other beverages that contain little or no energy can consume more nourishing foods that will support their wellness.

A Healthful Diet Is Balanced

A **balanced diet** contains the combinations of foods that provide the proper proportions of nutrients. As you will learn in this course, the body needs many types of foods in varying amounts to maintain health. For example, fruits and vegetables are excellent sources of fiber, vitamin C, potassium, and magnesium. In contrast, meats are not good sources of fiber and these nutrients. However, meats are excellent sources of protein, iron, zinc, and copper. By eating the proper balance of all healthful foods, including fruits, vegetables, and meats or meat substitutes, we can be confident that we're consuming the balanced nutrition we need to maintain health.

A Healthful Diet Is Varied

Variety refers to eating many different foods from the different food groups on a regular basis. With thousands of healthful foods to choose from, trying new foods is a fun and easy way to vary your diet. Eat a new vegetable each week or substitute one food for another, such as raw spinach on your turkey sandwich in place of iceberg lettuce. Selecting a variety of foods increases the likelihood that you will consume the multitude of nutrients your body needs. As an added benefit, eating a varied diet prevents boredom and helps you avoid the potential of getting into a "food rut." Later in this chapter, we'll provide suggestions for eating a varied diet.

RECAP A healthful diet provides adequate nutrients and energy, and it includes sweets, fats, and salty foods in moderate amounts only. A healthful diet includes an appropriate balance of nutrients and a wide variety of foods.

iStockphoto

⬆ The serving size on a nutrition label may not be the same as the amount you eat.

What Tools Can Help Me Design a Healthful Diet?

Many people feel it is impossible to eat a healthful diet. They may mistakenly believe that the foods they would need to eat are too expensive or not available to them, or they may feel too busy to do the necessary planning, shopping, and cooking. Some people rely on dietary supplements to get enough nutrients instead of focusing on eating a variety of foods. But is it really that difficult to eat healthfully?

Although designing and maintaining a healthful diet is not as simple as eating whatever you want, most of us can improve our diets with a little practice and a little help. Let's look at some tools for designing a healthful diet.

Food Labels

To design and maintain a healthful diet, it's important to read and understand food labels. It may surprise you to learn that, prior to the 1970s, there were no federal regulations for including nutrition information on food labels. The U.S. Food and Drug Administration (FDA) first established such regulations in 1973. Throughout the 1970s and 1980s, consumer interest in food quality grew substantially, leading the U.S. Congress to pass the Nutrition Labeling and Education Act in 1990. This act specifies which foods require a food label, provides detailed descriptions of the information that must be included on the label, and describes the companies and food products that are exempt from publishing complete nutrition information on food labels. For example, detailed food labels are not required for meat or poultry, as these products are regulated by the U.S. Department of Agriculture, not the FDA. In addition, foods such as coffee and most spices are not required to follow the FDA labeling guidelines, as they contain insignificant amounts of all nutrients that must be listed in nutrition labeling.

balanced diet A diet that contains the combinations of foods that provide the proper proportions of nutrients.

variety Eating a lot of different foods each day.

In this text, you will learn how to read food labels, a skill that can help you meet your nutritional goals.

AP Photo

Five Components Must Be Included on Food Labels

Five primary components of information must be included on food labels (**Figure 1**):

1. *A statement of identity:* The common name of the product or an appropriate identification of the food product must be prominently displayed on the label. This information tells us very clearly what the product is.
2. *The net contents of the package:* The quantity of the food product in the entire package must be accurately described. Information may be listed as weight (such as "grams"), volume (such as "fluid ounces"), or numerical count (such as "4 each").
3. *Ingredient list:* The ingredients must be listed by their common names, in descending order by weight. This means that the first product listed is the predominant ingredient in that food. This information can be very useful in many situations, such as when you are looking for foods that are lower in fat or sugar or when you are attempting to identify foods that contain whole-grain flour instead of processed wheat flour.
4. *The name and address of the food manufacturer, packer, or distributor:* You can use this information to find out more details about a food product and to contact the company if there is something wrong with the product or you suspect that it has caused an illness.
5. *Nutrition information:* The Nutrition Facts Panel contains the nutrition information required by the FDA. This panel is the primary tool to assist you in choosing more healthful foods. An explanation of the components of the Nutrition Facts Panel follows.

Figure 1 The five primary components that are required for food labels.
© ConAgra Brands, Inc.

How to Read and Use the Nutrition Facts Panel on Foods

Figure 2 shows an example of a **Nutrition Facts Panel.** You can use the information on this panel to learn more about an individual food, and you can use the panel to compare one food to another. Let's start at the top of the panel and work our way down to better understand how to use this information.

1. *Serving size and servings per container:* This section describes the serving size in a common household measure (such as a cup) and a metric measure (such as grams), as well as how many servings are contained in the package. The FDA has defined serving sizes based on the amounts of each food people typically eat. However, keep in mind that the serving size listed on the package may not be the same as the amount *you* eat. You must factor in how much of the food you eat when determining the amount of nutrients that this food contributes to your diet.

2. *Calories and Calories from fat per serving:* This section describes the total number of Calories and the total number of Calories that come from fat in 1 serving of that food. By looking at this section of the label, you can determine whether a food is relatively high in fat. For example, 1 serving of the food on this label (as prepared) contains 320 total Calories, with 90 of those Calories coming from fat. This means that this food contains 28% of its total Calories as fat (90 fat Calories ÷ 320 total Calories).

3. *List of nutrients:* This section states the nutrients this food contains. In this food, the nutrients listed toward the top, including total fat, saturated fat, *trans* fat, cholesterol, and sodium, are generally the nutrients you should strive to limit in a healthful diet. Some of the nutrients listed toward the bottom, including fiber, vitamins A and C, calcium, and iron, are those you should try to consume more of.

Nutrition Facts Panel The label on a food package that contains the nutrition information required by the FDA.

◆**Figure 2** The Nutrition Facts Panel contains a variety of information to help you make more healthful food choices.

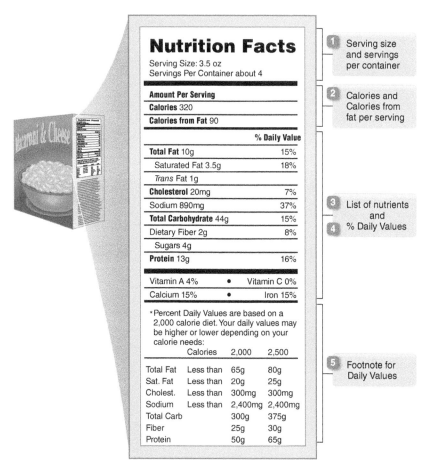

4. *Percent Daily Values (%DV):* This section tells you how much a serving of food contributes to your overall intake of the nutrients listed on the label. For example, 10 grams of fat constitutes 15% of your total daily recommended fat intake. Because we are all individuals, with unique nutritional needs, it is impractical to include nutrition information that applies to each person consuming a food. That would require thousands of labels! Thus, when defining the %DV, the FDA based its calculations on a 2,000-Calorie diet. Even if you do not consume 2,000 Calories each day, you can still use the %DV to figure out whether a food is high or low in a given nutrient. For example, foods that contain less than 5% DV of a nutrient are considered low in that nutrient, whereas foods that contain more than 20% DV are considered high in that nutrient. If you are trying to consume more calcium in your diet, select foods that contain more than 20% DV for calcium. In contrast, if you are trying to consume lower-fat foods, select foods that contain less than 5% or 10% fat. By comparing the %DV of foods for any nutrient, you can quickly decide which food is higher or lower in that nutrient without having to know how many Calories you need.

5. *Footnote (lower part of the panel):* This section tells you that the %DV are based on a 2,000-Calorie diet and that your needs may be higher or lower based on your caloric needs. The remainder of the footnote includes a table with values that illustrate the differences in recommendations between 2,000-Calorie and 2,500-Calorie diets; for instance, someone eating 2,000 Calories should strive to eat less than 65 grams of fat per day, whereas a person eating 2,500 Calories should eat less than 80 grams of fat per day. The table may not be present if the food label is too small. When present, the footnote and table are always the same, because the information refers to general dietary advice for all Americans, rather than to a specific food.

By comparing labels from various foods, you can start designing a more healthful diet today. Let's assume you are trying to limit your intake of sodium. Look at the soup label in Figure 1 and the macaroni and cheese label in Figure 2. How much sodium would a serving of these foods provide? If you had a choice of either of these products for lunch or a veggie burrito with 280 mg of sodium, which would you choose?

Food Labels Can Contain a Variety of Nutrient Claims

Have you ever noticed a food label displaying a claim such as "This food is low in sodium" or "This food is part of a heart-healthy diet"? The claim may have influenced you to buy the food, even if you weren't sure what it meant. Let's take a look.

The FDA regulates two types of claims that food companies put on food labels: nutrient claims and health claims. Food companies are prohibited from using a nutrient or health claim that is not approved by the FDA.

The Daily Values on the food labels serve as a basis for nutrient claims. For instance, if the label states that a food is "low in sodium," the food contains 140 mg or less of sodium per serving. Table 1 defines the terms approved for use in nutrient claims.

The FDA also allows food labels to display certain claims related to health and disease (Table 2). To help consumers gain a better understanding of nutritional information related to health, the FDA has developed a Health Claims Report Card (Figure 3), which grades the level of confidence in a health claim based on current scientific evidence. For example, if current scientific evidence about a particular health claim is not convincing, the label may have to include a disclaimer, so that consumers are not misled. Complete the Nutrition Label Activity to determine the strengths of certain health claims made for foods that are commonly consumed.

In addition to nutrient and health claims, labels may also contain structure–function claims. These are claims that can be made without approval from the FDA. While these claims can be generic statements about a food's impact on the body's structure and function, they cannot refer to a specific disease or symptom. Examples

This Cheerios cover is an example of an approved health claim.

percent Daily Values (%DV) Information on a Nutrition Facts Panel that identifies how much a serving of food contributes to your overall intake of the nutrients listed on the label; based on an energy intake of 2,000 Calories per day.

TABLE 1 United States Food and Drug Administration (FDA)–Approved Nutrient-Related Terms and Definitions

Nutrient	Claim	Meaning
Energy	Calorie free	Less than 5 kcal per serving
	Low Calorie	40 kcal or less per serving
	Reduced Calorie	At least 25% fewer kcal than reference (or regular) food
Fat and Cholesterol	Fat free	Less than 0.5 g of fat per serving
	Low fat	3 g or less fat per serving
	Reduced fat	At least 25% less fat per serving than reference food
	Saturated fat free	Less than 0.5 g of saturated fat **AND** less than 0.5 g of *trans* fat per serving
	Low saturated fat	1 g or less saturated fat and less than 0.5 g *trans* fat per serving **AND** 15% or less of total kcal from saturated fat
	Reduced saturated fat	At least 25% less saturated fat **AND** reduced by more than 1 g saturated fat per serving as compared to reference food
	Cholesterol free	Less than 2 mg of cholesterol per serving **AND** 2 g or less saturated fat and *trans* fat combined per serving
	Low cholesterol	20 mg or less cholesterol **AND** 2 g or less saturated fat per serving
	Reduced cholesterol	At least 25% less cholesterol than reference food **AND** 2 g or less saturated fat per serving
Fiber and Sugar	High fiber	5 g or more fiber per serving*
	Good source of fiber	2.5 g to 4.9 g fiber per serving
	More or added fiber	At least 2.5 g more fiber per serving than reference food
	Sugar free	Less than 0.5 g sugars per serving
	Low sugar	Not defined; no basis for recommended intake
	Reduced/less sugar	At least 25% less sugars per serving than reference food
	No added sugars or without added sugars	No sugar or sugar-containing ingredient added during processing
Sodium	Sodium free	Less than 5 mg sodium per serving
	Very low sodium	35 mg or less sodium per serving
	Low sodium	140 mg or less sodium per serving
	Reduced sodium	At least 25% less sodium per serving than reference food
Relative Claims	Free, without, no, zero	No or a trivial amount of given nutrient
	Light (or lite)	This term can have three different meanings: (1) a serving provides 1/3 fewer kcal than or half the fat of the reference food; (2) a serving of a low-fat, low-Calorie food provides half the sodium normally present; or (3) lighter in color and texture, with the label making this clear (for example, light molasses)
	Reduced, less, fewer	Contains at least 25% less of a nutrient or kcal than reference food
	More, added, extra, or plus	At least 10% of the Daily Value of nutrient as compared to reference food (may occur naturally or be added); may be used only for vitamins, minerals, protein, dietary fiber, and potassium
	Good source of, contains, or provides	10% to 19% of Daily Value per serving (may not be used for carbohydrate)
	High in, rich in, or excellent source of	20% or more of Daily Value per serving for protein, vitamins, minerals, dietary fiber, or potassium (may not be used for carbohydrate)

Data from U.S. Food and Drug Administration. 2008. Food Labeling Guide. Available at www.fda.gov/Food/GuidanceComplianceRegulatoryInformation/GuidanceDocuments/FoodLabelingNutrition/FoodLabelingGuide/default.htm.

*High fiber claims must also meet the definition of low fat; if not, then the level of total fat must appear next to the high fiber claim.

of structure–function claims include "Builds stronger bones," "Improves memory," "Slows signs of aging," and "Boosts your immune system." It is important to remember that these claims can be made with no proof, and thus there are no guarantees that any benefits identified in structure–function claims are true about that food. Thus, just because something is stated on the label doesn't guarantee it is always true!

In recent years, a variety of foods referred to as functional foods have become available to consumers. The Institute of Food Technologists defines a **functional food** as a food or food component that provides a health benefit beyond basic nutrition. You may be wondering what are some examples of functional foods, if they are safe, and if they are effective. Find the answers in the Nutrition Debate later in this chapter.

functional food A food or food component that provides a health benefit beyond basic nutrition.

TABLE 2 U.S. Food and Drug Administration–Approved Health Claims on Labels

Disease/Health Concern	Nutrient	Example of Approved Claim Statement
Osteoporosis	Calcium	Regular exercise and a healthy diet with enough calcium help teens and young white and Asian women maintain good bone health and may reduce their high risk for osteoporosis later in life.
Coronary heart disease	Saturated fat and cholesterol Fruits, vegetables, and grain products that contain fiber, particularly soluble fiber Soluble fiber from whole oats, psyllium seed husk, and beta glucan soluble fiber from oat bran, rolled oats (or oatmeal), and whole oat flour Soy protein Plant sterol/stanol esters Whole-grain foods	Diets low in saturated fat and cholesterol and rich in fruits, vegetables, and grain products that contain some types of dietary fiber, particularly soluble fiber, may reduce the risk for heart disease, a disease associated with many factors.
Cancer	Dietary fat Fiber-containing grain products, fruits, and vegetables Fruits and vegetables Whole-grain foods	Low-fat diets rich in fiber-containing grain products, fruits, and vegetables may reduce the risk for some types of cancer, a disease associated with many factors.
Hypertension and stroke	Sodium Potassium	Diets containing foods that are a good source of potassium and that are low in sodium may reduce the risk of high blood pressure and stroke.*
Neural tube defects	Folate	Healthful diets with adequate folate may reduce a woman's risk of having a child with a brain or spinal cord defect.
Dental caries	Sugar alcohols	Frequent between-meal consumption of foods high in sugars and starches promotes tooth decay. The sugar alcohols in [name of food] do not promote tooth decay.

Data from U.S. Food and Drug Administration. 2008. Food Labeling Guide. Available at www.fda.gov/Food/GuidanceComplianceRegulatoryInformation/GuidanceDocuments/FoodLabelingNutrition/FoodLabelingGuide/default.htm.
*Required wording for this claim. Wordings for other claims are recommended model statements but not required verbatim.

Figure 3 The U.S. Food and Drug Administration's Health Claims Report Card.

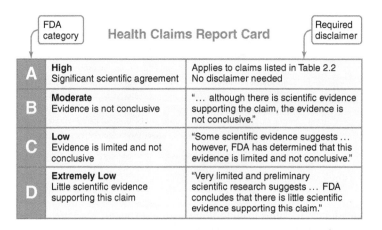

RECAP The ability to read and interpret food labels is important for planning and maintaining a healthful diet. Food labels must list the identity of the food, the net contents of the package, the contact information for the food manufacturer or distributor, the ingredients in the food, and a Nutrition Facts Panel. The Nutrition Facts Panel provides specific information about Calories, macronutrients, and selected vitamins and minerals. Food labels may also contain claims related to nutrients, health, and body structure and function.

NUTRITION LABEL ACTIVITY

How Do Health Claims on Food Labels Measure Up?

The U.S. Food and Drug Administration has published a Health Claims Report Card to assist consumers in deciphering health claims on food labels (Figure 3). It is important to note that the claims that are based on high scientific agreement do not require a label disclaimer. The claims reported in Table 2 are those that are based on high scientific agreement. Included here is a food label listing health claims: based on the Health Claims Report Card criteria listed in Figure 3, what level of confidence do scientists currently have about these health claims? Taking this level of confidence into consideration, would you recommend this product to relatives or friends if they were concerned about heart disease? Why or why not?

NUTRI-CASE GUSTAVO

"Until last night, I hadn't stepped inside a grocery store for 10 years, maybe more. But then my wife fell and broke her hip and had to go to the hospital. On my way home from visiting her, I remembered that we didn't have much food in the house, so I thought I'd do a little shopping. Was I ever in for a shock. I don't know how my wife does it, choosing between all the different brands, reading those long labels. She never went to school past sixth grade, and she doesn't speak English very well, either! I bought a frozen chicken pie for my dinner, but it didn't taste right, so I got the package out of the trash and read all the labels, and that's when I realized there wasn't any chicken in it at all! It was made out of tofu! This afternoon, my daughter is picking me up, and we're going to do our grocery shopping together!"

Given what you've learned about FDA food labels, what parts of a food package would you advise Gustavo to be sure to read before he makes a choice? What other advice might you give him to make his grocery shopping easier? Imagine that, like Gustavo's wife, you have only limited skills in mathematics and reading. In that case, what other strategies might you use when shopping for nutritious foods?

Ned Frisk Photography/Corbis; 2.4 Creative Digital Visions

Dietary Guidelines for Americans

The **Dietary Guidelines for Americans** are a set of principles developed by the U.S. Department of Agriculture and the U.S. Department of Health and Human Services to assist Americans in designing a healthful diet and lifestyle.[2] They are updated approximately every 5 years, and the current Guidelines were published in 2005. You can look to these general directives for assistance with eating a healthful diet and altering your physical activity habits to help reduce your risk for chronic diseases.

Following is a brief description of each of the chapters and key recommendations of the Dietary Guidelines for Americans. Refer to Table 3 for specific examples of how you can alter your current diet and physical activity habits according to some of these guidelines.

Adequate Nutrients Within Energy Needs

It is important to consume adequate nutrients to promote health while staying within your energy needs. Key recommendations include consuming a variety of nutrient-dense foods and beverages within and among the basic food groups while choosing foods that are limited in saturated and *trans* fats, cholesterol, added sugars, salt, and alcohol. **Nutrient-dense foods** are foods that supply the highest level of nutrients for the least amount of energy (Calories). Figure 4 compares 1 day of meals that are high in **nutrient density** to meals that are low in nutrient density. As you can see in this figure, skim milk is more nutrient-dense than whole milk, and a peeled orange is more nutrient-dense than an orange soft drink. This example can assist you in selecting the most nutrient-dense foods when planning your meals.

People can meet their recommended intakes within energy needs by adopting a balanced eating pattern, such as the USDA Food Guide, discussed later in this chapter.

Weight Management

Being overweight or obese increases our risk for many chronic diseases, including heart disease, type 2 diabetes, stroke, and some forms of cancer. A key recommendation is to maintain body weight in a healthful range by balancing Calories from foods and beverages with Calories expended.

Physical Activity

Key recommendations include engaging in regular physical activity and reducing sedentary activities to promote health, psychological well-being, and a healthful body weight. People are also encouraged to achieve physical fitness by including cardiovascular conditioning, stretching exercises for flexibility, and resistance exercises or calisthenics for muscle strength and endurance. By accumulating at least 30 minutes of

Dietary Guidelines for Americans A set of principles developed by the U.S. Department of Agriculture and the U.S. Department of Health and Human Services to assist Americans in designing a healthful diet and lifestyle. These Guidelines are updated every 5 years.

nutrient-dense foods Foods that provide the most nutrients for the least amount of energy (Calories).

nutrient density The relative amount of nutrients per amount of energy (or number of Calories).

TABLE 3 Ways to Incorporate the Dietary Guidelines for Americans into Your Daily Life

If You Normally Do This	Try Doing This Instead
Watch television when you get home at night	Do 30 minutes of stretching or lifting of hand weights in front of the television
Drive to the store down the block	Walk to and from the store
Go out to lunch with friends	Take a 15- or 30-minute walk with your friends at lunchtime 3 days each week
Eat white bread with your sandwich	Eat whole-wheat bread or some other bread made from whole grains
Eat white rice or fried rice with your meal	Eat brown rice or even try wild rice
Choose cookies or a candy bar for a snack	Choose a fresh nectarine, peach, apple, orange, or banana for a snack
Order french fries with your hamburger	Order a green salad with low-fat salad dressing on the side
Spread butter or margarine on your white toast each morning	Spread fresh fruit compote on whole-grain toast
Order a bacon double cheeseburger at your favorite restaurant	Order a turkey burger or grilled chicken sandwich without the cheese and bacon, and add lettuce and tomato
Drink nondiet soft drinks to quench your thirst	Drink iced tea, ice water with a slice of lemon, seltzer water, or diet soft drinks
Eat regular potato chips and pickles with your favorite sandwich	Eat carrot slices and crowns of fresh broccoli and cauliflower dipped in low-fat or nonfat ranch dressing

| Meals with Foods High in Nutrient Density | Meals with Foods Low in Nutrient Density |

Breakfast
1 cup cooked oatmeal with
 1/2 cup skim milk
1 slice whole-wheat toast with
 1 tsp. butter
6 fl. oz grapefruit juice

Breakfast
1 cup puffed rice cereal with
 1/2 cup whole milk
1 slice white toast with
 1 tsp. butter
6 fl. oz grape drink

Snack
1 peeled orange
1 cup nonfat yogurt

Snack
1 12-oz can orange soft drink
1.5 oz cheddar cheese

Lunch
Turkey sandwich
 3 oz turkey breast
 2 slices whole-grain bread
 2 tsp. Dijon mustard
 3 slices fresh tomato
 2 leaves red leaf lettuce
1 cup baby carrots with
 broccoli crowns
20 fl. oz (2.5 cups) water

Lunch
Hamburger
 3 oz regular ground beef
 1 white hamburger bun
 2 tsp. Dijon mustard
 1 tbsp. tomato ketchup
 2 leaves iceberg lettuce
1 snack-sized bag potato chips
20 fl. oz cola soft drink

Snack
1/2 whole-wheat bagel
1 tbsp. peanut butter
1 medium apple

Snack
3 chocolate sandwich cookies
1 12-oz can diet soft drink
10 Gummi Bears candy

Dinner
Spinach salad
 1 cup fresh spinach leaves
 1/4 cup sliced tomatoes
 1/4 cup diced green pepper
 1/2 cup kidney beans
 1 tbsp. fat-free Italian
 salad dressing
3 oz broiled chicken breast
1/2 cup cooked brown rice
1/2 cup steamed broccoli
8 fl. oz (1 cup) skim milk

Dinner
Green salad
 1 cup iceberg lettuce
 1/4 cup diced tomatoes
 1 tsp. green onions
 1/4 cup bacon bits
 1 tbsp. regular Ranch
 salad dressing
3 oz beef round steak,
 breaded and fried
1/2 cup cooked white rice
1/2 cup sweet corn
8 fl. oz (1 cup) iced tea

Figure 4 A comparison of one day's meals containing foods high in nutrient density to meals with foods low in nutrient density.

moderate physical activity on most, preferably all, days of the week, Americans can reduce their risk for chronic diseases. Moderate physical activity includes walking, riding a bike, mowing the lawn with a push mower, and performing heavy yard work. Other beneficial activities include those that build strength, such as lifting weights, groceries, or other objects; carrying your golf clubs while you walk around the course: and participating in yoga or other flexibility activities.

The 30-minute guideline is a minimum; people who are already doing more activity than this should continue on their healthful path. For most people, greater health benefits can be obtained by engaging in more vigorous or longer physical activity. If someone is currently inactive, 30 minutes is a realistic and healthful goal. Being physically active 60 to 90 minutes per day on most days of the week is recommended to prevent weight gain and to promote weight loss in those who are overweight.

Food Groups to Encourage

Eating a variety of fruits and vegetables is important to ensure that we consume the various nutrients we need to enhance our health. A few of the nutrients provided by fruits and vegetables are vitamin A, vitamin C, folate, and potassium. Fruits and vegetables also provide non-nutrient substances called *phytochemicals*. As explained **In Depth** at the end of this chapter, these plant chemicals are thought to have many beneficial effects on health. Key recommendations include consuming a sufficient amount of fruits and vegetables each day while staying within energy needs. In addition, we should choose a variety of fruits and vegetables, selecting from all five vegetable subgroups: dark-green, orange, legumes (peas, beans, and lentils), starchy vegetables, and other vegetables. Americans are also encouraged to eat 3 or more ounces of whole-grain foods each day and to consume 3 cups per day of low-fat or fat-free milk or equivalent milk products.

Fats

Fat is an important part of a healthful diet because it provides energy and important nutrients, such as essential fatty acids and fat-soluble vitamins. However, because fats are energy-dense, eating a diet high in total fat can lead to overweight and obesity. In addition, eating a diet high in saturated fats, *trans* fats, and cholesterol is linked to an increased risk for heart disease. Key recommendations include consuming less than 10% of your total energy intake as saturated fats and less than 300 mg/day of cholesterol. *Trans* fat intake should be as low as possible. Total fat intake should be 20% to 35% of total energy intake, with most fats coming from fish, nuts, and vegetable oils.

Carbohydrates

High-carbohydrate foods are an important source of energy and essential nutrients. Key recommendations include choosing fiber-rich fruits, vegetables, and whole grains often and choosing and preparing foods and beverages with little added sugars. It is important to moderate our intake of foods high in sugar and starch, as these foods promote tooth decay. To reduce the risk for dental caries (cavities), it is recommended that people practice good oral hygiene and consume foods and beverages that contain sugar and starch less frequently.

Sodium and Potassium

Both sodium and potassium are major minerals that are essential for health in appropriate amounts. Whereas potassium is linked to healthful blood pressure levels, excessive sodium consumption is linked to high blood pressure in some people. Eating a lot of sodium also can cause some people to lose calcium from their bones, which can increase their risk for bone loss and bone fractures. Table salt contains the mineral sodium, but much of the salt we consume in our diets comes from processed and prepared foods. Key recommendations include consuming less than 2,300 mg of sodium (approximately 1 tsp. of salt) per day, choosing and preparing foods with little salt, and consuming potassium-rich foods, such as fruits and vegetables. Some

Being physically active for at least 30 minutes each day can reduce your risk for chronic diseases.

When grocery shopping, try to select a variety of fruits and vegetables.

ways to decrease salt intake include eating fresh, plain frozen, or canned vegetables without added salt; limiting your intake of processed meats, such as cured ham, sausage, bacon, and most canned meats; and looking for foods with labels that say "low sodium." In addition, adding little or no salt to foods at home and limiting your intake of salty condiments, such as ketchup, mustard, pickles, soy sauce, and olives, can help reduce your sodium intake.

Alcoholic Beverages

Alcohol provides energy, but it does not contain any nutrients. In the body, it depresses the nervous system and is toxic to liver and other body cells. Drinking alcoholic beverages in excess can lead to serious health and social problems; therefore, those who choose to drink are encouraged to do so sensibly and in moderation: no more than one drink per day for women and no more than two drinks per day for men. People who should not drink alcohol include those who cannot restrict their intake, women of childbearing age who may become pregnant, pregnant and lactating women, children and adolescents, individuals taking medications that can interact with alcohol, people with certain medical conditions, and people who are engaging in activities that require attention, skill, or coordination.

Food Safety

A healthful diet is one that is safe from foodborne illnesses, such as those caused by microorganisms and their toxins. Important tips to remember include storing and cooking foods at the proper temperatures, avoiding unpasteurized juices and milk products and raw or undercooked meats and shellfish, and washing your hands and cooking surfaces before cooking and after handling raw meats, shellfish, and eggs.

RECAP The Dietary Guidelines for Americans emphasize healthful food choices and physical activity behaviors. The Guidelines include achieving a healthful weight; being physically active each day; eating whole-grain foods, fruits, and vegetables daily; eating foods low in saturated and *trans* fats and cholesterol and moderate in total fat; moderating sugar intake; eating less salt; eating more potassium-rich foods; keeping foods safe to eat; and drinking alcohol in moderation, if at all.

Andrew Whittuck/Dorling Kindersley

◆ Eating a diet rich in whole-grain foods and fiber-rich fruits and vegetables can enhance your overall health.

The USDA Food Guide

The U.S. Department of Agriculture (USDA) pyramid-based food guidance system is another tool that can help you design a healthful diet. It was created in 2005 to provide a conceptual framework for the types and amounts of foods that make up a healthful diet. It is important to remember that the USDA Food Guide is an evolving document, and it will continue to change as more is learned about the roles of specific nutrients and foods in promoting health and preventing certain diseases.

The graphic representation of the USDA Food Guide is called **MyPyramid** (Figure 5). MyPyramid is an interactive, personalized guide that you can access on the Internet to assess your current diet and physical activity levels and to plan appropriate changes. MyPyramid is intended to help Americans:

- eat in moderation
- eat a variety of foods
- consume the right proportion of each recommended food group
- personalize their eating plan
- increase their physical activity
- set goals for gradually improving their food choices and lifestyle.

Food Groups in the USDA Food Guide

The food groups emphasized in the USDA Food Guide are grains, vegetables, fruits, milk, and meat and beans. Oils are also recommended. These are represented in the

MyPyramid The graphic representation of the USDA Food Guide.

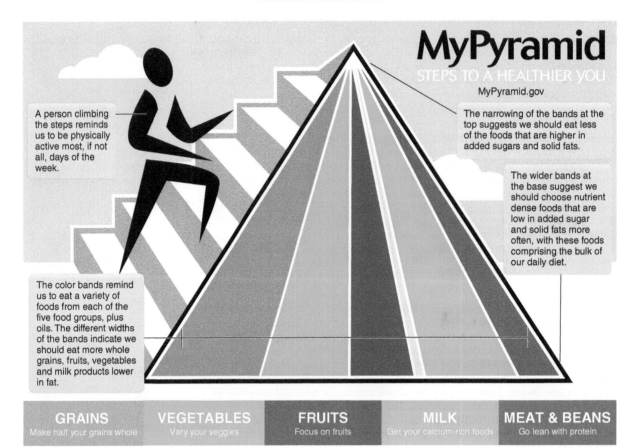

🔺 **Figure 5** The USDA MyPyramid. This pyramid is an interactive food guidance system based on the 2005 Dietary Guidelines for Americans and the Dietary Reference Intakes from the National Academy of Sciences. MyPyramid is a personalized guide that people can use to assess their current diet and physical activity levels and to make changes in their food intake and physical activity patterns. The yellow band in the pyramid represents oils. There are six components of this symbol: activity, moderation, personalization, proportionality, variety, and gradual improvement.

pyramid graphic with bands of six different colors. **Figure 6** illustrates each of these food groups and provides more detailed information on the nutrients they provide and recommended servings each day.

The Concept of Discretionary Calories

One concept introduced in the 2005 USDA Food Guide is that of **discretionary Calories.** Discretionary Calories represent the extra amount of energy you can consume after you've met all of your essential needs by eating nutrient-dense foods. The number of discretionary Calories you can allow yourself depends on your age, gender, and physical activity level. This number is small for most people, between about 100 and 300 kcal/day. Foods that use up discretionary Calories include butter, margarine, lard, salad dressings, mayonnaise, sour cream, cream, and gravy. High-sugar foods, such as candies, desserts, gelatin, soft drinks, fruit drinks, and alcoholic beverages, are also included in the discretionary Calorie allowance. You can also use your discretionary Calories to eat more healthful foods.

discretionary Calories A term used in the USDA Food Guide that represents the extra amount of energy you can consume after you have met all of your essential needs by consuming the most nutrient-dense foods that are low-fat or fat-free and that have no added sugars.

Grains

Make half your grains whole. At least half of the grains you eat each day should come from whole-grain sources.

Eat at least 3 oz of whole-grain bread, cereal, crackers, rice, or pasta every day.

Whole-grain foods provide fiber-rich carbohydrates, riboflavin, thiamin, niacin, iron, folate, zinc, protein, and magnesium.

Vegetables

Vary your veggies. Eat a variety of vegetables and increase consumption of dark-green and orange vegetables, and dry beans and peas.

Eat at least 2½ cups of vegetables each day.

Vegetables provide fiber and phytochemicals, carbohydrates, vitamins A and C, folate, potassium, and magnesium.

Fruits

Focus on fruits. Eat a greater variety of fruits (fresh, frozen, or dried) and go easy on the fruit juices.

Eat at least 2 cups of fruit every day.

Fruits provide fiber, phytochemicals, vitamins A and C, folate, potassium, and magnesium.

Dairy Foods

Get your calcium-rich foods. Choose low-fat or fat-free dairy products, such as milk, yogurt and cheese. People who can't consume dairy foods can choose lactose-free dairy products or other souces, such as calcium-fortified juices and soy and rice beverages.

Get 3 cups of low-fat dairy foods, or the equivalent, every day.

Dairy foods provide calcium, phosphorus, riboflavin, protein, and vitamin B12 and are often fortified with vitamins D and A.

Meats & Beans

Go lean on protein. Choose low-fat or lean meats and poultry. Switch to baking, broiling, or grilling more often, and vary your choices to include more fish, beans, nuts, and seeds. Legumes, including beans, peas, and lentils, are included both in the meat and beans group and the vegetables group.

Eat about 5½ oz of lean protein foods each day.

These foods provide protein, phosphorus, vitamin B6, vitamin B12, magnesium, iron, zinc, niacin, riboflacin, and thiamin.

Oils

Know your fats. Select health-promoting forms of fat, including fat from fish, nuts, and vegetable oils.

Eat small amounts of health-promoting oils each day and limit or eliminate solid fats, such as butter, stick margarine, shortening, lard, and visible fat on meat.

Oils provide vitamin E and essential faty acids.

Figure 6 Food groups of the USDA Food Guide.

Number of Servings in the USDA Food Guide

The USDA Food Guide also helps you decide *how much* of each food you should eat. The number of servings is based on the recommended Calorie level. **Figure 7** shows how much food four people at four different energy intake levels could eat from each food group. As you can see in this figure, people who need more energy should eat more foods from each group. A term used in this figure that may be new to you is **ounce-equivalent (oz-equivalent).** It is defined as a serving size that is 1 ounce, or equivalent to an ounce, for the grains and meats and beans sections. For instance, both a slice of bread and 1/2 cup of cooked brown rice qualify as ounce-equivalents.

Serving Size in the USDA Food Guide

What is considered a serving size for the foods recommended in the USDA Food Guide? **Figure 8** identifies the number of cups or oz-equivalent servings recommended for a 2,000-kcal diet and gives examples of amounts equal to 1 cup or 1 oz-equivalent for foods in each group. As you study this figure, notice the variety of examples for each group. For instance, an oz-equivalent serving from the grains group can mean one slice of bread or two pancakes. Because of their low density, 2 cups of raw, leafy vegetables, such as spinach, actually constitutes a 1-cup serving from the vegetables group. Although an oz-equivalent serving of meat is actually 1 oz, 1/2 oz of nuts also qualifies. One egg, 1 tablespoon of peanut butter, and 1/4 cup cooked legumes are also considered 1 oz-equivalents from the meat and beans group. Although it may seem unnatural and inconvenient to measure food servings, understanding the size of a serving is crucial to planning a nutritious diet. **Figure 9** shows you a practical way to estimate serving sizes.

It is important to understand that no nationally standardized definition for a serving size exists for any food. Thus, a serving size as defined in the USDA Food Guide may not be equal to a serving size identified on a food label. For instance, the serving size for crackers in the USDA Food Guide is 3 to 4 small crackers, whereas a serving size for crackers on a food label can range from 5 to 18 crackers, depending on the size and weight of the cracker. When comparing serving sizes from the USDA Food Guide to serving sizes on packaged foods, check the Nutrition Facts Panel. Try the Nutrition Label Activity to determine whether the serving sizes listed on assorted food labels match the serving sizes you normally eat.

ounce-equivalent (oz-equivalent) A serving size that is 1 ounce, or equivalent to an ounce, for the grains section and the meats and beans section of the USDA Food Guide.

For items consumed individually, such as muffins, frozen burgers, bottled juices, and so on, the serving sizes in the USDA Food Guide are typically much smaller than the items we buy. In addition, serving sizes in restaurants, cafes, and movie theatres have grown substantially over the past 30 years.[3] This "super-sizing" phenomenon, now seen even at home, indicates a major shift in accessibility to foods and in ac-

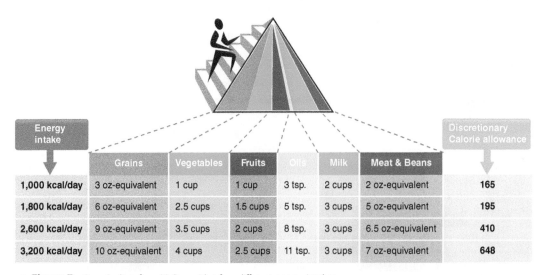

Energy intake	Grains	Vegetables	Fruits	Oils	Milk	Meat & Beans	Discretionary Calorie allowance
1,000 kcal/day	3 oz-equivalent	1 cup	1 cup	3 tsp.	2 cups	2 oz-equivalent	165
1,800 kcal/day	6 oz-equivalent	2.5 cups	1.5 cups	5 tsp.	3 cups	5 oz-equivalent	195
2,600 kcal/day	9 oz-equivalent	3.5 cups	2 cups	8 tsp.	3 cups	6.5 oz-equivalent	410
3,200 kcal/day	10 oz-equivalent	4 cups	2.5 cups	11 tsp.	3 cups	7 oz-equivalent	648

Figure 7 Sample diets from MyPyramid at four different energy intakes.

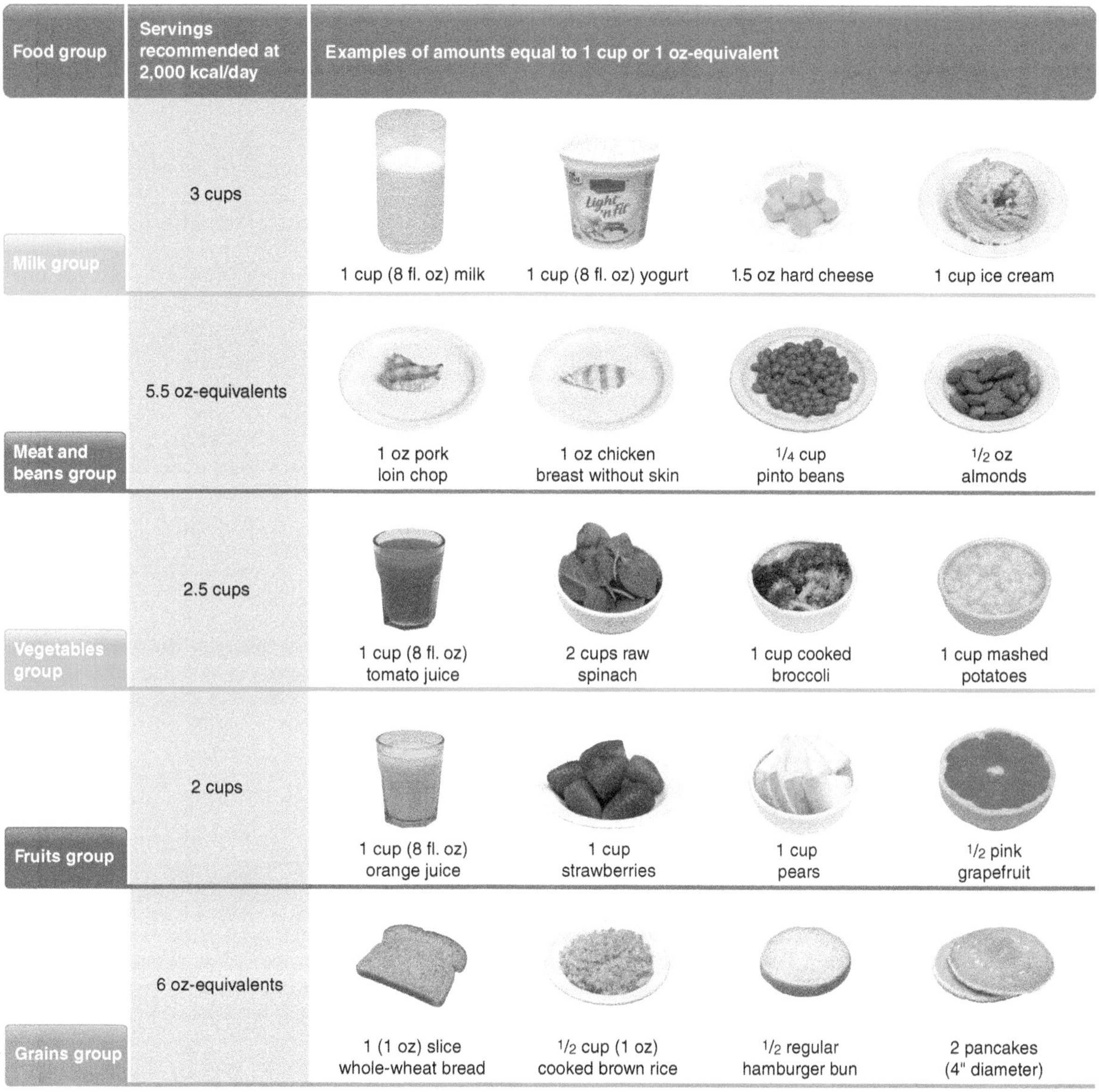

Food group	Servings recommended at 2,000 kcal/day	Examples of amounts equal to 1 cup or 1 oz-equivalent			
Milk group	3 cups	1 cup (8 fl. oz) milk	1 cup (8 fl. oz) yogurt	1.5 oz hard cheese	1 cup ice cream
Meat and beans group	5.5 oz-equivalents	1 oz pork loin chop	1 oz chicken breast without skin	1/4 cup pinto beans	1/2 oz almonds
Vegetables group	2.5 cups	1 cup (8 fl. oz) tomato juice	2 cups raw spinach	1 cup cooked broccoli	1 cup mashed potatoes
Fruits group	2 cups	1 cup (8 fl. oz) orange juice	1 cup strawberries	1 cup pears	1/2 pink grapefruit
Grains group	6 oz-equivalents	1 (1 oz) slice whole-wheat bread	1/2 cup (1 oz) cooked brown rice	1/2 regular hamburger bun	2 pancakes (4" diameter)

PLG/Pearson Education

Figure 8 Examples of serving sizes for foods in each food group of MyPyramid for a 2,000 kcal food intake pattern. Here are some examples of household items that can help you to estimate serving sizes: 1.5 oz of hard cheese is equal to 4 stacked dice, 3 oz of meat is equal in size to a deck of cards, and half of a regular hamburger bun is the size of a yo-yo.

cepted eating behaviors. It has also become an important contributor to the rise in obesity rates around the world. If you don't want to gain weight, it's important to become educated about portion size. In a study conducted by Young and Nestle,[11] introductory nutrition students were asked to take to class a "medium-sized" bagel, baked potato, muffin, apple, or cookie. The foods the students took to class were then weighed, and most well exceeded the USDA's definition of a serving. Young and Nestle[4] report that the discrepancy between USDA serving sizes and the portion size of many common foods sold outside of the home is staggering—chocolate chip cookies are seven times larger than USDA standards, a serving of cooked pasta in a restaurant is almost five times larger, and steaks are more than twice as large.[5] Thus, when using diet-planning tools, such as food labels and the USDA Food Guide, it is essential to

A woman's palm is approximately the size of 3 ounces of cooked meat, chicken, or fish

(a)

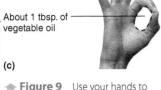

A woman's fist is about the size of 1 cup of pasta or vegetables (a man's fist is the size of about 2 cups)

(b)

About 1 tbsp. of vegetable oil

(c)

Kristin Piljay

⬆ **Figure 9** Use your hands to help you estimate the serving sizes of common foods.

learn the definition of a serving size for the tool you are using and *then* measure your food intake to determine whether you are meeting the guidelines. Refer to the You Do the Math box to estimate how much physical activity you would need to do to expend the excess energy you consume because of increasing food portion sizes.

Ethnic Variations of MyPyramid

As you know, the population of the United States is culturally and ethnically diverse, and this diversity influences our food choices. Foods that we may typically consider a part of an Asian, a Latin American, or a Mediterranean diet can also fit into a healthful diet. You can easily incorporate foods that match your specific ethnic, religious, or other lifestyle preferences into your own personal MyPyramid. You can also use one of the many ethnic and cultural variations of the previous USDA Food Guide Pyramid. These include the Latin American Diet Pyramid and the Asian Diet Pyramid, shown in **Figure 10**. There are also variations for Native Americans, African Americans, and many others.[6] These variations illustrate that anyone can design a healthful diet to accommodate his or her food preferences.

Of these variations, the Mediterranean diet has enjoyed considerable popularity. Does it deserve its reputation as a healthful diet? Check out the Hot Topic three pages ahead.

Limitations of the USDA Food Guide

Although the USDA Food Guide is a very useful tool for designing a healthful diet, it has limitations. As discussed in the previous section, the serving sizes as defined in the USDA Food Guide are relatively small and do not always coincide with the standard amounts of food we buy, prepare, and serve. Some nutrition professionals believe these serving sizes are unrealistic, and it has been suggested that the serving sizes should be redefined to match more closely the amount of food Americans typically eat.

NUTRITION LABEL ACTIVITY

How Realistic Are the Serving Sizes Listed on Food Labels?

Many people read food labels to determine the energy (caloric) value of foods, but it is less common to pay close attention to the actual serving size that corresponds to the listed caloric value. To test how closely your "naturally selected" serving size matches the actual serving size of certain foods, try these label activities:

- Choose a breakfast cereal that you commonly eat. Pour the amount of cereal you would normally eat into a bowl. Before adding milk, use a measuring cup to measure the amount of cereal you poured. Now read the label of the cereal to determine the serving size (for example, 1/2 cup or 1 cup) and the caloric value listed on the label. How do your "naturally selected" serving size and the label-defined serving size compare?

iStockphoto/Thinkstock

- At your local grocery store, locate various boxes of snack crackers. Look at the number of crackers and total Calories per serving listed on the labels of crackers such as regular Triscuits, reduced-fat Triscuits, Vegetable Thins, and Ritz crackers. How do the number of crackers and total Calories per serving differ for the serving size listed on each box? How do the serving sizes listed in the Nutrition Facts Panel compare to how many crackers you would usually eat?

These activities are just two examples of ways to understand how nutrition labels can help you make balanced and healthful food choices. As many people do not know what constitutes a serving size, they are inclined to consume too much of some foods (such as snack foods and meat) and too little of other foods (such as fruits and vegetables).

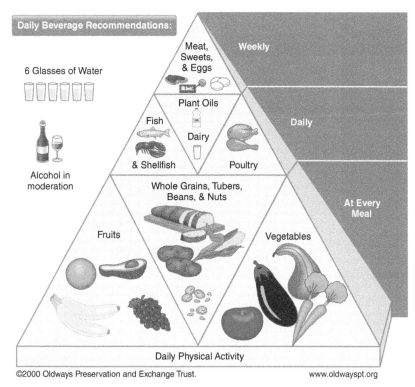

(a) Latin American Diet Pyramid

⬇ **Figure 10** Ethnic and cultural variations of an earlier version of the USDA Food Guide Pyramid. **(a)** The Latin American Diet Pyramid **(b)** The Asian Diet Pyramid

© 2000 Oldways Preservation and Exchange Trust. The Food Issues Think Tank. Healthy Eating Pyramids & Other Tools. www.oldwayspt.org.

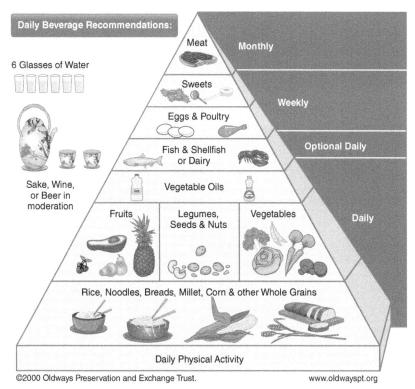

(b) Asian Diet Pyramid

YOU DO THE MATH
How Much Exercise Is Needed to Combat Increasing Food Portion Sizes?

Although the causes of obesity are complex and result from different factors, most researchers agree that one reason obesity rates are rising is a combination of increased energy intake due to expanding portion sizes and a reduction in overall daily physical activity. This box explores how portion sizes have increased over the past 30 years and how much physical activity you would need to expend the excess energy provided by these larger portion sizes.

The two photos in **Figure 11** show foods whose portion sizes have increased substantially. A few decades ago, a bagel had a diameter of approximately 3 inches and contained 140 kcal. Today, a bagel is about 6 inches in diameter and contains 350 kcal. Similarly, 30 years ago, a cup of coffee was 8 fl. oz and, if consumed without milk and sugar, contained about 2 kcal. Today, a standard coffee mocha is twice that size and contains 350 kcal; this excess energy comes from sugar, milk, and flavored syrup.

On her morning break at work, Judy routinely consumes a bagel and a coffee drink like the ones described here. How much physical activity would Judy need to do to "burn" this excess energy? Let's do some simple math to answer this question.

1. Calculate the excess energy Judy consumes from both of these foods:
   a. Bagel: 350 kcal in larger bagel − 140 kcal in smaller bagel = 210 kcal extra
   b. Coffee: 350 kcal in large coffee mocha − 2 kcal in small regular coffee = 348 kcal extra

   Total excess energy for these two larger portions = 558 kcal

2. Judy has started walking each day in an effort to lose weight. Judy currently weighs 200 lb. Based on her relatively low fitness level, Judy walks at a slow pace (approximately 2 miles per hour); it is estimated that walking at this pace expends 1.2 kcal per pound of body weight per hour. How long does Judy need to walk each day to expend 558 kcal?
   a. First, calculate how much energy Judy expends if she walks for a full hour by multiplying her body weight by the energy cost of walking per hour:
   1.2 kcal/lb body weight × 200 lb = 240 kcal.
   b. Next, you need to calculate how much energy she expends each minute she walks by dividing the energy cost of walking per hour by 60 minutes:
   240 kcal/hour ÷ 60 minutes/hour = 4 kcal/minute.
   c. To determine how many minutes she would need to walk to expend 558 kcal, divide the total amount of energy she needs to expend by the energy cost of walking per minute: 558 kcal ÷ 4 kcal/minute = 139.5 minutes.

Thus, Judy would need to walk for approximately 140 minutes, or about 2 hours and 20 minutes, to expend the excess energy she consumes by eating the larger bagel and coffee. If she wanted to burn off all of the energy in her morning snack, she would have to walk even longer, especially if she enjoyed her bagel with cream cheese!

Now use your own weight to determine how much walking you would have to do if you consumed the same foods:
a. 1.2 kcal/lb × (your weight in pounds) − _____ kcal/hour (If you walk at a brisk pace, use 2.4 kcal/lb.)
b. _____ kcal/hour ÷ 60 minutes/hour = _____ kcal/minute
c. 558 extra kcal in bagel and coffee ÷ _____ kcal/minutes = _____ minutes

For more information about large portion sizes and the physical activities necessary to avoid weight gain, see Web Resources at the end of this chapter.

20 Years Ago   **Today**

3-inch diameter, 140 Calories   6-inch diameter, 350 Calories

(a) Bagel

8 fluid ounces, 42 Calories   16 fluid ounces, 350 Calories

(b) Coffee

Image Source Pink/Alamy   Envision/Corbis   F. Schussler/PhotoLink/Getty Images   Ragnar Schmuck/Getty Images

Figure 11 Examples of increases in food portion sizes over the past 20 years. **(a)** A bagel has increased in diameter from 3 inches to 6 inches; **(b)** a cup of coffee has increased from 8 fl. oz to 16 fl. oz and now commonly contains Calorie-dense flavored syrup as well as steamed whole milk.

The Mediterranean Diet

A Mediterranean-style diet has received significant attention in recent years, as the rates of cardiovascular disease in many Mediterranean countries are substantially lower than the rates in the United States. These countries include Portugal, Spain, Italy, France, Greece, Turkey, and Israel. Each country has unique dietary patterns; however, they share the following characteristics:

- Meat is eaten monthly, and eggs, poultry, fish, and sweets are eaten weekly, making the diet low in saturated fats and refined sugars.
- The fat used predominantly for cooking and flavor is olive oil, making the diet high in monounsaturated fats.
- Foods eaten daily include grains, such as bread, pasta, couscous, and bulgur; fruits; beans and other legumes; nuts; vegetables; and cheese and yogurt. These choices make this diet high in fiber and rich in vitamins and minerals.

Figure 12 illustrates the Mediterranean Diet Pyramid. Its similarities to the USDA Food Guide include suggestions for daily physical activity and a daily intake of breads, cereals, other grains, fruits, and vegetables. It is different from the USDA Food Guide in that it includes the daily consumption of beans, other legumes, and nuts and the infrequent consumption of meat, fish, poultry, and eggs. Cheese and yogurt, rather than milk, are the primary dairy sources. A unique feature of the Mediterranean diet is the consumption of wine and olive oil daily.

Another drawback of the USDA Food Guide is that low-fat and low-Calorie food choices are not clearly defined in each food category. For instance, 1 oz-equivalent servings of meat, poultry, fish, dry beans, eggs, and nuts are suggested, but these foods differ significantly in their fat content and in the types of fat they contain. Fish is well recognized for being low in fat and containing a healthier type of fat than that found in red meats. However, these two choices are treated equally in the USDA Food Guide. Thus, the revised dietary guidelines and USDA Food Guide may not have gone far enough in encouraging people to consume more healthful foods.

RECAP The USDA Food Guide can be used to plan a healthful, balanced diet that includes foods from the grains group, vegetables group, fruits group, milk group, oil group, and meat and beans group. As defined in the USDA Food Guide, serving sizes typically are smaller than the amounts we normally eat or are served, so it is important to learn the definitions of serving sizes when using the USDA Food Guide to design a healthful diet. There are many ethnic and cultural variations of the USDA Food Guide. Its flexibility enables anyone to design a diet that meets the goals of adequacy, moderation, balance, variety, and nutrient density. Some of the limitations of the USDA Food Guide are relatively small serving sizes and its failure to distinguish between higher-fat and lower-fat food choices within some food groups.

Dorling Kindersley

Nutrient-packed foods—such as kale, which is an excellent source of calcium—should be part of a well-rounded diet.

Can Eating Out Be Part of a Healthful Diet?

How many times a week do you eat out? A report from the Pew Research Center states that about one-third of Americans eat out once a week, and another one-third eat out two or more times a week.[7] Almost half (47%) of the men and 35% of the women surveyed reported eating a meal at a fast-food restaurant at least once a week. Over the past 20 years, there has been phenomenal growth in the restaurant industry, particularly in the fast-food market. During the same time period, obesity increased by more than 60%, and an estimated 66% of U.S. adults are either overweight or obese.[8]

Figure 12 The Mediterranean Diet Pyramid. Interestingly, the Mediterranean diet is not lower in fat; in fact, about 40% of the total energy in this diet is derived from fat, which is much higher than the dietary fat recommendations made in the United States. However, the majority of fat in the Mediterranean diet is from plant oils, which are more healthful sources than the animal fats found in the U.S. diet, making the Mediterranean diet more protective against cardiovascular disease.

© 2000 Oldways Preservation and Exchange Trust. The Food Issues Think Tank. Healthy Eating Pyramids & Other Tools. www.oldwayspt.org.

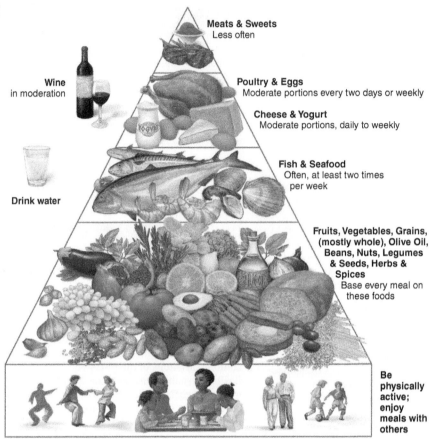

Illustration by Geoge Middleton © 2009 Oldways Preservation and Exchange Trust www.oldwayspt.org

Joe Raedle/Getty Images

Foods served at fast-food chains are often high in Calories, total fat, and sodium. The popular McDonald's sausage, egg, and cheese McGriddles breakfast sandwiches, for example, contain 560 kcal, 32 grams of fat, and 1,360 milligrams of sodium.

The Hidden Costs of Eating Out

Table 4 lists some of the foods served at McDonald's and Burger King restaurants. As you can see, a regular McDonald's hamburger has only 270 kcal, whereas the Big Xtra with Cheese has 810 kcal. A meal of the Quarter Pounder with Cheese, Super Size french fries, and a Super Size Coke provides 1,550 kcal. This meal has almost enough energy to support an entire day's needs for a small, lightly active woman! Similar meals at other fast-food chains are also very high in Calories, not to mention total fat and sodium.

Fast-food restaurants are not alone in serving large portions. Most sit-down restaurants also serve large meals, which may include bread with butter, a salad with dressing, sides of potatoes and other vegetables, and free refills of sugar-filled drinks. Combined with a high-fat appetizer, such as potato skins, fried onions, fried mozzarella sticks, or buffalo wings, it is easy to eat more than 2,000 kcal at one meal.

Does this mean that eating out cannot be a part of a healthful diet? Not necessarily. By becoming an educated consumer and making wise meal choices, you can enjoy both a healthful diet and the social benefits of eating out. An example is shown in **Figure 13**.

TABLE 4 Nutritional Value of Selected Fast Foods				
Menu Item	kcal	Fat (g)	Fat (% kcal)	Sodium (mg)
McDonald's				
Hamburger	250	9	32	520
Cheeseburger	300	12	37	750
Quarter Pounder	410	19	41	730
Quarter Pounder with Cheese	510	26	45	1,190
Big Mac	540	29	48	1,040
French fries, small	250	13	48	140
French fries, medium	380	20	47	220
French fries, large	570	30	47	330
Burger King				
Hamburger	260	16	38	520
Cheeseburger	310	20	42	740
Whopper	670	40	54	1,020
Double Whopper	920	58	57	1,090
Bacon Double Cheeseburger	510	30	53	1,180
French fries, small	340	17	47	530
French fries, medium	440	22	45	670
French fries, large	540	27	44	830

Sigrid Estrada/Getty Images

Eating out can be a part of a healthful diet, if you are careful to choose wisely.

The Healthful Way to Eat Out

Most restaurants, even fast-food restaurants, offer lower-fat menu items. For instance, eating a regular McDonald's hamburger, a small order of french fries, and a diet beverage or water provides 480 kcal and 19 g of fat (35% of kcal from fat). To provide some vegetables for the day, you can add a side salad with low-fat or nonfat salad dressing. Other fast-food restaurants also offer smaller portions, sandwiches made with whole-grain bread, grilled chicken or other lean meats, and side salads. Many sit-down restaurants offer "lite" menu items, such as grilled chicken and a variety of vegetables, which are usually a much better choice than foods from the regular menu.

Here are some other suggestions on how to eat out in moderation. Practice some of these Quick Tips every time you eat out.

QUICK TIPS

Eating Right When You're Eating Out

- Avoid all-you-can-eat buffet-style restaurants.
- Avoid appetizers that are breaded, fried, or filled with cheese or meat, or skip the appetizer completely.
- Order a healthful appetizer as an entrée instead of a larger meal.
- Order your meal from the children's menu.
- Share an entrée with a friend.
- Order broth-based soups instead of cream-based soups.
- Order any meat dish grilled or broiled, and avoid fried or breaded meat dishes.
- If you order a meat dish, select lean cuts of meat.
- Order a meatless dish filled with vegetables and whole grains. Avoid dishes with cream sauces and a lot of cheese.
- Instead of a beef burger, order a chicken burger, fish burger, or veggie burger.
- Order a salad with low-fat or nonfat dressing served on the side.
- Order steamed vegetables on the side instead of potatoes or rice. If you order potatoes, make sure to get a baked potato (with very little butter or sour cream, on the side).
- Order beverages with few or no Calories, such as water, tea, or diet drinks. Avoid coffee drinks made with syrups, as well as those made with cream, whipping cream, or whole milk.
- Don't feel you have to eat everything you're served. If you feel full, take the rest home for another meal.
- Skip dessert or share one dessert with a lot of friends, or order fresh fruit for dessert.
- Watch out for those "yogurt parfaits" offered at some fast-food restaurants. Many are loaded with sugar, fat, and Calories.

About 1,430 kcal			About 610 kcal
McDonald's Big Mac hamburger French fries, extra large 3 tbsp. ketchup Apple pie			Subway cold cut trio 6" sandwich Granola bar, hard, with chocolate chips, 1 bar (24 g) 1 fresh medium apple

Creative Digital Visions

🔺 **Figure 13** The energy density of two fast-food meals. The meal on the left is higher in total kilocalories and fat, while the meal on the right is lower in kilocalories and fat and is the preferred choice for someone trying to lose weight.

Koichi Kamoshida/Getty Images

🔺 When ordering your favorite coffee drink, avoid flavored syrups, cream, and whipping cream and request reduced-fat or skim milk instead.

Table 5 lists some examples of low-fat foods you can choose when you eat out.[17] Although provided as examples for people with diabetes, they are useful for anyone who is interested in making more healthful food choices while eating out. By choosing healthful foods and appropriate portion sizes, you can eat out regularly and still maintain a healthful body weight.

RECAP Healthful ways to eat out include choosing smaller menu items, ordering meats that are grilled or broiled, avoiding fried foods, choosing items with steamed vegetables, avoiding energy-rich appetizers and desserts, and eating less than half of the food you are served.

TABLE 5　Low-Fat Food Choices Available in Restaurants

Appetizers	Salads	Breads	Entrées	Fats	Desserts
Minestrone soup	Tossed with mixed greens, lettuce, tomato, and cucumber	Whole-grain rolls	Baked halibut with thyme and fresh-squeezed lemon	Diet margarine	Fresh fruit
Chicken soup with vegetables		Corn tortillas		Low-fat/low-Calorie salad dressing	Fruit sorbet
Raw celery and carrots with low-fat or nonfat ranch dressing	Spinach salad with crab meat, raw vegetables, and nonfat salad dressing	Whole-wheat or pumpernickel bread	Grilled skinless chicken breast with tomato salsa	Low-fat sour cream or yogurt	Fat-free or low-fat yogurt

Data from American Diabetes Association. 2007. Your Guide to Eating Out. www.diabetes.org/nutrition-and-recipes/nutrition/eatingoutguide.jsp. Printed with permission.

Nutrition DEBATE

Can Functional Foods Improve Our Health?

Many conventional foods "provide a health benefit beyond basic nutrition" and therefore qualify as functional foods. For example, oatmeal provides carbohydrates, but its soluble fiber also improves bowel function. Other types of functional foods (also called *nutraceuticals*) are processed to create fortified, enriched, or enhanced foods, which provide a higher level of micronutrients than the same foods would supply in an unprocessed form. For example, iodine is added to salt, orange juice is fortified with calcium, and milk is enriched with extra calcium. Sometimes, the health-promoting substances are developed in a functional food by altering the way in which the food is produced. For example, eggs with higher levels of omega-3 fatty acids result from feeding hens a special diet. And produce can be genetically engineered to contain higher levels of nutrients. Dietary supplements also qualify as functional foods.[9]

Are Functional Foods Safe?

The FDA regulates functional foods in the same way it regulates conventional foods. This means that, in order for a food to be allowed on the market, any "functional" ingredient added to that food must be generally recognized as safe.

Recently, other federal agencies and consumer advocacy groups have petitioned the FDA to reevaluate the way it regulates functional foods.[10] They contend that many food companies are making unsubstantiated health claims for their products. They also warn that dozens of products currently sold as foods contain ingredients, such as herbs, that are not FDA-approved for use in foods. They caution that such products could have adverse health effects on vulnerable consumers.

In response to these and other concerns, the FDA is considering a new regulatory system by which any product bearing health claims would be subject to FDA oversight. Thus, not only herbs, but even conventional food ingredients promoted for use in the treatment or prevention of disease in humans, would be subject to FDA control.[11] But until such a system is in effect, consumers should remain skeptical about the safety and effectiveness of functional foods.

Are Functional Foods Effective?

Is there any research to support the claims of health benefits made by manufacturers of functional foods? That depends on the product. So if you're considering regular consumption of a functional food, do your homework. To give you some practice, let's consider one currently on the market—designer yogurt.

People have been consuming yogurt for thousands of years. Yogurt contains live bacteria, called *probiotics* ("pro-life"), which are known to benefit human health. These helpful bacteria reproduce in the food naturally during the production process. Probiotics are also available in supplement form.

How do probiotics work? When a person consumes a product containing probiotics, the bacteria adhere to the intestinal wall for a few days, exerting their beneficial effects. Although their exact actions are currently being researched, it is believed that some crowd out harmful bacterial, viral, and fungal species; some produce nutrients and other helpful substances; and others influence the immune system.[12] They may be beneficial for conditions such as some forms of diarrhea, irritable bowel syndrome, inflammatory bowel disease, lactose intolerance, and certain types of infections.[12-14]

It is important to remember that, in order to be effective, foods containing probiotics must provide an adequate number of bacteria, thought to be 1 to 10 billion.[15] In the United States, the National Yogurt Association has created a "Live Active Culture" seal to be placed on yogurt containers to indicate that the yogurt has an adequate amount of active bacteria per gram. Also, because they can survive in the body for only a limited period of time, probiotics should be consumed daily, and they must be stored properly (usually refrigerated) and consumed within a relatively brief period of time.

Some food manufacturers are employing researchers to find and cultivate strains of probiotic bacteria that have specific health benefits. For example, Activia, a yogurt made by Dannon, contains a probiotic species said to promote regular bowel movements by reducing the time stool stays in the colon. The longer fecal matter remains in the colon, the more water is removed from it, and the harder it gets, so reduced transit time means softer bowel movements. Is this claim valid?

Four studies published in peer-reviewed journals found that consuming three 4-oz servings of Activia a day for 10 to 14 days sped up stool transit time by 10% to 40%. This effect was seen in both men and women. Convinced? If constipation were a problem for you, would you eat Activia three times a day?

Consuming Activia yogurt may improve bowel function.

Kristin Piljay

Chapter Review

Test Yourself ANSWERS

1. False. A healthful diet can be achieved by food alone; particular attention must be paid to adequacy, variety, moderation, and balance. However, some individuals may need to take vitamin supplements under certain circumstances.

2. False. The fact that something is stated on a food label doesn't guarantee it is true! Structure–function claims—such as "Supports healthy bones!" and "Promotes regularity!"—are not regulated by the FDA and may or may not be backed with solid research evidence.

3. False. A cup of black coffee has about 2 kcal. Adding a teaspoon of sugar and a tablespoon of whole milk would increase that amount to about 27 kcal. In contrast, a coffee mocha might contain from 350 to 500 kcal, depending on its size and precise contents.

Find the Quack

Jimena is a 19-year-old sophomore in a small liberal arts college. Everyone in Jimena's family is either overweight or obese, but now that she is away from home and living at an out-of-state school Jimena has become determined to break out of her "family pattern" and lose weight. In a fashion magazine, she reads about a grapefruit diet called the Mayo Clinic Diet. Jimena figures that any diet with a medical clinic behind it must be reputable, so she decides to try it. The diet requires that Jimena eat two eggs and two slices of bacon every morning with an 8-oz glass of grapefruit juice or half a grapefruit; eat a salad, red meat or poultry, and another serving of grapefruit at lunch; and eat a salad, red meat or poultry, and another serving of grapefruit at dinner. No snacks between meals are allowed. The diet is to be followed for 8 weeks: 12 days on the diet followed by 2 days off, then resumption of the diet again.

The magazine article makes the following claims:

- The consumption of grapefruit or grapefruit juice is absolutely essential because the grapefruit "is a catalyst that starts the fat-burning process."
- The consumption of bacon and eggs at breakfast and salad at lunch and dinner is also absolutely essential because these foods combine to promote fat burning.
- Anyone following the diet will lose 52 lb in 8 weeks. No weight loss will occur during the first 4 days, but the average weight loss for the remainder of the 8-week period will be 1 lb a day.

- The diet is safe and healthful if followed as described for 8 weeks.

1. Although you have not yet studied digestion and the absorption of food, do you believe the article's claim that there is something unique about grapefruit that catalyzes (initiates and speeds up) fat burning? Why or why not?

2. If the loss of 1 lb of body weight requires the body to expend 3,500 kcal more than it takes in, do you think it is possible for anyone trying the grapefruit diet to lose 52 lb in 56 days, without any prescribed physical activity and the daily consumption of two eggs, two strips of bacon, three servings of grapefruit, two salads, and two servings of meat or poultry? Why or why not?

3. What two food groups are entirely missing from this diet? Do you think this is problematic for some dieters? Why or why not?

4. Do you believe that this grapefruit diet, which the article refers to as the Mayo Clinic Diet, is truly endorsed by the Mayo Clinic—the medical institution based in Rochester, Minnesota, and known internationally for its high-quality healthcare? Go online and, using your favorite search engine, type in the search terms "grapefruit diet" and "Mayo Clinic." What do you discover?

Answers can be found on the companion website, at www.pearsonhighered.com/thompsonmanore.

 **NutriTools** Check out the companion website at www.pearsonhighered.com/thompsonmanore, or use MyNutritionLab.com, to access interactive animations, including:

- MyPyramid Food Groups
- What's Missing on This Label?

Review Questions

1. The Nutrition Facts Panel identifies which of the following?
   a. all of the nutrients and Calories in the package of food
   b. the Recommended Dietary Allowance for each nutrient in the package of food
   c. a footnote identifying the Tolerable Upper Intake Level for each nutrient in the package of food
   d. the % Daily Values of select nutrients in a serving of the packaged food

2. An adequate diet
   a. provides enough energy to meet minimum daily requirements.
   b. provides enough of the energy, nutrients, and fiber to maintain a person's health.
   c. provides a sufficient variety of nutrients to maintain a healthful weight and to optimize the body's metabolic processes.
   d. contains combinations of foods that provide healthful proportions of nutrients.

3. The USDA Food Guide recommends eating
   a. at least half your grains as whole grains each day.
   b. 6 to 11 servings of milk, cheese, and yogurt each day.
   c. 200 to 500 kcal of discretionary Calories each day.
   d. 2 to 3 servings of fruit juice each day.

4. The Dietary Guidelines for Americans recommend which of the following?
   a. choosing and preparing foods without salt
   b. consuming two alcoholic beverages per day
   c. being physically active each day
   d. following the Mediterranean diet

5. What does it mean to choose foods for their nutrient density?
   a. Dense foods, such as peanut butter and chicken, are more nutritious choices than transparent foods, such as mineral water and gelatin.
   b. Foods with a lot of nutrients per Calorie, such as fish, are more nutritious than foods with fewer nutrients per Calorie, such as candy.
   c. Calorie-dense foods, such as cheesecake, should be avoided.
   d. Fat makes foods dense; thus, foods high in fat should be avoided.

6. True or false? For most foods, the USDA has written a standardized definition of a serving size.

7. True or false? Structure–function claims on food labels must be approved by the FDA.

8. True or false? Discretionary Calories are the extra amount of energy a person can consume after meeting all essential needs through eating nutrient-dense foods.

9. True or false? The USDA Food Guide classifies beans, peas, and lentils in both the vegetables group and the meat and beans group.

10. True or false? More than half of all Americans eat out at least once a week.

Answers to Review Questions can be found at the back of this text, and additional essay questions and answers are located on the companion website, at www.pearsonhighered.com/thompsonmanore.

Web Resources

www.fda.gov
U.S. Food and Drug Administration (FDA)

Learn more about the government agency that regulates our food and first established regulations for nutrition information on food labels.

www.nccam.nih.gov/health/probiotics
National Center for Complementary and Alternative Medicine

The brochure "An Introduction to Probiotics" provides additional information on probiotics.

www.healthierus.gov/dietaryguidelines
Dietary Guidelines for Americans

Use these guidelines to make healthful changes in your food choices and physical activity habits to help reduce your risk for chronic disease.

www.MyPyramid.gov
USDA MyPyramid Steps to a Healthier You

Use the MyPyramid Tracker on this website to assess the overall quality of your diet based on the USDA MyPyramid.

www.oldwayspt.org
Oldways Preservation and Exchange Trust

Find variations of ethnic and cultural food pyramids.

www.hp2010.nhlbihin.net/portion
The National Institutes of Health (NIH) Portion Distortion Quiz

Take this fun quiz to see if you know how today's food portions compare to those of 20 years ago.

www.eatright.org
The American Dietetic Association

Visit the food and nutrition information section of this website for additional resources to help you achieve a healthful lifestyle.

www.hsph.harvard.edu
The Harvard School of Public Health

Search this site to learn more about the Healthy Eating Pyramid, an alternative to the USDA Food Guide Pyramid.

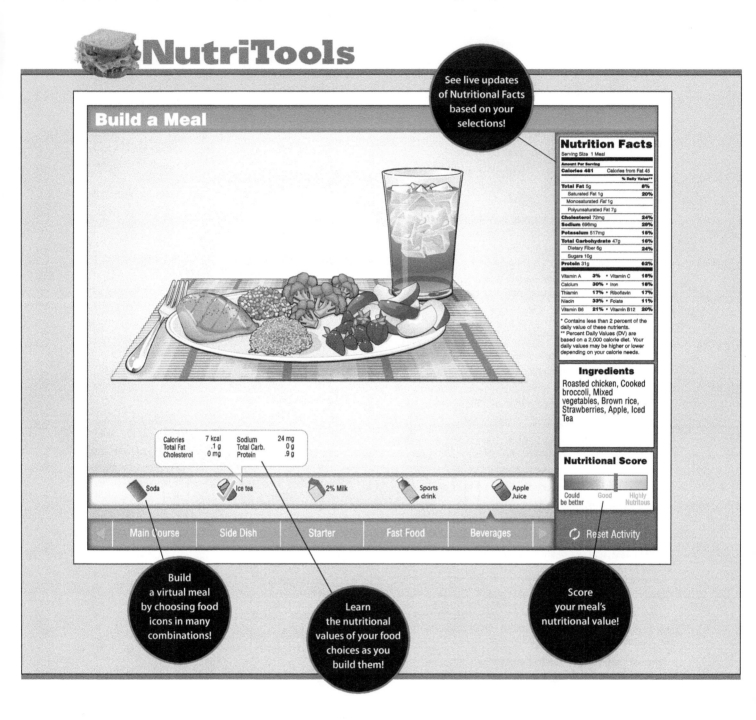

NutriTools

Build a Meal

See live updates of Nutritional Facts based on your selections!

Nutrition Facts
Serving Size 1 Meal

Amount Per Serving		
Calories 481	Calories from Fat 45	
		% Daily Value**
Total Fat 5g		**8%**
Saturated Fat 1g		**20%**
Monosaturated *Fat* 1g		
Polyunsaturated Fat 7g		
Cholesterol 72mg		**24%**
Sodium 696mg		**29%**
Potassium 517mg		**15%**
Total Carbohydrate 47g		**16%**
Dietary Fiber 6g		**24%**
Sugars 10g		
Protein 31g		**62%**

Vitamin A	**3%**	Vitamin C	**15%**
Calcium	**30%**	Iron	**15%**
Thiamin	**17%**	Riboflavin	**17%**
Niacin	**33%**	Folate	**11%**
Vitamin B6	**21%**	Vitamin B12	**20%**

* Contains less than 2 percent of the daily value of these nutrients.
** Percent Daily Values (DV) are based on a 2,000 calorie diet. Your daily values may be higher or lower depending on your calorie needs.

Ingredients

Roasted chicken, Cooked broccoli, Mixed vegetables, Brown rice, Strawberries, Apple, Iced Tea

Nutritional Score

Could be better — Good — Highly Nutritous

Calories	7 kcal	Sodium	24 mg
Total Fat	.1 g	Total Carb.	0 g
Cholesterol	0 mg	Protein	.9 g

Soda · Ice tea · 2% Milk · Sports drink · Apple Juice

Main Course | Side Dish | Starter | Fast Food | Beverages | ↻ Reset Activity

Build a virtual meal by choosing food icons in many combinations!

Learn the nutritional values of your food choices as you build them!

Score your meal's nutritional value!

To build your meal, just visit www.pearsonhighered.com/thompsonmanore or www.mynutritionlab.com

After building your meal, you should be able to answer these questions:

1. Is your meal meeting your kcalorie needs as well as your nutrient needs?
2. How can you build a highly nutritious meal when you do not eat meat?
3. How do you know you're selecting the best options for fruits and vegetables?
4. In what ways can your meal meet your calcium needs if you do not drink milk?
5. Is your beverage choice adding to or subtracting from your overall nutritional score?

References

1. Ogden, C. L., M. D. Carroll, and K. M. Flegal. 2008. High body mass index for age among US children and adolescents, 2003–2006. *JAMA* 299(20): 2401–2405.
2. U.S. Department of Health and Human Services (USDHHS) and U.S. Department of Agriculture (USDA). 2005. Dietary Guidelines for Americans, 2005, 6th edn. Washington, DC: U.S. Government Printing Office. www.healthierus.gov/dietaryguidelines.
3. Nielsen, S. J., and B. M. Popkin. 2003. Patterns and trends in food portion sizes, 1977–1998. *JAMA* 289(4):450–453.
4. Young, L. R., and M. Nestle. 1998. Variation in perceptions of a "medium" food portion: implications for dietary guidance. *J. Am. Diet. Assoc.* 98:458–459.
5. Young, L. R., and M. Nestle. 2002. The contribution of expanding portion sizes to the US obesity epidemic. *Am. J. Pub. Health* 92(2):246–249.
6. Food and Nutrition Information Center. 2006. Dietary Guidance. Ethnic/Cultural Food Pyramid. http://fnic.nal.usda.gov/nal_display/index.php?info_center=4&tax_level=3&tax_subject=256&topic_id=1348&level3_id=5732.
7. Taylor, P., C. Funk, and P. Craighill. 2006. Eating More; Enjoying Less. Pew Research Center. A Social Trends Report. http://pewresearch.org/assets/social/pdf/Eating.pdf. (Accessed March 2007.)
8. Ogden, C. L., M. D. Carroll, M. A. McDowell, and K. M. Flegal. 2007. Obesity Among Adults in the United States—No Change Since 2003-2004. NCHS data brief no 1. Hyattsville, MD: National Center for Health Statistics. Available at http://www.cdc.gov/nchs/data/databriefs/db01.pdf.
9. Institute of Food Technologists. Functional foods: Opportunities and challenges. IFT Expert Report. Available at http://members.ift.org/NR/rdonlyres/4D40132D-B06B-4F2B-9753-CE18B73E187E/0/OnePagerIntro.pdf.
10. Federal Register, October 25, 2006 (Volume 71, Number 206). From the Federal Register Online via GPO Access [wais.access.gpo.gov] [DOCID:fr25oc06-12] Food and Drug Administration, HHS; 21 CFR Parts 101 and 170 [Docket No. 2002P-0122] (formerly 02P-0122). Conventional Foods Being Marketed as "Functional Foods"; Public Hearing; Request for Comments.
11. U.S. Food and Drug Administration (FDA). 2006. Docket No. 2006D-0480. Draft Guidance for Industry on Complementary and Alternative Medicine Products and Their Regulation by the Food and Drug Administration.
12. Saier, M. H., Jr., and N. M. Mansour. 2005. Probiotics and prebiotics in human health. *J. Mol. Microbiol. Biotechnol.* 10(1):22–25.
13. Doron, S., and S. L. Gorbach. 2006. Probiotics: Their role in the treatment and prevention of diseases. *Expert Rev. Anti-Infect. Ther.* 4(2):261–275.
14. Ezendam, J., and H. van Loveren. 2006. Probiotics: Immunomodulation and evaluation of safety and efficacy. *Nutr. Rev.* 64(1):1–14.
15. Sanders, M. E., D. C. Walker, K. M. Walker, K. Aoyama, and T. R. Klaenhammer. 1996. Performance of commercial cultures in fluid milk applications. *J. Dairy Sci.* 79:943–955.

Answers to Review Questions

Answers to Review Questions 11-15 (essay questions) for this chapter are located on the Companion Website at **www.pearsonhighered.com/thompsonmanore**

1. **d.** The % Daily Values of select nutrients in a serving of the packaged food.
2. **b.** provides enough of the energy, nutrients, and fiber to maintain a person's health.
3. **a.** at least half your grains as whole grains each day.
4. **c.** Being physically active each day.
5. **b.** Foods with a lot of nutrients per calorie, such as fish, are more nutritious choices than foods with fewer nutrients per calorie, such as candy.
6. False. There is no standardized definition for a serving size for foods.
7. False. Structure-function claims can be made wihout FDA approval.
8. True.
9. True.
10. False. A Pew Research Center report states that about one-third of Americans eat out about once a week, and another one-third eat out two or more times per week.

The Human Body: Are We Really What We Eat?

From Chapter 3 of *Nutrition: An Applied Approach*, Third Edition. Janice Thompson, Melinda Manore. Copyright © 2012 by Pearson Education, Inc. Published by Pearson Benjamin Cummings. All rights reserved.

The Human Body: Are We Really What We Eat?

CHAPTER OBJECTIVES

After reading this chapter you will be able to:

1. Distinguish between appetite and hunger, describing the mechanisms that stimulate each.

2. Describe what is meant by the expression "You are what you eat".

3. Identify two functions of the cell membrane.

4. Draw a picture of the gastrointestinal tract, labeling all major and accessory organs.

5. Describe the contribution of each organ of the gastrointestinal system to the digestion, absorption, and elimination of food.

6. Discuss the causes, symptoms, and treatments of gastroesophageal reflux disease, ulcers, diarrhea, constipation, and irritable bowel syndrome.

JGI/Jamie Grill/Getty Images

Test Yourself

1. (T) (F) Sometimes we have an appetite even though we are not hungry.

2. (T) (F) The entire process of the digestion and absorption of one meal takes about 24 hours.

3. (T) (F) Most ulcers result from a type of infection.

Test Yourself answers can be found at the end of the chapter.

Two months ago, Andrea's lifelong dream of becoming a lawyer came one step closer to reality: she moved out of her parents' home in the Midwest to attend law school in Boston. Unfortunately, adjusting to a new city and new friends, and her intensive course work has been more stressful than she'd imagined, and Andrea has been experiencing insomnia and exhaustion. What's more, her always "sensitive stomach" has been getting worse: after almost every meal, she gets cramps so bad she can't stand up, and twice she has missed classes because of sudden attacks of pain and diarrhea. She suspects that the problem is related to stress and wonders if she is going to experience it throughout her life. She is even thinking of dropping out of school if that would make her feel well again.

Almost everyone experiences brief episodes of abdominal pain, diarrhea, or other symptoms from time to time. Such episodes are usually caused by food poisoning or an infection, such as influenza. But do you know anyone who experiences these symptoms periodically for days, weeks, or even years? If so, has it made you wonder why? What are the steps in normal digestion and absorption of food, and at what points can the process break down?

We begin this chapter with a look at some of the factors that make us feel as if we want to eat. We'll then discuss the physiologic processes by which the body digests and absorbs food and eliminates waste products. Finally, we'll look at some disorders that affect these processes.

Why Do We Want to Eat What We Want to Eat?

Jean Luc Morales/Getty Images

Food stimulates our senses.

You've just finished eating at your favorite Thai restaurant. As you walk back to the block where you parked your car, you pass a bakery window displaying several cakes and pies, each of which looks more enticing than the last, and through the door wafts a complex aroma of coffee, cinnamon, and chocolate. You stop. You know you're not hungry, but you go inside and buy a slice of chocolate torte and an espresso, anyway. Later that night, when the caffeine from the chocolate and espresso keeps you awake, you wonder why you succumbed.

Two mechanisms prompt us to seek food: hunger and appetite. **Hunger** is a physiologic drive for food that occurs when our body senses that we need to eat. The drive is *nonspecific;* when you're hungry, a variety of foods could satisfy you. If you've recently finished a nourishing meal, then hunger probably won't compel you toward a slice of chocolate torte. Instead, the culprit is likely to be **appetite,** a psychological desire to consume *specific* foods. It is aroused when environmental cues—such as the sight of chocolate cake or the smell of coffee—stimulate your senses, triggering pleasant emotions and memories.

People commonly experience appetite in the absence of hunger. That's why you can crave cake and coffee even after eating a full meal. On the other hand, it is possible to have a physiologic need for food yet have no appetite. This state, called **anorexia,** can accompany a variety of illnesses from infectious diseases to mood disorders. It can also occur as a side effect of certain medications, such as the chemotherapy used in treating cancer patients. Although the following sections describe hunger and appetite as separate entities, ideally the two states coexist: we seek specific, appealing foods to satisfy a physiologic need for nutrients.

The Hypothalamus Prompts Hunger in Response to Various Signals

Howard Kingsnorth/Getty Images

Hunger is a physiologic stimulus that prompts us to find food and eat.

Because hunger is a physiologic stimulus that drives us to find food and eat, we often feel it as a negative or unpleasant sensation. The primary organ producing that sensation is the brain. That's right—it's not our stomach but our brain that tells us when we're hungry. The region of brain tissue responsible for prompting us to seek food is called the **hypothalamus (Figure 1)**. It's located above the pituitary gland in the forebrain, a region that regulates many types of involuntary activity. The hypothalamus triggers feelings of either hunger or satiation (fullness) by integrating signals from three sources: nerve cells, chemicals called *hormones*, and the amount and type of food we eat. Let's review these three types of signals.

The Role of Nerve Cells

One important signal comes from nerve cells lining the stomach and small intestine that detect changes in pressure according to whether the organ is empty or distended with food. The cells relay these data to the hypothalamus. For instance, if you have not eaten for many hours and your stomach and small intestine do not contain food, these data are sent to the hypothalamus, which in turn prompts you to experience the sensation of hunger.

The Role of Hormones

Hormones are chemical messengers that are secreted into the bloodstream by one of the many *glands* of the body. The presence of different hormones in the blood helps regulate body functions. Insulin and glucagon are two hormones responsible for maintaining blood glucose levels. Glucose is our body's most readily available fuel supply. It's not surprising, then, that its level in the blood is an important signal af-

hunger A physiologic sensation that prompts us to eat.

appetite A psychological desire to consume specific foods.

anorexia An absence of appetite.

hypothalamus A region of forebrain above the pituitary gland, where visceral sensations, such as hunger and thirst, are regulated.

hormone A chemical messenger secreted into the bloodstream by one of the many glands of the body, which acts as a regulator of physiologic processes at a site remote from the gland that secreted it.

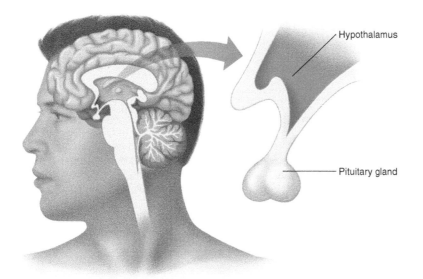

Figure 1 The hypothalamus triggers hunger by integrating signals from nerve cells throughout the body, as well as from messages carried by hormones.

fecting hunger. When we have not eaten for a while, our blood glucose levels fall, prompting a change in the level of insulin and glucagon. This chemical message is relayed to the hypothalamus, which then prompts us to eat in order to supply our body with more glucose.

After we eat, the hypothalamus picks up the sensation of a distended stomach, other signals from the gut, and a rise in blood glucose levels. When it integrates these signals, you have the experience of feeling full, or *satiated*. However, as we have noted, even though our brain sends us clear signals about hunger, most of us become adept at ignoring them and eat when we are not truly hungry.

In addition to insulin and glucagon, a variety of other hormones and hormone-like substances signal the hypothalamus to cause us to feel hungry or satiated. More details about the hormones involved in digestion are provided later in this chapter.

The Role of the Amount and Type of Food

Although the reason behind this observation is not understood, researchers have long recognized that foods containing protein have the highest satiety value.[1] This means that a ham and egg breakfast will cause us to feel satiated for a longer period of time than will pancakes with maple syrup, even if both meals have exactly the same number of Calories.

Another factor affecting hunger is how bulky the meal is—that is, how much fiber and water is within the food. Bulky meals tend to stretch the stomach and small intestine, which sends signals back to the hypothalamus telling us that we are full, so we stop eating. Beverages tend to be less satisfying than semisolid foods, and semisolid foods have a lower satiety value than solid foods. For example, if you were to eat a bunch of grapes, you would feel a greater sense of fullness than if you drank a glass of grape juice.

RECAP In contrast to appetite, hunger is a physiologic sensation triggered by the hypothalamus in response to cues about stomach and intestinal distention and the levels of certain hormones and hormone-like substances. High-protein foods make us feel satiated for longer periods of time, and bulky meals fill us up quickly, causing the distention that signals us to stop eating.

Environmental Cues Trigger Appetite

Whereas hunger is prompted by internal signals, appetite is triggered by aspects of our environment. The most significant factors influencing our appetite are sensory data, social and cultural cues, and learning **(Figure 2)**.

The Role of Sensory Data

Foods stimulate our five senses. Foods that are artfully prepared, arranged, or ornamented, with several different shapes and colors, appeal to our sense of sight. The aromas of foods such as freshly brewed coffee and baked goods can also be powerful stimulants. Much of our ability to taste foods actually comes from our sense of smell. This is why foods are not as appealing when we have a stuffy nose due to a cold. Certain tastes, such as sweetness, are almost universally appealing, while others, such as the astringent taste of some foods (for instance, spinach and kale), are quite individual. Texture, or "mouth feel," is also important in food choices, as it stimulates nerve endings sensitive to touch in our mouth and on our tongue. Even our sense of hearing can be stimulated by foods, from the fizz of cola to the crunch of pretzels.

The Role of Social and Cultural Cues

In addition to sensory cues, our brain's association with certain social events, such as birthday parties and holiday gatherings, can stimulate our appetite. At these times, our culture gives us permission to eat more than usual or to eat "forbidden" foods. Even when we feel full, these cues can motivate us to accept a second helping.

For some people, being in a certain location, such as at a baseball game or a movie theatre, can trigger appetite. Others may be influenced by activities such as watching television or at certain times of the day associated with mealtimes. Many people feel an increase or a decrease in appetite according to whom they are with; for example, they may eat more when at home with family members and less when out on a date.

In some people, appetite masks an emotional response to an external event. For example, a person might experience a desire for food rather than a desire for emo-

Figure 2 Appetite is a drive to consume specific foods, such as popcorn at the movies. It is aroused by social and cultural cues and sensory data and is influenced by learning.

66

Prescription Appetite Suppressants: Help or Harm?

The manufacturers of three new appetite suppressants are hoping for Food and Drug Administration (FDA) approval of their drugs, but smooth sailing isn't guaranteed. Such drugs typically work by influencing the central nervous system, and they can cause serious psychological side effects. In 2007, for example, a similar drug failed to win FDA approval because of its links to depression and suicidal thoughts. Another concern related to appetite suppressants is their effect on the heart and circulatory system. In the 1990s, two were removed from the market because of drug-related damage to heart valves, and one drug currently on the market, Meridia, can increase blood pressure and heart rate. Another problem is the drugs' limited effectiveness: many work for a short while, but, when weight goes down, appetite surges back again.[2]

tional comfort after receiving a failing grade or arguing with a close friend. Many people crave food when they're frustrated, worried, or bored or when they're at a gathering where they feel anxious or awkward. Others subconsciously seek food as a "reward." For example, have you ever found yourself heading out for a burger and fries after handing in a term paper?

The Role of Learning

Pigs' feet, anyone? What about blood sausage, stewed octopus, or snakes? These are delicacies in various cultures. Would you eat grasshoppers? If you'd grown up in certain parts of Africa or Central America, you might. That's because your preference for particular foods is largely a learned response. The culture in which you are raised teaches you what plant and animal products are appropriate to eat. If your parents fed you cubes of plain tofu throughout your toddlerhood, then you are probably still eating tofu.

That said, early introduction to foods is not essential: we can learn to enjoy new foods at any point in our lives. For instance, many immigrants adopt a diet typical of their new home, especially when their traditional foods are not readily available. This happens temporarily when we travel: the last time you were away from home, you probably sampled a variety of dishes that are not normally part of your diet.

Food preferences also change when people learn what foods are most healthful. Chances are, as you learn more about the health benefits of specific types of carbohydrates, fats, and proteins, you'll start incorporating more of these foods in your diet.

We can also "learn" to dislike foods we once enjoyed. For example, if we experience an episode of food poisoning after eating undercooked scrambled eggs, we might develop a

Paul Poplis/Foodpix/Jupiter Images

🔺 Food preferences are influenced by the family and culture you are raised in.

strong distaste for all types of eggs. Many adults who become vegetarians do so after learning about the treatment of animals in slaughterhouses: they might have eaten meat daily when young but no longer have any appetite for it.

Now that you understand the differences between appetite and hunger, as well as the influence of learning on food choices, you might be curious to investigate your own reasons for eating what and when you do. If so, check out the self-assessment box What About You: Do You Eat in Response to External or Internal Cues?

RECAP In contrast to hunger, appetite is a psychological desire to consume specific foods. It is triggered when external stimuli arouse our senses, and it often occurs in combination with social and cultural cues. Our preference for certain foods is largely learned from the culture in which we were raised, but our food choices can change with exposure to new foods or through new learning experiences.

What About You?

Do You Eat in Response to External or Internal Cues?

Whether you're trying to lose weight, gain weight, or maintain your current weight, you might find it intriguing to keep a log of the reasons behind your decisions about what, when, where, and why you eat. Are you eating in response to internal sensations telling you that your body needs food, or in response to your emotions, your situation, or a prescribed diet? Keeping a "cues" log for 1 full week would give you the most accurate picture of your eating habits, but even logging 2 days of meals and snacks should increase your cue awareness.

Each day, every time you eat a meal, snack, or beverage other than water, make a quick note of the following:

- **When you eat:** Many people eat at certain times (for example, 6 PM) whether they are hungry or not.
- **What you eat, and how much:** Do you choose a cup of yogurt and a 6-oz glass of orange juice or a candy bar and a 20-oz cola?
- **Where you eat:** At home, watching television; on the subway; and so on.
- **With whom you eat:** Are you alone or with others? If with others, are they also eating? Have they offered you food?
- **Your emotions:** Some people overeat when they are happy, others when they are anxious, depressed, bored, or frustrated. Still others eat as a way of denying feelings they don't want to identify and deal with. For some, food becomes a substitute for emotional fulfillment.
- **Your sensations—what you see, hear, or smell:** Are you eating because you just saw a TV commercial for pizza, or smelled homemade cookies?

- **Any dietary restrictions:** Are you choosing a particular food because it is allowed on your current diet plan? Or are you hungry for a meal but drinking a diet soda to stay within a certain allowance of Calories? Are you restricting yourself because you feel guilty about having eaten too much at another time?
- **Your physiologic hunger:** Finally, rate your hunger on a scale from 1 to 5 as follows:

  1 = you feel uncomfortably full or even stuffed
  2 = you feel satisfied but not uncomfortably full
  3 = neutral; you feel no discernible satiation or hunger
  4 = you feel hungry and want to eat
  5 = you feel strong physiologic sensations of hunger and need to eat

After keeping a log for 2 or more days, you might become aware of patterns you'd like to change. For example, maybe you notice that you often eat when you are not actually hungry but are worried about homework or personal relationships. Or maybe you notice that you can't walk past the snack bar without going in. This self-awareness may prompt you to change those patterns. For instance, instead of stifling your worries with food, you could write down exactly what you are worried about, including steps you can take to address your concerns. And the next time you approach the snack bar, you could check with your gut: are you truly hungry? If so, then purchase a healthful snack, maybe a piece of fruit or a bag of peanuts. If you're not really hungry, then take a moment to acknowledge the strength of this visual cue— and then walk on by.

NUTRI-CASE JUDY

"Ever since I was diagnosed with type 2 diabetes, I've felt as if there's a 'food cop' spying on me. Sometimes I feel like I have to look over my shoulder when I pull into the Dunkin' Donuts parking lot. My doctor says I'm supposed to eat fresh fruits and vegetables, fish, brown bread, brown rice . . . I didn't bother telling him I don't like that stuff and I don't have the money to buy it or the time to cook it even if I did. Besides, that kind of diet is for movie stars. All the real people I know eat the same way I do."

According to what you learned in Designing a Healthful Diet, is the diet Judy's doctor described really just for "movie stars"? Of the many factors influencing why we eat what we eat, identify at least two that might be affecting Judy's food choices. If you learned that Judy had not finished high school, would that fact have any bearing on your answer? If so, in what way?

George Doyle & Ciaran Griffin/Stockbyte/Getty Images

Are We Really What We Eat?

You've no doubt heard over and over again the saying "You are what you eat." Is this scientifically true? To answer that question, and to better understand how we digest and process foods, we'll need to look at how our body is organized **(Figure 3)**.

Atoms Bond to Form Molecules

Like all substances on earth, our body is made up of atoms. Atoms are tiny units of matter that cannot be broken down by natural means. Atoms almost constantly bind to each other in nature. When they do, they form groups called molecules. For example, a molecule of water is composed of two atoms of hydrogen and an atom of oxygen, which is abbreviated H_2O.

Every bite of food we eat is composed of molecules. The actions of digestion break food down into molecules small enough to be absorbed easily through the gastrointestinal wall and transported in the bloodstream to every part of the body. We use these molecules to help build body structures, to assemble whatever chemicals we need, and to provide the energy we must have to live.

Molecules Join to Form Cells

Cells are the smallest units of life. That is, cells can grow, reproduce, and perform certain basic functions, such as taking in nutrients, transmitting impulses, producing chemicals, and excreting wastes. The human body is composed of billions of cells, many of which have short life spans and must be replaced continually. To support this demand for new cells, we need a ready supply of nutrient molecules to serve as building blocks. All cells, whether of the skin, bones, or brain, are made of the same basic nutrient molecules, which are derived from the foods we eat.

cell The smallest unit of matter that exhibits the properties of living things, such as growth, reproduction, and metabolism.

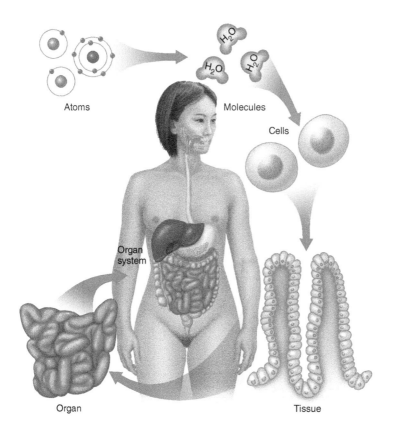

Atoms

Molecules

Cells

Organ system

Organ

Tissue

◀ **Figure 3** The organization of the human body. Atoms bind together to form molecules, and the body's cells are composed of molecules of the food we eat. Cells join to form tissues, one or more types of which form organs, such as the small intestine. Body systems, such as the gastrointestinal system, are made up of several organs, each of which performs a discrete function within that system.

69

Cells Are Encased in a Functional Membrane

Cells are encased by a thin covering called a **cell membrane** (Figure 4). This membrane defines the cell's boundaries: it encloses the cell's contents and acts as a gatekeeper, either allowing or denying the entry and exit of molecules, such as nutrients and wastes.

Cell membranes are composed of two layers of molecules called phospholipids, which consist of a long lipid "tail" that repels water, bound to a round phosphate "head" that interacts with water. Located throughout the membrane are molecules of another lipid, cholesterol, which helps keep the membrane flexible. The membrane is also studded with various proteins, which assist in the gatekeeper function, allowing the transport of nutrients and other substances across the cell membrane.

Cells Contain Organelles, Which Support Life

The cell membrane encloses the semiliquid **cytoplasm** (Figure 4), which includes a variety of **organelles**. These tiny structures accomplish some surprisingly sophisticated functions. A full description of all the organelles and their roles is beyond the scope of this book. In terms of nutrition, the most important are the following:

- *Nucleus.* The nucleus is where our genetic information, in the form of deoxyribonucleic acid (DNA), is located. The cell nucleus is darkly colored because DNA is a huge molecule that is tightly packed within it. A cell's DNA contains the instructions that the cell uses to make certain proteins.
- *Ribosomes.* Ribosomes use the instructions from DNA to assemble proteins.
- *Endoplasmic reticulum (ER).* Proteins assembled on the ribosomes enter this network of channels and are further processed and packaged for transport. The ER is also responsible for the breakdown of lipids and for storage of the mineral calcium.

cell membrane The boundary of an animal cell that separates its internal cytoplasm and organelles from the external environment.

cytoplasm The interior of an animal cell, not including its nucleus.

organelle A tiny "organ" within a cell that performs a discrete function necessary to the cell.

▶ **Figure 4** Representative cell of the small intestine, showing the cell membrane, cytoplasm, and a variety of organelles. The cell membrane is a double layer of phospholipid molecules, aligned such that the lipid tails form a water-repellant interior, whereas the phosphate heads interact with the fluids inside and outside the cell. The fluid inside the cell is the cytoplasm. Within it are a variety of organelles.

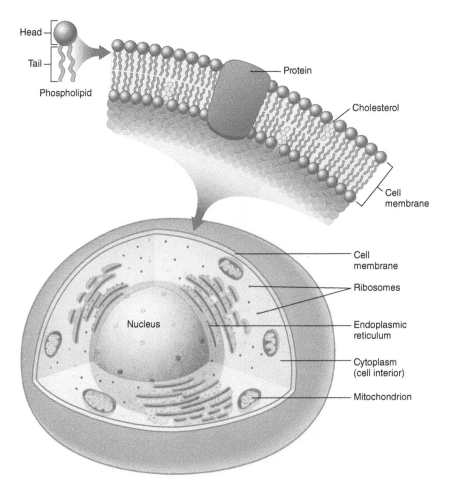

- *Mitochondria.* Often called the cell's powerhouses, mitochondria produce the energy molecule adenosine triphosphate (ATP) from basic food components. ATP can be thought of as a stored form of energy that can be drawn upon as we need it. Cells that have high energy needs—such as muscle cells—contain more mitochondria than do cells with lower energy needs.

Cells Join to Form Tissues, Organs, and Systems

Cells of a single type, such as muscle cells, join to form functional sheets or cords of cells called **tissues.** We'll cover some of the unique tissues of the gastrointestinal tract later in this chapter. In general, several types of tissues join together to form **organs,** which are sophisticated structures that perform a unique body function. The stomach and the small intestine are examples of organs.

Organs are further grouped into **systems** that perform integrated functions. The stomach, for example, is an organ that is part of the gastrointestinal system. It holds and partially digests a meal, but it can't perform all the system functions—digestion, absorption, and elimination—by itself. These functions require the cooperation of several organs. In the next section, we'll see how the organs of the gastrointestinal system work together to accomplish digestion and the absorption of foods and elimination of waste products.

RECAP Atoms join to form molecules. Cells, the smallest units of life, are encased in a membrane and contain functional units called organelles. Different cell types give rise to different tissue types and ultimately to all of the different organs of the body. A system is a group of organs that together accomplish a discrete body function, such as digestion.

What Happens to the Food We Eat?

When we eat, the food is digested, then the useful nutrients are absorbed, and finally the waste products are eliminated. But what does each of these processes really entail? In the simplest terms, **digestion** is the process by which foods are broken down into their component molecules, either mechanically or chemically. **Absorption** is the process of taking these products of digestion through the wall of the small intestine into the circulation. **Elimination** is the process by which the remaining waste is removed from the body.

Digestion, absorption, and elimination occur in the **gastrointestinal (GI) tract,** the organs of which work together to process foods. The GI tract is a long tube: if held out straight, an adult GI tract would be close to 30 feet long. Food within this tube is digested into molecules small enough to be absorbed by the cells lining the GI tract and thereby passed into the bloodstream.

The GI tract begins at the mouth and ends at the anus **(Figure 5)**. It is composed of several distinct organs, including the mouth, esophagus, stomach, small intestine, and large intestine. The flow of food between these organs is controlled by muscular **sphincters,** which are tight rings of muscle that open when a nerve signal indicates that food is ready to pass into the next section. Surrounding the GI tract are several accessory organs, including the salivary glands, liver, pancreas, and gallbladder, each of which has a specific role in digestion and the absorption of nutrients.

Now let's take a look at the role of each of these organs in processing the food we eat. Imagine that you ate a turkey sandwich for lunch today. It contained two slices of bread spread with mayonnaise, some turkey, two lettuce leaves, and a slice of tomato. Let's travel along with the sandwich and see what happens as it enters your GI tract and is digested and absorbed into your body.

Digestion Begins in the Mouth

Believe it or not, the first step in the digestive process is not your first bite of that sandwich. It is your first thought about what you want for lunch and your first whiff

tissue A grouping of like cells that performs a function; for example, muscle tissue.

organ A body structure composed of two or more tissues and performing a specific function; for example, the esophagus.

system A group of organs that work together to perform a unique function; for example, the gastrointestinal system.

digestion The process by which foods are broken down into their component molecules, either mechanically or chemically.

absorption The physiologic process by which molecules of food are taken from the gastrointestinal tract into the circulation.

elimination The process by which undigested portions of food and waste products are removed from the body.

gastrointestinal (GI) tract A long, muscular tube consisting of several organs: the mouth, esophagus, stomach, small intestine, and large intestine.

sphincter A tight ring of muscle separating some of the organs of the GI tract and opening in response to nerve signals indicating that food is ready to pass into the next section.

Figure 5 An overview of the gastrointestinal (GI) tract. The GI tract begins in the mouth and ends at the anus and is composed of numerous organs.

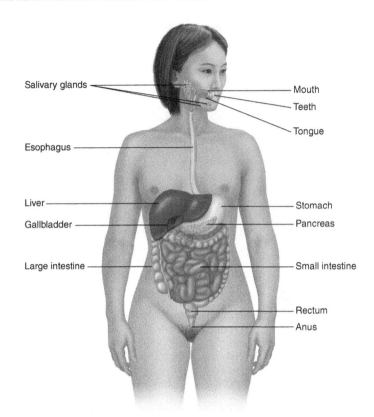

Jonelle Weaver/Taxi/Getty Images

Digestion of a sandwich starts before you even take a bite.

cephalic phase The earliest phase of digestion, in which the brain thinks about and prepares the digestive organs for the consumption of food.

saliva A mixture of water, mucus, enzymes, and other chemicals that moistens the mouth and food, binds food particles together, and begins the digestion of carbohydrates.

salivary glands A group of glands found under and behind the tongue and beneath the jaw that release saliva continually as well as in response to the thought, sight, smell, or presence of food.

enzymes Small chemicals, usually proteins, that act on other chemicals to speed up body processes but are not apparently changed during those processes.

of turkey and freshly baked bread as you stand in line at the deli. In this **cephalic phase** of digestion, hunger and appetite work together to prepare the GI tract to digest food. The nervous system stimulates the release of digestive juices in preparation for food entering the GI tract, and sometimes we experience some involuntary movement commonly called "hunger pangs."

Now let's stop smelling that sandwich and take a bite and chew! Chewing moistens the food and breaks it down into pieces small enough to swallow **(Figure 6)**. Thus, chewing initiates the mechanical digestion of food. The tough coating surrounding the lettuce fibers and tomato seeds is also broken open, facilitating digestion. This is especially important when we're eating foods that are high in fiber, such as grains, fruits, and vegetables. Chewing also mixes everything in your sandwich together: the protein in the turkey; the carbohydrates in the bread, lettuce, and tomato; the fat in the mayonnaise; and the vitamins, minerals, and water in all of the foods.

The presence of food in your mouth also initiates chemical digestion. As your teeth cut and grind the different foods in your sandwich, more surface area is exposed to the digestive juices in your mouth. Foremost among these is **saliva,** which you secrete from your **salivary glands.** Saliva not only moistens your food but also begins the process of chemical breakdown. One component of saliva, called *amylase,* starts the process of carbohydrate digestion. Saliva also contains other components, such as antibodies that protect the body from foreign bacteria entering the mouth and keep the oral cavity free from infection.

Salivary amylase is the first of many **enzymes** that assist the body in digesting and absorbing food. Since we will encounter enzymes throughout our journey through the GI tract, let's discuss them briefly here. Enzymes are small chemicals, usually proteins, that act on other chemicals to speed up body processes. Imagine them as facilitators: a chemical reaction that might take an hour to occur independently might happen in a few seconds with the help of one or more enzymes. Because they remain essentially unchanged by the chemical reactions they facilitate, enzymes can be reused repeatedly. The action of enzymes can result in the production of new substances or can assist in breaking substances apart. Our body makes hundreds of enzymes, and the process of

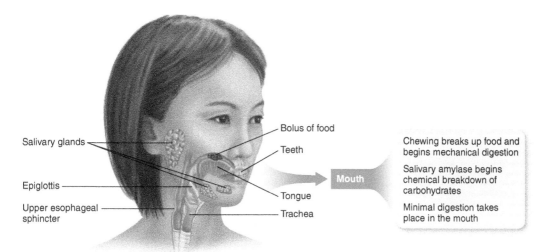

Salivary glands

Epiglottis

Upper esophageal
sphincter

Bolus of food

Teeth

Tongue

Trachea

Mouth

Chewing breaks up food and
begins mechanical digestion

Salivary amylase begins
chemical breakdown of
carbohydrates

Minimal digestion takes
place in the mouth

Figure 6 Where your food is now: the mouth. Chewing moistens food and mechanically breaks it down into pieces small enough to swallow, while salivary amylase begins the chemical digestion of carbohydrates.

digestion—as well as many other biochemical processes that go on in our body—could not happen without them. By the way, enzyme names typically end in –*ase* (as in *amylase*), so they are easy to recognize as we look at the digestive process.

In reality, very little digestion occurs in the mouth. This is because we do not hold food in the mouth for very long and because not all of the enzymes needed to break down food are present in saliva. Salivary amylase starts the digestion of carbohydrates in the mouth, and this digestion continues until food reaches the stomach. There, salivary amylase is destroyed by the acidic environment of the stomach.

RECAP Digestion, absorption, and elimination take place in the gastrointestinal (GI) tract. In the cephalic phase of digestion, hunger and appetite work together to prepare the GI tract for digestion and absorption. Chewing initiates mechanical digestion by breaking the food mass apart and mixing it together. The release of saliva moistens food and starts the process of chemical digestion of carbohydrates through the action of the enzyme salivary amylase.

The Esophagus Propels Food into the Stomach

The mass of food that has been chewed and moistened in the mouth is referred to as a **bolus.** This bolus is swallowed **(Figure 7)** and propelled to the stomach through the esophagus. Most of us take swallowing for granted. However, it is a very complex process involving voluntary and involuntary motion. A tiny flap of tissue called the *epiglottis* acts as a trapdoor covering the entrance to the trachea (windpipe). The epiglottis is normally open, allowing us to breathe freely even while chewing (Figure 7a). As a food bolus moves to the very back of the mouth, the brain is sent a signal to temporarily raise the soft palate and close the openings to the nasal passages, preventing the aspiration of food or liquid into the sinuses (Figure 7b). The brain also signals the epiglottis to close during swallowing, so that food and liquid cannot enter the trachea.

Sometimes this protective mechanism goes awry—for instance, when we try to eat and talk at the same time. When this happens, food or liquid enters the trachea. Typically, this causes us to cough involuntarily and repeatedly until the offending food or liquid is expelled.

As the trachea closes, the sphincter muscle at the top of the esophagus, called the *upper esophageal sphincter*, opens to allow the passage of food. The **esophagus** is a

bolus A mass of food that has been chewed and moistened in the mouth.

esophagus A muscular tube of the GI tract connecting the back of the mouth to the stomach.

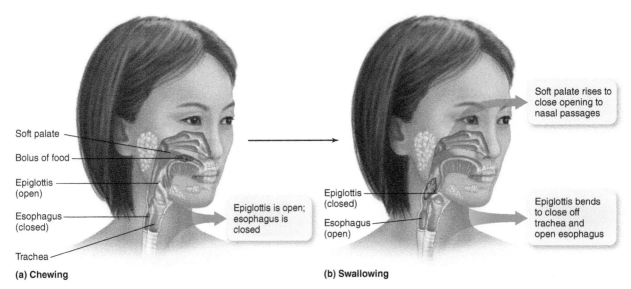

Soft palate

Bolus of food

Epiglottis
(open)

Esophagus
(closed)

Trachea

Epiglottis is open;
esophagus is
closed

(a) Chewing

Soft palate rises to
close opening to
nasal passages

Epiglottis
(closed)

Esophagus
(open)

Epiglottis bends
to close off
trachea and
open esophagus

(b) Swallowing

◆ **Figure 7** Chewing and swallowing are complex processes. **(a)** During the process of chewing, the epiglottis is open and the esophagus is closed, so that we can continue to breathe as we chew. **(b)** During swallowing, the epiglottis closes, so that food does not enter the trachea and obstruct our breathing. Also, the soft palate rises to seal off our nasal passages to prevent the aspiration of food or liquid into the sinuses.

peristalsis Waves of squeezing and pushing contractions that move food in one direction through the length of the GI tract.

muscular tube that connects and transports food from the mouth to the stomach (Figure 8). It does this by contracting two sets of muscles: inner sheets of circular muscle squeeze the food while outer sheets of longitudinal muscle push food along the length of the tube. Together, these rhythmic waves of squeezing and pushing are called **peristalsis.** We will see later in this chapter that peristalsis occurs throughout the GI tract.

Gravity also helps transport food down the esophagus, which explains why it is wise to sit or stand upright while eating. Together, peristalsis and gravity can transport a bite of food from our mouth to the opening of the stomach in 5 to 8 seconds. At the end of the esophagus is a sphincter muscle, the *gastroesophageal sphincter* (*gastro-* means "stomach"), which is normally tightly closed. When food reaches the end of the esophagus, this sphincter relaxes to allow the food to pass into the stomach. In some people, this sphincter is continually somewhat relaxed. Later in the chapter, we'll discuss this disorder and the unpleasant symptoms it causes.

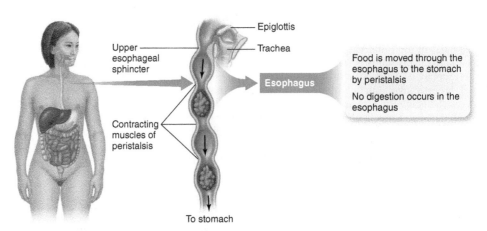

Upper
esophageal
sphincter

Epiglottis

Trachea

Esophagus

Food is moved through the
esophagus to the stomach
by peristalsis

No digestion occurs in the
esophagus

Contracting
muscles of
peristalsis

To stomach

◆ **Figure 8** Where your food is now: the esophagus. Peristalsis, the rhythmic contraction and relaxation of both circular and longitudinal muscles in the esophagus, propels food toward the stomach. Peristalsis occurs throughout the GI tract.

The Stomach Mixes, Digests, and Stores Food

The **stomach** is a J-shaped organ. Its size is fairly individual; in general, its volume is about 6 fl. oz (3/4 cup) when it is empty. When the stomach is full, it can expand to hold about 32 fl. oz, or about 4 cups. Before any food reaches the stomach, the brain sends signals, telling it to be ready for the food to arrive. This causes an increased secretion of **gastric juice,** which contains several important compounds:

- *Hydrochloric acid (HCl)* keeps the stomach interior very acidic—more so than many citrus juices. This acidic environment kills many of the bacteria that may have entered your body with your sandwich. HCl also starts to **denature** proteins, which means it uncoils the bonds that maintain their structure. This is an important preliminary step in protein digestion.
- HCl also converts *pepsinogen,* an inactive substance, into the active enzyme *pepsin,* which begins to digest proteins into smaller components. In addition, pepsin activates many other GI enzymes needed to digest your meal.
- *Gastric lipase* is an enzyme responsible for fat (lipid) digestion. It begins to break apart the fat in the turkey and the mayonnaise in your sandwich; however, only minimal digestion of fat occurs in the stomach.
- Your stomach also secretes *mucus,* which protects its lining from being digested by the HCl and pepsin.

With these gastric juices already present, the chemical digestion of proteins and fats begins as soon as food enters your stomach **(Figure 9)**. In this *gastric phase* of digestion, the hormone *gastrin* is secreted. Gastrin increases the secretions of the gastric cells, making the gastric juices even more acidic. It also stimulates stomach contractions, which begin to mix and churn the food until it becomes a liquid called **chyme.** This physical mixing and churning of food is another example of mechanical digestion. Enzymes can access the liquid chyme more readily than solid forms of food. This access facilitates chemical digestion.

Although most absorption occurs in the small intestine, the stomach lining does begin absorbing a few substances. These include water, some medium-chain fatty acids (components of certain types of fats), some minerals, and some drugs, including aspirin and alcohol.[3]

Another of your stomach's jobs is to store your sandwich (or what's left of it!) while the next part of the digestive tract, the small intestine, gets ready for the next wave of food. Remember that the stomach can hold about 4 cups of food. If this amount were to move suddenly into the small intestine all at once, it would overwhelm it. Instead, chyme stays in your stomach about 2 to 4 hours (a high-fat meal

stomach A J-shaped organ where food is partially digested, churned, and stored until it is released into the small intestine.

gastric juice Acidic liquid secreted within the stomach; it contains hydrochloric acid, pepsin, and other compounds.

denature The action of the unfolding of proteins in the stomach. Proteins must be denatured before they can be digested.

chyme A semifluid mass consisting of partially digested food, water, and gastric juices.

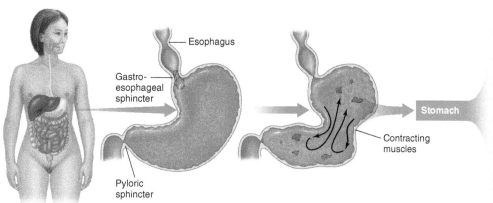

Mechanical digestion occurs when peristaltic waves mix contents of stomach

Gastric juice is secreted by stomach

Pepsin initiates protein digestion

Gastric lipase initiates lipid digestion

Small amounts of water, some minerals, drugs, and alcohol are absorbed

Figure 9 Where your food is now: the stomach. In the stomach, the protein and fat in your sandwich begin to be digested. Your meal is churned into chyme and stored until released into the small intestine.

may remain for up to 6 hours) before being released periodically in spurts into the duodenum, which is the first part of the small intestine. Regulating this release is the *pyloric sphincter* (Figure 9).

RECAP The esophagus is a muscular tube that transports food from the mouth to the stomach via waves of peristalsis. The stomach prepares itself for digestion by secreting gastric juice. It also secretes mucus to protect its lining. As the hormone gastrin causes the stomach to churn food into a liquid called chyme, the digestion of proteins and fats begins. The stomach stores chyme and releases it periodically into the small intestine through the pyloric sphincter.

Most Digestion and Absorption Occurs in the Small Intestine

The **small intestine** is the longest portion of the GI tract, accounting for about two-thirds of its length. However, it is called "small" because it is only an inch in diameter.

The small intestine is composed of three sections **(Figure 10)**. The *duodenum* is the section that is connected via the pyloric sphincter to the stomach. The *jejunum* is the middle portion, and the last portion is the *ileum*. It connects to the large intestine at another sphincter, called the *ileocecal valve*.

Most digestion and absorption takes place in the small intestine. Here, food is broken down into its smallest components, molecules that the body can then absorb into its internal environment. In the next section, we'll identify a variety of accessory organs, enzymes, and unique anatomical features of the small intestine that permit maximal absorption of most nutrients.

The Gallbladder and Pancreas Aid in Digestion

We left your sandwich as chyme, being released periodically into the small intestine. As the chyme enters the duodenum, a hormone-like substance called cholecystokinin (CCK) is released in response to the presence of protein and fat from the turkey and mayonnaise. The **gallbladder,** an accessory organ located beneath the

small intestine The longest portion of the GI tract, where most digestion and absorption takes place.

gallbladder A tissue sac beneath the liver that stores bile and secretes it into the small intestine.

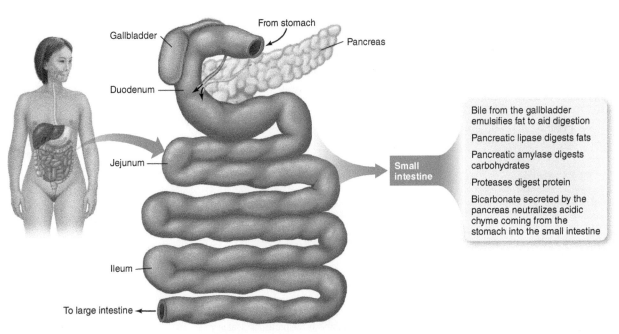

Figure 10 Where your food is now: the small intestine. Here, most of the digestion and absorption of the nutrients in your sandwich takes place.

liver (see Figures 5 and 10), stores a greenish fluid called **bile,** which the liver produces. The release of CCK signals the gallbladder to contract, sending bile through the *common bile duct* into the duodenum. Bile then *emulsifies* the fat; that is, it reduces the fat into smaller globules and disperses them, so that they are more accessible to digestive enzymes. If you've ever noticed how a drop of liquid detergent breaks up a film of fat floating at the top of a basin of greasy dishes, you understand the function of bile.

The **pancreas,** another accessory organ, manufactures, holds, and secretes different digestive enzymes. It is located behind the stomach (see Figures 5 and 10). Enzymes secreted by the pancreas include *pancreatic amylase,* which continues the digestion of carbohydrates, and *pancreatic lipase,* which continues the digestion of fats. *Proteases* secreted in pancreatic juice digest proteins. The pancreas is also responsible for manufacturing hormones that are important in metabolism. Earlier we mentioned insulin and glucagon, two pancreatic hormones that help regulate the amount of glucose in the blood.

Another essential role of the pancreas is to secrete bicarbonate into the duodenum. Bicarbonate is a base; like all bases, it is capable of neutralizing acids. Recall that chyme leaving the stomach is very acidic. The pancreatic bicarbonate neutralizes the acidic chyme. This action helps the pancreatic enzymes work more effectively. It also ensures that the lining of the duodenum is not eroded.

Now the protein, carbohydrate, and fat in your sandwich have been processed into a liquid that contains molecules of nutrients small enough for absorption. This molecular "soup" continues to move along the small intestine via peristalsis, encountering the absorptive cells of the intestinal lining all along the way.

A Specialized Lining Enables the Small Intestine to Absorb Food

The lining of the GI tract is especially well suited for absorption. If you were to look at the inside of the lining, which is also referred to as the mucosal membrane, you would notice that it is heavily folded (Figure 11). This feature increases the surface area of the small intestine and allows it to absorb more nutrients than if it were smooth. Within these larger folds, you would notice even smaller, finger-like projections called *villi*, whose constant movement helps them encounter and trap nutrient molecules. Inside each villus are *capillaries*, or tiny blood vessels, and a **lacteal,** which is a small lymph vessel. The capillaries absorb water-soluble nutrients directly into the bloodstream, whereas lacteals absorb fat-soluble nutrients into a watery fluid called *lymph.*

Covering the villi are specialized cells carpeted with hairlike structures called *microvilli.* Since this makes them look like tiny scrub brushes, these cells are sometimes referred to collectively as the **brush border.** The carpet of microvilli multiplies the surface area of the small intestine more than 500 times, tremendously increasing its absorptive capacity.

Intestinal Cells Readily Absorb Vitamins, Minerals, and Water

The turkey sandwich you ate contained several vitamins and minerals in addition to protein, carbohydrate, and fat. The vitamins and minerals are not really "digested" in the same way that macronutrients are. Vitamins do not have to be broken down because they are small enough to be readily absorbed by the small intestine. For example, fat-soluble vitamins, such as vitamins A, D, E, and K, are soluble in lipids and are absorbed into the intestinal cells along with the fats in our foods. Water-soluble vitamins, such as the B-vitamins and vitamin C, typically use some type of transport process to cross the intestinal lining. Minerals don't need to be digested because they are already the smallest possible units of matter. Thus, they are absorbed all along the small intestine, and in some cases in the large intestine as well, by a wide variety of mechanisms.

Finally, a large component of food is water, and, of course, you also drink lots of water throughout the day. Water is readily absorbed along the entire length of the GI tract because it is a small molecule that can easily pass through the cell membrane. However, as we will see shortly, a significant percentage of water is absorbed in the large intestine.

Bon Appetit/Alamy

A small amount of vinegar emulsifies the oil in this container.

bile Fluid produced by the liver and stored in the gallbladder; it emulsifies fats in the small intestine.

pancreas A gland located behind the stomach that secretes digestive enzymes.

lacteal A small lymph vessel located inside the villi of the small intestine.

brush border The microvilli-covered lining cells of the small intestine's villi. These microvilli tremendously increase the small intestine's absorptive capacity.

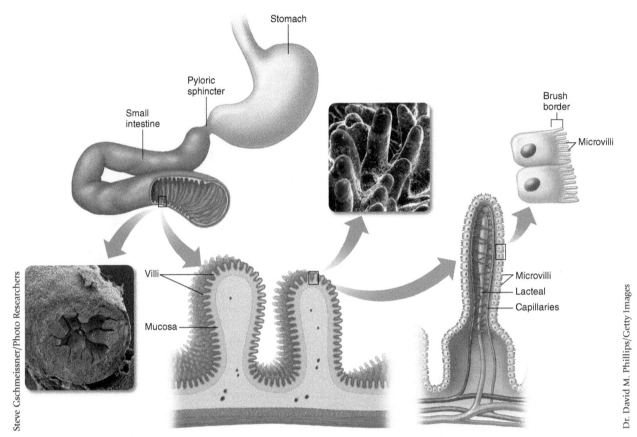

Steve Gschmeissner/Photo Researchers

Dr. David M. Phillips/Getty Images

Figure 11 Absorption of nutrients occurs via the specialized lining of the small intestine. The lining of the small intestine is heavily folded and has thousands of finger-like projections called *villi*. The cells covering the villi end in hairlike projections called *microvilli*, which together form the brush border. These features significantly increase the absorptive capacity of the small intestine.

Bruce Shippee/Shutterstock

Water is readily absorbed along the entire length of the GI tract.

Blood and Lymph Transport Nutrients and Fluids

We noted earlier that, within the intestinal villi, capillaries and lacteals absorb water-soluble and fat-soluble nutrients, respectively, into blood and lymph. These two fluids then transport the nutrients throughout the body. Blood travels through the cardiovascular system, and lymph travels through the lymphatic system (Figure 12).

The oxygen we inhale into our lungs is absorbed by our red blood cells. This oxygen-rich blood then travels to the heart, where it is pumped out to the rest of the body. Blood travels to all of our tissues to deliver nutrients and other materials and pick up waste products. As blood travels through the GI tract, it picks up most of the nutrients, including water, that are absorbed through the mucosal membrane of the small intestine. This nutrient-rich blood is then transported to the liver. The role of the liver in packaging the arriving nutrients is described in the following section.

The lymphatic vessels pick up most fats, fat-soluble vitamins, and fluids that have escaped from the cardiovascular system and transport them in lymph. In its journey through the lymphatic vessels of the body, this lymph is filtered through *lymph nodes*, clusters of immune and other cells that trap particles and destroy harmful microbes. Eventually, lymph returns to the bloodstream in an area near the heart where the lymphatic and blood vessels join together.

Bear in mind that circulation also allows for the elimination of metabolic wastes. The waste products picked up by the blood as it circulates around the body are filtered and excreted by the kidneys in urine. In addition, much of the carbon dioxide remain-

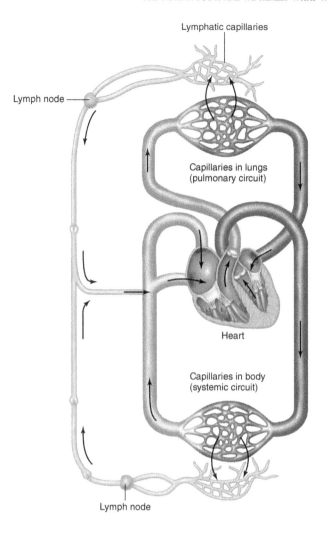

Lymphatic capillaries

Lymph node

Capillaries in lungs
(pulmonary circuit)

Heart

Capillaries in body
(systemic circuit)

Lymph node

◀ **Figure 12** Blood travels through the cardiovascular system to transport nutrients and fluids and pick up waste products. Lymph travels through the lymphatic system and transports most fats and fat-soluble vitamins.

ing in the blood once it reaches the lungs is exhaled into the outside air, making room for oxygen to attach to the red blood cells and repeat this cycle of circulation.

The Liver Regulates Blood Nutrients

Once nutrients are absorbed from the small intestine, most enter the *portal vein*, which carries them to the **liver.** The liver is a triangular, wedge-shaped organ weighing about 3 pounds and resting almost entirely within the protection of the rib cage on the right side of the body (see Figure 5). It is not only the largest digestive organ but also one of the most important organs in the body, performing more than 500 discrete functions.

One function of the liver is to receive the products of digestion and then release into the bloodstream those nutrients needed throughout the body. The liver also processes and stores simple sugars, fats, and amino acids and plays a major role in regulating their levels in the bloodstream. For instance, after we eat a meal, the liver picks up excess glucose (a simple sugar) from the blood and stores it as glycogen, releasing it into the bloodstream when we need energy later in the day. It also stores certain vitamins. But the liver is more than a nutrient warehouse: it also manufactures blood proteins and can even make glucose when necessary to keep our blood glucose levels constant.

Have you ever wondered why people who abuse alcohol are at risk for liver damage? It's because another of the liver's functions is to filter the blood, removing wastes and toxins such as alcohol, medications, and other drugs. When you drink,

liver The largest auxiliary organ of the GI tract and one of the most important organs of the body. Its functions include the production of bile and processing of nutrient-rich blood from the small intestine.

your liver works hard to break down the alcohol; but with heavy drinking over time, liver cells become damaged and scar tissue forms. The scar tissue blocks the free flow of blood through the liver, so that any further toxins accumulate in the blood, causing confusion, coma, and ultimately death.

Another important job of the liver is to synthesize many of the chemicals the body uses to carry out metabolic processes. For example, the liver synthesizes bile, which, as we just discussed, is then stored in the gallbladder until the body needs it to emulsify fats.

RECAP Most digestion and absorption occurs in the small intestine. Its three sections are the duodenum, the jejunum, and the ileum. The gallbladder stores bile, which emulsifies fats, and the pancreas synthesizes and secretes digestive enzymes that break down carbohydrates, fats, and proteins. The lining of the small intestine is heavily folded, with the surface area expanded by villi and microvilli. Nutrients are absorbed across the mucosal membrane. The liver processes all the nutrients absorbed from the small intestine and stores and regulates energy nutrients.

The Large Intestine Stores Food Waste Until It Is Excreted

The **large intestine** (also called the *colon*) is a thick, tubelike structure that frames the small intestine on three-and-a-half sides (Figure 13). It begins with a tissue sac called the *cecum*, which explains the name of the sphincter—the *ileocecal valve*—that connects it to the ileum of the small intestine. From the cecum, the large intestine continues up along the left side of the small intestine as the *ascending colon*. The *transverse colon* runs across the top of the small intestine, and then the *descending colon* comes down on the right. The *sigmoid colon* is the last segment of the colon; it extends from the bottom right corner to the *rectum*. The last segment of the large intestine is the *anal canal,* which is about an inch and a half long.

What has happened to your turkey sandwich? The undigested food components in the chyme finally reach the large intestine. By this time, the digestive mass entering the large intestine does not resemble the chyme that left the stomach several hours before. This is because most of the nutrients have been absorbed, leaving mainly nondigestible food material, such as fiber, bacteria, and water. As in the stomach, cells lining the large intestine secrete mucus, which helps protect it from the abrasive materials passing through it.

Bacteria colonizing the large intestine are normal and helpful residents, since they finish digesting some of the nutrients from your sandwich. The by-products of this digestion, such as short-chain fatty acids, are reabsorbed into the body, where they re-

large intestine The final organ of the GI tract, consisting of the cecum, colon, rectum, and anal canal and in which most water is absorbed and feces are formed.

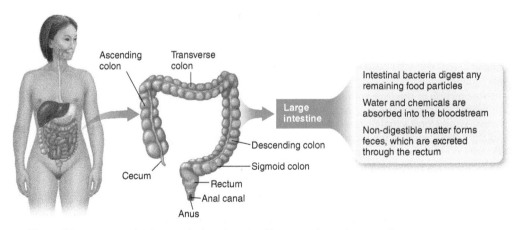

Ascending colon

Transverse colon

Descending colon

Sigmoid colon

Cecum

Rectum

Anal canal

Anus

Large intestine

Intestinal bacteria digest any remaining food particles

Water and chemicals are absorbed into the bloodstream

Non-digestible matter forms feces, which are excreted through the rectum

Figure 13 Where your food is now: the large intestine. Most water absorption occurs here, as does the formation of food wastes into semisolid feces. Peristalsis propels the feces to the body exterior.

turn to the liver and are either stored or used as needed. Intestinal bacteria, called *intestinal flora*, also help synthesize certain vitamins and are thought to promote intestinal motility. In fact, the types of bacteria that thrive in our large intestine are so helpful that many people consume them deliberately in yogurt and probiotics supplements!

No other digestion occurs in the large intestine. Instead, its main functions are to store the digestive mass for 12 to 24 hours and, during that time, to absorb nutrients and water from it, leaving a semisolid mass called *feces*. Peristalsis occurs weakly to move the feces through the colon, except for one or more stronger waves of peristalsis each day, which force the feces more powerfully toward the rectum for elimination.

Some people believe that so-called toxins in the colon are responsible for a wide variety of health problems. They say that colon cleansing—in which the person consumes a liquid "detox" diet, takes laxatives, uses a series of enemas, or undergoes a procedure called colonic irrigation—flushes away these toxins and restores health. What do the experts say? Check out the Nutrition Debate near the end of this chapter to find out!

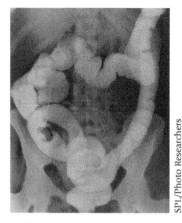

The large intestine is a thick, tubelike structure that stores the undigested mass exiting the small intestine, and also absorbs any remaining nutrients and water.

RECAP The large intestine is composed of six sections: the cecum, ascending colon, descending colon, sigmoid colon, rectum, and anal canal. Small amounts of undigested and indigestible food material, bacteria, and water enter the large intestine. Intestinal bacteria accomplish the final digestion of any remaining digestible food products. The main functions of the large intestine are to store the digestive mass and to absorb any remaining nutrients and water. A semisolid mass, called feces, is then eliminated from the body.

The Neuromuscular System Regulates the Activities of the GI Tract

Now that you can identify the organs involved in digestion, absorption, and elimination, and the job each performs, you might be wondering—who's the boss? In other words, what organ or system directs and coordinates all of these interrelated processes? The answer is the neuromuscular system. Both of its components, the nervous and muscular systems, are essential partners in regulating the activities of the GI tract.

The Muscles of the Gastrointestinal Tract Mix and Move Food

The purpose of the muscles of the GI tract is to mix food and move it in one direction—that is, from the mouth toward the anus. When food is present, nerves respond to the stretching of the tract walls and send signals to its muscles, stimulating peristalsis. As with an assembly line, the entire GI tract functions together so that materials are moved in one direction in a coordinated manner and wastes are removed as needed.

In order to process the large amount of food we consume daily, we use both voluntary and involuntary muscles. Muscles in the mouth are primarily voluntary; that is, they are under our conscious control. Once we swallow, involuntary muscles largely take over to propel food through the rest of the GI tract. This enables us to continue digesting and absorbing our food while we're working, exercising, and even sleeping. Let's now reveal the master controller behind these involuntary muscular actions.

The Enteric Nerves Coordinate and Regulate Digestive Activities

The nervous system in your body is like the communications system in a manufacturing plant. Within this communications system, the central nervous system (CNS), composed of the brain and spinal cord, is like the main control desk. For example, as discussed earlier in this chapter, the hypothalamus of the brain plays an important role in the control of hunger and satiation.

An intricate system of nerves branches out from the CNS; this system is called the peripheral nervous system. It includes the nerves of the GI tract, which are collectively known as the **enteric nervous system.**

enteric nervous system The nerves of the GI tract.

Enteric nerves work both independently of and in collaboration with the CNS. For example, they can respond independently to signals produced within the GI tract without first relaying them to the CNS for interpretation or assistance. On the other hand, many jobs require the involvement of the CNS. For instance, as we discussed earlier, special nerves in the GI tract pick up mechanical signals indicating how far the tract wall is stretched—that is, how full it is. These receptors signal the brain that your digestive tract is full, and then your brain sends out messages that prompt you to stop eating. Another type of enteric nerve picks up chemical signals about how acidic the digestive environment is or if there is protein or fat present. The CNS receives and responds to these signals; for example, it may send out a message to the pancreas to secrete enzymes for fat digestion.

All along the GI tract are a series of glands whose actions are also controlled by the nervous system. When food digestion products reach various locations within the GI tract, these glands are stimulated to release digestive enzymes, mucus, or water and electrolytes. For example, as chyme moves from the stomach into the small intestine, nerve signals are sent to stimulate the pancreas, gallbladder, and mucosal cells lining the intestinal tract. These signals cause these glands and cells to secrete digestive enzymes, bile, bicarbonate, and water, secretions necessary to continue digestion in the small intestine.

RECAP The coordination and regulation of digestion are directed by the neuromuscular system. Voluntary muscles assist us with chewing and swallowing. Once food is swallowed, the involuntary muscles along the entire length of the GI tract function together, so that materials are moved in one direction in a coordinated manner and wastes are removed as needed. The enteric nerves of the GI tract work with the central nervous system to achieve the digestion, absorption, and elimination of food.

◆ When we eat, both voluntary and involuntary muscles help us digest the food.
David Sacks/Stone/Getty Images

What Disorders Are Related to Digestion, Absorption, and Elimination?

Considering the complexity of digestion, absorption, and elimination, it's no wonder that sometimes things go wrong. Clinical disorders can disturb gastrointestinal functioning, as can merely consuming the wrong types or amounts of food for our unique needs. Whenever there is a problem with the GI tract, the absorption of nutrients can be affected and, over time, malnutrition can result. Let's look more closely at some GI tract disorders and what you might be able to do if they affect you.

Heartburn and Gastroesophageal Reflux Disease (GERD) Are Caused by Reflux of Stomach Acid

When you eat food, your stomach secretes hydrochloric acid to start the digestive process. In many people, the amount of HCl secreted is occasionally excessive, or the gastroesophageal sphincter opens too soon. In either case, the result is that HCl seeps back up into the esophagus (Figure 14). Although the stomach is protected from HCl by a thick coat of mucus, the esophagus does not have this mucous coating. Thus, the HCl burns it. When this happens, a person experiences a painful sensation in the region of the chest behind the sternum (breastbone). This condition, clinically known as *gastroesophageal reflux* (*GER*), is commonly called **heartburn**. Many people take over-the-counter antacids to neutralize the HCl, thereby relieving the heartburn. A nondrug approach is to repeatedly swallow: this action causes any acid within the esophagus to be swept down into the stomach, eventually relieving the symptoms.

Gastroesophageal reflux disease (GERD) is a more painful type of GER that occurs more than twice per week. Although people who experience occasional GER

heartburn (gastroesophageal reflux [GER]) A painful sensation that occurs over the sternum when hydrochloric acid backs up into the lower esophagus.

gastroesophageal reflux disease (GERD) A more painful type of GER that occurs more than twice per week.

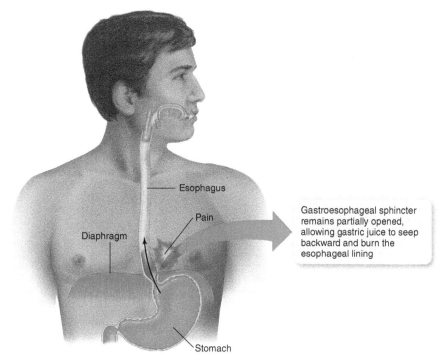

Esophagus

Pain

Diaphragm

Stomach

Gastroesophageal sphincter remains partially opened, allowing gastric juice to seep backward and burn the esophageal lining

◀ **Figure 14** The mechanism of gastroesophageal reflux: acidic gastric juices seep backward through an open or relaxed sphincter into the lower portion of the esophagus, burning its lining. The pain is felt behind the sternum (breastbone), over the heart.

usually have no structural abnormalities, many people with GERD have an overly relaxed or damaged esophageal sphincter or damage to the esophagus itself. Although the classic symptom of GERD is GER, some people instead experience chest pain, trouble swallowing, burning in the mouth, the feeling that food is stuck in the throat, or hoarseness in the morning.[4]

The exact causes of GERD are unknown. However, a number of factors may contribute, including the following:[4]

- A hiatal hernia, which occurs when the upper part of the stomach lies above the diaphragm muscle. Normally, the horizontal diaphragm muscle separates the stomach from the chest cavity and helps keep acid from seeping into the esophagus. Stomach acid can more easily enter the esophagus in people with a hiatal hernia.
- Cigarette smoking
- Alcohol use
- Overweight
- Pregnancy
- Foods such as citrus fruits, chocolate, caffeinated drinks, fried foods, garlic and onions, spicy foods, and tomato-based foods, such as chili, pizza, and spaghetti sauce
- Large, high-fat meals. These meals stay in the stomach longer and increase stomach pressure, making it more likely that acid will be pushed up into the esophagus.
- Lying down soon after a meal. In susceptible people, this is almost certain to bring on symptoms, since it positions the body so it is easier for the stomach acid to back up into the esophagus.

One way to reduce the symptoms of GERD is to identify the types of foods or situations that trigger episodes, and then avoid them. Eating smaller meals also helps. After a meal, wait at least 3 hours before lying down. Some people relieve their nighttime symptoms by elevating the head of their bed 4 to 6 inches—for instance, by placing a wedge between the mattress and the box spring. This keeps the chest area elevated and minimizes the amount of acid that can back up into the esophagus. People with GERD who smoke should stop, and, if they are overweight, they should lose

Getty Images

◀ Although the exact causes of gastroesophageal reflux disease (GERD) are unknown, smoking and being overweight may be contributing factors.

NUTRITION MYTH OR FACT?
Are Ulcers Caused by Stress, Alcohol, or Spicy Foods?

For decades, physicians believed that experiencing high levels of stress, drinking alcohol, and eating spicy foods were the primary factors responsible for ulcers. But in 1982, Australian gastroenterologists Robin Warren and Barry Marshall detected the same species of bacteria in the majority of their ulcer patients' stomachs.[5] Treatment with an antibiotic effective against the bacterium *Helicobacter pylori* (*H. pylori*), cured the ulcers. It is now known that *H. pylori* plays a key role in the development of most peptic ulcers. The hydrochloric acid in gastric juice kills most bacteria, but *H. pylori* is unusual in that it thrives in acidic environments. Approximately 40% of people have this bacterium in their stomachs, but most people do not develop ulcers. The reason for this is not known.[6]

Prevention of infection with *H. pylori*, as with any infectious microorganism, includes regular hand washing and safe

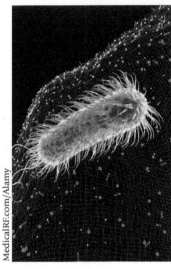

The *Helicobacter pylori* (*H. pylori*) bacterium plays a key role in the development of most peptic ulcers.

MedicalRF.com/Alamy

food-handling practices. Because of the role of *H. pylori* in ulcer development, treatment usually involves antibiotics and acid-suppressing medications. Special diets and stress-reduction techniques are no longer typically recommended because they do not reduce acid secretion. However, people with ulcers should avoid specific foods they identify as causing them discomfort.

Although most peptic ulcers are caused by *H. pylori* infection, some are caused by prolonged use of nonsteroidal anti-inflammatory drugs (NSAIDs); these drugs include pain relievers, such as aspirin, ibuprofen, and naproxen sodium. They appear to cause ulcers by suppressing the secretion of mucus and bicarbonate, which normally protect the stomach from its acidic gastric juice. Ulcers caused by NSAID use generally heal once a person stops taking the medication.[7]

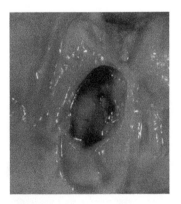

Figure 15 A peptic ulcer.
Dr. E. Walker/Science Photo Library/
Photo Researchers

peptic ulcer An area of the GI tract that has been eroded away by the acidic gastric juice of the stomach.

weight. Taking an antacid before a meal can help prevent symptoms, and many other medications are now available to treat GERD.

It is important to treat GERD, as it can cause serious health problems. GERD can lead to bleeding and ulcers in the esophagus. Scar tissue can develop in the esophagus, making swallowing very difficult. Some people can also develop a condition called Barrett's esophagus, which can lead to cancer. Asthma can also be aggravated or even caused by GERD.

An Ulcer Is an Area of Erosion in the GI Tract

A **peptic ulcer** is an area of the GI tract that has been eroded away by a combination of hydrochloric acid and the enzyme pepsin **(Figure 15)**. In almost all cases, it is located in the stomach area (*gastric ulcer*) or the part of the duodenum closest to the stomach (*duodenal ulcer*). It causes a burning pain in the abdominal area, typically 1 to 3 hours after eating a meal. In serious cases, eroded blood vessels bleed into the GI tract, causing vomiting of blood and/or blood in the stools, as well as anemia. If the ulcer entirely perforates the tract wall, stomach contents can leak into the abdominal cavity, causing a life-threatening infection.

You might have heard the advice that people with an ulcer should try to reduce their stress and avoid caffeine and spicy foods. But do these factors really cause or contribute to ulcers? Find the answer in the Nutrition Myth or Fact? box.

RECAP Heartburn is clinically known as gastroesophageal reflux (GER). It is caused by the seepage of gastric juices into the esophagus. Gastroesophageal reflux disease (GERD) is a more painful type of GER that occurs more than twice per week. Peptic ulcers are caused by erosion of the GI tract by hydrochloric acid and pepsin.

Some Disorders Affect Intestinal Function

GERD and ulcers involve the upper GI tract. In this section, we'll discuss disorders affecting intestinal function.

Diarrhea

Diarrhea is the frequent passage (more than three times in 1 day) of loose, watery stools. Other symptoms may include cramping, abdominal pain, bloating, nausea, fever, and blood in the stools. Diarrhea is usually caused by an infection of the gastrointestinal tract, a chronic disease, stress, or reactions to medications.[8] It can also occur as a reaction to a particular food or food ingredient. Disorders related to specific foods include food intolerances, allergies, and celiac disease. These are discussed *In Depth* following this chapter.

Whatever the cause, diarrhea can be harmful if it persists for a long period of time because the person can lose large quantities of water and minerals and become severely dehydrated. Table 1 reviews the signs and symptoms of dehydration, which is particularly dangerous in infants and young children. In fact, a child can die from dehydration in just a few days. Adults, particularly the elderly, can also become dangerously ill if severely dehydrated. A doctor should be seen immediately if diarrhea persists for more than 24 hours in children or more than 3 days in adults or if diarrhea is bloody, fever is present, or there are signs of dehydration.

A condition referred to as *traveler's diarrhea* has become a common health concern due to the expansion in global travel. *Traveler's diarrhea* is experienced by people traveling to countries outside of their own and is usually caused by viral or bacterial infections. Diarrhea represents the body's way of ridding itself of an invasive agent. The large intestine and even some of the small intestine become irritated by the microbes and the body's defense against them. This irritation leads to increased secretion of fluid and increased motility of the large intestine, causing watery and frequent bowel movements. In some cases, the person may also experience nausea, vomiting, and low-grade fever. Usually, people who are otherwise healthy recover completely within 4 to 6 days.[9]

People generally get traveler's diarrhea from consuming water or food that is contaminated with fecal matter. Very risky foods include any raw or undercooked fish, meats, and raw fruits and vegetables. Tap water, ice made from tap water, and unpasteurized milk and dairy products are also common sources of infection.

What can you do to prevent traveler's diarrhea? The following Quick Tips from the National Institutes of Health should help.[10]

If you do suffer from traveler's diarrhea, it is important to replace the fluid and nutrients lost as a result of the illness. Specially formulated oral rehydration solutions are available in most countries. Antibiotics may also be taken to kill bacteria. Once treatment is initiated, the diarrhea should cease within 2 to 3 days. If the diarrhea persists for more than 10 days after the initiation of treatment, or if there is blood in your stools, you should see a physician immediately.

Constipation

At the opposite end of the spectrum from diarrhea is **constipation,** which is typically defined as a condition in which no stools are passed for 2 or more days; however, it is important to recognize that some people normally experience bowel movements only every second or third day. Thus, the definition of constipation varies from one person to another. In addition to being infrequent, the stools are usually hard, small, and somewhat difficult to pass.

Many people experience temporary constipation at some point in their lives such as when they travel,

⬆ When traveling, it is wise to avoid food from street vendors.
Susan Van Etten/Photo Edit

diarrhea A condition characterized by the frequent passage of loose, watery stools.

constipation A condition characterized by the absence of bowel movements for a period of time that is significantly longer than normal for the individual. When a bowel movement does occur, stools are usually small, hard, and difficult to pass.

TABLE 1 Signs and Symptoms of Dehydration in Adults and Children

Symptoms in Adults	Symptoms in Children
Thirst	Dry mouth and tongue
Light-headedness	No tears when crying
Less frequent urination	No wet diapers for 3 hours or more
Dark colored urine	High fever
Fatigue	Sunken abdomen, eyes, or cheeks
Dry skin	Irritable or listless
	Skin does not rebound when pinched and released

Data from National Digestive Diseases Information Clearinghouse (NDDIC). 2003. Diarrhea. NIH Publication No. 04–2749. http://digestive.niddk.nih.gov/ddiseases/pubs/diarrhea/index.htm.

QUICK TIPS

Avoiding Traveler's Diarrhea

✓ Do not drink tap water or use it to brush your teeth.

✓ Do not drink unpasteurized milk or dairy products.

✓ Do not use ice made from tap water. Freezing does not kill all microbes.

✓ Avoid raw or rare meats, and raw fruits and vegetables, including lettuce and fruit salads, unless they can be peeled and you peel them yourself.

✓ Do not eat meat or shellfish that is not hot when served.

✓ Do not eat food from street vendors.

✓ Do drink bottled water. Make sure you are the one to break the seal, and wipe the top of the bottle clean before doing so. You can also safely choose canned carbonated soft drinks and hot drinks made with boiling water, such as coffee or tea.

✓ Consult your doctor when planning your trip. Depending on where you are going and how long you will stay, your doctor may recommend that you take antibiotics before leaving to protect you from possible infection.

when their schedule is disrupted, if they change their diet, or if they are on certain medications. Many healthcare providers suggest increasing fiber and fluid in the diet. Five to nine servings of fruits and vegetables each day and six or more servings of whole grains is recommended. If you eat breakfast cereal, make sure you buy a cereal containing at least 2 to 3 g of fiber per serving. Staying well hydrated is important when increasing your fiber intake. Regular exercise may also help reduce your risk for constipation.

Irritable Bowel Syndrome

Irritable bowel syndrome (IBS) is a disorder that interferes with the normal functions of the colon (commonly referred to as the "large bowel"). It is one of the most common medical diagnoses, applied to approximately 20% of the U.S. population, and it affects more women than men.[11,12] Symptoms include abdominal cramps, bloating, and either constipation or diarrhea: in some people with IBS, food moves too quickly through the colon and fluid cannot be absorbed fast enough, which causes diarrhea. In others, the movement of the colon is too slow and too much fluid is absorbed, leading to constipation.

IBS shows no sign of underlying disease that can be observed or measured. However, it appears that the colon is more sensitive to physiologic or emotional stress in people with IBS than in healthy people. Some researchers believe that the problem stems from conflicting messages between the central nervous system and the enteric nervous system. The immune system may also trigger symptoms of IBS. Some of the foods thought to cause physiologic stress linked to IBS include caffeinated tea, coffee, & colas; chocolate, alcohol, dairy products, and wheat. Certain medications may also increase the risk.

If you think you have IBS, it is important to have a complete physical examination to rule out any other health problems, including celiac disease (see the **In Depth** essay following this chapter). Treatment options include taking certain medications to treat diarrhea or constipation, managing stress, engaging in regular physical activity, eating smaller meals, avoiding foods that exacerbate symptoms, eating a higher-fiber diet, and drinking at least six to eight glasses of water each day.[15] Although IBS is uncomfortable, it does not appear to endanger long-term health. However, severe IBS can be disabling and can prevent people from leading normal lives; thus, an accurate diagnosis and effective treatment are critical.

◄ Consuming caffeinated drinks is one of several factors that have been linked with irritable bowel syndrome. Nataliya Peregudova/Fotolia

irritable bowel syndrome (IBS) A bowel disorder that interferes with normal functions of the colon.

RECAP Diarrhea is the frequent passage of loose or watery stools. It should be treated quickly to avoid dehydration or even death. Constipation is failure to have a bowel movement within a time period that is normal for the individual. Irritable bowel syndrome (IBS) causes abdominal cramps, bloating, and constipation or diarrhea. The causes of IBS are unknown; however, physiologic and emotional stress is implicated.

Nutrition DEBATE

Colon Cleansing: Does the Body Need Help Flushing Toxins Away?

Are you struggling with weight gain? Fatigue? Headaches? Sluggish bowel movements? Allergies? Joint pain? Recurring infections? Inability to concentrate? If so, have you ever thought that your symptoms might be due to a build-up of toxins in your colon, and that flushing out those toxins might cure you?

You're probably thinking that this pitch sounds too good to be true. But isn't there something about it that seems sort of—logical? After all, the colon is the body's "solid waste disposal facility," so isn't it possible that toxins could build up in its tissues, and if so shouldn't regular cleansing be beneficial?

Before we consider the arguments for and against it, let's find out what colon cleansing really entails. In essence, the term refers to a single goal that can be achieved by any of several different activities. One form of colon cleansing is the use of standard enemas—often twice or even three times within a couple of hours—to force the expulsion of the contents of the colon. Another method is the consumption of laxative drugs or tablets, powders, or teas, some containing potent herbs. These either draw water into feces, making them easier to pass, or irritate the colon, promoting strong bowel contractions. Another method is the so-called detox liquid diet—such as the combination of water, lemon juice, maple syrup, and cayenne pepper that some pop stars have endorsed—which is supposed to be followed for a week to 10 days. A more sophisticated and expensive method, called *colonic irrigation*, is available only in clinics staffed by trained colonic therapists. In colonic irrigation, the person lies on a table while water (or a watery solution that may also contain herbs or other substances) is pumped into the colon through a tube inserted in the rectum.

Adherents say that colon cleansing is beneficial because it removes toxins from the colon before they have a chance to enter the body. They claim that toxins enter the body in foods, water, and air—for instance, in pesticide residues and in chemicals that leach into foods from packaging materials. They say that such toxins build up on the walls of the colon and are readily absorbed into the bloodstream via the colon's lining cells. They conclude that these chemicals are responsible for a wide variety of health problems, including those listed earlier, as well as life-threatening illnesses, such as cancer.

So what does the research say about colon cleansing? Unfortunately, not much. There is very little evidence to either support or refute the claims for the benefits of this therapy.[13]

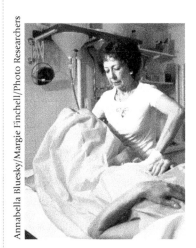

Annabella Bluesky/Margie Finchell/Photo Researchers

⬆ The colonic irrigation, or "colon cleansing," procedure. There is currently little scientific evidence to either support or refute claims about its benefits.

Nonetheless, certain aspects of normal GI functioning suggest that colon cleansing is unnecessary. For instance, as you've learned in this chapter, helpful bacteria that are normal residents of the colon detoxify food wastes. In addition, both the liver and the kidneys remove blood-borne toxins, and lymph nodes cleanse harmful substances circulating in lymph. Moreover, the lining cells of the colon are shed about every 3 days! Thus, physicians argue that your body doesn't need special procedures to protect against toxins.

So why do some people report improvements in health from colon cleansing? First, their positive response may be due in part to the placebo effect. In addition, if they've been experiencing sluggish bowel movements, then simply emptying the colon of its contents—toxins or no toxins—will relieve a wide range of symptoms. Also, liquid "detox" fasts may make adherents feel more spirited because they're consuming very little energy: voluntary calorie restriction can lead to heightened feelings of psychological well-being.[14]

Finally, many physicians warn that colon cleansing regimes can be harmful. Their primary danger is dehydration which can seriously deplete the body of essential minerals. Other adverse effects include nausea, vomiting, cramps, an allergic reaction, and even bowel perforation (complete penetration of the intestinal wall). A safer alternative is a healthful intake of fiber from foods, such as fruits, vegetables, legumes, whole grains, and seeds, accompanied by an adequate fluid intake.[15]

Chapter Review

Test Yourself ANSWERS

1. True. Sometimes we may have an appetite even though we are not hungry. These feelings are referred to as *cravings* and are associated with physical or emotional cues.

2. True. Although there are individual variations in how we respond to food, the entire process of digestion and absorption of one meal usually takes about 24 hours.

3. True. Most ulcers result from an infection of the bacterium *Helicobacter pylori* (*H. pylori*). Contrary to popular belief, ulcers are not caused by stress or spicy food.

Find the Quack

When Petra left her home in the Czech Republic a year ago to enroll in an acting school in Los Angeles, she regarded her figure as *curvaceous*. Now when she looks in the mirror, she sees herself as *fat*. Convinced that she has been turned down at auditions because of her weight, she has been maintaining a strict high-protein, low-carbohydrate diet, plus diet pills and exercise, but the weight hasn't been coming off fast enough. What's more, she's constipated. At a step aerobics class, she sees a flyer recommending an all-natural weight-loss "tonic." The flyer states that the regular use of this "pleasant-tasting tonic" will take weight off and keep it off. It lists a website address where Petra can learn more. When Petra gets home, she goes online to the site. Here is what she reads:

- "Your colon can contain up to 25 pounds of undigested food and trapped fecal matter. Over time, these ferment and release toxins. Our patented tonic will flush this waste out of your body."

- "If you don't naturally have a bowel movement after every meal, then your intestines are very likely blocked. If you have difficulty losing weight, low energy, headaches, insomnia, bloating, or constipation, you almost certainly need our laxative tonic."

- "Our tonic was developed by a chemist and a nutritionist. It is a pleasant-tasting syrup containing a proprietary blend of organically grown herbs, roots, and other medicinals. Simply mix 2 tablespoons with a cup of pure water and drink each morning upon rising. Taken daily, it will help you maintain your new figure and trimmer waistline. It will also increase your energy level, relieve headaches,

help you sleep better, and prevent diseases of the digestive system."

- "Never before has it been so easy to eliminate up to 25 pounds of trapped wastes from your body! A 30-day supply is available for a limited time at the special price of just $29.99! That's less than a dollar a day to a slimmer, healthier you!"

1. Comment on the website's statements that the product was developed by a chemist and a nutritionist and that it is a "patented" formula containing a "proprietary" blend of ingredients.

2. In this chapter, you learned about the normal functions of digestion and elimination. Comment on the website's assertion "If you don't naturally have a bowel movement after every meal, then your intestines are very likely blocked."

3. Petra has been maintaining a diet high in meat, eggs, and other protein sources and low in carbohydrates, including fruits, vegetables, and grains. She has also been using diet pills, which typically act as diuretics, flushing fluids from the body. Could there be a link between these behaviors and her constipation? If so, identify the link.

4. If the tonic is actually just a very strong laxative, and Petra were to ingest the recommended dose daily, what do you think she might experience?

Answers can be found on the companion website, at www.pearsonhighered.com/thompsonmanore.

 **NutriTools** Check out the companion website at www.pearsonhighered.com/thompsonmanore, or use MyNutritionLab.com, to access interactive animations, including:

- Digestion and Absorption: Carbohydrates
- Digestion and Absorption: Protein
- Digestion and Absorption: Lipids

Review Questions

1. Which of the following represents the levels of organization in the human body from smallest to largest?
   a. cells, molecules, atoms, tissues, organs, systems
   b. atoms, molecules, cells, organs, tissues, systems
   c. atoms, molecules, cells, tissues, organs, systems
   d. molecules, atoms, cells, tissues, organs, systems

2. Bile is a greenish fluid that
   a. is stored by the pancreas.
   b. is produced by the gallbladder.
   c. denatures proteins.
   d. emulsifies fats.

3. The region of brain tissue that is responsible for prompting us to seek food is the
   a. pituitary gland.
   b. cephalic phase.
   c. hypothalamus.
   d. peripheral nervous system.

4. Heartburn is caused by
   a. seepage of gastric acid into the esophagus.
   b. seepage of gastric acid into the cardiac muscle.
   c. seepage of bile into the stomach.
   d. seepage of salivary amylase into the stomach.

5. Most digestion of carbohydrates, fats, and proteins takes place in the
   a. mouth.
   b. stomach.
   c. small intestine.
   d. large intestine.

6. True or false? Hunger is more physiologic, and appetite is more psychological.

7. True or false? The nerves of the GI tract are collectively known as the enteric nervous system.

8. True or false? Vitamins and minerals are digested in the small intestine.

9. True or false? Diarrhea can usually be corrected by adhering to a high-fiber diet.

10. True or false? Atoms are the smallest units of life.

Answers to Review Questions can be found at the back of this text, and additional essay questions and answers are located on the companion website, at www.pearsonhighered.com/thompsonmanore.

Web Resources

www.digestive.niddk.nih.gov
National Institute of Diabetes and Digestive and Kidney Diseases (NIDDK)

Explore this site to learn more about gastroesophageal reflux disease (GERD), ulcers, diarrhea, constipation, and irritable bowel syndrome (IBS).

www.healthfinder.gov
Health Finder

Search this site to learn more about disorders related to digestion, absorption, and elimination.

www.ibsgroup.org
Irritable Bowel Syndrome Self-Help and Support Group

Visit this site for information on self-help measures and support for people diagnosed with IBS.

References

1. Orr, J., and B. Davy. 2005. Dietary influences on peripheral hormones regulating energy intake: potential applications for weight management. *J. Am. Diet. Assoc.* 105:1115–1124; Astrup, A. 2005. The satiating power of protein—a key to obesity prevention? *Am. J. Cl. Nutr.* Vol. 82 No. 1, 1–2, July 2005. Available at www.ajcn.org/cgi/content/full/82/1/1.

2. Pollack, A. 2009. Medicine's Elusive Goal: A Safe Weight-Loss Drug. *The New York Times*, October 17, 2009. www.nytimes.com/2009/10/17/business/17obesity.html?_r=1&scp=1&sq=appetite%20suppressants&st=cse.

3. Davidson, N. O. 2003. Intestinal lipid absorption. In: Yamada, T., D. H. Alpers, N. Kaplowitz, L. Laine, C. Owyang, and D. W. Powell, eds. *Textbook of Gastroenterology*, Vol. 1, 4th edn. Philadelphia: Lippincott Williams & Wilkins.

4. National Institute of Diabetes and Digestive and Kidney Diseases (NIDDK). 2007. Heartburn, Gastroesophageal Reflux (GER), and Gastroesophageal Reflux Disease (GERD). NIH Publication No. 07-0882. http://digestive.niddk.nih.gov/ddiseases/pubs/gerd/index.htm.

5. Bauman, R. 2011. *Microbiology*, 3rd edn. San Francisco: Benjamin Cummings.

6. National Institute of Diabetes and Digestive and Kidney Diseases (NIDDK). 2004. H. pylori and Peptic Ulcer. NIH Publication No. 05-4225. http://digestive.niddk.nih.gov/ddiseases/pubs/hpylori/.

7. National Institute of Diabetes and Digestive and Kidney Diseases (NIDDK). 2004. NSAIDs and Peptic Ulcers. NIH Publication No. 04-4644. Available at http://digestive.niddk.nih.gov/ddiseases/pubs/nsaids/index.htm.

8. National Institute of Diabetes and Digestive and Kidney Diseases (NIDDK). 2007. Diarrhea. NIH Publication No. 07-2749. http://digestive.niddk.nih.gov/ddiseases/pubs/diarrhea/index.htm.

9. DuPont, H. L. 2006. New insights and directions in traveler's diarrhea. Gastroenterol. *Clin. N. Am.* 35(2):337–353, viii–ix.

10. National Institute of Diabetes and Digestive and Kidney Diseases (NIDDK). 2007. Diarrhea. NIH Publication No. 07-2749. http://digestive.niddk.nih.gov/ddiseases/pubs/diarrhea/index.htm.

11. Lewis, C. July–August 2001. Irritable Bowel Syndrome: A Poorly Understood Disorder. *FDA Consumer Magazine.* www.fda.gov/fdac/features/2001/401_ibs.html.

12. National Institute of Diabetes and Digestive and Kidney Diseases (NIDDK). 2007. Irritable Bowel Syndrome. NIH Publication No. 07-693. http://digestive.niddk.nih.gov/ddiseases/pubs/ibs/.

13. Mayo Clinic. 2009. Colon cleansing: Is it helpful or harmful? Mayo Foundation for Medical Education and Research. Available at: www.mayoclinic.com/health/colon-cleansing/AN00065; WebMD. 2009. Natural Colon Cleansing: Is It Necessary? WebMD Medical Reference. Available at www.webmd.com/balance/natural-colon-cleansing-is-it-necessary.

14. Picco, M. 2008. Detox diets: Do they offer any health benefits? Mayo Foundation for Medical Education and Research. Available at: www.mayoclinic.com/health/detox-diets/AN015334.

15. Mayo Clinic, op. cit.; Picco, op. cit.; Ellin, A. 2009. Flush Those Toxins! Eh, Not So Fast. *The New York Times.* January 22, 2009. Available at www.nytimes.com/2009/01/22/fashion/22skin.html.

Answers to Review Questions

Answers to Review Questions 11-15 (essay questions) for this chapter are located on the Companion Website at **www.pearsonhighered.com/thompsonmanore**

1. **c.** atoms, molecules, cells, tissues, organs, systems
2. **d.** emulsifies fats.
3. **c.** hypothalamus.
4. **a.** seepage of gastric acid into the esophagus.
5. **c.** small intestine.
6. True.
7. True.
8. False. Vitamins and minerals are not really "digested" the same way that macronutrients are. These compounds do not have to be broken down because they are small enough to be readily absorbed by the small intestine. For example, fat-soluble vitamins, such as vitamins A, D, E, and K, are soluble in lipids and are absorbed into the intestinal cells along with the fats in our foods. Water-soluble vitamins, such as the B vitamins and vitamin C, typically undergo some type of active transport process that helps assure the vitamin is absorbed by the small intestine. Minerals are absorbed all along the small intestine, and in some cases in the large intestine as well, by a wide variety of mechanisms.

9. False. If you have diarrhea, bowel rest is recommended. In contrast, increasing your fiber might be advised if you're prone to constipation.

10. False. Cells are the smallest units of life. Atoms are the smallest units of matter in nature.

Carbohydrates: Plant-Derived Energy Nutrients

From Chapter 4 of *Nutrition: An Applied Approach*, Third Edition. Janice Thompson, Melinda Manore. Copyright © 2012 by Pearson Education, Inc. Published by Pearson Benjamin Cummings. All rights reserved.

Carbohydrates: Plant-Derived Energy Nutrients

CHAPTER OBJECTIVES

After reading this chapter you will be able to:

1. Describe the difference between simple and complex carbohydrates.

2. List four functions of carbohydrates in our body.

3. Discuss how carbohydrates are digested and absorbed by our body.

4. Define the Acceptable Macronutrient Distribution Range for carbohydrates, and the Adequate Intake for fiber.

5. Identify the potential health risks associated with diets high in refined sugars.

6. List five foods that are good sources of carbohydrates.

7. Identify three alternative sweeteners.

Suzannah Skelton/iStockphoto

W

hen Khalil lived at home, he snacked on whatever was around. That typically meant fresh fruit or his mom's home-made flatbread, and either plain water or skim milk. His parents never drank soda, and the only time he ate sweets was on special occasions. Now Khalil is living on campus. When he gets hungry between classes, he visits the snack shack in the Student Union for one of their awesome chocolate-chunk cookies, a cinnamon roll, or a brownie and washes it down with a large cola. Studying at night, he munches on cheese curls or corn chips and drinks more cola to help him stay awake. Not suprisingly, Khalil has noticed lately that his clothes feel tight. When he steps on the scale, he's shocked to discover that, since starting college 3 months ago, he's gained 7 pounds!

Several popular diets—including the Zone Diet, Sugar Busters, and Dr. Atkins' New Diet Revolution—claim that carbohydrates are bad for your health. They recommend reducing carbohydrate consumption and eating more protein and fat.[1-3] Is this good advice? If you had a friend like Khalil who regularly consumed several soft drinks a day, plus chips, cookies, candy, and other high-carbohydrate snacks, would you say anything? Are carbohydrates a health menace, and is one type of carbohydrate as bad as another?

In this chapter, we'll explore the differences between simple and complex carbohydrates and learn why some carbohydrates really are better than others. We'll also learn how the human body breaks down carbohydrates and uses them to maintain our health and to fuel our activity and exercise.

What Are Carbohydrates?

Carbohydrates are one of the three macronutrients. As such, they are an important energy source for the entire body and are the preferred energy source for nerve cells, including those of the brain. We will say more about their functions later in this chapter.

The term **carbohydrate** literally means "hydrated carbon." Water (H_2O) is made of hydrogen and oxygen, and, when something is said to be *hydrated*, it contains water. Thus, the chemical abbreviation for carbohydrate (CHO) indicates the atoms it contains: **c**arbon, **h**ydrogen, and **o**xygen.

We obtain carbohydrates predominantly from plant foods, such as fruits, vegetables, and grains. Plants make the most abundant form of carbohydrate, called **glucose**, through a process called **photosynthesis**. During photosynthesis, the green pigment of plants, called *chlorophyll*, absorbs sunlight, which provides the energy needed to fuel the manufacture of glucose. As shown in **Figure 1**, water absorbed from the earth by the roots of plants combines with the carbon dioxide present in the leaves to produce the carbohydrate glucose. Plants continually store glucose and use it to support their own growth. Then, when we eat plant foods, our body digests, absorbs, and uses the stored glucose.

Carbohydrates can be classified as *simple* or *complex*. These terms are used to describe carbohydrates based on the number of molecules of sugar present.[4] Simple carbohydrates contain either one or two molecules, whereas complex carbohydrates contain hundreds to thousands of molecules.

carbohydrate One of the three macronutrients, a compound made up of carbon, hydrogen, and oxygen that is derived from plants and provides energy.

glucose The most abundant sugar molecule, a monosaccharide generally found in combination with other sugars; it is the preferred source of energy for the brain and an important source of energy for all cells.

photosynthesis The process by which plants use sunlight to fuel a chemical reaction that combines carbon and water into glucose, which is then stored in their cells.

Figure 1 Plants make carbohydrates through the process of photosynthesis. Water, carbon dioxide, and energy from the sun are combined to produce glucose.

Simple Carbohydrates Include Monosaccharides and Disaccharides

Simple carbohydrates are commonly referred to as *sugars*. Four of these sugars are called **monosaccharides** because they consist of a single sugar molecule (*mono* means "one," and *saccharide* means "sugar"). The other three sugars are **disaccharides**, which consist of two molecules of sugar joined together (*di* means "two").

Glucose, Fructose, Galactose, and Ribose Are Monosaccharides

Glucose, *fructose*, and *galactose* are the three most common monosaccharides in our diet. Each of these monosaccharides contains six carbon atoms, twelve hydrogen atoms, and six oxygen atoms (Figure 2). Very slight differences in the arrangement of the atoms in these three monosaccharides cause major differences in their levels of sweetness.

Given what you've just learned about how plants manufacture glucose, it probably won't surprise you to discover that glucose is the most abundant sugar molecule in our diets and in our body. Glucose does not generally occur by itself in foods, but attaches to other sugars to form disaccharides and complex carbohydrates. In our body, glucose is the preferred source of energy for the brain, and it is a very important source of energy for all cells.

Fructose, the sweetest natural sugar, is found in fruits and vegetables. Fructose is also called *levulose,*or *fruit sugar*. In many processed foods, it comes in the form of *high-fructose corn syrup*. This syrup is manufactured from corn and is used to sweeten soft drinks, desserts, candies, and jellies.

Galactose does not occur alone in foods. It joins with glucose to create lactose, one of the three most common disaccharides.

Ribose is a five-carbon monosaccharide. Very little ribose is found in our diets; our body produces ribose from the foods we eat, and ribose is contained in the genetic material of our cells: deoxyribonucleic acid (DNA) and ribonucleic acid (RNA).

Lactose, Maltose, and Sucrose Are Disaccharides

The three most common disaccharides found in foods are *lactose, maltose,* and *sucrose* (Figure 3). **Lactose** (also called *milk sugar*) consists of one glucose molecule and one galactose molecule. Interestingly, human breast milk has more lactose than cow's milk does, making human breast milk taste sweeter.

In our body, glucose is the preferred source of energy for the brain.

Brocreativ/Shutterstock

simple carbohydrate Commonly called *sugar;* can be either a monosaccharide (such as glucose) or a disaccharide.

monosaccharide The simplest of carbohydrates, consisting of one sugar molecule, the most common form of which is glucose.

disaccharide A carbohydrate compound consisting of two sugar molecules joined together.

fructose The sweetest natural sugar; a monosaccharide that occurs in fruits and vegetables; also called levulose, or fruit sugar.

galactose A monosaccharide that joins with glucose to create lactose, one of the three most common disaccharides.

ribose A five-carbon monosaccharide that is located in the genetic material of cells.

lactose A disaccharide consisting of one glucose molecule and one galactose molecule. It is found in milk, including human breast milk; also called *milk sugar.*

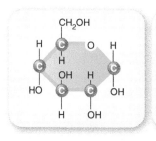

Glucose

Most abundant sugar molecule in our diet; good energy source

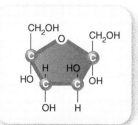

Fructose

Sweetest natural sugar; found in fruit, high-fructose corn syrup

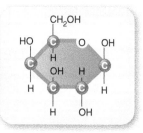

Galactose

Does not occur alone in foods; binds with glucose to form lactose

Figure 2 The three most common monosaccharides. Notice that all three contain identical atoms: six carbon, twelve hydrogen, and six oxygen. It is only the arrangement of these atoms that differs among them.

Figure 3 Galactose, glucose, and fructose join together to make the disaccharides lactose, maltose, and sucrose.

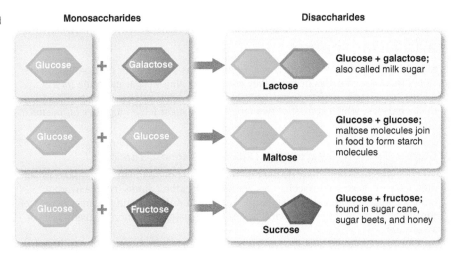

Monosaccharides

Disaccharides

Glucose + Galactose → Lactose — Glucose + galactose; also called milk sugar

Glucose + Glucose → Maltose — Glucose + glucose; maltose molecules join in food to form starch molecules

Glucose + Fructose → Sucrose — Glucose + fructose; found in sugar cane, sugar beets, and honey

Maltose (also called *malt sugar*) consists of two molecules of glucose. It does not generally occur by itself in foods but, rather, is bound together with other molecules. As our body breaks these larger molecules down, maltose results as a by-product. Maltose is also the sugar that is fermented during the production of beer and liquor products. **Fermentation** is a process in which an agent, such as yeast, causes an organic substance to break down into simpler substances and results in the production of the energy molecule adenosine triphosphate (ATP). Maltose is formed during the breakdown of sugar in grains and other foods into alcohol. Contrary to popular belief, very little maltose remains in alcoholic beverages after the fermentation process is complete; thus, alcoholic beverages are not good sources of carbohydrate.

Sucrose is composed of one glucose molecule and one fructose molecule. Because sucrose contains fructose, it is sweeter than lactose or maltose. Sucrose provides much of the sweet taste found in honey, maple syrup, fruits, and vegetables. Table sugar, brown sugar, powdered sugar, and many other products are made by refining the sucrose found in sugarcane and sugar beets. Are honey and other naturally occurring forms of sucrose more healthful than manufactured forms? The Nutrition Myth or Fact? box investigates this question.

RECAP Carbohydrates contain carbon, hydrogen, and oxygen. Plants make one type of carbohydrate, glucose, through the process of photosynthesis. Simple carbohydrates include monosaccharides and disaccharides. Glucose, fructose, and galactose are monosaccharides; lactose, maltose, and sucrose are disaccharides.

Polysaccharides Are Complex Carbohydrates

Complex carbohydrates, the second major type of carbohydrate, generally consist of long chains of glucose molecules called **polysaccharides** (*poly* means "many"). They include starch, glycogen, and most fibers **(Figure 4)**.

Starch Is a Polysaccharide Stored in Plants

Plants store glucose not as single molecules but as polysaccharides in the form of **starch**. Excellent food sources of starch include grains (wheat, rice, corn, oats, and barley), legumes (peas, beans, and lentils), and tubers (potatoes and yams). Our cells cannot use the complex starch molecules exactly as they exist in plants. Instead, our body must break them down into the monosaccharide glucose, from which we can then meet our energy needs.

maltose A disaccharide consisting of two molecules of glucose. It does not generally occur independently in foods but results as a by-product of digestion; maltose is also called *malt sugar*.

fermentation A process in which an agent causes an organic substance to break down into simpler substances and results in the production of ATP.

sucrose A disaccharide composed of one glucose molecule and one fructose molecule; sucrose is sweeter than lactose or maltose.

complex carbohydrate A nutrient compound consisting of long chains of glucose molecules, such as starch, glycogen, and fiber.

polysaccharide A complex carbohydrate consisting of long chains of glucose.

starch A polysaccharide stored in plants; the storage form of glucose in plants.

NUTRITION MYTH OR FACT?
Is Honey More Nutritious Than Table Sugar?

Liz's friend Tiffany is dedicated to eating healthful foods. She advises Liz to avoid sucrose and to eat foods that contain honey, molasses, or raw sugar. Like many people, Tiffany believes these sweeteners are more natural and nutritious than refined table sugar. How can Liz sort sugar fact from fiction?

Remember that sucrose consists of one glucose molecule and one fructose molecule joined together. From a chemical perspective, honey is almost identical to sucrose, since honey also contains glucose and fructose molecules in almost equal amounts. However, enzymes in bees' "honey stomachs" separate some of the glucose and fructose molecules, resulting in honey looking and tasting slightly different than sucrose. As you know, bees store honey in combs and fan it with their wings to reduce its moisture content. This also alters the appearance and texture of honey.

Honey does not contain any more nutrients than sucrose, so it is not a more healthful choice than sucrose. In fact, per tablespoon, honey has more Calories (energy) than table sugar. This is because the crystals in table sugar take up more space on a spoon than the liquid form of honey, so a tablespoon contains less sugar. However, some people argue that honey is sweeter, so you use less.

It is important to note that honey commonly contains bacteria that can cause fatal food poisoning in infants. The more mature digestive system of older children and adults is immune to the effects of these bacteria, but babies younger than 12 months should never be given honey.

Are raw sugar and molasses more healthful than table sugar? Actually, the "raw sugar" available in the United States is not really raw. Truly raw sugar is made up of the first crystals obtained when sugar is processed. Sugar in this form contains dirt, parts of insects, and other by-products that make it illegal to sell in the United States. The raw sugar products in American stores have actually gone through more than half of the same steps in the refining process used to make table sugar. Raw sugar has a coarser texture than white sugar and is unbleached; in most markets, it is also significantly more expensive.

Molasses is the syrup that remains when sucrose is made from sugarcane. It is reddish brown in color with a distinctive taste that is less sweet than table sugar. It does contain some iron, but this iron does not occur naturally. It is a contaminant from the machines that process the sugarcane! Incidentally, blackstrap molasses is the residue of a third boiling of the syrup. It contains less sugar than light or dark molasses but more minerals.

Table 1 compares the nutrient content of white table sugar, raw sugar, honey, and blackstrap molasses. As you can see, none of them contains many nutrients that are important for health. This is why highly sweetened products are referred to as "empty Calories."

TABLE 1	Nutrient Comparison of Four Different Sugars			
	Table Sugar	Raw Sugar	Honey	Molasses
Energy (kcal)	49	49	64	58
Carbohydrate (g)	12.6	12.6	17.3	14.95
Fat (g)	0	0	0	0
Protein (g)	0	0	0.06	0
Fiber (grams)	0	0	0	0
Vitamin C (mg)	0	0	0.1	0
Vitamin A (IU)	0	0	0	0
Thiamin (mg)	0	0	0	0.008
Riboflavin (mg)	0.002	0.003	0.008	0
Folate (µg)	0	0	0	0
Calcium (mg)	0	0.042	1	41
Iron (mg)	0	0	0.09	0.94
Sodium (mg)	0	0	1	7
Potassium (mg)	0	0.25	11	293

Data from U.S. Department of Agriculture, Agricultural Research Service. 2009. USDA National Nutrient Database for Standard Reference, Release 22. Nutrient Data Laboratory Home Page, www.ars.usda.gov/ba/bhnrc/ndl.
Note: Nutrient values are identified for 1 tablespoon of each product.

Our body easily digests most starches; however, some starches in plants are not digestible and are called *resistant*. Technically, resistant starch is classified as a type of fiber. When our intestinal bacteria ferment resistant starch, a fatty acid called *butyrate* is produced. Consuming resistant starch may be beneficial: some research suggests that butyrate consumption reduces the risk for cancer.[5] Legumes contain more resistant starch than do grains, fruits, or vegetables. This quality, plus their high protein and fiber content, makes legumes a healthful food.

Figure 4 Polysaccharides include starch, glycogen, and fiber.

Starch
Storage form of glucose in plants; found in grains, legumes, and tubers

Glycogen
Storage form of glucose in animals; stored in liver and muscles

Fiber
Forms the support structures of leaves, stems, and plants

Monkey Business Images/Shutterstock

Tubers, such as these sweet potatoes, are excellent food sources of starch.

glycogen A polysaccharide; the storage form of glucose in animals.

dietary fiber The nondigestible carbohydrate parts of plants that form the support structures of leaves, stems, and seeds.

functional fiber The nondigestible forms of carbohydrates that are extracted from plants or manufactured in a laboratory and have known health benefits.

total fiber The sum of dietary fiber and functional fiber.

soluble fibers Fibers that dissolve in water.

viscous Having a gel-like consistency; viscous fibers form a gel when dissolved in water.

Glycogen Is a Polysaccharide Stored by Animals

Glycogen is the storage form of glucose for animals, including humans. After an animal is slaughtered, most of the glycogen is broken down by enzymes found in animal tissues. Thus, very little glycogen exists in meat. As plants contain no glycogen, it is not a dietary source of carbohydrate. As explained later in this chapter, we can break down glycogen into glucose when we need it for energy. We store glycogen in our liver and muscles; the storage and use of glycogen are discussed in more detail later on in this chapter.

Fiber Is a Polysaccharide That Gives Plants Their Structure

Like starch, fiber is composed of long polysaccharide chains; however, our body does not easily break down the bonds that connect fiber molecules. This means that most fibers pass through the digestive system without being digested and absorbed, so they contribute no energy to our diet. However, fiber offers many other health benefits, as we will see shortly.

There are currently a number of definitions of fiber. Recently, the Food and Nutrition Board of the Institute of Medicine proposed three distinctions: *dietary fiber, functional fiber,* and *total fiber.*[6]

- **Dietary fiber** is the nondigestible parts of plants that form the support structures of leaves, stems, and seeds (see Figure 4). In a sense, you can think of dietary fiber as a plant's "skeleton."
- **Functional fiber** consists of the nondigestible forms of carbohydrates that are extracted from plants or manufactured in a laboratory and have known health benefits. Functional fiber is added to foods and is the form used in fiber supplements. Examples of functional fiber you might see on nutrition labels include cellulose, guar gum, pectin, and psyllium.
- **Total fiber** is the sum of dietary fiber and functional fiber.

Fiber can also be classified according to its chemical and physical properties as soluble or insoluble.

Soluble Fibers **Soluble fibers** dissolve in water. They are also **viscous**, forming a gel when wet, and fermentable; that is, they are easily digested by bacteria in the colon. Soluble fibers are typically found in citrus fruits, berries, oat products, and beans.

Research suggests that the regular consumption of soluble fibers reduces the risks for cardiovascular disease and type 2 diabetes by lowering blood cholesterol and blood glucose levels.

Soluble fibers include:

- *Pectins*, which contain chains of galacturonic acid and other monosaccharides. Pectins are found in the cell walls and intracellular tissues of many fruits and berries. They can be isolated and used to thicken foods, such as jams and yogurts.
- *Gums*, which contain galactose, glucuronic acid, and other monosaccharides. Gums are a diverse group of polysaccharides that are viscous. They are typically

isolated from seeds and are used as thickening, gelling, and stabilizing agents. Guar gum and gum arabic are common gums used as food additives.

- *Mucilages,* which are similar to gums and contain galactose, mannose, and other monosaccharides. Two examples are psyllium and carrageenan. Psyllium is the husk of psyllium seeds, which are also known as plantago or flea seeds. Carrageenan comes from seaweed. Mucilages are used as food stabilizers.

Insoluble Fibers **Insoluble fibers** are those that do not typically dissolve in water. These fibers are usually nonviscous and typically cannot be fermented by bacteria in the colon. Insoluble fibers are generally found in whole grains, such as wheat, rye, and brown rice, and are found in many vegetables. These fibers are not associated with reducing cholesterol levels but are known for promoting regular bowel movements, alleviating constipation, and reducing the risk for diverticulosis (discussed later in this chapter). Examples of insoluble fibers include the following:

- *Lignins* are noncarbohydrate forms of fiber. Lignins are found in the woody parts of plant cell walls and in carrots and the seeds of fruits and berries. Lignins are also found in brans (the outer husk of grains such as wheat, oats, and rye) and other whole grains.
- *Cellulose* is the main structural component of plant cell walls. Cellulose is a chain of glucose units similar to amylose but, unlike amylose, cellulose contains bonds that are nondigestible by humans. Cellulose is found in whole grains, fruits, vegetables, and legumes. It can also be extracted from wood pulp or cotton, and it is added to foods as an agent for anticaking, thickening, and texturizing of foods.
- *Hemicelluloses* contain glucose, mannose, galacturonic acid, and other monosaccharides. Hemicelluloses are found in plant cell walls and they surround cellulose. They are the primary component of cereal fibers and are found in whole grains and vegetables. Although many hemicelluloses are insoluble, some are also classified as soluble.

RECAP The three types of polysaccharides are starch, glycogen, and fiber. Starch is the storage form of glucose in plants, whereas glycogen is the storage form of glucose in animals. Fiber forms the support structures of plants. Soluble fibers dissolve in water, are viscous, and can be digested by bacteria in the colon, whereas insoluble fibers do not dissolve in water, are not viscous, and cannot be digested.

Why Do We Need Carbohydrates?

We have seen that carbohydrates are an important energy source for our body. Let's learn more about this and discuss other functions of carbohydrates.

Carbohydrates Provide Energy

Carbohydrates, an excellent source of energy for all our cells, provide 4 kilocalories (kcal) of energy per gram. Some of our cells can also use fat and even protein for energy if necessary. However, our red blood cells can utilize only glucose, and our brain and other nervous tissues primarily rely on glucose. This is why we get tired, irritable, and shaky when we haven't eaten any carbohydrate for a prolonged period of time.

Carbohydrates Fuel Daily Activity

Many popular diets—such as Dr. Atkins' New Revolution Diet and the Sugar Busters plan—are based on the idea that our body actually "prefers" to use fat and/or protein for energy. They claim that current carbohydrate recommendations are much higher than we really need.

In reality, the body relies mostly on both carbohydrates and fat for energy. In fact, as shown in **Figure 5**, our body always uses some combination of carbohydrates and fat to fuel daily activities. Fat is the predominant energy source used by our body at rest and during low-intensity activities, such as sitting, standing, and walking. Even during rest, however, our brain cells and red blood cells still rely on glucose.

Kristin Piljay

◆ Dissolvable laxatives are an example of one type of soluble fiber.

Rob Lewine/Bettmann/Corbis

◆ Our red blood cells can utilize only glucose and other monosaccharides, and our brain and other nervous tissues rely primarily on glucose. This is why we get tired, irritable, and shaky when we haven't eaten for a prolonged period of time.

insoluble fibers Fibers that do not dissolve in water.

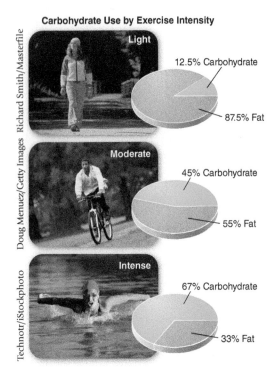

Figure 5 Amounts of carbohydrate and fat used during light, moderate, and intense exercise.[7]

Carbohydrates Fuel Exercise

When we exercise, whether running, briskly walking, bicycling, or performing any other activity that causes us to breathe harder and sweat, we begin to use more glucose than fat. Whereas fat breakdown is a slow process and requires oxygen, we can break down glucose very quickly either with or without oxygen. Even during very intense exercise, when less oxygen is available, we can still break down glucose very quickly for energy. That's why when you are exercising at maximal effort carbohydrates are providing almost 100% of the energy your body requires.

If you are physically active, it is important to eat enough carbohydrates to provide energy for your brain, red blood cells, and muscles. In general, if you do not eat enough carbohydrate to support regular exercise, your body will have to rely on fat and protein as alternative energy sources. One advantage of becoming highly trained for endurance-type events, such as marathons and triathlons, is that our muscles are able to store more glycogen, which provides us with additional glucose we can use during exercise.

Low Carbohydrate Intake Can Lead to Ketoacidosis

When we do not eat enough carbohydrate, our body seeks an alternative source of fuel for our brain and begins to break down stored fat. This process, called **ketosis**, produces an alternative fuel called **ketones**.

Ketosis is an important mechanism for providing energy to the brain during situations of fasting, low carbohydrate intake, or vigorous exercise.[5] However, ketones also suppress appetite and cause dehydration and acetone breath (the breath smells like nail polish remover). If inadequate carbohydrate intake continues for an extended period of time, the body will produce excessive amounts of ketones. Because many ketones are acids, high ketone levels cause the blood to become very acidic, leading to a condition called **ketoacidosis**. The high acidity of the blood interferes with basic body functions, causes the loss of lean body mass, and damages many body tissues. People with untreated diabetes are at high risk for ketoacidosis, which can lead to coma and even death.

Carbohydrates Spare Protein

If the diet does not provide enough carbohydrate, the body will make its own glucose from protein. This involves breaking down the proteins in blood and tissues into amino acids, then converting them to glucose. This process is called **gluconeogenesis** ("generating new glucose").

When our body uses amino acids for energy, they are not available to make new cells, repair tissue damage, support our immune system, or perform any of their other functions. During periods of starvation or when eating a diet that is very low in carbohydrate, our body will take amino acids from the blood first, and then from other tissues, such as muscles, heart, liver, and kidneys. Using amino acids in this manner over a prolonged period of time can cause serious, possibly irreversible, damage to these organs.

Carbohydrates and Body Weight

Proponents of low-carbohydrate diets claim that eating carbohydrates makes you gain weight. However, anyone who consumes more Calories than he or she expends will gain weight, whether those Calories are in the form of simple or complex carbohydrates, protein, or fat. Moreover, fat is more energy dense than carbohydrate: it contains 9 kcal per gram, whereas carbohydrate contains only 4 kcal per gram. Thus, gram for gram, fat is twice as "fattening" as carbohydrate. In fact, eating

ketosis The process by which the breakdown of fat during fasting states results in the production of ketones.

ketones Substances produced during the breakdown of fat when carbohydrate intake is insufficient to meet energy needs. Ketones provide an alternative energy source for the brain when glucose levels are low.

ketoacidosis A condition in which excessive ketones are present in the blood, causing the blood to become very acidic, which alters basic body functions and damages tissues. Untreated ketoacidosis can be fatal. This condition is found in individuals with untreated diabetes mellitus.

gluconeogenesis The generation of glucose from the breakdown of proteins into amino acids.

carbohydrate sources that are high in fiber and other nutrients has been shown to reduce the overall risk for obesity, heart disease, and diabetes. Thus, all carbohydrates are not bad, and even a small amount of refined sugars can be included in a healthful diet.

Fiber Helps Us Stay Healthy

The terms *simple* and *complex* can cause confusion when discussing the health effects of carbohydrates. As we explained earlier, these terms are used to designate the number of sugar molecules present in the carbohydrate. However, when distinguishing carbohydrates in terms of their effect on our health, it is more appropriate to talk about them in terms of their nutrient density and their fiber content. Although we cannot digest fiber, it is a very important substance in our diet. Research indicates that it helps us stay healthy and may prevent many digestive and chronic diseases. The following are potential benefits of fiber consumption:

- May reduce the risk of colon cancer. Although there is some controversy surrounding this issue, many researchers believe that fiber binds cancer-causing substances and speeds their elimination from the colon. However, recent studies of colon cancer and fiber have shown that the relationship between them is not as strong as previously thought.
- Helps prevent hemorrhoids, constipation, and other intestinal problems by keeping our stools moist and soft. Fiber gives gut muscles "something to push on" and makes it easier to eliminate stools.
- Reduces the risk for *diverticulosis*, a condition that is caused in part by trying to eliminate small, hard stools. A great deal of pressure must be generated in the large intestine to pass hard stools. This increased pressure weakens intestinal walls, causing them to bulge outward and form pockets (Figure 6). Feces and fibrous materials can get trapped in these pockets, which become infected and inflamed. This is a painful condition that must be treated with antibiotics or surgery.
- May reduce the risk of heart disease by delaying or blocking the absorption of dietary cholesterol into the bloodstream (Figure 7). In addition, when soluble fibers are digested, bacteria in the colon produce short-chain fatty acids that may lower the production of low-density lipoprotein (LDL) to healthful levels in our body.
- May enhance weight loss, as eating a high-fiber diet causes a person to feel more full. Fiber absorbs water, expands in the large intestine, and slows the movement of food through the upper part of the digestive tract. Also, people who eat a fiber-rich diet tend to eat fewer fatty and sugary foods.
- May lower the risk for type 2 diabetes. In slowing digestion and absorption, fiber also slows the release of glucose into the blood. It thereby improves the body's regulation of insulin production and blood glucose levels.

Peter Weber/Shutterstock

◀ When we exercise or perform any activity that causes us to breathe harder and sweat, we begin to use more glucose than fat.

Dorling Kindersley

◀ Brown rice is a good food source of dietary fiber.

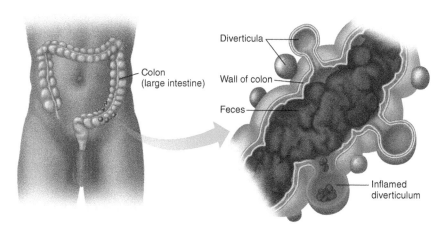

Colon (large intestine)

Diverticula

Wall of colon

Feces

Inflamed diverticulum

◀ **Figure 6** Diverticulosis occurs when bulging pockets form in the wall of the large intestine (colon). These pockets become infected and inflamed, requiring proper treatment.

Figure 7 How fiber might help decrease blood cholesterol levels. **(a)** When eating a high-fiber diet, fiber binds to the bile that is produced from cholesterol, resulting in relatively more cholesterol being excreted in the feces. **(b)** When a lower-fiber diet is consumed, less fiber (and thus less cholesterol) is bound to bile and excreted in the feces.

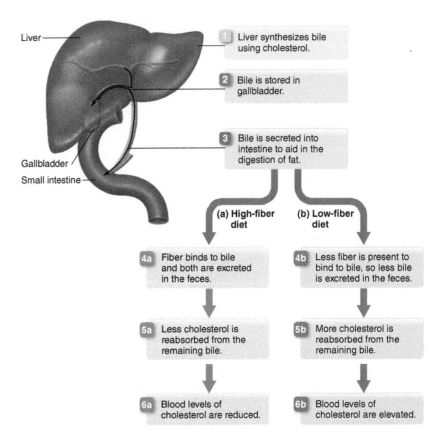

Liver

1 Liver synthesizes bile using cholesterol.

2 Bile is stored in gallbladder.

3 Bile is secreted into intestine to aid in the digestion of fat.

Gallbladder

Small intestine

(a) High-fiber diet

4a Fiber binds to bile and both are excreted in the feces.

5a Less cholesterol is reabsorbed from the remaining bile.

6a Blood levels of cholesterol are reduced.

(b) Low-fiber diet

4b Less fiber is present to bind to bile, so less bile is excreted in the feces.

5b More cholesterol is reabsorbed from the remaining bile.

6b Blood levels of cholesterol are elevated.

RECAP Carbohydrates are an important energy source at rest and during exercise, and they provide 4 kcal of energy per gram. Carbohydrates are necessary in the diet to spare body protein and prevent ketosis. Carbohydrate sources that contain fiber and other nutrients can reduce the risk for obesity, heart disease, and diabetes. Fiber helps prevent hemorrhoids, constipation, and diverticulosis; may reduce the risk for colon cancer and heart disease; and may assist with weight loss.

How Does Our Body Break Down Carbohydrates?

Glucose is the form of sugar that our body uses for energy, and the primary goal of carbohydrate digestion is to break down polysaccharides and disaccharides into monosaccharides, which can then be converted to glucose. We focus specifically and in a bit more detail on the digestion and absorption of carbohydrates. **Figure 8** provides a visual tour of carbohydrate digestion.

Digestion Breaks Down Most Carbohydrates into Monosaccharides

Carbohydrate digestion begins in the mouth (Figure 8, step 1). The starch in the foods you eat mixes with your saliva during chewing. Saliva contains an enzyme called **salivary amylase,** which breaks starch into smaller particles and eventually into the disaccharide maltose. The next time you eat a piece of bread, notice that you can actually taste it becoming sweeter; this indicates the breakdown of starch into maltose. Disaccharides are not digested in the mouth.

salivary amylase An enzyme in saliva that breaks starch into smaller particles and eventually into the disaccharide maltose.

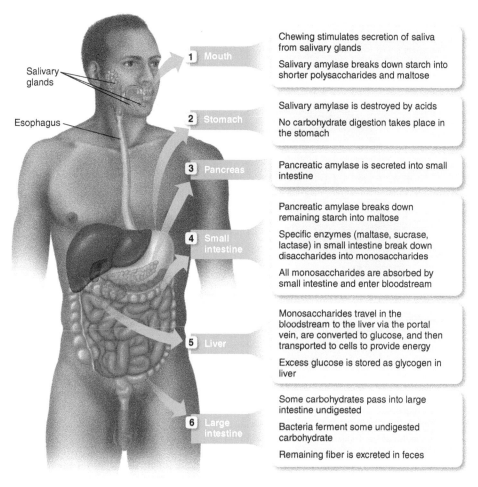

Salivary glands

Esophagus

1 Mouth
Chewing stimulates secretion of saliva from salivary glands

Salivary amylase breaks down starch into shorter polysaccharides and maltose

2 Stomach
Salivary amylase is destroyed by acids

No carbohydrate digestion takes place in the stomach

3 Pancreas
Pancreatic amylase is secreted into small intestine

4 Small intestine
Pancreatic amylase breaks down remaining starch into maltose

Specific enzymes (maltase, sucrase, lactase) in small intestine break down disaccharides into monosaccharides

All monosaccharides are absorbed by small intestine and enter bloodstream

5 Liver
Monosaccharides travel in the bloodstream to the liver via the portal vein, are converted to glucose, and then transported to cells to provide energy

Excess glucose is stored as glycogen in liver

6 Large intestine
Some carbohydrates pass into large intestine undigested

Bacteria ferment some undigested carbohydrate

Remaining fiber is excreted in feces

Figure 8 A review of carbohydrate digestion and absorption.

As the bolus of food leaves the mouth and enters the stomach, all digestion of carbohydrates ceases. This is because the acid in the stomach inactivates most of the salivary amylase enzyme (Figure 8, step 2).

The majority of carbohydrate digestion occurs in the small intestine. As the contents of the stomach enter the small intestine, the pancreas secretes an enzyme called **pancreatic amylase** into the small intestine (Figure 8, step 3). Pancreatic amylase continues to digest any remaining starch into maltose. Additional enzymes in the microvilli of the mucosal cells that line the intestinal tract work to break down disaccharides into monosaccharides. Maltose is broken down into glucose by the enzyme **maltase.** Sucrose is broken down into glucose and fructose by the enzyme **sucrase.** The enzyme **lactase** breaks down lactose into glucose and galactose (Figure 8, step 4). Notice that enzyme names are identifiable by the *–ase* suffix. All monosaccharides are then absorbed into the mucosal cells lining the small intestine, where they pass through and enter into the bloodstream.

The Liver Converts Most Non-Glucose Monosaccharides into Glucose

Once the monosaccharides enter the bloodstream, they travel to the liver, where fructose and galactose are converted to glucose (Figure 8, step 5). If needed immediately for energy, the glucose is released into the bloodstream, where it can travel to

pancreatic amylase An enzyme secreted by the pancreas into the small intestine that digests any remaining starch into maltose.

maltase A digestive enzyme that breaks maltose into glucose.

sucrase A digestive enzyme that breaks sucrose into glucose and fructose.

lactase A digestive enzyme that breaks lactose into glucose and galactose.

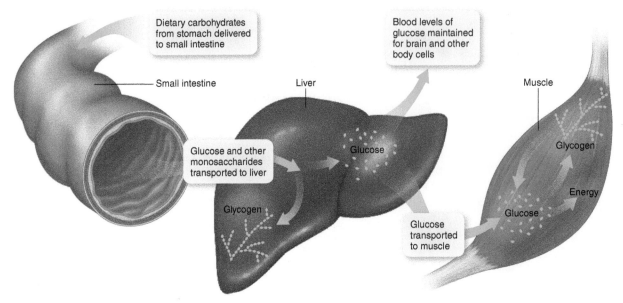

Dietary carbohydrates from stomach delivered to small intestine

Blood levels of glucose maintained for brain and other body cells

Small intestine

Liver

Muscle

Glucose and other monosaccharides transported to liver

Glucose

Glycogen

Glycogen

Energy

Glycogen

Glucose

Glucose transported to muscle

Figure 9 Glucose is stored as glycogen in both liver and muscle. The glycogen stored in the liver maintains blood glucose between meals; muscle glycogen provides immediate energy to the muscle during exercise.

the cells to provide energy. If glucose is not needed immediately for energy, it is stored as glycogen in our liver and muscles. Enzymes in liver and muscle cells combine glucose molecules to form glycogen (an anabolic, or building, process) and break glycogen into glucose (a catabolic, or destructive, process), depending on the body's energy needs. On average, the liver can store 70 g (280 kcal) and the muscles can normally store about 120 g (480 kcal) of glycogen. Between meals, our body draws on liver glycogen reserves to maintain blood glucose levels and support the needs of our cells, including those of our brain, spinal cord, and red blood cells **(Figure 9)**.

The glycogen stored in our muscles continually provides energy to our muscle cells, particularly during intense exercise. Endurance athletes can increase their storage of muscle glycogen from two to four times the normal amount through a process called *carbohydrate loading*. Any excess glucose is stored as glycogen in the liver and muscles and saved for such future energy needs as exercise. Once the storage capacity of the liver and muscles is reached, any excess glucose can be stored as fat in adipose tissue.

Fiber Is Excreted from the Large Intestine

As previously mentioned, humans do not possess enzymes in the small intestine that can break down fiber. Thus, fiber passes through the small intestine undigested and enters the large intestine, or colon. There, bacteria ferment some previously undigested carbohydrates, causing the production of gases and a few short-chain fatty acids. The cells of the large intestine use these short-chain fatty acids for energy. The fiber remaining in the colon adds bulk to our stools and is excreted (Figure 8, step 6) in feces. In this way, fiber assists in maintaining bowel regularity.

RECAP Carbohydrate digestion starts in the mouth and continues in the small intestine. Glucose and other monosaccharides are absorbed into the bloodstream and travel to the liver, where non-glucose sugars are converted to glucose. Glucose either is used by the cells for energy or is converted to glycogen and stored in the liver and muscle for later use.

Is it Hunger—or Hypoglycemia?

After going for several hours without eating, have you ever felt spaced out, shaky, irritable, and weak? And did the symptoms subside once you'd eaten? If so, maybe you wondered if your symptoms were due to hypoglycemia.

In **hypoglycemia,** blood glucose falls to lower-than-normal levels. This commonly occurs in people with diabetes who aren't getting proper treatment, but it can also happen in people who don't have diabetes if their pancreas secretes too much insulin after a high-carbohydrate meal. The characteristic symptoms usually appear about 1 to 4 hours after the meal and occur because the body clears glucose from the blood too quickly. People with this form of hypoglycemia must eat smaller meals more frequently to level out their blood insulin and glucose levels.

The trouble is, ordinary hunger can make you experience symptoms just like those of true hypoglycemia. So which is it— hunger or hypoglycemia? You can only find out for sure by getting a blood test, but unless you have diabetes it's probably not necessary. For most healthy people, eating regular meals and healthy snacks is the only "treatment" needed.

A Variety of Hormones Regulates Blood Glucose Levels

Our body regulates blood glucose levels within a fairly narrow range to provide adequate glucose to the brain and other cells. A number of hormones, including insulin, glucagon, epinephrine, norepinephrine, cortisol, and growth hormone, assist the body with maintaining blood glucose.

When we eat a meal, our blood glucose level rises. But glucose in our blood cannot help our nerves, muscles, and other organs function unless it can cross into their cells. Glucose molecules are too large to cross cell membranes independently. To get in, glucose needs assistance from the hormone **insulin,** which is secreted by the pancreas **(Figure 10a)**. Insulin is transported in the blood throughout the body, where it stimulates special molecules located in cell membranes to transport glucose into the cell. Insulin can be thought of as a key that opens the gates of the cell membrane, enabling the transport of glucose into the cell interior, where it can be used for energy. Insulin also stimulates the liver and muscles to take up glucose and store it as glycogen.

When you have not eaten for a period of time, your blood glucose level declines. This decrease in blood glucose stimulates the pancreas to secrete another hormone, **glucagon** (Figure 10b). Glucagon acts in an opposite way to insulin: it causes the liver to convert its stored glycogen into glucose, which is then secreted into the bloodstream and transported to the cells for energy. Glucagon also assists in the breakdown of body proteins to amino acids, so that the liver can stimulate *gluconeogenesis*, the production of new glucose from amino acids.

Epinephrine, norepinephrine, cortisol, and growth hormone are additional hormones that work to increase blood glucose. Epinephrine and norepinephrine are secreted by the adrenal glands and nerve endings when blood glucose levels are low. They act to increase glycogen breakdown in the liver, resulting in a subsequent increase in the release of glucose into the bloodstream. They also increase gluconeogenesis. These two hormones are also responsible for our "fight-or-flight" reaction to danger; they are released when we need a burst of energy to respond quickly. Cortisol and growth hormone are secreted by the adrenal glands to act on liver, muscle, and adipose tissue. Cortisol increases gluconeogenesis and decreases the use of glucose by muscles and other body organs. Growth hormone decreases glucose uptake by our muscles, increases our mobilization and use of the fatty acids stored in our adipose tissue, and increases our liver's output of glucose.

Normally, the effects of these hormones balance each other to maintain blood glucose within a healthy range. An alteration in this balance can lead to health conditions such as diabetes or hypoglycemia.

insulin The hormone secreted by the beta cells of the pancreas in response to increased blood levels of glucose; it facilitates the uptake of glucose by body cells.

glucagon The hormone secreted by the alpha cells of the pancreas in response to decreased blood levels of glucose; it causes the breakdown of liver stores of glycogen into glucose.

hypoglycemia A condition marked by blood glucose levels that are below normal fasting levels.

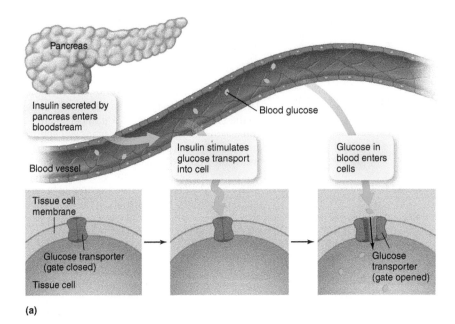

(a)

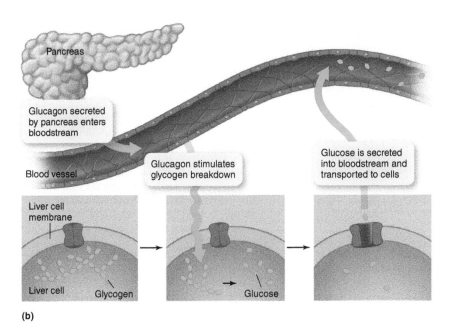

(b)

Figure 10 Regulation of blood glucose by the hormones insulin and glucagon. **(a)** When blood glucose levels increase after a meal, the pancreas secretes insulin. Insulin opens "gates" in the cell membrane to allow the passage of glucose into the cell. **(b)** When blood glucose levels are low, the pancreas secretes glucagon. Glucagon enters liver cells, where it stimulates the breakdown of stored glycogen into glucose. This glucose is then released into the bloodstream.

The Glycemic Index Shows How Foods Affect Our Blood Glucose Level

The **glycemic index** is a measure of the potential of foods to raise blood glucose levels. Foods with a high glycemic index cause a sudden surge in blood glucose. This in turn triggers a surge in insulin, which may then be followed by a dramatic drop in blood glucose. Foods with a low glycemic index cause low to moderate fluctuations in blood glucose. When foods are assigned a glycemic index value, they are often compared to the glycemic effect of pure glucose.

The glycemic index of a food is not always easy to predict. Figure 11 ranks certain foods according to their glycemic index. Do any of these rankings surprise you? Most people assume that foods containing simple sugars have a higher glycemic index than starches, but this is not always the case. For instance, compare the glycemic indexes for apples and instant potatoes. Although instant potatoes are a starchy food, they have a glycemic index value of 85, whereas the value for an apple is only 38!

The type of carbohydrate, the way the food is prepared, and its fat and fiber content can all affect how quickly the body absorbs it. It is important to note that we eat most of our foods combined into a meal. In this case, the glycemic index of the total meal becomes more important than the ranking of each food.

For determining the effect of a food on a person's glucose response, some nutrition experts believe that a food's **glycemic load** is more useful than the glycemic index. A food's glycemic load is the number of grams of carbohydrate it contains multiplied by the glycemic index of that carbohydrate. For instance, carrots are recognized as a vegetable having a relatively high glycemic index of about 68; however, the glycemic load of carrots is only 3.[8] This is because there is very little total carbohydrate in a serving of carrots. The low glycemic load of carrots means that carrot consumption is unlikely to cause a significant rise in glucose and insulin levels.

Steve Shott/Dorling Kindersley

Ryan McVay/Getty Images

An apple has a lower glycemic index (38) than a serving of white rice (56).

glycemic index The system that assigns ratings (or values) for the potential of foods to raise blood glucose and insulin levels.

glycemic load The amount of carbohydrate in a food multiplied by the glycemic index of the carbohydrate.

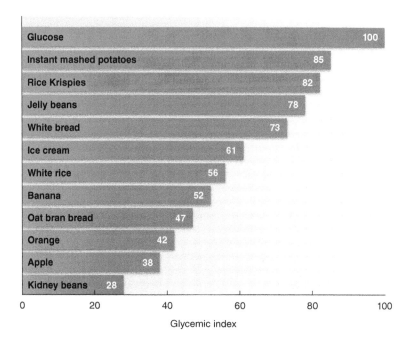

Glycemic index values:

Food	Glycemic index
Glucose	100
Instant mashed potatoes	85
Rice Krispies	82
Jelly beans	78
White bread	73
Ice cream	61
White rice	56
Banana	52
Oat bran bread	47
Orange	42
Apple	38
Kidney beans	28

Figure 11 Glycemic index values for various foods as compared to pure glucose.

Data from Foster-Powell, K., S. H. A. Holt, and J. C. Brand-Miller. 2002. International table of glycemic index and glycemic load values. *Am. J. Clin. Nutr.* 76:5–56.

Why do we care about the glycemic index and glycemic load? Foods and meals with a lower glycemic load are better choices for someone with diabetes because they will not trigger dramatic fluctuations in blood glucose. They may also reduce the risk for heart disease and colon cancer because they generally contain more fiber, and fiber helps decrease fat levels in the blood. Recent studies have shown that people who eat lower glycemic index diets have more healthful blood lipid levels and their blood glucose values are more likely to be normal.[9–11] Diets with a low glycemic index and low glycemic load are also associated with a reduced risk for prostate cancer.[12] Despite some encouraging research findings, the glycemic index and glycemic load remain controversial. Many nutrition researchers feel that the evidence supporting their health benefits is weak. In addition, many believe the concepts of the glycemic index/load are too complex for people to apply to their daily lives. Other researchers insist that helping people choose foods with a lower glycemic index/load is critical in the prevention and treatment of many chronic diseases. Until this controversy is resolved, people are encouraged to eat a variety of fiber-rich and less processed carbohydrates, such as beans and lentils, fresh vegetables, and whole-wheat bread, because these forms of carbohydrates have a lower glycemic load and they contain a multitude of important nutrients.

RECAP Various hormones are involved in regulating blood glucose. Insulin lowers blood glucose levels by facilitating the entry of glucose into cells. Glucagon, epinephrine, norepinephrine, cortisol, and growth hormone raise blood glucose levels by a variety of mechanisms. The glycemic index is a value that indicates the potential of foods to raise blood glucose and insulin levels. The glycemic load is the amount of carbohydrate in a food multiplied by the glycemic index of the carbohydrate in that food. Foods with a high glycemic index/load cause surges in blood glucose and insulin, whereas foods with a low glycemic index/load cause more moderate fluctuations in blood glucose.

How Much Carbohydrate Should We Eat?

Carbohydrates are an important part of a balanced, healthful diet. The Recommended Dietary Allowance (RDA) for carbohydrate is based on the amount of glucose the brain uses.[6] The current RDA for adults 19 years of age and older is 130 g of carbohydrate per day. It is important to emphasize that this RDA does not cover the amount of carbohydrate needed to support daily activities; it covers only the amount of carbohydrate needed to supply adequate glucose to the brain.

Carbohydrates have been assigned an Acceptable Macronutrient Distribution Range (AMDR) of 45% to 65% of total energy intake. Table 2 compares the carbohydrate recommendations from the Institute of Medicine with the Dietary Guidelines for Americans related to carbohydrate-containing foods.[6,13] As you can see, the Institute of Medicine provides specific numeric recom-

Ian O'Leary/Dorling Kindersley

🍎 Eating the suggested daily amounts of vegetables and fruit, such as apricots, will ensure that you're getting enough fiber-rich carbohydrate in your diet.

TABLE 2	Dietary Recommendations for Carbohydrates
Institute of Medicine Recommendations*	**Dietary Guidelines for Americans†**
Recommended Dietary Allowance (RDA) for adults 19 years of age and older is 130 g of carbohydrate per day.	Choose fiber-rich fruits, vegetables, and whole grains often.
The Acceptable Macronutrient Distribution Range (AMDR) for carbohydrate is 45–65% of total daily energy intake.	Choose and prepare foods and beverages with little added sugars or caloric sweeteners, such as amounts suggested by the USDA Food Guide and the DASH eating plan.
Added sugar intake should be 25% or less of total energy intake each day.	Reduce the incidence of dental caries by practicing good oral hygiene and consuming sugar- and starch-containing foods and beverages less frequently.

* Data from "Dietary Reference Intakes for Energy, Carbohydrates, Fiber, Fat, Fatty Acids, Cholesterol, Protein, and Amino Acids (Macronutrients)," © 2002 by the National Academy of Sciences, courtesy of the National Academies Press, Washington, DC. Used by permission.
† U.S. Department of Health and Human Services (USDHHS) and U.S. Department of Agriculture (USDA). 2005. *Dietary Guidelines for Americans, 2005.* 6th ed. Washington, DC: U.S. Government Printing Office, www.healthierus.gov/dietaryguidelines.

mendations, whereas the Dietary Guidelines for Americans are general suggestions about foods high in fiber and low in added sugars. Most health agencies agree that most of the carbohydrates you eat each day should be high in fiber, whole-grain and unprocessed. As recommended in the USDA Food Guide, eating at least half your grains as whole grains and eating the suggested amounts of fruits and vegetables each day will ensure that you get enough fiber-rich carbohydrates in your diet. Keep in mind that fruits are predominantly composed of simple sugars and contain little or no starch. They are healthful food choices, however, as they are good sources of vitamins, some minerals, and fiber.

Most Americans Eat Too Much Sugar

The average carbohydrate intake per person in the United States is approximately 50% of total energy intake. For some people, almost half of this amount consists of sugars. Where does all this sugar come from? Some sugar comes from healthful food sources, such as fruit and milk. However, much of our sugar intake comes from *added sugars*. **Added sugars** are defined as sugars and syrups that are added to foods during processing or preparation.[6]

The most common source of added sugars in the U.S. diet is sweetened soft drinks; we drink an average of 40 gallons per person each year. Consider that one 12-oz cola contains 38.5 g of sugar, or almost 10 teaspoons. If you drink the average amount, you are consuming more than 16,420 g of sugar (about 267 cups) each year! Other common sources of added sugars include cookies, cakes, pies, fruit drinks, fruit punches, and candy. In addition, a surprising number of processed foods you may not think of as "sweet" actually contain a significant amount of added sugar, including many brands of peanut butter, flavored rice mixes, and even some canned soups!

Added sugars are not chemically different from naturally occurring sugars. However, foods and beverages with added sugars have lower levels of vitamins, minerals, and fiber than foods that naturally contain simple sugars. Given these nutrient limitations, it's best to choose and prepare foods and beverages with little added sugars. People who are very physically active are able to consume relatively more added sugars, whereas smaller or less active people should consume relatively less. The Nutrition Facts Panel includes a listing of total sugars, but a distinction is not generally made between added sugars and naturally occurring sugars. Thus, you may need to check the ingredients list. Refer to Table 3 for a list of forms of sugar commonly used in foods. To maintain a diet low in added sugars, limit foods in which a form of added sugar is listed as one of the first few ingredients on the label.[14]

Sugars Are Blamed for Many Health Problems

Why do sugars have such a bad reputation? First, they are known to cause tooth decay. Second, many people believe they cause hyperactivity in children. Third, eating a lot of sugar could increase the levels of unhealthful lipids, or fats, in our blood, increasing our risk for heart disease. High intakes of sugar have also been blamed for causing diabetes and obesity. Let's learn the truth about these accusations.

Sugar Causes Tooth Decay

Sugars do play a role in dental problems because the bacteria that cause tooth decay thrive on sugar. These bacteria produce acids, which eat away at tooth enamel and can eventually cause cavities and gum disease (Figure 12). Eating sticky foods that adhere to teeth—such as caramels, crackers, sugary cereals, and licorice—and sipping sweetened beverages over a period of time are two behaviors that increase the risk for tooth decay. This means that people shouldn't suck on hard candies or caramels, slowly sip soda or juice, or put babies to bed with a bottle unless it contains water. As we have seen, even breast milk contains sugar, which can slowly drip onto the baby's gums. As a result, infants should not routinely be allowed to fall asleep at the breast.

Foods with added sugars, such as candy, have lower levels of vitamins and minerals than foods that naturally contain simple sugars.
Joe Raedle/Getty Images

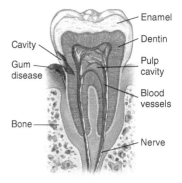

Figure 12 Eating simple carbohydrates can cause an increase in cavities and gum disease. This is because bacteria in the mouth consume simple carbohydrates present on the teeth and gums and produce acids, which eat away at these tissues.

added sugars Sugars and syrups that are added to food during processing or preparation.

TABLE 3   Forms of Sugar Commonly Used in Foods

Name of Sugar	Definition
Brown sugar	A highly refined sweetener made up of approximately 99% sucrose and produced by adding to white table sugar either molasses or burnt table sugar for coloring and flavor.
Concentrated fruit juice sweetener	A form of sweetener made with concentrated fruit juice, commonly pear juice.
Confectioner's sugar	A highly refined, finely ground white sugar with added cornstarch to reduce clumping; also referred to as powdered sugar.
Corn sweetener	A general term for any sweetener made with cornstarch.
Corn syrup	A syrup produced by the partial hydrolysis of cornstarch.
Dextrose	An alternative term for glucose.
Fructose	A monosaccharide in fruits and vegetables, also called levulose or fruit sugar.
Glucose	The most abundant monosaccharide; it is the preferred source of energy for the brain and an important source of energy for all cells.
Granulated sugar	Another terms for white sugar, or table sugar.
High-fructose corn syrup	A type of corn syrup in which part of the sucrose is converted to fructose, making it sweeter than sucrose or regular corn syrup; most high-fructose corn syrup contains 42% to 55% fructose.
Honey	A sweet, sticky liquid sweetener made by bees from the nectar of flowers; contains glucose and fructose.
Invert sugar	A sugar created by heating a sucrose syrup with a small amount of acid; inverting sucrose results in its breakdown into glucose and fructose, which reduces the size of the sugar crystals; its smooth texture makes it ideal for use in making candies, such as fondant, and some syrups.
Lactose	A disaccharide formed by one molecule of glucose and one molecule of galactose; occurs naturally in milk and other dairy products.
Levulose	Another term for fructose, or fruit sugar.
Maltose	A disaccharide consisting of two molecules of glucose; it does not generally occur independently in foods but is a by-product of digestion; also called malt sugar.
Mannitol	A type of sugar alcohol.
Maple sugar	A sugar made by boiling maple syrup.
Molasses	A thick, brown syrup that is separated from raw sugar during manufacturing; it is considered the least refined form of sucrose.
Natural sweetener	A general term used for any naturally occurring sweetener, such as sucrose, honey, or raw sugar.
Raw sugar	The sugar that results from the processing of sugar beets or sugarcane; approximately 96% to 98% sucrose; true raw sugar contains impurities and is not stable in storage; the raw sugar available to consumers has been purified to yield an edible sugar.
Sorbitol	A type of sugar alcohol.
Turbinado sugar	The form of raw sugar that is purified and safe for human consumption; sold as "Sugar in the Raw" in the United States.
White sugar	Another name for sucrose, or table sugar.
Xylitol	A type of sugar alcohol.

To reduce your risk for tooth decay, brush your teeth after each meal, especially after drinking sugary drinks and eating candy. Drinking fluoridated water and using a fluoride toothpaste will also help protect your teeth.

There Is No Link Between Sugar and Hyperactivity in Children

Although many people believe that eating sugar causes hyperactivity and other behavioral problems in children, there is little scientific evidence to support this claim. Some children actually become less active shortly after a high-sugar meal! However, it is important to emphasize that most studies of sugar and children's behavior have only looked at the effects of sugar a few hours after ingestion. We know very little about the long-term effects of sugar intake on the behavior of children. Behavioral and learning problems are complex issues, most likely caused by a multitude of factors. Because of this complexity, the Institute of Medicine has stated that, overall, there does not appear to be enough evidence to state that eating too much sugar causes hyperactivity or other behavioral problems in children.[6] Thus, there is no Tolerable Upper Intake Level for sugar.

High Sugar Intake Can Lead to Unhealthful Levels of Blood Lipids

Research evidence suggests that consuming a diet high in sugars, particularly fructose, can lead to unhealthful changes in blood lipids. Briefly, higher intakes of sugars are associated with increases in our blood of both low-density lipoproteins (LDL, commonly referred to as "bad cholesterol") and triglycerides. At the same time, high sugar intake appears to *decrease* our high-density lipoproteins (HDL), which are protective and are often referred to as "good cholesterol."[6,15] These changes are of concern, as increased levels of triglycerides and LDL and decreased levels of HDL are risk factors for heart disease. However, there is not enough scientific evidence at the present time to state with confidence that eating a diet high in sugar causes heart disease. Still, based on current knowledge, it is prudent for a person at risk for heart disease to eat a diet low in sugars. Because fructose, especially in the form of high-fructose corn syrup, is a component of many processed foods and beverages, careful label reading is advised.

High Sugar Intake Does Not Cause Diabetes but May Contribute to Obesity

There is no scientific evidence that eating a diet high in sugar causes diabetes. In fact, studies examining the relationship between sugar intake and type 2 diabetes report no association between sugar intake and diabetes, or an increased risk for diabetes associated with increased sugar intake and weight gain, or a decreased risk for diabetes with increased sugar intake.[16–18] However, people who have diabetes need to moderate their intake of sugar and closely monitor their blood glucose levels.

There is somewhat more evidence linking sugar intake with obesity. For example, a recent study found that overweight children consumed more sugared soft drinks than did children of normal weight.[18] Another study found that for every extra sugared soft drink a child consumes per day, the risk for obesity increases by 60%.[19] We also know that if you consume more energy than you expend, you will gain weight. It makes intuitive sense that people who consume extra energy from high-sugar foods are at risk for obesity, just as people who consume extra energy from fat or protein gain weight. In addition to the increased potential for obesity, another major concern about high-sugar diets is that they tend to be low in nutrient density because the intake of high-sugar foods tends to replace that of more nutritious foods. The relationship between sugared soft drinks and obesity is highly controversial and is discussed in more detail in the Nutrition Debate later in this chapter.

RECAP The RDA for carbohydrate is 130 g per day; this amount is only sufficient to supply adequate glucose to the brain. The AMDR for carbohydrate is 45% to 65% of total energy intake. Added sugars are sugars and syrups added to foods during processing or preparation. Sugar causes tooth decay but does not appear to cause hyperactivity in children. High intakes of sugars are associated with increases in unhealthful blood lipids. Diets high in sugar are not confirmed to cause diabetes but may contribute to obesity.

Whole-grain foods provide more nutrients and fiber than foods made with enriched flour.

Dorling Kindersley

Most Americans Eat Too Little Fiber-Rich Carbohydrates

Do you get enough fiber-rich carbohydrates each day? If you are like most people in the United States, you eat only about 2 servings of fruits or vegetables each day; this is far below the recommended amount.

Breads and cereals are another potential source of fiber-rich carbohydrates, and they're part of most Americans' diets. But are the breads and cereals you eat made with whole grains? If you're not sure, check out the ingredients lists on the labels of your favorite breads and breakfast cereals. Do they list *whole-wheat flour* or just

TABLE 4   Terms Used to Describe Grains and Cereals on Nutrition Labels

Term	Definition
Brown bread	Bread that may or may not be made using whole-grain flour. Many brown breads are made with white flour with brown (caramel) coloring added.
Enriched (or fortified) flour or grain	Enriching or fortifying grains involves adding nutrients back to refined foods. In order for a manufacturer to use this term in the United States, a minimum amount of iron, folate, niacin, thiamin, and riboflavin must be added. Other nutrients can also be added.
Refined flour or grain	Refining involves removing the coarse parts of food products; refined wheat flour is flour in which all but the internal part of the kernel has been removed. Refined sugar is made by removing the outer portions of sugar beets or sugarcane.
Stone ground	Refers to a milling process in which limestone is used to grind any grain. Stone ground does not mean that bread is made with whole grain, as refined flour can be stone ground.
Unbleached flour	Flour that has been refined but not bleached; it is very similar to refined white flour in texture and nutritional value.
Wheat flour	Any flour made from wheat, which includes white flour, unbleached flour, and whole-wheat flour.
White flour	Flour that has been bleached and refined. All-purpose flour, cake flour, and enriched baking flour are all types of white flour.
Whole-grain flour	A grain that is not refined; whole grains are milled in their complete form, with only the husk removed.
Whole-wheat flour	An unrefined, whole-grain flour made from whole-wheat kernels.

wheat flour? And what's the difference? To help you answer this question, in Table 4 we've defined some terms commonly used on labels for breads and cereals. As you can see, whole-wheat flour is made from whole grains; only the husk of the wheat kernel has been removed. In contrast, the term *wheat flour* can be used to signify a flour that has been highly refined, with the bran and other fiber-rich portions removed.

In addition to stripping a grain of its fiber, the refining process reduces many of the grain's original nutrients. To make up for some of the lost nutrients, manufacturers sometimes enrich the product. **Enriched foods** are foods in which nutrients that were lost during processing have been added back, so that the food meets a specified standard. Notice that the terms *enriched* and *fortified* are not synonymous: **fortified foods** have nutrients added that did not originally exist in the food (or existed in insignificant amounts). For example, some breakfast cereals have been fortified with iron, a mineral that is not present in cereals naturally.

We Need at Least 25 Grams of Fiber Daily

How much fiber do we need? The Adequate Intake for fiber is 25 g per day for women and 38 g per day for men, or 14 g of fiber for every 1,000 kcal per day that a person eats.[5] Most people in the United States eat only 12 to 18 g of fiber each day, getting only half of the fiber they need. Although fiber supplements are available, it is

Eating Right All Day

Breakfast — Oatmeal instead of sugary cereal!

Lunch — Bean soup instead of pizza!

Dinner — Sweet potato instead of french fries!

Snack — Fresh fruit instead of a candy bar!

John Shepherd/iStockphoto · Dusan Zidar/Shutterstock · Dorling Kindersley · Bgphoto/Dreamstime

QUICK TIPS

Hunting for Fiber

✓ Select breads made with *whole* grains, such as wheat, oats, barley, and rye. Two slices of whole-grain bread provide 4–6 grams of fiber.

✓ Switch from a low-fiber breakfast cereal to one that has at least 4 grams of fiber per serving.

✓ For a mid-morning snack, stir 1–2 tablespoons of whole ground flaxseed meal (4 grams of fiber) into a cup of low-fat or nonfat yogurt. Or choose an apple or a pear, with the skin left on (approximately 5 grams of fiber).

✓ Instead of potato chips with your lunchtime sandwich, have a side of carrot sticks or celery sticks (approximately 2 grams of fiber per serving).

✓ Eat legumes every day, if possible (approximately 6 grams of fiber per serving). Have them as your main dish, as a side, or in soups, chili, and other dishes.

✓ Don't forget the vegetables! A cup of cooked leafy greens provides about 4 grams of fiber, and a salad is rich in fiber.

✓ For dessert, try fresh, frozen, or dried fruit or a high-fiber granola with sweetened soy milk.

✓ When shopping, choose fresh fruits and vegetables whenever possible. Buy frozen vegetables and fruits when fresh produce is not available. Check frozen selections to make sure there is no sugar or salt added.

✓ Be careful when buying canned fruits, vegetables, and legumes, as they may be high in added sugar or sodium. Select versions without added sugar or salt, or rinse before serving.

---

best to get fiber from food because foods contain additional nutrients, such as vitamins and minerals.

It is also important to drink plenty of fluid as you increase your fiber intake, as fiber binds with water to soften stools. Inadequate fluid intake with a high-fiber diet can actually result in hard, dry stools that are difficult to pass through the colon. At least eight 8-oz glasses of fluid each day are commonly recommended.

Can you eat too much fiber? Excessive fiber consumption can lead to problems such as intestinal gas, bloating, and constipation. Because fiber binds with water, it causes the body to eliminate more water in the feces, so a very-high-fiber diet could result in dehydration. Fiber also binds many vitamins and minerals, so a high-fiber diet can reduce our absorption of important nutrients, such as iron, zinc, and calcium. In children, some elderly, the chronically ill, and other at-risk populations, extreme fiber intake can even lead to malnutrition—they feel full before they have eaten enough to provide adequate energy and nutrients. So, although some societies are accustomed to a very-high-fiber diet, most people in the United States find it difficult to tolerate more than 50 g of fiber per day.

Food Sources of Fiber

Eating the amounts of whole grains, vegetables, fruits, nuts, and legumes recommended in the USDA Food Guide will ensure that you eat enough fiber. **Figure 13** shows some common foods and their fiber content. You can use this information to design a diet that includes adequate fiber.

To help you eat right all day, see the menu choices high in fiber. Each of these choices is also packed with vitamins, minerals, and phytochemicals. For instance, a sweet potato is loaded with beta-carotene, a phytochemical the body converts to vitamin A.

See the Quick Tips box above for suggestions on selecting carbohydrate sources rich in fiber.

enriched foods Foods in which nutrients that were lost during processing have been added back, so that the food meets a specified standard.

fortified foods Foods in which nutrients are added that did not originally exist in the food, or which existed in insignificant amounts.

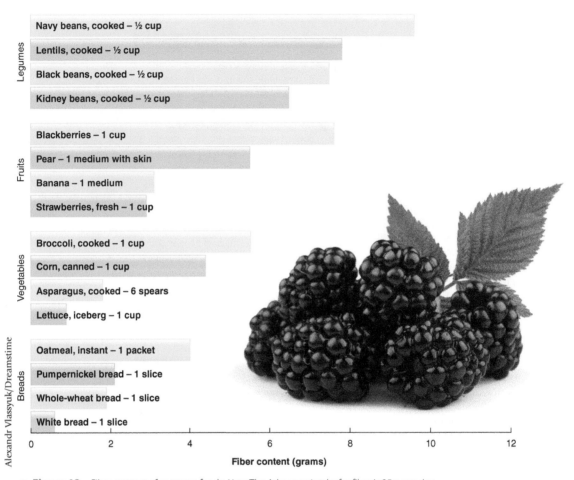

Figure 13 Fiber content of common foods. *Note:* The Adequate Intake for fiber is 25 g per day for women and 38 g per day for men.

Data from U.S. Department of Agriculture, Agricultural Research Service. 2009. USDA National Nutrient Database for Standard Reference, Release 22. Nutrient Data Laboratory Home Page, www.ars.usda.gov/ba/bhnrc/ndl.

Try the Nutrition Label Activity coming up to learn how to recognize various carbohydrates on food labels. Armed with this knowledge, you are now ready to make more healthful food choices.

RECAP The Adequate Intake for fiber is 25 g per day for women and 38 g per day for men. Most Americans eat only half of the fiber they need each day. Foods high in fiber and nutrient density include whole grains and cereals, fruits, and vegetables. The more processed the food, the fewer fiber-rich carbohydrates it contains.

What's the Story on Alternative Sweeteners?

Most of us love sweets but want to avoid the extra Calories and tooth decay that go along with eating refined sugars. That's why we turn to alternative sweeteners.

Contrary to reports claiming severe health consequences related to the consumption of alternative sweeteners, major health agencies have determined that they are safe to consume.

NUTRITION LABEL ACTIVITY

Recognizing Carbohydrates on the Label

Figure 14 shows portions of labels for two breakfast cereals. The cereal on the left (a) is processed and sweetened, whereas the one on the right (b) is a whole-grain product with no added sugar.

- Check the center of each label to locate the amount of total carbohydrate. Notice that it is almost the same, although the sweetened cereal has a larger serving size.

- Now look at the information listed as subgroups under total carbohydrate. Notice that the sweetened cereal contains 13 g of sugar—half of its total carbohydrates—but only 1 g of dietary fiber. In contrast, the whole-grain cereal contains 4 g of fiber and only 1 g of sugar!

- Now look at the percent values listed to the right of the Total Carbohydrate section. For both cereals (without milk), their percent contribution to daily carbohydrate is 9%. This does not mean that 9% of the Calories in these cereals come from carbohydrates. Instead, it refers to the Daily Values listed at the bottom of each label. For a person who eats 2,000 kcal, the recommended amount of carbohydrate each day is 300 g. One serving of each cereal contains 26–27 g, which is about 9% of 300 g.

To compare the percent of total Calories that comes from carbohydrate in each cereal, do the following:

a. Calculate the *Calories* in 1 serving of the cereal that come from carbohydrate. Multiply the total grams of carbohydrate per serving by the energy value of carbohydrate. For the sweetened cereal:

$$26 \text{ g of carbohydrate} \times 4 \text{ kcal/g} = 104 \text{ kcal from carbohydrate}$$

b. Calculate the *percent of Calories* in the cereal that come from carbohydrate. Divide the Calories from carbohydrate by the total Calories for each serving and multiply by 100. For the sweetened cereal:

$$(104 \text{ kcal} \div 120 \text{ kcal}) \times 100 = 87\% \text{ Calories from carbohydrate}$$

c. Now do the same calculations for the whole-grain cereal and compare.

Which has a *lower* percentage of carbohydrate? What macronutrients does this cereal provide in *greater* amounts than the other product? Finally, check the ingredients for the sweetened cereal. Remember that they are listed in order from highest to lowest amount. The second and third ingredients listed are sugar and brown sugar, and the corn and oat flours are not whole-grain flours. Now look at the ingredients for the other cereal— whole-grain oats. Although the sweetened product is enriched with more B-vitamins, iron, and zinc, the whole-grain cereal packs 4 g of fiber per serving and contains no added sugars. Which cereal should you choose, and why?

Nutritive Sweeteners Include Sugars and Sugar Alcohols

Remember that all carbohydrates, including simple and complex, contain 4 kcal of energy per gram. Because sweeteners such as sucrose, fructose, honey, and brown sugar contribute Calories (or energy), they are called **nutritive sweeteners.**

Other nutritive sweeteners are the *sugar alcohols,* such as mannitol, sorbitol, isomalt, and xylitol. Popular in sugar-free gums and mints, sugar alcohols are less sweet than sucrose. Foods with sugar alcohols have health benefits that foods made with sugars do not have, such as a reduced glycemic response and a decreased risk for dental caries. Also, because sugar alcohols are absorbed slowly and incompletely from the small intestine, they provide less energy than sugar, usually 2 to 3 kcal of energy per gram. However, because they are not completely absorbed from the small intestine, they can attract water into the large intestine and cause diarrhea.

nutritive sweeteners Sweeteners, such as sucrose, fructose, honey, and brown sugar, that contribute Calories (energy).

Nutrition Facts

Serving Size: 3/4 cup (30g)
Servings Per Package: About 14

Amount Per Serving	Cereal	Cereal With 1/2 Cup Skim Milk
Calories	120	160
Calories from Fat	15	15
	% Daily Value**	
Total Fat 1.5g*	2%	2%
Saturated Fat 0g	0%	0%
Trans Fat 0g		
Polyunsaturated Fat 0g		
Monounsaturated Fat 0.5g		
Cholesterol 0mg	0%	1%
Sodium 220mg	9%	12%
Potassium 40mg	1%	7%
Total Carbohydrate 26g	9%	11%
Dietary Fiber 1g	3%	3%
Sugars 13g		
Other Carbohydrate 12g		
Protein 1g		

INGREDIENTS: Corn Flour, Sugar, Brown Sugar, Partially Hydrogenated Vegetable Oil (Soybean and Cottonseed), Oat Flour, Salt, Sodium Citrate (a flavoring agent), Flavor added [Natural & Artificial Flavor, Strawberry Juice Concentrate, Malic Acid (a flavoring agent)], Niacinamide (Niacin), Zinc Oxide, Reduced Iron, Red 40, Yellow 5, Red 3, Yellow 6, Pyridoxine Hydrochloride (Vitamin B6), Riboflavin (Vitamin B2), Thiamin Mononitrate (Vitamin B1), Folic Acid (Folate) and Blue 1.

iStockphoto

(a)

Nutrition Facts

Serving Size: 1/2 cup dry (40g)
Servings Per Container: 13

Amount Per Serving	
Calories	150
Calories from Fat	25
	% Daily Value*
Total Fat 3g	5%
Saturated Fat 0.5g	2%
Trans Fat 0g	
Polyunsaturated Fat 1g	
Monounsaturated Fat 1g	
Cholesterol 0mg	0%
Sodium 0mg	0%
Total Carbohydrate 27g	9%
Dietary Fiber 4g	15%
Soluble Fiber 2g	
Insoluble Fiber 2g	
Sugars 1g	
Protein 5g	

INGREDIENTS: 100% Natural Whole Grain Rolled Oats.

(b)

◆ **Figure 14** Labels for two breakfast cereals: **(a)** processed and sweetened cereal; **(b)** whole-grain cereal with no added sugar.

Alternative Sweeteners Are Non-Nutritive

A number of other products have been developed to sweeten foods without promoting tooth decay and weight gain. Because these products provide little or no energy, they are called **non-nutritive,** or *alternative*, **sweeteners.** Contrary to popular belief, alternative sweeteners have been determined to be safe for adults, children, and individuals with diabetes to consume. Although women who are pregnant should discuss the use of alternative sweeteners with their healthcare provider, in general, it appears safe for pregnant women to consume alternative sweeteners in amounts within the Food and Drug Administration (FDA) guidelines.[19] The **Acceptable Daily Intake (ADI)** is an FDA estimate of the amount of a sweetener that someone can consume each day over a lifetime without adverse effects. The estimates are based on studies conducted on laboratory animals, and they include a 100-fold safety factor. It is important to emphasize that actual intake by humans is typically well below the ADI.

The major alternative sweeteners currently available on the market are saccharin, acesulfame-K, aspartame, and sucralose.

non-nutritive sweeteners Manufactured sweeteners that provide little or no energy; also called *alternative sweeteners.*

Acceptable Daily Intake (ADI) An FDA estimate of the amount of a non-nutritive sweetener that someone can consume each day over a lifetime without adverse effects.

Saccharin

Discovered in the late 1800s, *saccharin* is about 300 times sweeter than sucrose. Evidence to suggest that saccharin may cause bladder tumors in rats surfaced in the 1970s; however, more than 20 years of scientific research has shown that saccharin is not related to bladder cancer in humans. Based on this evidence, in May of 2000 the National Toxicology Program of the U.S. government removed saccharin from its list of products that may cause cancer. No ADI has been set for saccharin, and it is used in foods and beverages and sold as a tabletop sweetener. Saccharin is sold as Sweet 'N Low (also known as "the pink packet") in the United States.

Acesulfame-K

Acesulfame-K (acesulfame potassium) is marketed under the names Sunette and Sweet One. It is a Calorie-free sweetener that is 200 times sweeter than sugar. It is used to sweeten gums, candies, beverages, instant tea, coffee, gelatins, and puddings. The taste of acesulfame-K does not change when it is heated, so it can be used in cooking. The body does not metabolize acesulfame-K, so it is excreted unchanged by the kidneys.

Aspartame

Aspartame, also called Equal ("the blue packet") and NutraSweet, is one of the most popular alternative sweeteners in foods and beverages. Aspartame is composed of two amino acids, phenylalanine and aspartic acid. When these amino acids are separate, one is bitter and the other has no flavor—but joined together they make a substance that is 180 times sweeter than sucrose. Although aspartame contains 4 kcal of energy per gram, it is so sweet that only small amounts are necessary; thus, it ends up contributing little or no energy. Because aspartame is made from amino acids, its taste is destroyed with heat, so it cannot be used in cooking.

A significant amount of research has been done to test the safety of aspartame. Although a number of false claims have been published, especially on the Internet, there is no scientific evidence to support the claim that aspartame causes brain tumors, Alzheimer's disease, or nerve disorders.

The ADI for aspartame is 50 mg per kg body weight per day. Table 5 shows how many servings of aspartame-sweetened foods would have to be consumed to exceed the ADI. Although eating less than the ADI is considered safe, note that children who consume many powdered drinks, diet sodas, and other aspartame-flavored products could potentially exceed this amount. Drinks sweetened with aspartame are extremely popular among children and teenagers, but they are very low in nutritional value and should not replace healthful beverages, such as milk, water, and 100% fruit juice.

Some people should not consume any aspartame: those with the disease *phenylketonuria (PKU)*. This is a genetic disorder that prevents the breakdown of the

---

TABLE 5 The Amount of Food that a 50-Pound Child and a 150-Pound Adult Would Have to Consume Each Day to Exceed the ADI for Aspartame

Food	50-Pound Child	150-Pound Adult
12 fl. oz carbonated soft drink	7	20
8 fl. oz powdered soft drink	11	34
4 fl. oz gelatin dessert	14	42
Packets of tabletop sweetener	32	97

Data from International Food Information Council. 2003. *Everything You Need to Know About Aspartame*. Available at http://ific.org/publications/brochures/aspartamebroch.cfm.

amino acid phenylalanine. Because a person with PKU cannot metabolize phenylalanine, it builds up in the tissues of the body and causes irreversible brain damage. In the United States, all newborn babies are tested for PKU; those who have it are placed on a phenylalanine-limited diet. Some foods that are common sources of protein and other nutrients for growing children, such as meats and milk, contain phenylalanine. Thus, it is critical that children with PKU not waste what little phenylalanine they can consume on nutrient-poor products sweetened with aspartame.

Sucralose

The FDA has recently approved the use of *sucralose* as an alternative sweetener. It is marketed under the brand name Splenda and is known as "the yellow packet." It is made from sucrose, but chlorine atoms are substituted for the hydrogen and oxygen normally found in sucrose, and it passes through the digestive tract unchanged, without contributing any energy. It is 600 times sweeter than sucrose and is stable when heated, so it can be used in cooking. It has been approved for use in many foods, including chewing gum, salad dressings, beverages, gelatin and pudding products, canned fruits, frozen dairy desserts, and baked goods. Safety studies have not shown sucralose to cause cancer or to have other adverse health effects.

RECAP Alternative sweeteners can be used in place of sugar to sweeten foods. Most of these products do not promote tooth decay and contribute little or no energy. The alternative sweeteners approved for use in the United States are considered safe when eaten in amounts less than the acceptable daily intake.

NUTRI-CASE HANNAH

"Last night, my mom called and said she'd be late getting home from work, so I made dinner. I made vegetarian quesadillas with flour tortillas, canned green chilies, cheese, and sour cream, plus a few baby carrots on the side. Later that night, I got really hungry, so I ate a package of sugar-free cookies. They're sweetened with sorbitol and taste just like real cookies! I ate maybe three or four, but I didn't think it was a big deal because they're sugar-free. When I checked the package label, I found out that each cookie has 90 Calories!

Without knowing the exact ingredients in Hannah's dinner and snack, would you agree that, prior to the cookies, she'd been making healthy choices? Why or why not? How might she have changed the ingredients in her quesadillas to increase their fiber content? And, if the cookies were sugar-free, how can you explain the fact that each cookie still contained 90 Calories?

PhotoDisc/Getty Images

Nutrition DEBATE

Is High-Fructose Corn Syrup the Cause of the Obesity Epidemic?

Over the past 30 years, obesity rates have increased dramatically for adults and children. Obesity has become public health enemy number one, as many chronic diseases, such as type 2 diabetes, heart disease, high blood pressure, and arthritis, go hand in hand with obesity.

Factors contributing to obesity include genetic influences, lack of adequate physical activity, and excessive consumption of energy. Genetics cannot be held solely responsible for the rapid rise in obesity that has occurred over the past 30 years. Our genetic makeup takes thousands of years to change; humans who lived 100 years ago had essentially the same genetic makeup as we do. We need to look at the effect of our lifestyle changes over the same period.

One lifestyle factor that has come to the forefront of nutrition research is the contribution of high-fructose corn syrup (HFCS) to overweight and obesity. HFCS is made by converting the starch in corn to glucose and then converting some of the glucose to fructose, which is sweeter. Unfortunately, fructose is metabolized differently than glucose, because it is absorbed farther down in the small intestine and, unlike glucose, it does not stimulate insulin release from the pancreas. Since insulin inhibits food intake in humans, this failure to stimulate insulin release could increase energy intake. In addition, fructose enters body cells via a transport protein not present in brain cells; thus, unlike glucose, fructose cannot enter brain cells and stimulate satiety signals. If we don't feel full, we are likely to continue eating or drinking.

However, the culprit in our increasing obesity rates may not be HFCS itself but, rather, the sweetened soft drinks and other products in which it is found. Bray et al.[20] emphasize that

HFCS is the sole caloric sweetener in sugared soft drinks and represents more than 40% of caloric sweeteners added to other foods and beverages in the United States. These researchers have linked the increased use and consumption of HFCS with the rising rates of obesity since the 1970s, when HFCS first appeared.

The potential contribution of sweetened soft drink consumption to rising obesity rates in young people has received a great deal of attention. Studies show that girls and boys ages 6 to 11 years drank about twice as many soft drinks in 1998 as children did in 1977.[21] Equally alarming is the finding that one-fourth of a group of adolescents studied drank at least 26 oz of soft drinks each day. This intake is equivalent to almost 400 extra Calories daily![22] Another study found that replacing sweetened soft drinks with noncaloric beverages in 13- to 18-year-olds resulted in a significant decrease in body mass index in the those who were the most overweight when starting the study.[23]

This alarming information has led to dramatic changes in soft drink availability in schools and at school-sponsored events. In 2006, the soft drink industry agreed to a voluntary ban on sales of all sweetened soft drinks in elementary and

high schools. Despite these positive changes, there is still ample availability of foods and beverages containing HFCS in the marketplace.

Although the evidence pinpointing HFCS as a major contributor to the obesity epidemic may appear strong, other nutrition professionals disagree. It has been proposed that soft drinks would have contributed to the obesity epidemic whether the sweetener was sucrose or fructose, and that their contribution to obesity is due to increased consumption as a result of advertising, increases in serving sizes, and virtually unlimited access to soft drinks.[24] Also, a recent study found that increased fructose consumption does not cause weight gain in humans.[25] It is possible that the obesity epidemic has resulted from increased consumption of energy (from sweetened soft drinks and other high-energy foods) *and* a reduction in physical activity levels, and HFCS itself is not to blame. Evidence to support this stems from the fact that obesity rates are rising around the world, and many countries experiencing this epidemic do not use HFCS as a sweetener.

This issue is extremely complex, and more research needs to be done in humans before we can fully understand how HFCS contributes to our diet and our health.[26]

Brian Buckley/Alamy Images

◀ It is estimated that the rate of overweight in children has increased 100% since the mid-1970s.

Chapter Review

Test Yourself ANSWERS

1. False. There is no evidence that diets high in sugar cause hyperactivity or diabetes in children.

2. False. At 4 kcal/g, carbohydrates have less than half the energy of a gram of fat. Eating a high-carbohydrate diet will not cause people to gain body fat unless their total diet contains more energy (kcal) than they expend. In fact, eating a diet high in complex, fiber-rich carbohydrates is associated with a lower risk for obesity.

3. True. Contrary to recent reports claiming harmful consequences related to the consumption of alternative sweeteners, major health agencies have determined that these products are safe for most of us to consume in limited quantities.

Find the Quack

Christina is surfing the Internet looking for information for a report on carbohydrates for her nutrition class, when she spots something that intrigues her: Cure Diseases with Sugar! She wonders what it's all about and clicks to bring up the site. Glyconutrients! the homepage proclaims, stating that these special nutrients will reverse aging, increase sports performance, and help you achieve optimal health. Beside a photo of a slender, tanned couple walking along a beach are statements claiming that:

- "Processed foods are devoid of nourishment and have no nutritional value. They are also toxic. We both starve and poison ourselves by consuming these foods. This is why every degenerative disease condition is on the rise."
- "Pharmaceuticals (prescription and over-the-counter medications) do not work."
- "Glyconutrients are plant monosaccharides, essential plant sugars that have recently been shown to be essential to human life. We must consume glyconutrient supplements to protect our health. Without them, our cells will lose the ability to communicate with one another and perform the functions they were designed to do. We will then develop chronic diseases, such as cancer and diabetes."
- "A total of ninety-six patents have been filed on a range of glyconutrient products."

- "Just about every respected scientific journal has now published documents and articles on glycobiology and glyconutrients."
- "Your doctor will not know about glyconutrients because the topic is only just beginning to be taught in medical schools."

1. You can now spot false nutrition claims. Discuss the validity of the website's statement about processed foods.

2. Comment on the website's definition of glyconutrients as plant monosaccharides that are essential for human life.

3. Are you impressed with the statement that "ninety-six patents have been filed on a range of glyconutrient products"? Why or why not?

4. What motive do you think might lurk behind the assertion that your doctor will not know about glyconutrients because the topic "is only just beginning to be taught in medical schools"?

Answers can be found on the companion website, at www.pearsonhighered.com/thompsonmanore.

 **NutriTools** Check out the companion website at www.pearsonhighered.com/thompsonmanore, or use MyNutritionLab.com, to access interactive animations, including:

- Food Label: Find the Carbohydrates
- Know Your Carbohydrate Sources
- Digestion and Absorption: Carbohydrates

Review Questions

1. The glycemic index rates
   a. the acceptable amount of alternative sweeteners to consume in 1 day.
   b. the potential of foods to raise blood glucose and insulin levels.
   c. the risk of a given food for causing diabetes.
   d. the ratio of soluble to insoluble fiber in a complex carbohydrate.

2. Carbohydrates contain
   a. carbon, nitrogen, and water.
   b. carbonic acid and a sugar alcohol.
   c. hydrated sugar.
   d. carbon, hydrogen, and oxygen.

3. The most common source of added sugar in the American diet is
   a. table sugar.
   b. white flour.
   c. alcohol.
   d. sweetened soft drinks.

4. Glucose, fructose, and galactose are
   a. monosaccharides.
   b. disaccharides.
   c. polysaccharides.
   d. complex carbohydrates.

5. Aspartame should not be consumed by people who have
   a. phenylketonuria.
   b. type 1 diabetes.
   c. lactose intolerance.
   d. diverticulosis.

6. True or false? Sugar alcohols are non-nutritive sweeteners.

7. True or false? Both insulin and glucagon are pancreatic hormones.

8. True or false? Adults need about 10 grams of fiber daily.

9. True or false? Plants store glucose as fiber.

10. True or false? Salivary amylase breaks down starches into galactose.

Answers to Review Questions can be found at the back of this text, and additional essay questions and answers are located on the companion website at www.pearsonhighered.com/ thompsonmanore.

Web Resources

www.ific.org
International Food Information Council Foundation (IFIC)

Search this site to find out more about sugars and low-calorie sweeteners.

www.ada.org
American Dental Association

Go to this site to learn more about tooth decay as well as other oral health topics.

www.nidcr.nih.gov
National Institute of Dental and Craniofacial Research (NIDCR)

Find out more about recent oral and dental health discoveries and obtain statistics and data on the status of dental health in the United States.

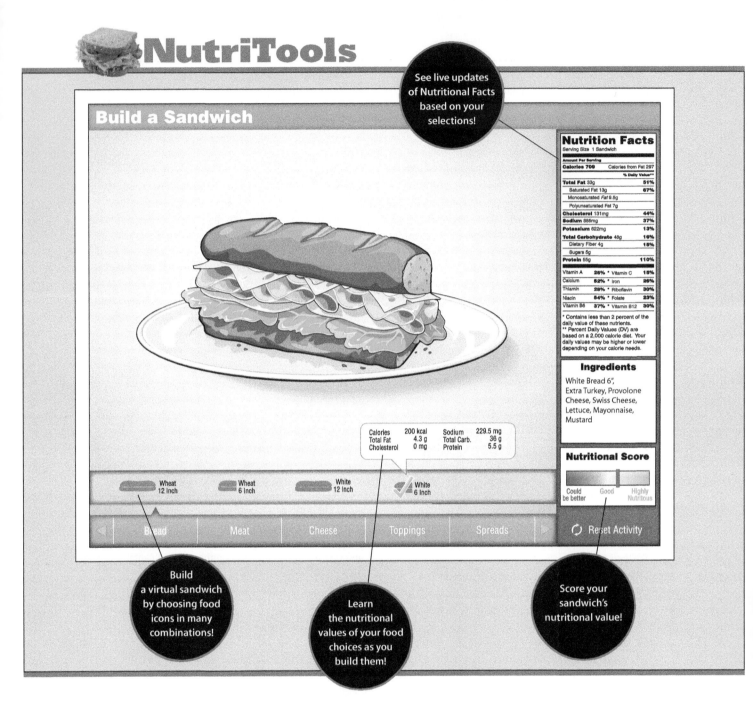

NutriTools

Build a Sandwich

See live updates of Nutritional Facts based on your selections!

Nutrition Facts
Serving Size 1 Sandwich

Amount Per Serving	
Calories 709	Calories from Fat 297

	% Daily Value**
Total Fat 33g	**51%**
Saturated Fat 13g	**67%**
Monosaturated Fat 9.5g	
Polyunsaturated Fat 7g	
Cholesterol 131mg	**44%**
Sodium 885mg	**37%**
Potassium 622mg	**13%**
Total Carbohydrate 48g	**16%**
Dietary Fiber 4g	**16%**
Sugars 5g	
Protein 55g	**110%**

Vitamin A	**25%**	* Vitamin C	**15%**
Calcium	**52%**	* Iron	**25%**
Thiamin	**28%**	* Riboflavin	**30%**
Niacin	**54%**	* Folate	**23%**
Vitamin B6	**37%**	* Vitamin B12	**30%**

* Contains less than 2 percent of the daily value of these nutrients.
** Percent Daily Values (DV) are based on a 2,000 calorie diet. Your daily values may be higher or lower depending on your calorie needs.

Ingredients
White Bread 6", Extra Turkey, Provolone Cheese, Swiss Cheese, Lettuce, Mayonnaise, Mustard

Nutritional Score
Could be better — Good — Highly Nutritous

Calories	200 kcal	Sodium	229.5 mg
Total Fat	4.3 g	Total Carb.	36 g
Cholesterol	0 mg	Protein	5.5 g

Wheat 12 Inch · Wheat 6 Inch · White 12 Inch · White 6 Inch

Bread | Meat | Cheese | Toppings | Spreads | ↻ Reset Activity

Build a virtual sandwich by choosing food icons in many combinations!

Learn the nutritional values of your food choices as you build them!

Score your sandwich's nutritional value!

To build your sandwich, just visit www.pearsonhighered.com/thompsonmanore **or** www.mynutritionlab.com

After building your sandwich, you should be able to answer these questions:

1. How is your selection of combination toppings making your sandwich nutritious?
2. Is your sandwich higher or lower in kcalories than you need for one meal?
3. Which ingredients could you combine to build a sandwich with a nutritional score of 100?
4. How are the condiments added to your sandwich affecting its nutritional score?
5. Would a six-inch sandwich have half the nutritional score of a twelve-inch?

References

1. Sears, B. 1995. The Zone. A Dietary Road Map. New York: HarperCollins Publishers.
2. Steward, H. L., M. C. Bethea, S. S. Andrews, and L. A. Balart. 1995. Sugar Busters! Cut Sugar to Trim Fat. New York: Ballantine Books.
3. Atkins, R. C. 1992. Dr. Atkins' New Diet Revolution. New York: M. Evans & Company, Inc.
4. Topping, D. L., and P. M. Clifton. 2001. Short-chain fatty acids and human colonic function: roles of resistant starch and nonstarch polysaccharides. *Physiol. Rev.* 81:1031–1064.
5. Pan, J. W., D. L. Rothman, K. L. Behar, D. T. Stein, and H. P. Hetherington. 2000. Human brain α-hydroxybutyrate and lactate increase in fasting-induced ketosis. *J. Cerebral Blood Flow Metabol.* 20:1502–1507.
6. Institute of Medicine, Food and Nutrition Board. 2002. Dietary Reference Intakes for Energy, Carbohydrates, Fiber, Fat, Protein and Amino Acids (Macronutrients). Washington, DC: The National Academy of Sciences.
7. Romijn, J. A., E. F. Coyle, L. S. Sidossis, A. Gastaldelli, J. F. Horowitz, E. Endert, and R. R. Wolfe. 1993. Regulation of endogenous fat and carbohydrate metabolism in relation to exercise intensity and duration. *Am. J. Physiol.* 265 [Endocrinol. Metab. 28]: E380–E391.
8. Foster-Powell, K., S. H. A. Holt, and J. C. Brand-Miller. 2002. International table of glycemic index and glycemic load values: 2002. *Am. J. Clin. Nutr.* 76:5–56.
9. Liu, S., J. E. Manson, M. J. Stampfer, M. D. Holmes, F. B. Hu, S. E. Hankinson, and W. C. Willett. 2001. Dietary glycemic load assessed by food-frequency questionnaire in relation to plasma high-density-lipoprotein cholesterol and fasting plasma triacylglycerols in postmenopausal women. *Am. J. Clin. Nutr.* 73:560–566.
10. Sloth, B., I. Krog-Mikkelsen, A. Flint, I. Tetens, I. Björck, S. Vinoy, H. Elmståhl, A. Astrup, V. Lang, and A. Raben. 2004. No difference in body weight decrease between a low-glycemic-index and a high-glycemic-index diet but reduced LDL cholesterol after 10-wk ad libitum intake of the low-glycemic-index diet. *Am. J. Clin. Nutr.* 80:337–347.
11. Buyken, A. E., M. Toeller, G. Heitkamp, G. Karamanos, B. Rottiers, R. Muggeo, and M. Fuller. 2001. Glycemic index in the diet of European outpatients with type 1 diabetes: relations to glycated hemoglobin and serum lipids. *Am. J. Clin. Nutr.* 73:574–581.
12. Augustin, L. S. A., C. Galeone, L. Dal Maso, C. Pelucchi, V. Ramazzotti, D. J. A. Jenkins, M. Montella, R. Talamini, E. Negri, S. Franceschi, and C. La Vecchia. 2004. Glycemic index, glycemic load and risk of prostate cancer. Int. *J. Cancer* 112: 446–450.
13. U.S. Department of Health and Human Services (USDHHS) and U.S. Department of Agriculture (USDA). 2005. Dietary Guidelines for Americans, 2005, 6th edn. Washington, DC: U.S. Government Printing Office. www.healthierus.gov/dietaryguidelines.
14. U.S. Department of Health and Human Services (USDHHS) and U.S. Department of Agriculture (USDA). 2006. Eating healthier and feeling better using the Nutrition Facts Label. www.cfsan.fda .gov/∼acrobat/nutfacts.pdf.
15. Howard, B. V., and J. Wylie-Rosett. 2002. Sugar and cardiovascular disease. A statement for healthcare professionals from the Committee on Nutrition of the Council on Nutrition, Physical Activity, and Metabolism of the American Heart Association. *Circulation* 106:523–527.
16. Meyer, K. A., L. H. Kushi, D. R. Jacobs, J. Slavin, T. A. Sellers, and A. R. Folsom. 2000. Carbohydrates, dietary fiber, and incident type 2 diabetes in older women. *Am. J. Clin. Nutr.* 71:921–930.
17. Schultze, M. B., J. E. Manson, D. S. Ludwig, G. A. Colditz, M. J. Stampfer, W. C. Willett, and F. B. Hu. 2004. Sugar-sweetened beverages, weight gain, and incidence of type 2 diabetes in young and middle-aged women. *JAMA.* 292:927–934.
18. Colditz, G. A., J. E. Manson, M. J. Stampfer, B. Rosner, W. C. Willett, and F. E. Speizer. 1992. Diet and risk of clinical diabetes in women. *Am. J. Clin. Nutr.* 55:1018–1023.
19. International Food Information Council Foundation. 2009. Facts About Low-Calorie Sweeteners. http://www.foodinsight.org/ Content/6/LCS%20Fact%20Sheet_11-09.pdf.
20. Bray, G. A., S. J. Nielsen, and B. M. Popkin. 2004. Consumption of high-fructose corn syrup in beverages may play a role in the epidemic of obesity. *Am. J. Clin. Nutr.* 79:537–543.
21. Wilkinson Enns, C., S. J. Mickle, and J. D. Goldman. 2002. Trends in food and nutrient intakes by children in the United States. Family Econ. *Nutr. Rev.* 14:56–68.
22. Harnack, L., J. Stang, and M. Story. 1999. Soft drink consumption among U.S. children and adolescents: nutritional consequences. *J. Am. Diet. Assoc.* 99:436–441.
23. Ebbeling, C. B., H. A. Feldman, S. K. Osganian, V. R. Chomitz, S. H. Ellenbogen, and D. S. Ludwig. 2006. Effects of decreasing sugar-sweetened beverage consumption on body weight in adolescents: a randomized, controlled pilot study. *Pediatrics* 117:673–680.
24. Jacobson, M. F. 2004. Letter to the editor. High-fructose corn syrup and the obesity epidemic. *Am. J. Clin. Nutr.* 80:1081–1090.
25. Lê, K.-A., D. Faeh, R. Stettler, M. Ith, R. Kreis, P. Vermathen, C. Boesch, E. Ravussin, and L. Tappy. 2006. A 4-wk high-fructose diet alters lipid metabolism without affecting insulin sensitivity or ectopic lipids in healthy humans. *Am. J. Clin. Nutr.* 84:1374–1379.26.
26. Elliott, S. S., N. L. Keim, J. S. Stern, K. Teff, and P. J. Havel. 2002. Fructose, weight gain, and the insulin resistance syndrome. *Am. J. Clin. Nutr.* 76:911–922.

Answers to Review Questions

Answers to Review Questions 11-15 (essay questions) for this chapter are located on the Companion Website at **www.pearsonhighered.com/thompsonmanore**

1. **b.** the potential of foods to raise blood glucose and insulin levels.
2. **d.** carbon, hydrogen, and oxygen.
3. **d.** sweetened soft drinks.
4. **a.** monosaccharides.
5. **a.** phenylketonuria.
6. False. Sugar alcohols are considered nutritive sweeteners because they contain 2 to 4 kcal of energy per gram.
7. True.
8. False. Adults need at least 25 grams of fiber daily.
9. False. Plants store glucose as starch.
10. False. Salivary amylase breaks starches into maltose and shorter polysaccharides.

Fats: Essential Energy-Supplying Nutrients

From Chapter 5 of *Nutrition: An Applied Approach,* Third Edition. Janice Thompson, Melinda Manore. Copyright © 2012 by Pearson Education, Inc. Published by Pearson Benjamin Cummings. All rights reserved.

Fats: Essential Energy-Supplying Nutrients

sasimoto/iStockphoto

CHAPTER OBJECTIVES

After reading this chapter you will be able to:

1. List and describe the three types of lipids found in foods.

2. Discuss how the level of saturation of a fatty acid affects its shape and the form it takes.

3. Explain the derivation of the term *trans* fatty acid and how *trans* fatty acids can negatively affect our health.

4. Identify the beneficial functions of the essential fatty acids.

5. List three functions of fat in our bodies.

6. Describe the steps involved in fat digestion.

7. Define the recommended dietary intakes for total fat, saturated fat, *trans* fats, and the two essential fatty acids.

8. Identify at least three common food sources of un-healthful fats and three common sources of beneficial fats.

Test Yourself

1. T F Some fats are essential for good health.
2. T F Fat is a primary source of energy during exercise.
3. T F Fried foods are relatively nutritious as long as vegetable shortening is used to fry the foods.

Test Yourself answers can be found at the end of the chapter.

How would you feel if you purchased a bag of potato chips and were charged an extra 5% "fat tax"? What if you ordered fish and chips in your favorite restaurant, only to be told that, in an effort to avoid lawsuits, fried foods were no longer being served? Sound surreal? Believe it or not, these and dozens of similar scenarios are being proposed, threatened, and defended in the current "obesity wars" raging around the globe. From Maine to California, from Iceland to New Zealand, local and national governments and healthcare policy advisors are scrambling to find effective methods for combating their rising rates of obesity. For reasons we explore in this chapter, many of their proposals focus on limiting consumption of foods high in saturated fats—for instance, requiring food vendors and manufacturers to reduce the portion size of such foods; taxing or increasing their purchase price; levying fines on manufacturers who produce them; removing them from vending machines; banning advertisements of these foods to children; and using food labels and public service announcements to warn consumers away from these foods. At the same time, "food litigation" lawsuits have been increasing, including allegations against restaurant chains and food companies for failing to warn consumers of the health dangers of eating their energy-dense, high-saturated-fat foods.

Is saturated fat really such a menace? If so, why? What is saturated fat, anyway? And are other fats just as bad? In this chapter, we'll answer these questions, plus identify some small changes you can make to shift your diet toward more healthful fats.

What Are Fats?

Fats are just one form of a much larger and more diverse group of organic substances called **lipids,** which are distinguished by the fact that they are insoluble in water. Think of a salad dressing made with vinegar, which is mostly water, and olive oil, which is a lipid. Shaking the bottle *disperses* the oil but doesn't *dissolve* it: that's why it separates back out again so quickly. Lipids are found in all sorts of living things, from bacteria to plants to human beings. In fact, their presence on your skin explains why you can't clean your face with water alone: you need some type of soap to break down the insoluble lipids before you can wash them away. In this chapter, we focus on the small group of lipids that are found in foods.

Fats and oils are two different types of lipids found in foods. Fats, such as butter, are solid at room temperature, whereas oils, such as olive oil, are liquid at room temperature. Because most people are more comfortable with the term *fats* instead of *lipids,* we will use that term generically throughout this book, including when we are referring to oils. Three types of fats are commonly found in foods; triglycerides, phospholipids, and sterols. Let's take a look at each.

Frances Roberts/Alamy

Dorling Kindersley

◆ Some fats, such as olive oil, are liquid at room temperature.

Triglycerides Are the Most Common Food-Based Fat

Most of the fat we eat (95%) is in the form of triglycerides (also called *triacylglycerols*), which is the same form in which most body fat is stored. As reflected in the prefix *tri-*, a **triglyceride** is a molecule consisting of *three* fatty acids attached to a *three*-carbon glycerol backbone. **Fatty acids** are long chains of carbon atoms bound to each other as well as to hydrogen atoms. They are acids because they contain an acid group (carboxyl group) at one end of their chain. **Glycerol,** the backbone of a triglyceride molecule, is an alcohol composed of three carbon atoms. One fatty acid attaches to each of these three carbons to make the triglyceride (Figure 1).

To understand why we want more of some fats than others, we need to know more about their properties and how they work in our body. In general, triglycerides can be classified by their chain length (number of carbons in each fatty acid), their level of saturation (how much hydrogen, H, is attached to each carbon atom in the fatty acid chain), and their shape, which is determined in some cases by how they

Triglyceride

Glycerol

Fatty acid

◆ **Figure 1**   A triglyceride consists of three fatty acids attached to a three-carbon glycerol backbone.

are commercially processed. All of these factors influence how we use the triglycerides within our bodies.

Chain Length Affects Triglyceride Function

The fatty acids attached to the glycerol backbone can vary in the number of carbons they contain, referred to as their *chain length*.

- Short-chain fatty acids are usually fewer than six carbon atoms in length.
- Medium-chain fatty acids are six to twelve carbons in length.
- Long-chain fatty acids are fourteen or more carbons in length.

Fatty acid chain length is important because it determines the method of fat digestion and absorption and affects how fats function within the body. For example, short- and medium-chain fatty acids are digested and transported more quickly than long-chain fatty acids. We will discuss the digestion and absorption of fats in more detail shortly. In addition, chain length can determine saturation, as discussed in the next section.

Saturated Fats Contain the Maximum Amount of Hydrogen

Triglycerides can also vary by the types of bonds found in the fatty acids. If a fatty acid has no carbons bonded together with a double bond, it is referred to as a **saturated fatty acid** (**SFA**) (Figures 2a and 3a). This is because every carbon atom in the chain is *saturated* with hydrogen: each has the maximum amount of hydrogen bound to it. Some foods that are high in saturated fatty acids are coconut oil, palm kernel oil, butter, cream, whole milk, and beef.

Unsaturated Fats Contain Less Hydrogen

If, within the chain of carbon atoms, two carbons are bound to each other with a double bond, then this double carbon bond excludes hydrogen. This lack of hydrogen at *one* part of the molecule results in a fat that is referred to as *monounsaturated*. A monounsaturated molecule is shown in Figures 2b and 3a. **Monounsaturated fatty acids** (**MUFAs**) are usually liquid at room temperature. Foods that are high in monounsaturated fatty acids are olive oil, canola oil, and cashew nuts.

If the fat molecules have *more than one* double bond, they contain even less hydrogen and are referred to as **polyunsaturated fatty acids** (**PUFAs**). (See Figure 3a.) Polyunsaturated fatty acids are also liquid at room temperature and include cottonseed, canola, corn, and safflower oils.

Although foods vary in the types of fatty acids they contain, in general we can say that animal-based foods tend to be high in saturated fats and plant foods tend to be high in unsaturated fats. Specifically, animal fats provide approximately 40–60% of their energy from saturated fats, whereas plant fats provide 80–90% of their energy from monounsaturated and polyunsaturated fats (Figure 4). Most oils are a good source of both MUFAs and PUFAs.

In general, saturated fats have a detrimental effect on our health, whereas unsaturated fats are protective. It makes sense, therefore, that diets high in plant foods—because they're low in saturated fats—are more healthful than diets high in animal products. We discuss the influence of various types of fatty acids on your risk for cardiovascular disease in the **In Depth** essay immediately following this chapter.

Carbon Bonding Affects Shape

Have you ever noticed how many toothpicks are packed into a small box? A hundred or more! But if you were to break a bunch of toothpicks into V shapes anywhere along their length, how many could you then fit into the same box? It would be very few because the bent toothpicks would jumble together, taking up much more space. Molecules of saturated fat are like straight toothpicks: they have no double carbon bonds and always form straight, rigid chains. As they have no kinks, these chains can pack together tightly (see Figure 3b). That is why saturated fats, such as the fat in meats, are solid at room temperature.

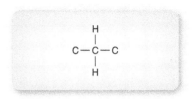

(a) Saturated fatty acid

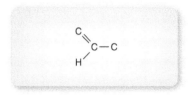

(b) Unsaturated fatty acid

Figure 2 An atom of carbon has four attachment sites. In fatty acid chains, two of these sites are filled by adjacent carbon atoms. **(a)** In saturated fatty acids, the other two sites are always filled by two hydrogen atoms. **(b)** In unsaturated fatty acids, at one or more points along the chain, a double bond to an adjacent carbon atom takes up one of the attachment sites that would otherwise be filled by hydrogen.

lipids A diverse group of organic substances that are insoluble in water; lipids include triglycerides, phospholipids, and sterols.

triglyceride A molecule consisting of three fatty acids attached to a three-carbon glycerol backbone.

fatty acids Long chains of carbon atoms bound to each other as well as to hydrogen atoms.

glycerol An alcohol composed of three carbon atoms; it is the backbone of a triglyceride molecule.

saturated fatty acids (SFAs) Fatty acids that have no carbons joined together with a double bond; these types of fatty acids are generally solid at room temperature.

monounsaturated fatty acids (MUFAs) Fatty acids that have two carbons in the chain bound to each other with one double bond; these types of fatty acids are generally liquid at room temperature.

polyunsaturated fatty acids (PUFAs) Fatty acids that have more than one double bond in the chain; these types of fatty acids are generally liquid at room temperature.

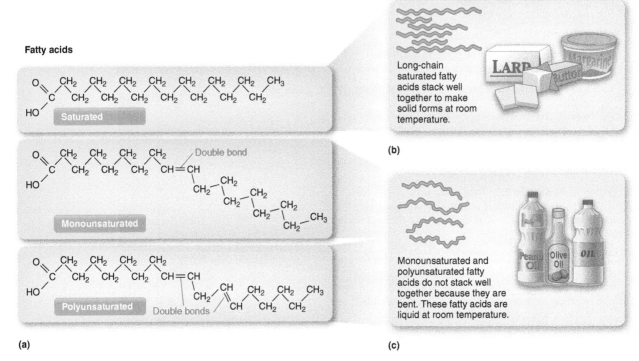

Fatty acids

▲ **Figure 3** Examples of levels of saturation among fatty acids and how these levels of saturation affect the shape of fatty acids. **(a)** Saturated fatty acids are saturated with hydrogen, meaning they have no carbons bonded together with a double bond. Monounsaturated fatty acids contain two carbons bound by one double bond. Polyunsaturated fatty acids have more than one double bond linking carbon atoms. **(b)** Saturated fats have straight fatty acids packed tightly together and are solid at room temperature. **(c)** Unsaturated fats have "kinked" fatty acids at the area of the double bond, preventing them from packing tightly together; they are liquid at room temperature.

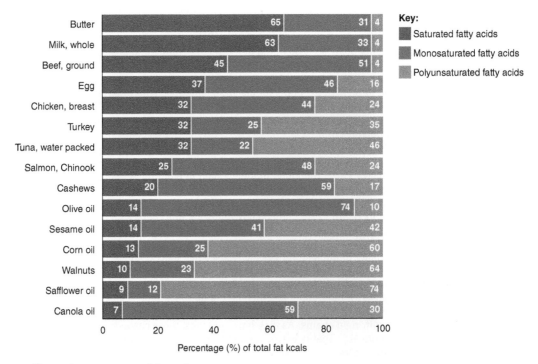

▲ **Figure 4** Major sources of dietary fat.

The Nuts and Bolts on Nuts

Nuts are rich in healthful unsaturated fats, not to mention protein, some minerals, and fiber. But they're also high in energy: 160–180 kcal for a 1-ounce serving (about 4 tablespoons, depending on the nut). So why are nuts the new "in" food on popular diet plans?

Well, in several studies, when researchers fed people an ounce or two of nuts every day, the participants failed to gain the expected weight. And, in general, people who eat nuts are typically leaner than people who don't. No one has a definitive explanation for these findings. Some researchers speculate that people find nuts satiating and therefore eat less later on. Others propose that the energy in nuts may not be fully absorbed in the GI (gastrointestinal) tract.

Will nuts help you control your weight? Maybe—if you can limit yourself to an ounce or two a day. Trouble is, they taste so good, it's easy to overdo it.

In contrast, each double carbon bond of unsaturated fats gives them a kink along their length (see Figure 3c). This means that they are unable to pack together tightly—for example, to form a stick of butter—and instead are liquid at room temperature. In our body, unsaturated fatty acids are part of our cell membranes. They help keep the cell membranes flexible, allowing substances to move into and out of the cells.

We've just said that unsaturated fatty acids are kinked. That's true when they occur naturally in plant foods and plant oils. But unsaturated fatty acids can be manipulated by food manufacturers to create a type of straight, rigid fatty acid called a *trans* fat. The Dietary Guidelines for Americans suggest that you keep your *trans* fat intake as low as possible. In fact, *trans* fats are considered at least as harmful to your health as saturated fats. We'll explain why in a moment. For now, let's make sure we know what *trans* fats really are.

Trans Fatty Acids Have Hydrogen Atoms on Opposite Sides

Unsaturated fatty acids can occur in either a *cis* or a *trans* shape. The prefix *cis* means things are located on the same side or near each other, whereas *trans* is a prefix that denotes across or opposite. These terms describe the positioning of the hydrogen atoms around the double carbon bond as follows:

- The prefix *cis* means "on the same side." A *cis fatty acid* has both hydrogen atoms located on the same side of the double bond **(Figure 5a)**. This positioning gives the *cis* molecule a pronounced kink at the double carbon bond. We typically find the *cis* fatty acids in nature, and thus in foods such as olive oil.

- In contrast, *trans* means "on the opposite side." In a *trans fatty acid*, the hydrogen atoms are attached on diagonally opposite sides of the double carbon bond (Figure 5b). This positioning makes *trans* fatty acid fats straighter and more rigid, just like saturated fats. Thus, "*trans* fats" is a collective term used to define fats with *trans* double bonds. Although a limited amount of natural *trans* fatty acids are found in cow's milk and meat, the majority of *trans* fatty acids in foods are produced by manipulating the fatty acids during food processing.

This process, called **hydrogenation,** was developed in the early 1900s in order to produce a type of cheap fat that could be stored in a solid form and would resist rancidity. During hydrogenation, pressurized hydrogen molecules are added directly to unsaturated fatty acids such as those found in corn and safflower oils. This causes the double bonds of the unsaturated fatty acids in the oil to be partially or totally removed. As a result, the fatty acid becomes more saturated and straighter.

The hydrogenation process can be controlled to make the oil more or less saturated: if only some of the double bonds are broken, the fat produced is called *partially hydrogenated*, a term you will see frequently on food labels. For example, corn oil margarine is a partially hydrogenated form of corn oil. Unless labeled as containing zero *trans* fatty acids, most margarines have more *trans* fatty acids than butter. So which is the more healthful choice—butter or margarine? Check out the Nutrition Myth or Fact? box two pages ahead to find out!

Walnuts and cashews are high in monounsaturated fatty acids.

hydrogenation The process of adding hydrogen to unsaturated fatty acids, making them more saturated and thereby more solid at room temperature.

cis arrangement

(a) *cis* polyunsaturated fatty acid

trans arrangement

(b) *trans* polyunsaturated fatty acid

🔸 **Figure 5** Structure of **(a)** a *cis* and **(b)** a *trans* polyunsaturated fatty acid. Notice that *cis* fatty acids have both hydrogen atoms located on the same side of the double bond. This positioning makes the molecule kinked. In the *trans* fatty acids, the hydrogen atoms are attached on diagonally opposite sides of the double carbon bond. This positioning makes them straighter and more rigid.

AP Photos

🔸 The U.S. FDA ruled that as of 2006, *trans* fatty acids, or *trans* fat, must be listed as a separate line item on the Nutrition Facts Panels for conventional foods and some dietary supplements.

essential fatty acids (EFAs) Fatty acids that must be consumed in the diet because they cannot be made by our bodies. The two essential fatty acids are linoleic acid and alpha-linolenic acid.

Incidentally, even when a product *is* labeled as having "zero" *trans* fats, there can still be *trans* fatty acids in the product! That's because the U.S. Food and Drug Administration (FDA) allows products that have less than 1 g of *trans* fat per serving to claim that they are *trans* fat free. So, even if the Nutrition Facts panel states 0 g *trans* fats, the product can still have 1/2 g of *trans* fat per serving. If the ingredients list states that the product contains partially hydrogenated oils, it contains *trans* fats.

For a period of several decades in the 20th century, partially hydrogenated oil products were in demand. Americans were being urged to reduce their intake of saturated fats and switched to partially hydrogenated oils, including spreadable margarines, assuming that these products were more healthful and could reduce the risk for heart disease. But as we discuss later in this chapter, this assumption did not turn out to be true.

Some Triglycerides Contain Essential Fatty Acids

There has been a lot of press lately about "omega" fatty acids, so you might be wondering what they are and why they're so important. First, let's explain the Greek name. As illustrated in **Figure 6**, one end of a fatty acid chain is designated the α (alpha) end (α is the first letter in the Greek alphabet). The other end of a fatty acid chain is called the ω (omega) end (ω is the last letter in the Greek alphabet). Two fatty acids with a unique structure are known to be essential to human growth and health: one of these has a double bond six carbons from the omega end (at ω-6), and the other has a double bond three carbons from the omega end (at ω-3). When synthesizing fatty acids, the body cannot insert double bonds before the ninth carbon from the omega end.[1] This means that we have to obtain ω-6 and ω-3 fatty acids from food. They are considered **essential fatty acids (EFAs)** because the body cannot make them, yet it requires them for healthy functioning.

NUTRITION MYTH OR FACT?
Is Margarine More Healthful Than Butter?

Your toast just popped up! Which will it be: butter or margarine? As you've just learned, butter is 65% saturated fat: 1 tablespoon provides 30 grams of cholesterol! In contrast, corn oil margarine is just 2% saturated fat, with no cholesterol. But how much *trans* fat does that margarine contain? And which is better—the more natural and more saturated butter or the more processed and less saturated margarine?

Comstock/Thinkstock

You're not the only one asking this question. Until recently, vegetable-based oils were hydrogenated to make margarines. These products were filled with *trans* fats that could increase the consumer's risk for heart disease, as well as harm cell membranes, weaken immune function, and inhibit the body's natural anti-inflammatory hormones. Some margarines also contained harmful amounts of toxic metals, such as nickel and aluminum, as by-products of the hydrogenation process. These are among some of the reasons researchers began warning consumers against using margarines several years ago.

So does that mean that the saturated-fat, cholesterol-rich butter is the better choice? A decade ago, that may have been the case, but, over the last ten years, food manufacturers have introduced "*trans* fat free margarines and spreads" that contain no cholesterol or *trans* fats and low amounts of saturated fats. The American Heart Association[2] advises that consumers choose these *trans* fat free margarines over butter.

Others point out that such manufactured products are still "non-foods" and recommend that those who prefer whole foods choose unprocessed nut butters (peanut, walnut, cashew, and almond butters). These natural alternatives are rich in essential fatty acids and other heart-healthy unsaturated fats but are still as energy-dense as butter.

Remember, a label claiming that a margarine has zero *trans* fatty acids doesn't guarantee that the product is *trans* fatty acid free (see the accompanying table). You have to look for margarines with no "partially hydrogenated" oil in them. That is the only way you will know your spread is entirely free of *trans* fatty acids. Check out the spreads listed in the table to help you decide which you're going to include in your diet.

Spreads for Your Bread*

Brand Name	Energy (kcal)	Sat fat (g)	*Trans* fat (g)	Sodium (mg)
Tubs and Squeezes Made Without Partially Hydrogenated Oil				
Promise Fat Free; I Can't Believe It's Not Butter (fat free)	5	0	0	90
Country Crock Omega Plus Light	50	1	0	80
Smart Balance Omega Light	50	1.5	0	80
Parkay Squeeze	70	1.5	0	110
Canola Harvest Original	100	1.5	0	100
Tubs Made with Partially Hydrogenated Oil				
Fleischmann's Light	50	0.5	NA	70
Blue Bonnet	60	1	0.4	130
I Can't Believe It's Not Butter! Original	80	2	0.3	90
Sticks				
Blue Bonnet Light	50	1	1	80
Fleischmann's Original	100	2	2.5	120
Butter				
Butter, any brand, stick	100	7.5	0.4	80
Land O'Lakes Light with Canola Oil	50	2	0	90
Shortening				
Crisco, stick or tub	100	3	0.5	0
Nut Butters				
Peanut butter	95	1.5	0	78
Almond butter	99	1	0	70

*All portion sizes are 1 tablespoon.
Data from Hurley, J., and B. Liebman. 2009. Covering the spreads: tracking down the butters and margarines. *Nutrition Action Healthletter*, Sept., pp. 13–15. Food Processor-SQL, Version 10.3, ESHA Research, Salem, OR.

Figure 6 The two essential fatty acids: linoleic acid (an omega-6 fatty acid) and alpha-linolenic acid (an omega-3 fatty acid).

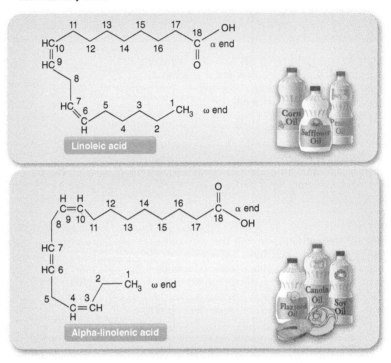

Essential fatty acids

Linoleic acid

Alpha-linolenic acid

Lyudmila Suvorova/iStockphoto

Salmon is high in omega-3 fatty acid content.

linoleic acid An essential fatty acid found in vegetable and nut oils; also known as omega-6 fatty acid.

alpha-linolenic acid An essential fatty acid found in leafy green vegetables, flaxseed oil, soy oil, fish oil, and fish products; an omega-3 fatty acid.

EFAs are essential to growth and health because they are precursors to important biological compounds called *eicosanoids*, which are produced in nearly every cell in the body.[3] Eicosanoids get their name from the Greek word *eicosa*, which means "twenty," as they are synthesized from fatty acids with twenty carbon atoms. In the body, eicosanoids are potent regulators of cellular function. For example, they help regulate gastrointestinal tract motility, blood clotting, blood pressure, the permeability of our blood vessels to fluid and large molecules, and the regulation of inflammation.

The body's synthesis of various eicosanoids depends in part on the abundance of the EFAs available as precursors. Since they play an important role in "regulating" biological processes, we need a balance of the various eicosanoids and thus a balance of EFAs. For example, we need just the right amount of blood clotting at the right time—too much and we get excessive blood clotting, and too little and we get excessive bleeding. As just noted, the two essential fatty acids in our diet are popularly known as omega-6 and omega-3 fatty acids. These are more technically referred to as linoleic acid and alpha-linolenic acid, respectively.

Linoleic Acid Linoleic acid, also known as an *omega-6 fatty acid*, is found in vegetable and nut oils, such as sunflower, safflower, corn, soy, and peanut oil. If you eat lots of vegetables or use vegetable-oil-based margarines or vegetable oils, you are probably getting adequate amounts of this essential fatty acid in your diet. Linoleic acid is metabolized in the body to arachidonic acid, which is a precursor to a number of eicosanoids. Linoleic acid is also needed for cell membrane structure and is required for the lipoproteins that transport fats in our blood.

Alpha-Linolenic Acid Alpha-linolenic acid, also known as an *omega-3 fatty acid*, was only recognized to be essential in the mid-1980s. It is found primarily in dark green, leafy vegetables, flaxseeds and flaxseed oil, soybeans and soybean oil, walnuts and walnut oil, and canola oil. You may also have read news reports of the health

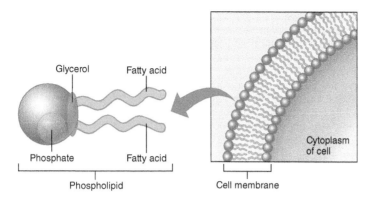

Figure 7 Structure of a phospholipid. Phospholipids consist of a glycerol backbone with two fatty acids and a compound that contains phosphate.

benefits of the omega-3 fatty acids found in many fish. The two omega-3 fatty acids found in fish, shellfish, and fish oils are **eicosapentaenoic acid (EPA)** and **docosahexaenoic acid (DHA)**. Fish that naturally contain more oil, such as salmon and tuna, are higher in EPA and DHA than lean fish, such as cod or flounder. Research indicates that diets high in EPA and DHA stimulate the production of regulatory compounds that reduce an individual's risk for heart disease.[4,5]

Phospholipids Combine Lipids with Phosphate

Along with the triglycerides just discussed, we also find phospholipids and sterols in the foods we eat. **Phospholipids** consist of two fatty acids and a glycerol backbone with another compound that contains phosphate **(Figure 7)**. This addition of a phosphate compound makes phospholipids soluble in water, a property that enables phospholipids to assist in transporting fats in our bloodstream. We discuss this concept in more detail later in this chapter. Also, phospholipids in our cell membranes regulate the transport of substances into and out of the cell. Phospholipids also help with the digestion of dietary fats: the liver uses phospholipids called *lecithins* to make bile. Note that our bodies manufacture phospholipids, so they are not essential for us to include in our diets. What *is* essential is phosphorus, a mineral that is combined with oxygen to make phosphate.

Sterols Have a Ring Structure

Sterols are also a type of lipid found in foods and in the body, but their multiple-ring structure is quite different from that of triglycerides **(Figure 8a)**. Sterols are found in both plant and animal foods and are produced in the body. Plants contain some sterols, but these sterols are not very well absorbed and appear to block the absorption of dietary cholesterol, the most commonly occurring sterol in the diet (Figure 8b). Cholesterol is found only in the fatty part of animal products such as

eicosapentaenoic acid (EPA) A metabolic derivative of alpha-linolenic acid.

docosahexaenoic acid (DHA) Another metabolic derivative of alpha-linolenic acid; together with EPA, it appears to reduce our risk for a heart attack.

phospholipids A type of lipid in which a fatty acid is combined with another compound that contains phosphate; unlike other lipids, phospholipids are soluble in water.

sterols A type of lipid found in foods and the body that has a ring structure; cholesterol is the most common sterol that occurs in our diets.

(a) Sterol ring structure

(b) Cholesterol

Figure 8 Sterol structure. **(a)** Sterols are lipids that contain multiple-ring structures. **(b)** Cholesterol is the most commonly occurring sterol in the diet.

butter, egg yolks, whole milk, meats, and poultry. Low- or reduced-fat animal products, such as lean meats and skim milk, have little cholesterol.

We don't need to consume cholesterol in our diet because our body continually synthesizes it, mostly in the liver and intestines. This continuous production is essential because cholesterol is part of every cell membrane, where it works in conjunction with fatty acids to help maintain cell membrane integrity. It is particularly plentiful in the neural cells that make up our brain, spinal cord, and nerves. The body also uses cholesterol to synthesize several important compounds, including sex hormones (estrogen, androgen, and progesterone), bile acids, adrenal hormones, and vitamin D. Thus, despite cholesterol's bad reputation, it is absolutely essential to human health.

RECAP Fat is essential for health. Three types of fat are found in foods: triglycerides, phospholipids, and sterols. Triglycerides are the most common. A triglyceride is made up of glycerol and three fatty acids. These fatty acids can be classified based on chain length, level of saturation, and shape. Saturated and *trans* fatty acids increase our risk for cardiovascular disease, whereas unsaturated fatty acids, including the essential fatty acids, are protective. Phospholipids combine two fatty acids and a glycerol backbone with a phosphate-containing compound, making them soluble in water. Sterols have a multiple-ring structure; cholesterol is the most commonly occurring sterol in our diet.

Why Do We Need Fats?

Dietary fat provides energy and helps our bodies perform some essential physiologic functions.

Fats Provide Energy

Dietary fat is a primary source of energy because fat has more than twice the energy per gram of carbohydrate or protein. Fat provides 9 kilocalories (kcal) per gram, whereas carbohydrate and protein provide only 4 kilocalories (kcal) per gram. This means that fat is much more energy dense. For example, 1 tbsp. of butter or oil contains approximately 100 kcal, whereas it takes 2.5 cups of steamed broccoli or 1 slice of whole-wheat bread to provide 100 kcal.

Fats Are a Major Fuel Source When We Are at Rest

At rest, we are able to deliver plenty of oxygen to our cells, so that metabolic functions can occur. Just as a candle needs oxygen for the flame to burn the tallow, our cells need oxygen to burn fat for energy. Thus, approximately 30–70% of the energy used at rest by the muscles and organs comes from fat.[6] The exact percentage varies, according to how much fat you are eating in your diet, how physically active you are, and whether you are gaining or losing weight. If you are dieting, more fat will be used for energy than if you are gaining weight. During times of weight gain, more of the fat consumed in the diet is stored in the adipose tissue, and the body uses more dietary protein and carbohydrate as fuel sources at rest.

Fats Fuel Physical Activity

Fat is a major energy source during physical activity, and one of the best ways to lose body fat is to exercise. During exercise, fat can be mobilized from any of the following sources: muscle tissue, adipose tissue, blood lipoproteins, and/or any dietary fat consumed during exercise. A number of hormonal changes signal the body to break down stored energy to fuel the working muscles. The hormonal responses, and the amount and source of the fat used, depend on your level of fitness; the type, intensity, and duration of the exercise; and how well fed you are before you exercise.

For example, adrenaline strongly stimulates the breakdown of stored fat. Blood levels of adrenaline rise dramatically within seconds of beginning exercise, and this

Andersen Floss/Photodisc/Getty Images

◆ Dietary fat provides energy.

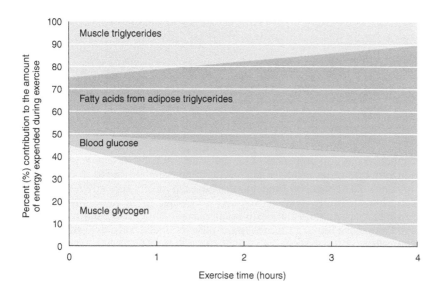

Figure 9 Various sources of energy used during exercise. As a person exercises for a prolonged period of time, fatty acids from adipose cells contribute relatively more energy than do carbohydrates stored in the muscle or circulating in our blood.

Data from Coyle, E. F. 1995. Substrate utilization during exercise in active people. *Am. J. Clin. Nutr.* 6[Suppl]: 958S–979S. Used with permission.

action activates additional hormones within the fat cell to begin breaking down fat. Adrenaline also signals the pancreas to *decrease* insulin production. This is important because insulin inhibits fat breakdown. Thus, when the need for fat as an energy source is high, blood insulin levels are typically low. As you might guess, blood insulin levels are high after eating, when our need for getting energy from stored fat is low and the need for fat storage is high.

Once fatty acids are released from the adipose cell, they travel in the blood attached to a protein, *albumin,* to the muscles, where they enter the mitochondria and use oxygen to produce ATP, which is the cell's energy source. Becoming more physically fit means you can deliver more oxygen to the muscle to use the fat that is delivered there. In addition, you can exercise longer when you are fit. Since the body has only a limited supply of stored carbohydrate as glycogen in muscle tissue, the longer you exercise, the more fat you use for energy. This point is illustrated in **Figure 9**. In this example, an individual is running for 4 hours at a moderate intensity. The longer the individual runs, the more depleted the muscle glycogen levels become and the more fat from adipose tissue is used as a fuel source for exercise.

Doug Pensinger/Getty Images

The longer you exercise, the more fat you use for energy. Cyclists in long-distance races use fat stores for energy.

Body Fat Stores Energy for Later Use

Our body stores extra energy in the form of body fat, which then can be used for energy at rest, during exercise, or during periods of low energy intake. Having a readily available energy source in the form of fat allows the body to always have access to energy, even when we choose not to eat (or are unable to eat), when we are exercising, and while we are sleeping. Our bodies have little stored carbohydrate—only enough to last about 1 to 2 days—and there is no place where our body can store extra protein. We cannot consider our muscles and organs as a place where "extra" protein is stored! For these reasons, the fat stored in our adipose and muscle tissues is necessary to keep the body going. Although we do not want too much stored adipose tissue, some fat storage is essential to good health.

Fats Enable the Transport of Fat-Soluble Vitamins

Dietary fat enables the transport of the fat-soluble vitamins (A, D, E, and K) our body needs for many essential metabolic functions. For example, vitamin A is especially important for normal vision and gives us the ability to see at night. Vitamin D is important for regulating blood calcium and phosphorus concentrations within normal ranges, which indirectly helps maintain bone health. If vitamin D is low, blood calcium levels will drop below normal, and the body will draw calcium from the bones

Odd Anderdsen/Getty Images

Adipose tissue pads our body and protects our organs when we fall or are bruised.

to maintain blood levels. Vitamin E functions primarily as an antioxidant in our body and keeps cell membranes healthy by preventing the oxidation of body fats. Finally, vitamin K is important for proteins involved in blood clotting and bone health.

Fats Help Maintain Cell Function

Fats are a critical part of every cell membrane. The types of fats in cell membranes help maintain membrane integrity, determine what substances are transported into and out of the cell, and regulate what substances can bind to the cell; thus, fats strongly influence the function of the cell. In addition, fats help maintain cell fluidity and other physical properties of the cell membrane. For example, wild salmon live in very cold water and have high levels of omega-3 fatty acids in their cell membranes. These fats stay fluid and flexible even in very cold environments, which allow the fish to swim in extremely cold water. In the same way, fats help our membranes stay fluid and flexible. For example, they enable our red blood cells to bend and move through the smallest capillaries in our body, delivering oxygen to all our cells.

Fats, especially PUFAs, are also primary components of the tissues of the brain and spinal cord, where they facilitate the transmission of information from one cell to another. We also need fats for the development, growth, and maintenance of these tissues.

Danny E. Hooks/Shutterstock

Stored Fat Provides Protection to the Body

Stored body fat also plays an important role in our body. Besides being the primary site of stored energy, adipose tissue pads our body and protects our organs, such as the kidneys and liver, when we fall or are bruised. The fat under our skin acts as insulation to help us retain body heat. Although we often think of body fat as "bad," it plays important roles in keeping our body healthy and functioning properly.

Fat adds texture and flavor to foods.

Fats Contribute to the Flavor and Texture of Foods

Dietary fat helps food taste good because it contributes to texture and flavor. Fat makes salad dressings smooth and ice cream "creamy," and it gives cakes and cookies their moist, tender texture. Frying foods in melted butter, lard, or oils gives them a crisp, flavorful coating; however, eating fried foods regularly is unhealthful because these foods are high in saturated and *trans* fatty acids.

Fats Help Us Feel Satiated

Fats in foods help us feel satiated after a meal. Two factors probably contribute to this effect: first, fat has a much higher energy density than carbohydrate or protein. For example, a pat of butter weighing 5 g contains 35 kcal; 5 g of an apple contain only 3 kcal. For every gram of fat you consume, you get 2.25 times the amount of energy that you get with the same number of grams consumed in protein or carbohydrate.

Second, fat takes longer to digest than protein or carbohydrate because more steps are involved in the digestion process, which may make you feel fuller for a longer period of time because energy is slowly being released into your body.

On the other hand, you can eat more fat in a meal without feeling overfull because fat is generally compact in its size. Going back to our apple and butter example, one medium apple weighs 117 g (approximately 4 oz) and has 70 kcal, but the same number of Calories of butter—two pats—would hardly make you feel full! Looked at another way, an amount of butter weighing the same number of grams as a medium apple would contain 840 kcal!

Kip Peticolas/Fundamental Photographs, NYC

Fats and oils do not dissolve readily in water.

RECAP Dietary fats provide more than twice the energy of protein and carbohydrate, at 9 kcal per gram, and provide the majority of the energy required at rest. Fats are also a major fuel source during exercise, especially endurance exercise. Dietary fats help transport the fat-soluble vitamins into the body and help regulate cell function and maintain membrane integrity. Stored body fat in the adipose tissue helps protect vital organs and pad the body. Fats contribute to the flavor and texture of foods and the satiety we feel after a meal.

How Does Our Body Process Fats?

Because fats are not soluble in water, they cannot enter our bloodstream easily from the digestive tract. Thus, fats must be digested, absorbed, and transported within the body differently than carbohydrates and proteins, which are water-soluble substances.

We briefly review the process of digestion and absorption of fat here (Figure 10). Dietary fats usually come mixed with other foods. Salivary enzymes released during chewing have a limited role in the breakdown of fats, so most fat reaches the stomach intact (Figure 10, step 1). The primary role of the stomach in fat digestion is to mix and break up the fat into small droplets. Because they are not soluble in water, these fat droplets typically float on top of the watery digestive juices in the stomach until they are passed into the small intestine (Figure 10, step 2).

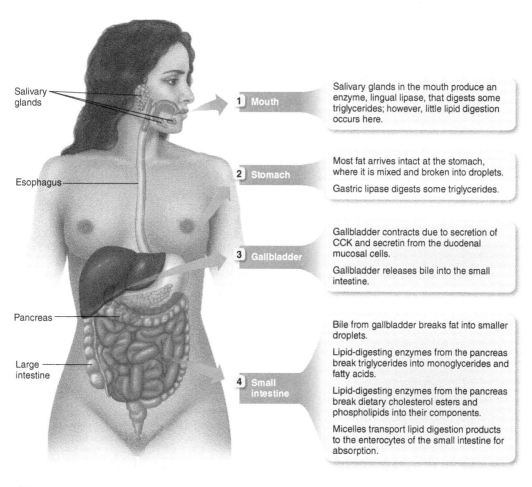

Salivary glands

Esophagus

Pancreas

Large intestine

1 Mouth
Salivary glands in the mouth produce an enzyme, lingual lipase, that digests some triglycerides; however, little lipid digestion occurs here.

2 Stomach
Most fat arrives intact at the stomach, where it is mixed and broken into droplets.
Gastric lipase digests some triglycerides.

3 Gallbladder
Gallbladder contracts due to secretion of CCK and secretin from the duodenal mucosal cells.
Gallbladder releases bile into the small intestine.

4 Small intestine
Bile from gallbladder breaks fat into smaller droplets.
Lipid-digesting enzymes from the pancreas break triglycerides into monoglycerides and fatty acids.
Lipid-digesting enzymes from the pancreas break dietary cholesterol esters and phospholipids into their components.
Micelles transport lipid digestion products to the enterocytes of the small intestine for absorption.

◆ **Figure 10** The process of fat digestion.

The Gallbladder, Liver, and Pancreas Assist in Fat Digestion

Because fat is not soluble in water, its digestion requires the help of digestive enzymes from the pancreas and mixing compounds from the gallbladder. The gallbladder is a sac attached to the underside of the liver and the pancreas is an oblong-shaped organ sitting below the stomach. Both have a duct connecting them to the small intestine. As fat enters the small intestine from the stomach, the gallbladder contracts and releases a substance called bile (Figure 10, step 3). Bile is produced in the liver from cholesterol and is stored in the gallbladder until needed. You can think of bile acting much as soap does, breaking up the fat into smaller and smaller droplets. At the same time, lipid-digesting enzymes produced in the pancreas travel through the pancreatic duct into the small intestine. Once bile has broken the fat into small droplets, these pancreatic enzymes take over, breaking the fatty acids away from their glycerol backbones. Each triglyceride molecule is broken down into two free fatty acids and one *monoglyceride*, a glycerol molecule with one fatty acid still attached.

Absorption of Fat Occurs Primarily in the Small Intestine

The majority of fat absorption occurs in the mucosal lining of the small intestine with the help of a micelle (Figure 10, step 4). A *micelle* is a spherical compound made up of bile and phospholipids that can trap the free fatty acids and the monoglycerides and transport them to the mucosal cells for absorption.

How does the absorbed fat get into the bloodstream? Because fats do not mix with water, most fats cannot be transported freely in the bloodstream. To solve this problem, the fatty acids are reformulated back into triglycerides and then packaged into lipoproteins before being released into the bloodstream. A **lipoprotein** is a spherical compound in which the fat clusters in the center and phospholipids and proteins form the outside of the sphere (Figure 11). The specific lipoprotein produced in the mucosal cell to transport fat from a meal is called a **chylomicron.** This unique compound is now soluble in water because phospholipids and proteins are water soluble. Once chylomicrons are formed, they are transported from the intestinal lining to the lymphatic system and then into the blood. In this way, dietary fat finally arrives in your blood.

As mentioned earlier, short- and medium-chain fatty acids (those fewer than fourteen carbons in length) can be transported in the body more readily than the long-chain fatty acids. When short- and medium-chain fatty acids are digested and transported to the mucosal cells of the small intestine, they do not have to be reformed into triglycerides and incorporated into chylomicrons. Instead, they can travel in the bloodstream bound to either a transport protein, such as albumin, or a phospholipid. For this reason, shorter-chain fatty acids can get into the system more quickly than long-chain fatty acids.

Imagine a "magic pill" that would block your body's absorption of fat, allowing you to eat all the fat you wanted without any effects on your weight or your heart. Does such a pill exist? Check out the Nutrition Debate later in this chapter to find out.

Fat Is Stored in Adipose Tissues for Later Use

The chylomicrons, which are filled with the dietary fat you just ate, now begin to circulate through the blood, looking for a place to deliver their load. There are three primary fates of this dietary fat:

1. It can immediately be taken up and used as a source of energy for the cells.
2. It can be used to make lipid-containing compounds in the body.
3. It can be stored in the muscle or adipose tissue as a triglyceride for later use. (Figure 12 shows an adipose cell.)

lipoprotein A spherical compound in which fat clusters in the center and phospholipids and proteins form the outside of the sphere.

chylomicron A lipoprotein produced in the mucosal cell of the intestine; transports dietary fat out of the intestinal tract.

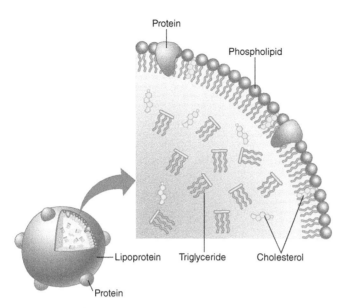

Figure 11 Structure of a lipoprotein. Notice that the fat clusters in the center of the molecule and the phospholipids and proteins, which are water soluble, form the outside of the sphere. This enables lipoproteins to transport fats in the bloodstream.

How does the fat get out of the chylomicrons and into the cell? This process occurs with the help of an enzyme called **lipoprotein lipase,** or LPL, which sits outside of our adipose cells. LPL comes in contact with the chylomicrons when they touch the surface of the adipose cell. As a result of this contact, LPL breaks apart the triglycerides in the core of the chylomicrons. This process results in the movement of individual fatty acids from within the core of the chylomicrons and out into the adipose cell. If the adipose cell needs the fat for energy, these fatty acids are quickly transported into the mitochondria and used as fuel. If the body doesn't need the fatty acids for immediate energy, the cell can re-create the triglycerides and store them for later use.

The primary storage site for this extra energy is the adipose cell. However, if you are physically active, your body will preferentially store this extra fat in the muscle tissue first, so, the next time you work out, the fat is readily available to the cell for energy. Thus, people who engage in physical activity are more likely to have extra fat stored in the muscle tissue and to have less body fat—something many of us would prefer. Of course, fat stored in the adipose tissue can also be used for energy during exercise, but it must be broken down first and then transported to the muscle cells.

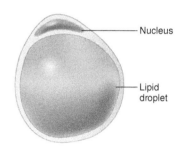

Figure 12 Diagram of an adipose cell.

RECAP Fat digestion begins when fats are broken into droplets by bile. Pancreatic enzymes subsequently digest the triglycerides into two free fatty acids and one monoglyceride. These are transported into the intestinal mucosal cells with the help of micelles. Once inside the mucosal cells, triglycerides are re-formed and packaged into lipoproteins called chylomicrons. Dietary fat is transported by the chylomicrons to cells within the body that need energy. Fat stored in the muscle tissue is used as a source of energy during physical activity. Excess fat is stored in the adipose tissue and can be used whenever the body needs energy.

How Much Fat Should We Eat?

Without a doubt, Americans think dietary fat is bad! How many people have you heard say they are trying to dramatically reduce the level of fat in their diet? Yet,

lipoprotein lipase An enzyme that sits on the outside of cells and breaks apart triglycerides, so that their fatty acids can be removed and taken up by the cell.

because fat plays such an important role in keeping our bodies healthy, we do need to include a moderate amount in our diet. But what, exactly, is a moderate amount? And what foods contain the most healthful fats? We'll explore these questions here.

Dietary Reference Intake for Total Fat

The Acceptable Macronutrient Distribution Range (AMDR) for fat is 20–35% of total energy.[7] This recommendation is based on evidence indicating that higher intakes of fat increase the risk for obesity and its complications, especially heart disease, but that diets too low in fat and too high in carbohydrate can also increase the risk for heart disease if they cause blood triglycerides to increase.[7] Within this range of fat intake, it is also recommended that we minimize our intake of saturated and *trans* fatty acids as much as possible; these changes will lower our risk for heart disease.

So how are Americans doing? According to the most recent U.S. data, on average Americans consume approximately 34% of their energy from fat, which is within the recommended range.[8] Yet, over the last 35 years, total fat intake (as grams per day) has gradually increased from 71 to 100 g/day, along with total energy intake.[8, 9, 10] Thus, it's not surprising that obesity is on the rise in America.

If you're an athlete, you've probably been advised to consume less fat and more carbohydrate to replenish your glycogen stores, especially if you participate in endurance activities. Specifically, you should consume 20–25% of your total energy from fat, 55–60% of energy from carbohydrate, and 12–15% of energy from protein.[11,12] This percentage of fat intake is still within the AMDR and represents approximately 45 to 55 g of fat per day for an athlete consuming 2,000 kcal per day, and 78 to 97 g of fat per day for an athlete consuming 3,500 kcal per day.

Although many people trying to lose weight consume less than 20% of their energy from fat, this practice may do more harm than good, especially if they are also limiting energy intake (eating fewer than 1,500 kcal per day). Research suggests that very-low-fat diets, those with less than 15% of energy from fat, do not provide additional health or performance benefits over moderate-fat diets and are usually very difficult to follow.[13] In fact, most people find they feel better, are more successful in weight maintenance, and are less preoccupied with food if they keep their fat intake at 20–25% of energy intake. Additionally, people attempting to reduce their dietary fat frequently eliminate foods such as meats, dairy, eggs, and nuts, which are sources of protein and many essential vitamins and minerals. Diets extremely low in fat may also be deficient in essential fatty acids.

Jeff Greenberg/AGE Fotostock

◄ In the United States, we eat too many saturated and *trans* fats.

TABLE 1 Omega-3 Fatty Acid Content of Selected Foods

Food Item	Total Omega-3	DHA	EPA*
		g/serving	
Flaxseed oil, 1 tbsp.	7.25	0.00	0.00
Salmon oil (fish oil), 1 tbsp.	4.39	2.48	1.77
Sardine oil, 1 tbsp.	3.01	1.45	1.38
Flaxseed, whole, 1 tbsp.	2.50	0.00	0.00
Herring, Atlantic, broiled, 3 oz	1.83	0.94	0.77
Anchovies w/oil, each	1.76	0.65	1.10
Herring oil, 1 tbsp.	1.53	0.57	0.85
Salmon, Coho, steamed, 3 oz	1.34	0.71	0.46
Canola oil, 1 tbsp.	1.28	0.00	0.00
Sardines, Atlantic, w/ bones and oil, 3 oz	1.26	0.43	0.40
Trout, rainbow fillet, baked, 3 oz	1.05	0.70	0.28
Walnuts, English, 1 tbsp.	0.66	0.00	0.00
Halibut, fillet, baked, 3 oz	0.53	0.31	0.21
Shrimp, Canned, 3 oz	0.47	0.21	0.25
Tuna, white, in oil, 3 oz	0.38	0.19	0.04
Crab, Alaska King, steamed, 3 oz	0.36	0.10	0.25
Scallops, broiled, 3 oz	0.31	0.14	0.17
Tuna, light, in water, 3 oz	0.23	0.19	0.04
Avocado, Calif., fresh, whole	0.22	0.00	0.00
Spinach, cooked, 1 cup	0.17	0.00	0.00

Note: *EPA = eicosapentaenoic acid; DHA = docosahexaenoic acid
Data from Food Processor SQL, Version 10.3, ESHA Research, Salem, OR.

Dietary Reference Intakes for Essential Fatty Acids

Dietary Reference Intakes (DRIs) for the two essential fatty acids were set for the first time in 2002.[7]

- *Linoleic acid.* The Adequate Intake (AI) for linoleic acid (an omega-6 FA) is 14 to 17 g per day for adult men and 11 to 12 g per day for women 19 years and older. Using the typical energy intakes for adult men and women, this translates into an AMDR of 5–10% of total energy intake.
- *Alpha-linolenic acid.* The AI for alpha-linolenic acid (an omega-3 FA) is 1.6 g per day for adult men and 1.1 g per day for adult women. This translates into an AMDR of 0.6–1.2% of total energy. These recommendations are for omega-3 fatty acids as a group. No DRIs have been set for DHA or EPA specifically. So how do you know if you're getting enough in your diet? Look through Table 1 to see if you are consuming any good food sources of these essential acids.

Baked goods are often high in hidden fats and may contain *trans* fats.

Following these recommendations, an individual consuming 2,000 kcal per day should consume about 11 to 22 g per day of linoleic acid and about 1.3 to 2.6 g per day of alpha-linolenic acid. Notice that the recommended intake of linoleic acid is close to ten times higher than the recommended intake of alpha-linolenic acid. This is in keeping with the 5:1 to 10:1 ratio of linoleic:alpha-linolenic acid recommended by the World Health Organization and supported by the Institute of Medicine.[7] Because these EFAs compete for the same enzymes to produce various eicosanoids, this ratio helps keep eicosanoid production in balance; that is, one isn't overproduced at the expense of the other.

RECAP The Acceptable Macronutrient Distribution Range (AMDR) for total fat is 20–35% of total energy. The Adequate Intake (AI) for linoleic acid is 14 to 17 g per day for adult men and 11 to 12 g per day for adult women. The AI for alpha-linolenic acid is 1.6 g per day for adult men and 1.1 g per day for adult women.

Don't Let the Fats Fool You!

Like many things, a little can be good, but too much can be harmful. We know that un-saturated fats are necessary for good health, but too much fat, regardless of type, can be unhealthful. That's one reason nutritionists have been recommending the reduction of dietary fat for over a decade. However, before you can make healthful reductions in your fat intake, you need to know where the fat in your diet is coming from.

Recognize the Fat in Foods

It is easy to eat a high-fat diet. First, we add fats, such as oils, butter, cream, shortening, margarine, mayonnaise, and salad dressings, to foods because they make food taste good. This type of fat is called **visible fat** because we can easily see that we are adding it to our food. When we add fat to foods ourselves, we generally know how much we are adding. Still, we may not be aware of the type of fat we're using and the number of Calories it adds to our meal. For instance, it's easy to make a salad into a high-fat meal by adding two or three tablespoons of full-fat salad dressing. Doing so also transforms the salad into a high-Calorie meal: concentrated fats, such as butter, oil, and salad dressings, have 100 kcal/tablespoon.

Limiting your intake of visible fats is important, but it's only the first step. You must also be on the lookout for **hidden fats**—that is, fats added to processed and pre-pared foods to improve taste and texture. Over the past decade, our intake of visible fats has decreased, while our intake of hidden fats has increased.[9] That's partly be-cause, when fat exists naturally within a food, or is added during food preparation,

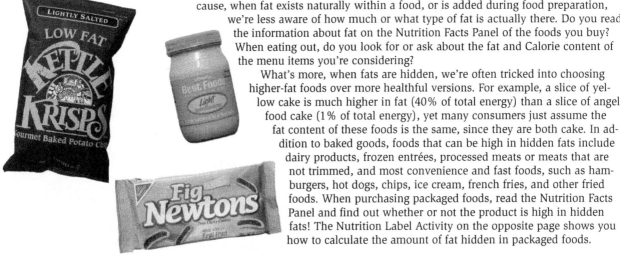

we're less aware of how much or what type of fat is actually there. Do you read the information about fat on the Nutrition Facts Panel of the foods you buy? When eating out, do you look for or ask about the fat and Calorie content of the menu items you're considering?

What's more, when fats are hidden, we're often tricked into choosing higher-fat foods over more healthful versions. For example, a slice of yellow cake is much higher in fat (40% of total energy) than a slice of angel food cake (1% of total energy), yet many consumers just assume the fat content of these foods is the same, since they are both cake. In addition to baked goods, foods that can be high in hidden fats include dairy products, frozen entrées, processed meats or meats that are not trimmed, and most convenience and fast foods, such as hamburgers, hot dogs, chips, ice cream, french fries, and other fried foods. When purchasing packaged foods, read the Nutrition Facts Panel and find out whether or not the product is high in hidden fats! The Nutrition Label Activity on the opposite page shows you how to calculate the amount of fat hidden in packaged foods.

Decipher Label Claims

Since high-fat diets have been associated with obesity, many Americans are trying to reduce their total fat intake. Because of this concern, food manufacturers have been more than happy to provide consumers with low-fat alternatives to their favorite foods—so you can have your cake and eat it, too! The FDA and the USDA have set specific regulations on allowable product descriptions for reduced-fat products. The following claims are defined for 1 serving:

- Fat-free = less than 0.5 g of fat
- Low-fat = 3 g or less of fat
- Reduced or less fat: at least 25% less fat as compared to a standard serving
- Light: one-third fewer Calories or 50% less fat as compared with a standard serving size

It is now estimated that there are more than 5,000 different fat-modified foods on the market.[14, 15] For example, you can purchase fat-modified dairy products, peanut butter, mayonnaise, cookies, crackers, and frozen meals. However, if you're choosing

visible fats Fat we can see in our foods or see added to foods, such as butter, margarine, cream, shortening, salad dressings, chicken skin, and untrimmed fat on meat.

hidden fats Fats that are hidden in foods, such as the fats found in baked goods, regular-fat dairy products, marbling in meat, and fried foods.

NUTRITION LABEL ACTIVITY

How Much Fat Is in This Food?

How can you figure out how much fat is in a food you buy? One way is to read the Nutrition Facts Panel on the label. By becoming a better label reader, you can make more healthful food selections. Two cracker labels are shown in Figure 13; one cracker is higher in fat than the other.

Let's review how you can use the label to find out what percentage of energy is coming from fat in each product. The calculations are relatively simple.

1. Divide the total Calories from fat by the total Calories per serving, and multiply the answer by 100.
   - For the regular wheat crackers: 50 kcal/150 kcal = 0.33 × 100 = 33%.

   Thus, for the regular crackers, the total energy coming from fat is 33%.
   - For the reduced-fat wheat crackers: 35 kcal/130 kcal = 0.269 × 100 = 27%.

   Thus, for the reduced-fat crackers, the total energy coming from fat is 27%.

   You can see that, although the total amount of energy per serving is not very different between these two crackers, the percentage from fat is quite different.

2. If the total Calories per serving from fat are not given on the label, you can quickly calculate this value by multiplying the grams of total fat per serving by 9 (there are 9 kcal per gram of fat).
   - For the regular wheat crackers: 6 g fat × 9 kcal/gram = 54 kcal of fat.
   - To calculate the percentage of Calories from fat: 54 kcal/150 kcal = 0.36 × 100 = 36%.

   You can see that this value is not exactly the same as the 50 kcal reported on the label or the 33% of Calories from fat calculated in example 1. The values on food labels are rounded off, so your estimations may not be identical when you do this second calculation.

   In summary, you can quickly calculate the percentage of fat per serving for any packaged food in three steps: (1) multiply the grams of fat per serving by 9 kcal per gram; (2) divide this number by the total kcal per serving; (3) multiply by 100.

Wheat Crackers

- **No Cholesterol**

Nutrition Facts

Serving Size: 16 Crackers (31g)
Servings Per Container: About 9

Amount Per Serving		
Calories		150
Calories from Fat		50
		% Daily Value*
Total Fat 6g		9%
Saturated Fat 1g		6%
Polyunsaturated Fat 0g		
Monounsaturated Fat 2g		
Trans Fat 0g		
Cholesterol 0mg		0%
Sodium 270mg		11%
Total Carbohydrate 21g		7%
Dietary Fiber 1g		4%
Sugars 3g		
Protein 2g		

(a)

Reduced-Fat Wheat Crackers

- **No Cholesterol**
- **Low Saturated Fat**
  Contains 4g Fat Per Serving

Nutrition Facts

Serving Size: 16 Crackers (29g)
Servings Per Container: About 9

Amount Per Serving		
Calories		130
Calories from Fat		35
		% Daily Value*
Total Fat 4g		6%
Saturated Fat 1g		4%
Polyunsaturated Fat 0g		
Monounsaturated Fat 1.5g		
Trans Fat 0g		
Cholesterol 0mg		0%
Sodium 260 mg		11%
Total Carbohydrate 21g		7%
Dietary Fiber 1g		4%
Sugars 3g		
Protein 2g		

(b)

Foodfolio/Alamy

Figure 13 Labels for two types of wheat crackers. **(a)** Regular wheat crackers. **(b)** Reduced-fat wheat crackers.

TABLE 2 Comparison of Full-Fat, Reduced-Fat, and Low-Fat Foods*

Product and Serving Size	Version	Energy (kcal)	Protein (g)	Carbohydrate (g)	Fat (g)	Saturated Fat (g)
Animal Products:						
Milk, 8 oz	Whole, 3.3% fat	150	8.0	11.4	8.2	4.6
	2% fat	121	8.1	11.7	4.7	3.0
	1% fat	102	8.0	11.7	2.6	1.5
	Skim (nonfat)	86	8.4	11.9	0.5	0.0
Cheese, cheddar, 1 oz	Regular	111	7.1	0.5	9.1	4.0
	Low-fat	81	9.1	0.0	5.1	2.7
	Nonfat	41	6.8	4.0	0.0	0.0
Cream cheese, 1 tbsp.	Soft regular	50	1.0	0.5	5.0	3.0
	Soft light	35	1.5	1.0	2.5	1.7
	Soft nonfat	15	2.5	1.0	0.0	0.0
Ground Beef, cooked (3 oz)	Regular (25% fat)	237	22	0	16	6.2
	Extra-lean (5% fat)	145	22	0	5.6	2.5
Chicken, frozen dinner (9–12 oz dinner cooked)	Fried breast with skin	470	20	30	30	10
	Grilled, skinless	360	20	38	14	4
Vegetable Spreads:						
Mayonnaise, 1 tbsp.	Regular	100	0.0	0.0	11.0	1.5
	Light	50	0.0	1.0	5.0	0.75
	Fat-free	10	0.0	2.0	0.0	0.08
Margarine, veg oil, 1 tbsp.	Regular	100	0.0	0.0	11.0	1.5
	Reduced-fat	60	0.0	0.0	7.0	1.3
Peanut butter, 1 tbsp.	Regular	95	4.1	3.1	8.0	1.5
	Reduced-fat	95	4.4	5.2	6.0	1.25
Grain Products:						
Cookies, Oreo, 3 cookies	Regular	160	2.0	24.0	7.0	1.5
	Reduced-fat	150	2.0	26.0	3.5	1.0
Cookies, Fig Newton, 3 cookies	Regular	174	3.0	29.0	4.4	1.45
	Fat-free	130	1.5	30.0	0.0	0.0
Muffin, 4 oz	Regular	429	6.0	54.0	21.0	3.0
	Low-fat	300	6.0	61.0	3.0	0.5

*The Food and Drug Administration and the U.S. Department of Agriculture have set specific regulations on allowable product descriptions for reduced-fat products. The following claims are defined for 1 serving: **fat-free**: less than 0.5 g of fat; **low-fat**: 3 g or less of fat; **reduced or less fat**: at least 25% less fat as compared to a standard serving; **light**: one-third fewer calories or 50% less fat as compared with a standard serving size.
Data from Food Processor-SQL, Version 10.3, ESHA Research, Salem, OR.

such foods because of a concern about your weight, let the buyer beware! Lower-fat versions of foods may not always be lower in Calories.

In **Table 2**, we list a number of full-fat foods with their lower-fat alternatives. If you were to incorporate such foods into your diet on a regular basis, you could significantly reduce the amount of fat you consume. Still, your choices may or may not reduce the amount of energy you consume. For example, as you can see in the table, drinking nonfat milk instead of whole milk would dramatically reduce both your fat and your energy intake. However, eating fat-free instead of regular Fig Newton cookies would not significantly reduce your energy intake.

Thus, if you think that eating fat-free foods means you're reducing your energy intake so significantly that you can eat all you want without gaining weight, you're mistaken. The reduced fat is often replaced with added carbohydrate, resulting in a very similar total energy intake. Thus, if you want to reduce both the amount of fat and energy you consume, you must read the labels of modified-fat foods carefully before you buy.[14]

◄ This skinless roasted chicken breast provides <1 g saturated fat and 131 kcal; with the skin, it would provide 3 g saturated fat and 235 kcal.

Limit Saturated and *Trans* Fats

Research over the last two decades has shown that diets high in saturated fatty acids negatively influence blood lipid levels, increasing our risk for heart disease. We now also know that *trans* fatty acids appear to function much like saturated fatty acids in our diet: both *trans* and saturated fatty acids lower "good" cholesterol and raise "bad" cholesterol, change cell membrane function, and alter the way cholesterol is removed from the blood. For these reasons, researchers believe that diets high in saturated and *trans* fatty acids can increase the risk for cardiovascular disease.

Reduce Your Intake of Saturated Fats

The recommended intake of saturated fats is less than 7–10% of our total energy; unfortunately, our average intake is between 11% and 12% of energy.[16] According to data from NHANES, about 64% of adults in the United States exceed the dietary recommendation for saturated fats.[17]

The last time you popped a frozen dinner into the microwave, did you stop and read the Nutrition Facts Panel on the box? If you had, you might have been shocked to learn how much saturated fat was in the meal. Where does it come from? Let's look at the primary sources of saturated fats in the American diet.

- *Animal products.* Meats contain saturated fats. The precise amount depends on the cut of the meat and how it is prepared. For example, red meats, such as beef, pork, and lamb, typically have more fat than skinless chicken or fish. Thus, lean meats are lower in saturated fat than regular cuts. In addition, broiled, grilled, or baked meats have less saturated fat than fried meats. Dairy products may also be high in saturated fat. Whole-fat milk has three times the saturated fat as low-fat milk, and nearly twice the energy. Whole eggs have just over a gram of saturated fat and are high in cholesterol.
- *Grain products.* Baked goods and snack foods are the main culprits in this food group. Pastries, cookies, and muffins may be filled with saturated fats, as well as *trans* fats, if they come from your local bakery. Tortilla chips, microwave and movie-theatre popcorn, snack crackers, and packaged rice and pasta mixes may also be high in saturated fat.

- *Vegetables and vegetable spreads/dressings.* We often don't think of plant foods as having high amounts of saturated fats, but if these foods are fried, breaded, or drenched in sauces they can become a source of saturated fat. For example, a small baked potato (138 g) has no fat and 134 kcal, whereas a medium serving (134 g) of french fries cooked in vegetable oil has 427 kcal, 23 g of fat, and 5.3 g of saturated fat. This is one-third of the saturated fat recommended for an entire day for a person on a 2,000-kcal/day diet. Some spreads, such as margarine, mayonnaise, and salad dressings, can also add saturated fats to your diet.

Avoid *Trans* Fatty Acids

The Institute of Medicine recommends that we keep our intake of *trans* fatty acids to an absolute minimum.[7] Currently, the average consumption of industrially produced *trans* fatty acids is only about 2–3% of total energy intake, with the majority coming from deep-fried fast or frozen foods, some tub margarines, and bakery products.[7, 18, 19] So, if our current consumption is already so low, why the advice to reduce it even further?

Although *trans* fatty acids make up only a small fraction of the average American diet, their negative effect on our health appears to be dramatic. Many health professionals feel that diets high in *trans* fatty acids increase the risk for heart disease even more than diets high in saturated fats.[20] A research review that involved over 140,000 individuals showed that, for every 2% increase in energy intake from *trans* fatty acids, there was a 23% increase in incidence of heart disease.[20] Other researchers have concluded that the scientific evidence showing that *trans* fatty acids negatively affect health is so strong that it is unethical to do any additional long-term human research trials comparing the health effects of *trans* fatty acids to other types of fatty acids.

Because of the evidence linking *trans* fatty acid consumption to heart disease, the FDA requires manufacturers to list the amount of *trans* fatty acids per serving on the Nutrition Facts Panel. In addition, many cities are considering total bans on *trans* fatty acids in restaurants. For example, in New York City, an amendment to the health code has phased out all artificial *trans* fats in restaurants and other food establishments operating within the city limits.[21] Unfortunately, no such requirement exists for the majority of food establishments in the United States.

As we noted at the beginning of this chapter, legislators and food policy experts around the world are lobbying for the labeling of *trans* fatty acids on menus and/or the elimination of artificial *trans* fatty acids from restaurant foods and other ready-to-eat foods. Although this is a step in the right direction, if we are to achieve our goals for public health, we need to make sure that, in eliminating *trans* fatty acids from foods, we don't simply substitute saturated fats. Food establishments and food manufacturers need to switch to unsaturated fats if we are to reduce our risk for heart disease.

Shop Smart!

Next time you're at the grocery store, how can you limit the level of saturated and *trans* fats in the foods you buy? Here are some Quick Tips to help guide your choices.

Cook Smart!

You can also significantly reduce your intake of saturated fats by making smart choices when you cook. Here are some more Quick Tips to guide you.

Select Beneficial Fats

As mentioned earlier, it's best to switch to healthful fats without increasing your total fat intake. Americans appear to get adequate amounts of omega-6 fatty acids, probably because of the large amount of salad dressings, vegetable oils, margarine, and mayonnaise we eat; however, our consumption of omega-3 fatty acids is more variable and can be low in the diets of people who do not eat leafy green vegetables, fish, or walnuts; drink soy milk; or use soybean, canola, or flaxseed oil.

How can you specifically increase your intake of omega-3 fatty acids? In Table 1, we identified the omega-3 fatty acid content of various foods and supple-

QUICK TIPS

Shopping for Foods Low in Saturated and *Trans* Fats

✓ Read food labels. Look for foods with no hydrogenated oils and low amounts of saturated fats per serving.

✓ Select liquid or tub margarine/butters over hard stick forms. Fats that are solid at room temperature are usually high in *trans* or saturated fatty acids. Also, select margarines made from healthful fats, such as canola oil.

✓ Buy naturally occurring oils, such as olive and canola oil. These types of oils have not been hydrogenated and contain healthful unsaturated fatty acids and no *trans* fatty acids.

✓ Select reduced-fat baked products, such as crackers, chips, cookies, and muffins, over full-fat versions. If you are watching your weight, choose products with fewer Calories per serving as well.

✓ Cut back on packaged pastries, such as Danish, croissants, donuts, cakes, tarts, pies, and brownies. These baked goods are typically high in saturated and *trans* fatty acids.

✓ Select reduced-fat salad dressing and mayonnaise or select those made with healthful fats, such as olive oil and vinegar. If you select the full-fat versions, remember that a tablespoon of oil or full-fat mayonnaise contains 100 kcal.

✓ Add fish, especially those high in omega-3 fatty acids, to your shopping list. For example, select salmon, line-caught tuna, herring, and sardines. Many specialty markets now carry line-caught canned tuna, which is low in mercury. These tuna are smaller, usually less than 20 pounds, and have had less exposure to mercury in their lifetime.

✓ For other healthful sources of protein, select lean cuts of meat and skinless poultry, meat substitutes made with soy, or beans or lentils.

✓ Select low-fat or nonfat versions of milk, cheese, cottage cheese, yogurt, sour cream, cream cheese, and ice cream.

ments. Use this table to determine how you can increase your intake of omega-3 fatty acids. For example, consider including fish in your diet at least twice a week, use canola oil when baking, and add ground flaxseeds to your cereal or walnuts to your salad. You might also consider taking a daily fish oil supplement, using flaxseed oil, or buying products with omega-3 fatty acids added. As a consumer, you need to read the labels of these products carefully to determine if the omega-3 fatty acid content of the product is worth the extra cost.

It is important to recognize that there can be some risk associated with eating large amounts of certain fish on a regular basis. Some species of fish, including shark, swordfish, and king mackerel, contain high levels of mercury and other environmental contaminants. Women who are pregnant or breastfeeding, women who may become pregnant, and small children are at particularly high risk for toxicity from these contaminants.

Of course, healthful fats include not only the essential fatty acids but also polyunsaturated and monounsaturated fats in general. Plant oils are excellent sources of unsaturated fats, as are avocados, olives, nuts and nut butters, and seeds. Substituting beneficial fats for saturated or *trans* fats isn't difficult. See the Eating Right All Day feature two pages ahead for some simple menu choices to help you eat right all day.

Watch Out When You're Eating Out!

Many college students eat most of their meals in dining halls, fast-food restaurants, and other food establishments. If that describes you, watch out! The menu items you choose each day may be increasing the amount of fat in your diet, including your intake of saturated and *trans* fats. A high fat intake is especially difficult to avoid if you regularly eat fast food. Based on 2003–2004 NHANES data, fast-food consumers have

QUICK TIPS

Reducing Saturated Fats When Preparing and Cooking Foods

✓ Trim visible fat from meats before cooking.

✓ Remove the skin from poultry before cooking.

✓ Instead of frying meats, poultry, fish, or potatoes or other vegetables, bake or broil them.

✓ If you normally eat two eggs for breakfast, discard the yolk from one for half the cholesterol. Do the same in recipes calling for two eggs.

✓ Cook with olive oil or canola oil instead of butter.

✓ Use cooking spray instead of butter or oils for stir-frying and baking.

✓ Substitute hard cheeses (such as parmesan), which are naturally lower in fat, for softer cheeses that are higher in fat (such as cheddar).

✓ Substitute low-fat or nonfat yogurt for cream, cream cheese, mayonnaise, or sour cream in recipes; on baked potatoes, tacos, and salads; and in dips.

---

higher total energy, total fat, and saturated fat intake than those who eat fast food infrequently.[22] And although many fast food restaurants have eliminated *trans* fatty acids from their menus, McDonald's still has a few items, such as desserts and shakes, that contain *trans* fatty acids. The following are some specific strategies for improving the amount and type of fat in your menu choices.

Be Aware of Fat Replacers

One way to lower the fat content of foods such as chips, muffins, cakes, and cookies is by replacing the fat in a food with a *fat replacer*. Snack foods have been the primary target for fat replacers because it is more difficult to eliminate the fat from these types of products without dramatically changing the taste. In the mid-1990s, the food industry and nutritionists thought that fat replacers would be the answer to our growing obesity problem. They reasoned that, if we substitute fat replacers for some of the traditional fats in snack and fast foods, we might be able to reduce both energy and fat intake and help Americans manage their weight better.

Products such as olestra (brand name Olean) hit the market in 1996 with a lot of fanfare, but the hype was short-lived. Initially, foods containing olestra had to bear a label warning of potential gastrointestinal side effects. In 2003, the FDA announced that this warning was no longer necessary, as research showed that olestra causes only mild, infrequent discomfort. However, even with the new labeling, only a limited number of foods in the marketplace contain olestra. It is also evident from our growing obesity problem that fat replacers, such as olestra, do not help Americans lose weight or even maintain their current weight.

RECAP Visible fats are those foods that can be easily recognized as containing fat. Hidden fats are those fats added to our food during the manufacturing or cooking process, so we are not aware of how much fat has been added. By making simple substitutions when shopping and eating out, you can reduce the quantity of saturated and *trans* fatty acids in your diet and increase your intake of healthful fats. Fat replacers are substances used to replace the typical fats found in foods.

What Role Do Fats Play in Chronic Disease?

There appears to be a generally held assumption that if you eat fat-free or low-fat foods you will lose weight and prevent chronic diseases. Certainly, we know that diets high in saturated and *trans* fatty acids can contribute to chronic diseases, including heart disease and cancer; however, as we have explored in this chapter, unsaturated fatty acids do not have this negative effect and some are essential to good health. Thus, a sensible health goal is to eat the appropriate amounts and types of fat.

The chronic disease most closely associated with diets high in saturated and *trans* fats is cardiovascular disease. This complex disorder is discussed **In Depth** following this chapter. In addition, high-fat diets have been linked to cancer. Is such a link supported by evidence?

Cancer develops as a result of a poorly understood interaction between the environment and genetic factors. In addition, most cancers take years to develop, so examining the impact of diet on cancer development can be a long and difficult process. Nevertheless, research does suggest that diet is one of several important environmental factors that influence the development of cancer.[23, 24]

Of the many dietary factors that have been studied, the influence of dietary fat intake on the development of cancer has been extensively researched. The relationship between type and amount of fat consumed and increased risk for breast cancer is controversial.[25, 26] Early research suggested an association between animal fat intake and increased risk for colon cancer, but more recent research indicates that the association involves factors other than fat that are found in red meat. Because we now know that physical activity can reduce the risk for colon cancer, earlier diet and colon cancer studies that did not control for this factor are now being questioned. The strongest association between dietary fat intake and cancer is for prostate cancer. Research shows that there is a consistent link between prostate cancer risk and consumption of animal fat, but not fat from plant sources. The exact mechanism by which animal fats may contribute to prostate cancer has not yet been identified.

Eating Right All Day

Breakfast
Non-fat yogurt with walnuts instead of bacon and eggs!

Shutterstock

Lunch
Veggie pita instead of a ham and cheese sandwich!

iStockphoto/Thinkstock

Dinner
Grilled salmon instead of steak!

Jacek Chabraszewski/Shutterstock

Snack
Whole-grain crackers with peanut butter instead of potato chips!

Scott Karcich/Dreamstime

QUICK TIPS

Limiting Fat When You're Eating Out

✓ Find eating establishments that allow you to order alternatives to the usual menu items. For instance, if you like burgers, look for a restaurant that will grill your burger instead of frying it and will let you substitute a salad for french fries.

✓ Ask about the types of fats used in salad dressing, baked goods, and cooking processes. Many establishments are working to replace *trans* fatty acids with healthful fats in their menu items. If you have a favorite restaurant that you visit frequently, make sure you know the kinds of fats they use in their products.

✓ Select healthful appetizers, such as salads, broth-based soups, vegetables, or fruit, over white bread with butter, nachos, or fried foods such as chicken wings.

✓ Select broth-based soups, which are lower in fat and Calories than cream-based soups, which are typically made with cream, cheese, and/or butter.

✓ Ask that all visible fat be trimmed from meats and that poultry be served without the skin.

✓ Select menu items that use cooking methods that add little or no additional fat, such as broiling, grilling, steaming, and sautéing. Be alert to menu descriptions such as *fried, crispy, creamed, buttered, au gratin, escalloped,* and *parmesan.* Also avoid foods served in sauces such as butter sauce, alfredo, and hollandaise. All of these types of food preparation typically add more fat to a meal.

✓ Avoid meat and vegetable pot pies, quiches, and other items with a pastry crust, as these may be high in *trans* fats.

✓ Ask for spreads and condiments, such as butter, salad dressings, sauces, and sour cream, to be served on the side instead of added in the kitchen.

✓ Request low-fat spreads on your sandwiches, such as mustards or chutneys, over full-fat mayonnaise or butter.

✓ Substitute a salad, veggies, or fruit for the chips or french fries that come with the meal.

✓ Select lower-fat desserts, such as sorbet or a small cookie, over full-fat ice cream or a brownie. Alternatively, share a full-fat dessert with friends or family members, which will reduce both the Calories and fat you consume.

✓ Keep counting at your favorite cafe! Consider that a Starbucks tall cafe latte (12 oz) made with whole milk contains 200 kcal and 11 g of fat (7 g from saturated fat). Whipped cream can add 80–130 kcal and 8–12 g of fat. The same drink made with non-fat milk and no whipped cream contains 120 kcal and no fat. So ask for your coffee, hot chocolate, tea, or chai with nonfat milk and eliminate the whipped cream.

✓ Select lower-fat options to accompany your coffee drink. For example, choose a biscotti or a small piece of dark chocolate instead of a croissant, a scone, a muffin, coffee cake or a large cookie.

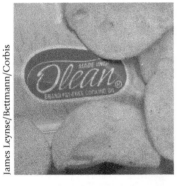

James Leynse/Bettmann/Corbis

⬤ Snack foods have been the primary target for fat replacers, such as Olean, since it is more difficult to eliminate the fat from these types of foods without dramatically changing the taste.

RECAP The types of fats we eat can significantly affect our health and risk for disease. Diets high in saturated and *trans* fatty acids increase our risk for heart disease. Selecting appropriate types of fat in the diet may also reduce your risk for some cancers, especially prostate cancer.

Nutrition DEBATE

Fat Blockers—Help or Hype?

In the last thirty years, the rate of obesity has steadily increased among Americans. And growing right alongside our waistlines is the market for weight-loss supplements. It's a multibillion-dollar industry, with new products continually tempting us with promises of quick, effortless, and dramatic results. Currently, there's no regulation of weight-loss supplements, so consumers have no way of knowing if the product they're considering is effective, or safe.

One popular group of weight-loss supplements are the so-called fat blockers. Do these products really "block" fat? Can they really help you lose weight?

What Are the Claims?

One way to reduce energy intake and body weight would be to block the absorption of energy-containing macronutrients—such as fat, which contains 9 kcals/gram. If we could block fat absorption, then we could eat large portions of our favorite high-fat foods, including fast foods, snacks, and desserts, without worrying about gaining weight. Fat blockers are said to decrease the amount of fat absorbed in the small intestine, leaving more to be excreted from the body.

The main ingredient in many of these supplements is chitosan, a nondigestible substance extracted mainly from the exoskeletons of marine crustaceans.[27] Chitosan is said to bind up to four to six times its weight in fat. Thus, for every gram of chitosan consumed, 4–6 g of fat should be "blocked." If this were true, then consuming 3 g of chitosan a day would block 12–18 g of fat a day, or 108–162 kcal/day. Chitosan is also thought to block the absorption of bile acids. (Recall that bile is delivered to the small intestine to emulsify fats.) If bile absorption is blocked, then the liver must produce new supplies. Since

Alex Potemkin/iStockphoto

the liver takes cholesterol from the blood to make bile, fat blockers might reduce serum cholesterol as well.[27]

It all sounds good, but is there any evidence that fat blockers work? Let's review the research.

What Does the Research Say?

Chitosan has been studied extensively as a weight-loss aid. Two recent meta-analyses reviewing the efficacy of chitosan for weight loss from fourteen double-blind randomized controlled trials (RCT) involving over 1,000 participants concluded that there is some limited evidence that chitosan reduces body weight in humans.[28, 29, 30] The authors found that chitosan produced a small, but significant, greater average weight loss (1.7 kg, or 3.7 lb) over an average of 8.6 weeks compared to the placebo group (the group with no supplements). In considering these results, ask yourself, is such a small weight loss what you would expect from a weight-loss supplement?

In another study, researchers reported a slightly greater weight loss.[31] Overweight adults taking 3 grams of chitosan per day experienced a weight loss of 2.8 kg (6 pounds) in 8 weeks compared to the placebo group that gained weight (+0.8 kg, or +1.8 lb). However, participants were not consuming a controlled diet, but were only

asked to record their food intake and physical activity. The average weight loss of less than a pound a week was still meager, but many people struggling with obesity might consider it significant—especially if, as indicated in this study, chitosan could help prevent further weight gain over time.

To learn more about the specific effects of chitosan, researchers at the University of California at Davis[32] studied its fat-trapping capacity in college students. They fed twelve men and twelve women a controlled diet for 4 days, followed by the same diet plus chitosan for 4 days. Fecal samples were collected to determine the amount of fat trapped by chitosan. They found that, with the control diet plus chitosan, fecal fat excretion increased by 1.8 g/day (16 kcal/day) for the men and 0.0 g/day for the women. They concluded that the amount of fat trapped by chitosan was clinically insignificant and that 7 weeks of supplementation (at 2.5 g/day) would be required for a 1-pound weight loss.

Are There Any Side Effects?

The most common side effects experienced by individuals using chitosan are gastrointestinal distress and flatulence. Also, some product formulations contain ingredients such as caffeine, herbs, and other substances that may cause problems in some people. Because chitosan is derived from shellfish, individuals who are allergic to shellfish should not use these products.

You Be the Judge

A quick Internet search reveals that chitosan-containing products range widely in price from five to forty dollars or more for a one-month supply. Would you want to try this product to prevent weight gain? How much is a potential weight loss of less than a pound a week worth to you?

Chapter Review

Test Yourself ANSWERS

1. True. Although eating too much fat, or too much of unhealthful fats (such as saturated and *trans* fatty acids), can increase our risk for diseases such as cardiovascular disease and obesity, some fats are essential to good health. We need to consume a certain minimum amount to provide adequate levels of essential fatty acids and fat-soluble vitamins.

2. True. Fat is our primary source of energy, both at rest and during low- and moderate-intensity exercise. Fat is also an important fuel source during prolonged exercise. During periods of high-intensity exercise, carbohydrate becomes the dominant fuel source.

3. False. Even foods fried in vegetable shortening can be unhealthful because they are higher in *trans* fatty acids. In addition, fried foods are high in fat and energy and can contribute to overweight and obesity.

Find the Quack

Like everyone else in his family, Luiz is overweight. In addition, both of Luiz's parents take prescription medications to manage their high blood pressure, and his paternal grandfather died at age 42 from a heart attack. Understandably, Luiz is concerned about his own risk for cardiovascular disease. On this morning's news broadcast, the health segment discusses the Dr. Dean Ornish Diet. It is supposed to be designed specifically for people at risk for cardiovascular disease. Luiz learns that the diet consists of the following:

* "Abundant consumption of legumes, fruits, vegetables, and whole grains"
* "Moderate consumption of nonfat dairy products and nonfat or very-low-fat processed foods (such as nonfat yogurt bars, very-low-fat frozen dinners, and so on)"
* "Avoidance of all of the following: meats, oils, oil-containing products (such as margarines and salad dressings), avocados, nuts, seeds, alcohol, and sugars (including honey, molasses, and high-fructose corn syrup)"
* "Adding 30 minutes a day of moderate physical activity or three 1-hour sessions per week"

The TV health segment states that the Dr. Dean Ornish Diet has been proven in clinical studies to reduce the risk factors for cardiovascular disease.

1. Compare the Dr. Dean Ornish Diet to the USDA Food Guide. What are the main similarities? What are the main differences you see?

2. Comment on the level of essential fatty acids the Dr. Dean Ornish Diet provides.

3. Based on the diet's recommendations, how much total fat do you think this diet provides?

4. Do you think the Dr. Dean Ornish Diet is a quack diet or a legitimate diet? If legitimate, do you think it is advisable for someone with a family history of cardiovascular disease, such as Luiz? Why or why not?

Answers can be found on the companion website, at www.pearsonhighered.com/thompsonmanore.

 **NutriTools** Check out the companion website at www.pearsonhighered.com/thompsonmanore, or use MyNutritionLab.com, to access interactive animations, including:

* Know Your Fat Sources
* Digestion and Absorption: Lipids

Review Questions

1. Omega-3 fatty acids are
   a. a form of *trans* fatty acid.
   b. metabolized in the body to arachidonic acid.
   c. synthesized in the liver and small intestine.
   d. found in leafy green vegetables, flaxseeds, soy milk, and fish.

2. One of the most sensible ways to reduce body fat is to
   a. limit intake of fat to less than 15% of total energy consumed.
   b. exercise regularly.
   c. avoid all consumption of *trans* fatty acids.
   d. restrict total Calories to 1,200 per day.

3. Fats in chylomicrons are taken up by cells with the help of
   a. lipoprotein lipase.
   b. micelles.
   c. sterols.
   d. pancreatic enzymes.

4. The risk for heart disease is increased in people who
   a. consume a diet high in saturated fats.
   b. consume a diet high in *trans* fats.
   c. consume a diet high in animal fats.
   d. all of the above.

5. Triglycerides with a double bond at one part of the molecule are referred to as
   a. monounsaturated fats.
   b. hydrogenated fats.
   c. saturated fats.
   d. sterols.

6. True or false? The Acceptable Macronutrient Distribution Range (AMDR) for fat is 20–35% of total energy.

7. True or false? During exercise, fat cannot be mobilized from adipose tissue for use as energy.

8. True or false? Triglycerides are the same as fatty acids.

9. True or false? *Trans* fatty acids are produced by food manufacturers; they do not occur in nature.

10. True or false? A serving of food labeled *reduced fat* has at least 25% less fat and 25% fewer Calories than a full-fat version of the same food.

Answers to Review Questions can be found at the back of this text, and additional essay questions and answers are located on the companion website at www.pearsonhighered.com/ thompsonmanore.

Web Resources

www.americanheart.org
American Heart Association

Learn the best way to help lower your blood cholesterol level. Access the AHA's online cookbook for healthy-heart recipes and cooking methods.

www.caloriecontrol.org
Calorie Control Council

Go to this site to find out more about fat replacers.

www.nhlbi.nih.gov/chd
Live Healthier, Live Longer

Take a cholesterol quiz, and test your heart disease IQ. Create a diet using the Heart Healthy Diet or the TLC Diet online software.

www.nhlbi.nih.gov
National Heart, Lung, and Blood Institute

Learn how a healthful diet can lower your cholesterol levels. Use the online risk assessment tool to estimate your 10-year risk of having a heart attack.

www.nih.gov
The National Institutes of Health (NIH), U.S. Department of Health and Human Services

Search this site to learn more about dietary fats.

www.nlm.nih.gov/medlineplus
MEDLINE Plus Health Information

Search for "fats" or "lipids" to obtain additional resources and the latest news on dietary lipids, heart diseases, and cholesterol.

www.hsph.harvard.edu/nutritionsource
The Nutrition Source: Knowledge for Healthy Eating Harvard School of Public Health

Go to this site, and click on "Fats & Cholesterol" to find out how selective fat intake can be part of a healthful diet.

www.ific.org
International Food Information Council Foundation

Access this site to find out more about fats and dietary fat replacers.

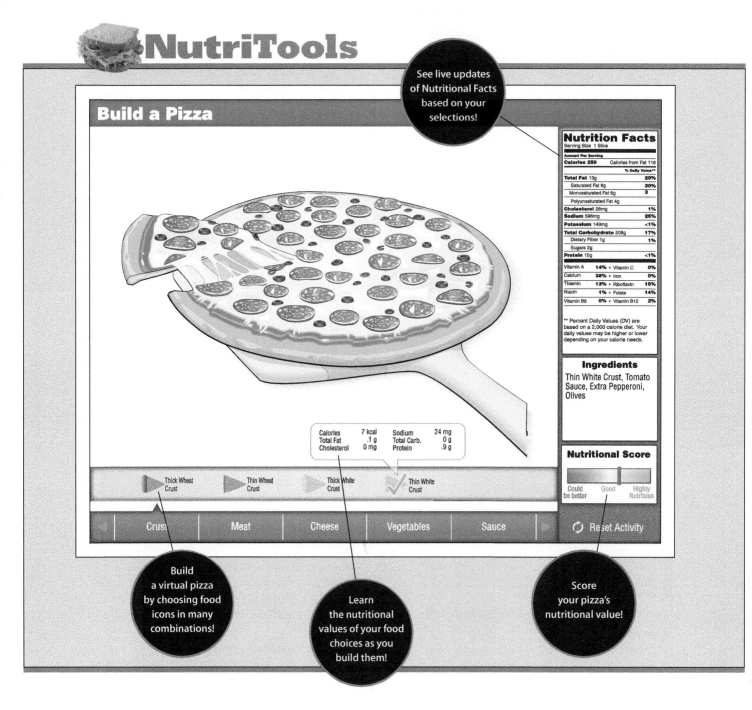

NutriTools

Build a Pizza

See live updates of Nutritional Facts based on your selections!

Nutrition Facts
Serving Size 1 Slice

Amount Per Serving		
Calories 250	Calories from Fat 116	
		% Daily Value
Total Fat 13g		**20%**
Saturated Fat 6g		**30%**
Monosaturated Fat 6g		**2**
Polyunsaturated Fat 4g		
Cholesterol 28mg		**1%**
Sodium 596mg		**25%**
Potassium 149mg		**<1%**
Total Carbohydrate 208g		**17%**
Dietary Fiber 1g		**1%**
Sugars 2g		
Protein 15g		**<1%**

Vitamin A	**14%**	Vitamin C	**0%**
Calcium	**38%**	Iron	**0%**
Thiamin	**13%**	Riboflavin	**15%**
Niacin	**1%**	Folate	**14%**
Vitamin B6	**0%**	Vitamin B12	**2%**

** Percent Daily Values (DV) are based on a 2,000 calorie diet. Your daily values may be higher or lower depending on your calorie needs.

Ingredients
Thin White Crust, Tomato Sauce, Extra Pepperoni, Olives

Calories	7 kcal	Sodium	24 mg
Total Fat	.1 g	Total Carb.	0 g
Cholesterol	0 mg	Protein	.9 g

Nutritional Score

Could be better — Good — Highly Nutritous

Thick Wheat Crust   Thin Wheat Crust   Thick White Crust   Thin White Crust

Crust | Meat | Cheese | Vegetables | Sauce | Reset Activity

Build a virtual pizza by choosing food icons in many combinations!

Learn the nutritional values of your food choices as you build them!

Score your pizza's nutritional value!

To build your pizza, just visit www.pearsonhighered.com/thompsonmanore or www.mynutritionlab.com

After building your pizza, you should be able to answer these questions:

1. How would you know if your pizza is "junk food" or a nutritious meal?
2. What toppings could you add to your pizza to make it highly nutritious?
3. In what ways is whole wheat crust better than white crust?
4. How can you build a lowfat, nutritious pizza that also tastes good?
5. Which sauce and topping combinations can give you the best nutritional score?

References

1. Champe, P. C., R. A. Harvey, and D. R. Ferrier. 2008. Lippincott's Illustrated Reviews: Biochemistry. 4th ed. Philadelphia: Lippincott Williams & Wilkins.
2. Lichtenstein A. H., L. J. Appel, M. Brands, M. Carnethon, S. Daniels, H. A. Franch, B. Franklin, P. Kris-Ethergon, W. S. Harris, B. Howard, N. Karanja, M. Lefevre, L. Rudel, F. Sancks, L. Van Horn, M. Winston, and J. Wylie-Rosett. 2006. Diet and lifestyle recommendations revision 2006: A scientific statement from the American Heart Association Nutrition Committee. *Circulation* 114:82–96.
3. Smith, C., A. D. Marks, and M. Lieberman. 2005. Mark's Basic Medical Biochemistry: A Clinical Approach. 2nd ed. Philadelphia: Lippincott Williams & Wilkins.
4. Wijendran, V., and K. C. Hayes. 2004. Dietary n-6 and n-3 fatty acid balance and cardiovascular health. *Annu. Rev. Nutr.* 24:597–615.
5. Din, J. N., D. E. Newby, and A. D. Flapan. 2004. Omega 3 fatty acids and cardiovascular disease—fishing for a natural treatment. *British Med. J.* 328(3):30–35.
6. Jebb, S. A., A. M. Prentice, G. R. Goldberg, P. R. Murgatroyd, A. E. Black, and W. A. Coward. 1996. Changes in macronutrient balance during over- and underfeeding assessed by 12-d continuous whole-body calorimetry. *Am. J. Clin. Nutr.* 64:259–266.
7. Institute of Medicine, Food and Nutrition Board. 2002. Dietary Reference Intakes for Energy, Carbohydrate, Fiber, Fat, Fatty Acids, Cholesterol, Protein, and Amino Acids (Macronutrients). Washington, DC: National Academies Press.
8. USDA, What we eat in America. Agricultural Research Service (ARS), 2009. http://www.ars.usdagov/research/projects/projects.htm?ACCN_NO=415257.
9. Jonnalagadda S. S. Jones J. M. 2005. Position of the American Dietetic Association: Fat Replacers. *J Am Diet Assoc.* 205:266–275.
10. Briefel, R. R., and C. L. Johnson. 2004. Secular trends in dietary intake in the United States. *Annu. Rev. Nutr.* 24:401–431.
11. Cialdella-Kam L. C., Manore M. M. 2009. Macronutrient requirements of active individuals: An Update. *Nutrition Today.* 44(3):104–111.
12. Rodriguez N. R., DiMarco N. M., Langley S. 2009. Postiion of the American Dietetic Association, Dietitians of Canada, and the American College of Sports Medicine: Nutrition and Athletic Performance. *J. Am. Diet. Assoc.* 109:509–527.
13. Lichtenstein, A. H., and L. Van Horn. 1998. Very low fat diets. *Circulation* 98:935–939.
14. Calloway, C. W. 1998. The role of fat-modified foods in the American diet. *Nutr. Today* 33:156–163.
15. Sigman-Grant, M. 1997. Can you have your low-fat cake and eat it too? The role of fat-modified products. *J. Am. Diet. Assoc.* 97(suppl.):S76–S81.
16. Expert Panel on Detection, Evaluation, and Treatment of High Blood Cholesterol in Adults, National Institutes of Health. 2001. Executive summary of the Third Report of the National Cholesterol Education Program (NCEP) Expert Panel on Detection, Evaluation, and Treatment of High Blood Cholesterol in Adults (Adult Treatment Panel III). *JAMA* 285(19):2486–2509.
17. USDA, Weighing in on Fats. Agricultural Research Service (ARS), 2008. http://www.ars.usda.gov/is/AR/archive/mar08/fats0308.htm.
18. Ratnayake W. M. N., M. R. L. L'Abee, S. Farnworth, L. Dumais, C. Gagnon, B. Lampi, V. Casey, D. Mohottalage, I. Rondeau, and L. Underhill. Trans fatty acids: Current contents in Canadian food and estimated intake levels for the Canadian population. *J AOAC International.* 92(5):1258–1276.
19. Teegala S. M., W. C. Willett, and D. Mazaffarian. 2009. Consumption and health effects of Trans fatty acids: a review. *J. AOAC International.* 92(5):1250–1257.
20. Mozaffarian, D., M. B. Katan, A. Ascherio, M. J. Stampher, and W. C. Willet. 2006. Trans fatty acids and cardiovascular disease. *N. Engl. J. Med.* 354(15):1601–1613.
21. New York Department of Health and Mental Hygiene, Board of Health. 2006. Notice of Adoption of an Amendment (81.08) to Article 81 of the New York City Health Code to Restrict the Service of Products Containing Artificial Trans Fats at All Food Service Establishments. December 5, 2006. www.nyc.gov/html/doh/downloads/pdf/public/notice-adoption-hc-art81-08.pdf.
22. Sabastian R., C. Enns, J. Goldman, and A. Moshfegh. 2008. Effect of fast food consumption on dietary intake and likelood of meeting MyPyramid recommendations in adults: Results from What We Eat in America, NHANES 2003–04. *FASEB Journal* 22:868.7.
23. Kim, Y. I. 2001. Nutrition and cancer. In: Bowman, B. A., and R. M. Russell, eds. Present Knowledge in Nutrition, 8th edn. Washington, DC: International Life Sciences Institute Press.
24. Kris-Etherton, P. M., and S. Innis. 2007. Position of the American Dietetic Association and Dietitians of Canada: Dietary fatty acid. *J. Am. Diet. Assoc.* 107:1599–1611.
25. Willett, W. C. 1999. Diet, nutrition and the prevention of cancer. In: Shils, M. E., J. A. Olsen, M. Shike, and A. C. Ross, eds. Modern Nutrition in Health and Disease, 9th edn. Baltimore: Williams & Wilkins.
26. Prentice, R. L., C. Bette, R. Chlebowski, et al. 2006. Low-fat dietary patterns and risk of invasive breast cancer. The Women's Health Initiative Randomized Controlled Dietary Modification Trial. *JAMA* 295:629–642.
27. Ormrod D. J., C. C. Holmes, and T. E. Miller. 1998. Dietary chitosan inhibits hypercholesterolaemia and atherogenesis in the apolipoprotein E-deficient mouse model of atherosclerosis. *Atherosclerosis.* 138(2):329–334.
28. Mhurchu C. N., C. Dunshea-Mooij, D. Bennet, and A. Rodgers. 2005a. Effect of chitosan on weight loss in overweight and obese individuals: a systemic review of randomized control trials. *Obesity Rev* 6:35–42.
29. Mhurchu C. N., C. A. Dunshea-Mooij, D. Bennett, and A. Rodgers. 2005b. Chitosan for overweight or obesity. Cochrane database of systematic reviews (Online) (Cochrane Database Syst Rev) 2005(3): CD003892. 2005b.
30. Pittler M. H., and E. Ernst. 2004 Dietary supplements for body-weight reduction: a systematic review. *Am. J. Clin. Nutr.* 79(4):529–536.
31. Kaats G. R., J. E. Michalek, and H. G. Preuss. 2006. Evaluating efficacy of a chitosan product using a double-blinded, placebo-controlled protocol. *J. Am. Coll. Nutr.* 25(5):389–394.
32. Gades M. D., and J. S. Stern. 2005. Chitosan supplementation and fat absorption in men and women. *J. Am. Diet. Assoc.* 105:72–77.

Answers to Review Questions

Answers to Review Questions 11-15 (essay questions) for this chapter are located on the Companion Website at **www.pearsonhighered.com/thompsonmanore**

1. **d.** found in leafy green vegetables, flax seeds, soy milk, and fish.
2. **b.** exercise regularly.
3. **a.** lipoprotein lipase.
4. **d.** all of the above.
5. **a.** monounsaturated fats.
6. True.
7. False. Fat is an important source of energy during rest and during exercise, and adipose tissue is our primary storage site for fat. We rely significantly on the fat stored in our adipose tissue to provide energy during rest and exercise.
8. False. A triglyceride is a lipid comprised of a glycerol molecule and three fatty acids. Thus, fatty acids are a component of triglycerides.
9. False. While most trans fatty acids result from the hydrogenation of vegetable oils by food manufacturers, a small amount of trans fatty acids are found in cow's milk.
10. False. A serving of food labeled reduced fat has at least 25% less fat than a standard serving, but may not have fewer calories than a full-fat version of the same food.

Proteins: Crucial Components of All Body Tissues

From Chapter 6 of *Nutrition: An Applied Approach*, Third Edition. Janice Thompson, Melinda Manore. Copyright © 2012 by Pearson Education, Inc. Published by Pearson Benjamin Cummings. All rights reserved.

Proteins: Crucial Components of All Body Tissues

CHAPTER OBJECTIVES

After reading this chapter you will be able to:

1. Describe how proteins differ from carbohydrates and fats.

2. Identify non-meat food combinations that are complete protein sources.

3. Describe four functions of proteins in our bodies.

4. Discuss how proteins are digested, absorbed, and synthesized by our bodies.

5. Calculate your recommended daily allowance for protein.

6. List five foods that are good sources of protein.

7. Identify the potential health risks associated with high-protein diets.

8. Describe two disorders related to inadequate protein intake.

Melissa Mai Yee Lo/iStockphoto

Test Yourself

1. (T) (F) Protein is a primary source of energy for our bodies.

2. (T) (F) Vegetarian diets are inadequate in protein.

3. (T) (F) Most people in the United States consume more protein than they need.

Test Yourself answers can be found at the end of the chapter.

W

hat do professional skateboarder Forrest Kirby, Olympic figure skating champion Surya Bonaly, wrestler "Killer" Kowalski, and hundreds of other athletes have in common? They're all vegetarians! Olympic track icon Carl Lewis states: "I've found that a person does not need protein from meat to be a successful athlete. In fact, my best year of track competition was the first year I ate a vegan diet."[1] Although precise statistics on the number of vegetarian American athletes aren't available, a total of 3% of the U.S. population—approximately 6 to 8 million American adults—are estimated to be vegetarians.[2]

What is a protein, and what makes it so different from carbohydrates and fats? How much protein do you really need, and do you get enough in your daily diet? What exactly is a vegetarian, anyway? Do you qualify? If so, how do you plan your diet to include sufficient protein, especially if you play competitive sports? Are there real advantages to eating meat, or is plant protein just as good?

It seems as if everybody has an opinion about protein, both how much you should consume and from what sources. In this chapter, we'll address these and other questions to clarify the importance of protein in the diet and dispel common myths about this crucial nutrient.

What Are Proteins?

Proteins are large, complex molecules found in the cells of all living things. Although proteins are best known as a part of our muscle mass, they are, in fact, critical components of all the tissues of the human body, including bones, blood, and skin. Proteins also function in metabolism, immunity, fluid balance, and nutrient transport, and they can provide energy in certain circumstances. The functions of proteins will be discussed in detail later in this chapter.

How Do Proteins Differ from Carbohydrates and Lipids?

Proteins are one of the three macronutrients. Like carbohydrates and lipids, proteins are found in a wide variety of foods; plus, the human body is able to synthesize them. But unlike carbohydrates and lipids, proteins are made according to instructions provided by our genetic material, or DNA. We'll explore how DNA dictates the structure of proteins shortly.

Another key difference between proteins and the other macronutrients lies in their chemical makeup. In addition to the carbon, hydrogen, and oxygen also found in carbohydrates and lipids, proteins contain a special form of nitrogen that our bodies can readily use. Our bodies are able to break down the proteins in foods and utilize the nitrogen for many important processes. Carbohydrates and lipids do not provide nitrogen.

The Building Blocks of Proteins Are Amino Acids

The proteins in our bodies are made from a combination of building blocks called **amino acids,** molecules composed of a central carbon atom connected to four other groups: an amine group, an acid group, a hydrogen atom, and a side chain **(Figure 1a)**. The word *amine* means nitrogen-containing, and nitrogen is indeed the essential component of the amine portion of the molecule.

As shown in Figure 1b, the portion of the amino acid that makes each unique is its side chain. The amine group, acid group, and carbon and hydrogen atoms do not vary. Variations in the structure of the side chain give each amino acid its distinct properties.

The singular term *protein* is misleading, as there are potentially an infinite number of unique types of proteins in living organisms. Most of the proteins in our bodies are made from combinations of just twenty amino acids, identified in **Table 1**. By

Proteins are an integral part of our body tissues, including our muscle tissue.
Shutterstock

proteins Large, complex molecules made up of amino acids and found as essential components of all living cells.

amino acids Nitrogen-containing molecules that combine to form proteins.

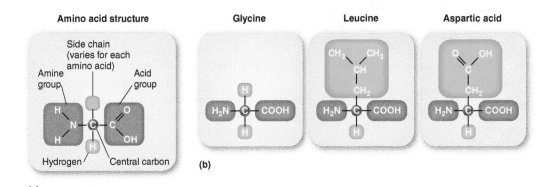

(b)

(a)

Figure 1   Structure of an amino acid. **(a)** All amino acids contain five parts: a central carbon atom, an amine group around the atom that contains nitrogen, an acid group, a hydrogen atom, and a side chain. **(b)** Only the side chain differs for each of the twenty amino acids, giving each its unique properties.

combining a few dozen to more than 300 copies of these twenty amino acids in various sequences, our bodies form an estimated 10,000 to 50,000 unique proteins. Two of the twenty amino acids listed in Table 1, cysteine and methionine, are unique in that, in addition to the components present in the other amino acids, they contain sulfur.

We Must Obtain Essential Amino Acids from Food

Of the twenty amino acids in our bodies, nine are classified as essential. This does not mean that they are more important than the others. Instead, an **essential amino acid** is one that our bodies cannot produce at all or cannot produce in sufficient quantities to meet our physiologic needs. Thus, we must obtain essential amino acids from our food. Without the proper amount of essential amino acids in our bodies, we lose our ability to make the proteins and other nitrogen-containing compounds we need.

The Body Can Make Nonessential Amino Acids

Nonessential amino acids are just as important to our bodies as essential amino acids, but our bodies can make them in sufficient quantities, so we do not need to consume them in our diet. We make nonessential amino acids by transferring the amine group from an essential amino acid to a different acid group and side chain. This process is called **transamination,** and it is shown in **Figure 2.** The acid groups and side chains can be donated by amino acids, or they can be made from the breakdown products of carbohydrates and fats. Thus, by combining parts of different amino acids, the nonessential amino acids can be made.

Under some conditions, a nonessential amino acid can become an essential amino acid. In this case, the amino acid is called a *conditionally essential amino acid.* Consider what occurs in the disease known as phenylketonuria (PKU). Someone with PKU cannot metabolize phenylalanine (an essential amino acid). Normally, the body uses phenylalanine to produce the nonessential amino acid tyrosine, so the inability to metabolize phenylalanine results in failure to make tyrosine. If PKU is not diagnosed immediately after birth, it results in irreversible brain damage. In this situation, tyrosine becomes a conditionally essential amino acid that must be provided by the diet. Other conditionally essential amino acids include arginine, cysteine, and glutamine.

RECAP Proteins are critical components of all the tissues of the human body. Like carbohydrates and lipids, they contain carbon, hydrogen, and oxygen. Unlike the other macronutrients, they also contain nitrogen and some contain sulfur, and their structure is dictated by DNA. The building blocks of proteins are amino acids. The amine group of the amino acid contains nitrogen. The portion of the amino acid that changes, giving each amino acid its distinct identity, is the side chain. The body cannot make essential amino acids, so we must obtain them from our diet. Our bodies can make nonessential amino acids from parts of other amino acids, carbohydrates, and fats.

TABLE 1 Amino Acids of the Human Body	
Essential Amino Acids	**Nonessential Amino Acids**
These amino acids must be consumed in the diet.	*These amino acids can be manufactured by the body.*
Histidine	Alanine
Isoleucine	Arginine
Leucine	Asparagine
Lysine	Aspartic acid
Methionine	Cysteine
Phenylalanine	Glutamic acid
Threonine	Glutamine
Tryptophan	Glycine
Valine	Proline
	Serine
	Tyrosine

essential amino acids Amino acids not produced by the body that must be obtained from food.

nonessential amino acids Amino acids that can be manufactured by the body in sufficient quantities and therefore do not need to be consumed regularly in our diet.

transamination The process of transferring the amine group from one amino acid to another in order to manufacture a new amino acid.

Figure 2 Transamination. Our bodies can make nonessential amino acids by transferring the amine group from an essential amino acid to a different acid group and side chain.

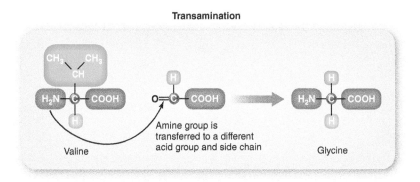

Transamination

Amine group is transferred to a different acid group and side chain

Valine

Glycine

How Are Proteins Made?

As we have stated, our bodies can synthesize proteins by selecting the needed amino acids from the pool of all amino acids available at any given time. Let's look more closely at how this occurs.

Amino Acids Bond to Form a Variety of Peptides

Figure 3 shows that, when two amino acids join together, the amine group of one binds to the acid group of another in a unique type of chemical bond called a **peptide bond.** In the process, a molecule of water is released as a by-product.

Two amino acids joined together form a *dipeptide,* and three amino acids joined together are called a *tripeptide.* The term *oligopeptide* is used to identify a string of four to nine amino acids, while a *polypeptide* is ten or more amino acids bonded together. As a polypeptide chain grows longer, it begins to fold into any of a variety of complex shapes that give proteins their sophisticated structure.

Genes Regulate Amino Acid Binding

Each of us is unique because we inherited a specific genetic "code" that integrates the code from each of our parents. Each person's genetic code dictates minor differences in amino acid sequences, which in turn lead to differences in our bodies' individual proteins. These differences in proteins result in the unique physical and physiologic characteristics each one of us possesses.

As mentioned earlier, DNA dictates the structure of each protein our bodies synthesize. **Figure 4** shows how this process occurs. Cells use segments of DNA called *genes* as templates for assembling—or *expressing*—particular proteins. Thus, this process is referred to as **gene expression.** Since proteins are manufactured at the site of ribosomes in the cytoplasm, and DNA never leaves the nucleus, a special molecule is needed to copy, or transcribe, the information from DNA and carry it to the ribosome. This is the job of *messenger RNA* (*messenger ribonucleic acid,* or *mRNA*); during **transcription,** mRNA copies the genetic information from DNA in the nucleus and carries it to the ribosomes in the cytoplasm. Once this genetic information is at the ribosome, **translation** occurs: genetic information from the mRNA is translated into a growing chain of amino acids that are bonded together to make a specific protein.

Although the DNA for making every protein in our bodies is contained within each cell nucleus, not all genes are expressed and each cell does not make every type of protein. For example, each cell contains the DNA to manufacture the hormone insulin. However, only the cells of the pancreas express the insulin gene; that is, they are the only cells that produce insulin. Our physiologic needs alter gene expression, as do various nutrients. For instance, a cut in the skin that causes bleeding leads to the production of various proteins that clot the blood. If we consume more dietary iron than we need, the gene for ferritin (a protein that stores iron) is expressed, so

peptide bonds Unique types of chemical bonds in which the amine group of one amino acid binds to the acid group of another in order to manufacture dipeptides and all larger peptide molecules.

gene expression The process of using a gene to make a protein.

transcription The process through which messenger RNA copies genetic information from DNA in the nucleus.

translation The process that occurs when the genetic information carried by messenger RNA is translated into a chain of amino acids at the ribosome.

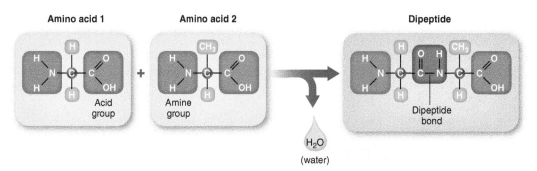

▲ **Figure 3** Amino acid bonding. Two amino acids join together to form a dipeptide. By combining multiple amino acids, proteins are made.

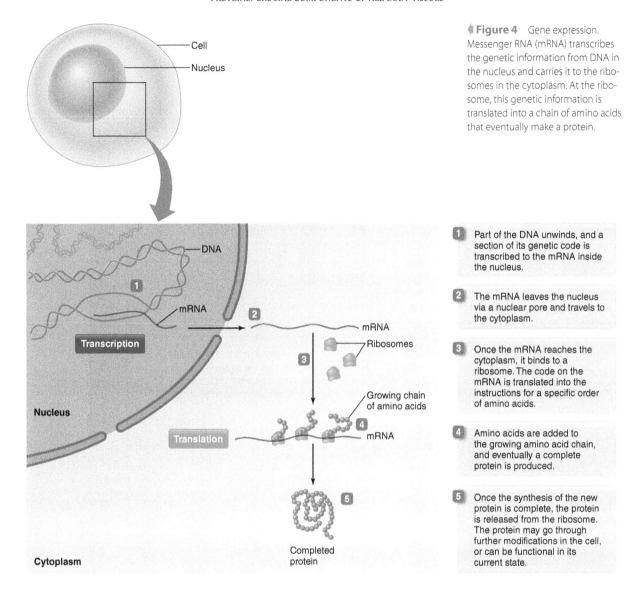

◀ Figure 4 Gene expression. Messenger RNA (mRNA) transcribes the genetic information from DNA in the nucleus and carries it to the ribosomes in the cytoplasm. At the ribosome, this genetic information is translated into a chain of amino acids that eventually make a protein.

1 Part of the DNA unwinds, and a section of its genetic code is transcribed to the mRNA inside the nucleus.

2 The mRNA leaves the nucleus via a nuclear pore and travels to the cytoplasm.

3 Once the mRNA reaches the cytoplasm, it binds to a ribosome. The code on the mRNA is translated into the instructions for a specific order of amino acids.

4 Amino acids are added to the growing amino acid chain, and eventually a complete protein is produced.

5 Once the synthesis of the new protein is complete, the protein is released from the ribosome. The protein may go through further modifications in the cell, or can be functional in its current state.

that we can store this excess iron. Our genetic makeup and how appropriately we express our genes are important factors in our health.

Protein Turnover Involves Synthesis and Degradation

Our bodies constantly require new proteins to function properly. *Protein turnover* involves both the synthesis of new proteins and the degradation of existing proteins to provide the building blocks for those new proteins (**Figure 5**). This process allows the cells to respond to the constantly changing demands of physiologic functions. For instance, skin cells live for only about 30 days and must continually be replaced. The amino acids needed to produce these new skin cells can be obtained from the body's *amino acid pool,* which includes those amino acids we consume in our diet as well as those that are released from the breakdown of other cells in our bodies. The body's pool of amino acids is used to produce not only new amino acids but also other products, including glucose and fat.

165

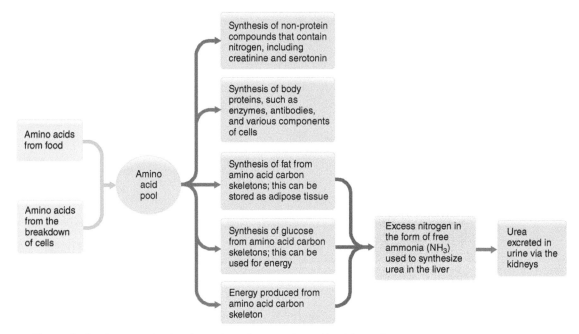

Figure 5 Protein turnover involves the synthesis of new proteins and breakdown of existing proteins to provide building blocks for new proteins. Amino acids are drawn from the body's amino acid pool and can be used to build proteins, fat, glucose, and non-protein nitrogen-containing compounds. Urea is produced as a waste product from any excess nitrogen, which is then excreted by the kidneys.

Nicholas Rjabow/iStockphoto

Stiffening egg whites denatures some of the proteins within them.

denaturation The process by which proteins uncoil and lose their shape and function when they are exposed to heat, acids, bases, heavy metals, alcohol, and other damaging substances.

Protein Organization Determines Function

Four levels of protein structure have been identified (Figure 6). The sequential order of the amino acids in a protein is called the *primary structure* of the protein. The different amino acids in a polypeptide chain possess unique chemical characteristics that cause the chain to twist and turn into a characteristic spiral shape, referred to as the protein's *secondary structure*. The stability of the secondary structure is achieved through the bonding of hydrogen atoms or sulfur atoms; these bonds create a bridge between two protein strands or two parts of the same strand of protein. The spiral of the secondary structure further folds into a unique three-dimensional shape, referred to as the protein's *tertiary structure;* this structure is critically important because it determines each protein's function in the body. Often, two or more separate polypeptides bond to form an even larger protein with a *quaternary structure,* which may be *globular* or *fibrous*.

The importance of the shape of a protein to its function cannot be overemphasized. For example, the protein strands in muscle fibers are much longer than they are wide (see Figure 6d). This structure plays an essential role in enabling muscle contraction and relaxation. In contrast, the proteins that form red blood cells are globular in shape, and they result in the red blood cells being shaped like flattened discs with depressed centers, similar to a miniature doughnut (Figure 7). This structure and the flexibility of the proteins in the red blood cells permit them to change shape and flow freely through even the tiniest capillaries to deliver oxygen and still return to their original shape.

Proteins can uncoil and lose their shape when they are exposed to heat, acids, bases, heavy metals, alcohol, and other damaging substances. The term used to describe this change in the shape of proteins is **denaturation.** Everyday examples of protein denaturation that we can see are the stiffening of egg whites when they are

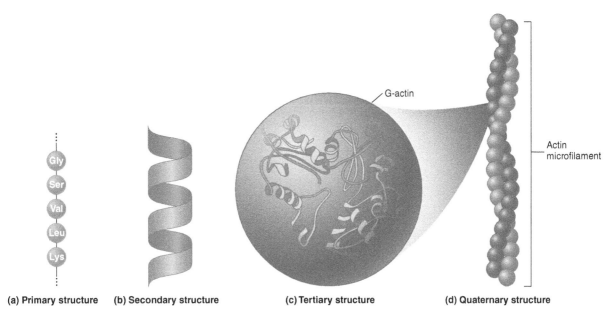

(a) Primary structure   (b) Secondary structure   (c) Tertiary structure   (d) Quaternary structure

Figure 6 Levels of protein structure. **(a)** The primary structure of a protein is the sequential order of amino acids. **(b)** The secondary structure of a protein is the folding of the amino acid chain. **(c)** The tertiary structure is a further folding that results in the three-dimensional shape of the protein. **(d)** The quaternary structure of a protein refers to molecules containing two or more polypeptides that bond to form a larger protein, such as the actin molecule illustrated here. In this figure, strands of actin molecules intertwine to form contractile elements involved in generating muscle contractions.

whipped, the curdling of milk when lemon juice or another acid is added, and the solidifying of eggs as they cook.

Denaturation does not affect the primary structure of proteins. However, when a protein is denatured, its function is lost. For instance, denaturation of a critical enzyme on exposure to heat or acidity is harmful, because it prevents the enzyme from doing its job. This type of denaturation can occur during times of high fever or when the level of acid in the blood is out of the normal range. In some cases, denaturation

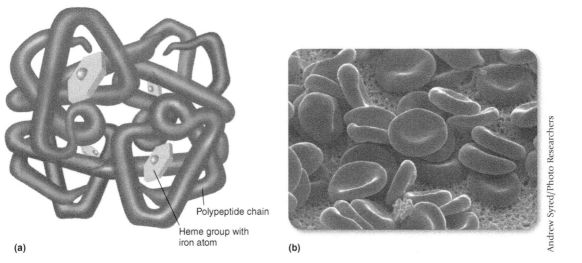

Figure 7 Protein shape determines function. **(a)** Hemoglobin, the protein that forms red blood cells, is globular in shape. **(b)** The globular shape of hemoglobin results in red blood cells being shaped like flattened discs.

is helpful. For instance, denaturation of proteins during the digestive process allows for their breakdown into amino acids and the absorption of these amino acids from the digestive tract into the bloodstream.

RECAP Amino acids bind together to form proteins. Genes regulate the amino acid sequence, and thus the structure, of all proteins. The shape of a protein determines its function. When a protein is denatured by damaging substances, such as heat and acids, it loses its shape and its function.

Protein Synthesis Can Be Limited by Missing Amino Acids

For protein synthesis to occur, all essential amino acids must be available to the cell. If this is not the case, the amino acid that is missing or in the smallest supply is called the **limiting amino acid.** Without the proper combination and quantity of essential amino acids, protein synthesis slows to the point at which proteins cannot be generated. For instance, the protein hemoglobin contains the essential amino acid histidine. If we do not consume enough histidine, it becomes the limiting amino acid in hemoglobin production. As no other amino acid can be substituted, our bodies become unable to make adequate hemoglobin, and we lose the ability to transport oxygen to our cells.

Inadequate energy consumption also limits protein synthesis. If there is not enough energy available from our diets, our bodies will use any accessible proteins for energy, thus preventing them from being used to build new proteins.

A protein that does not contain all of the essential amino acids in sufficient quantities to support growth and health is called an **incomplete** (*low-quality*) **protein.** Proteins that have all nine of the essential amino acids are considered **complete** (*high-quality*) **proteins.** The most complete protein sources are foods derived from animals and include egg whites, meat, poultry, fish, and milk. Soybeans are the most complete source of plant protein. In general, the typical American diet is very high in complete proteins, as we eat proteins from a variety of food sources.

Protein Synthesis Can Be Enhanced by Mutual Supplementation

Many people believe that we must consume meat or dairy products to obtain complete proteins. Not true! Consider a meal of beans and rice. Beans are low in the amino acids methionine and cysteine but have adequate amounts of isoleucine and lysine. Rice is low in isoleucine and lysine but contains sufficient methionine and cysteine. By combining beans and rice, we create a complete protein.

Mutual supplementation is the process of combining two or more incomplete protein sources to make a complete protein. The two foods involved are called complementary foods; these foods provide **complementary proteins (Figure 8),** which, when combined, provide all nine essential amino acids.

It is not necessary to eat complementary proteins at the same meal. Recall that we maintain a free pool of amino acids in the blood; these amino acids come from food and sloughed-off cells. When we eat one complementary protein, its amino acids join those in the free amino acid pool. These free amino acids can then combine to synthesize complete proteins. However, it is wise to eat complementary-protein foods during the same day, as partially completed proteins cannot be stored and saved for a later time. Mutual supplementation is important for people eating a vegetarian diet, particularly if they consume no animal products whatsoever.

RECAP When a particular amino acid is limiting, protein synthesis cannot occur. A complete protein provides all nine essential amino acids. Mutual supplementation combines two complementary-protein sources to make a complete protein.

limiting amino acid The essential amino acid that is missing or in the smallest supply in the amino acid pool and is thus responsible for slowing or halting protein synthesis.

incomplete proteins Foods that do not contain all of the essential amino acids in sufficient amounts to support growth and health.

complete proteins Foods that contain all nine essential amino acids.

mutual supplementation The process of combining two or more incomplete protein sources to make a complete protein.

complementary proteins Two or more foods that together contain all nine essential amino acids necessary for a complete protein. It is not necessary to eat complementary proteins at the same meal.

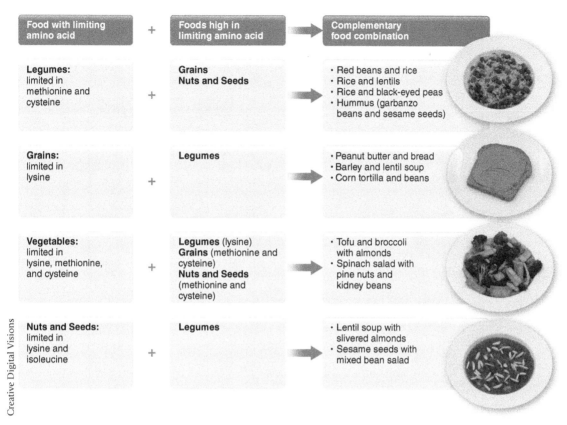

Food with limiting amino acid	+	Foods high in limiting amino acid	→	Complementary food combination
Legumes: limited in methionine and cysteine	+	**Grains** **Nuts and Seeds**		• Red beans and rice • Rice and lentils • Rice and black-eyed peas • Hummus (garbanzo beans and sesame seeds)
Grains: limited in lysine	+	**Legumes**		• Peanut butter and bread • Barley and lentil soup • Corn tortilla and beans
Vegetables: limited in lysine, methionine, and cysteine	+	**Legumes** (lysine) **Grains** (methionine and cysteine) **Nuts and Seeds** (methionine and cysteine)		• Tofu and broccoli with almonds • Spinach salad with pine nuts and kidney beans
Nuts and Seeds: limited in lysine and isoleucine	+	**Legumes**		• Lentil soup with slivered almonds • Sesame seeds with mixed bean salad

Creative Digital Visions

◄ **Figure 8** Complementary food combinations.

Why Do We Need Proteins?

The functions of proteins in the body are so numerous that only a few can be described in detail in this chapter. Note that proteins function most effectively when we also consume adequate amounts of energy as carbohydrates and fat. When there is not enough energy available, the body uses proteins as an energy source, limiting their availability for the functions described in this section.

Proteins Contribute to Cell Growth, Repair, and Maintenance

The proteins in our bodies are dynamic, meaning that they are constantly being broken down, repaired, and replaced. When proteins are broken down, many amino acids are recycled into new proteins. Think about all of the new proteins that are needed to allow an infant to develop and grow into a mature adult.

Even in adulthood, our cells are constantly turning over, as damaged or worn-out cells are broken down and their components are used to create new cells. Our red blood cells live for only 3 to 4 months and then are replaced by new cells that are produced in bone marrow. The cells lining our intestinal tract are replaced every 3 to 6 days. The "old" intestinal cells are treated just like the proteins in food; they are digested and the amino acids absorbed back into the body. The constant turnover of proteins from our diet is essential for such cell growth, repair, and maintenance.

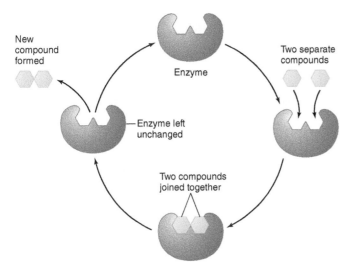

◆ Figure 9 Proteins act as enzymes. Enzymes facilitate chemical reactions, such as joining two compounds together.

Proteins Act as Enzymes and Hormones

Enzymes are compounds, usually proteins, that speed up chemical reactions, without being changed by the chemical reaction themselves. Enzymes can bind substances together or break them apart and can transform one substance into another. **Figure 9** shows how an enzyme can bind two substances together.

Each cell contains thousands of enzymes that facilitate specific cellular reactions. For example, the enzyme phosphofructokinase (PFK) is critical to driving the rate at which we break down glucose and use it for energy during exercise. Without PFK, we would be unable to generate energy at a fast enough rate to allow us to be physically active.

Hormones are substances that act as chemical messengers in the body. Some hormones are made from amino acids, whereas others are made from lipids. Hormones are stored in various glands in the body, which release them in response to changes in the body's environment. They then act on the body's organs and tissues to restore the body to normal conditions. Insulin, a hormone made from amino acids, acts on cell membranes to facilitate the transport of glucose into cells. Other examples of amino acid–containing hormones are glucagon, which responds to conditions of low blood glucose, and thyroid hormone, which helps control our resting metabolic rate.

Proteins Help Maintain Fluid and Electrolyte Balance

Electrolytes are electrically charged particles that assist in maintaining fluid balance. For our bodies to function properly, fluids and electrolytes must be maintained at healthy levels inside and outside cells and within blood vessels. Proteins attract fluids, and the proteins that are in the bloodstream, in the cells, and in the spaces surrounding the cells work together to keep fluids moving across these spaces in the proper quantities to maintain fluid balance and blood pressure. When protein intake is deficient, the concentration of proteins in the bloodstream is insufficient to draw fluid from the tissues and across the blood vessel walls; fluid then collects in the tissues, causing **edema** (Figure 10). In addition to being uncomfortable, edema can lead to serious medical problems.

Sodium (Na^+) and potassium (K^+) are examples of common electrolytes. Under normal conditions, Na^+ is more concentrated outside the cell, and K^+ is more concentrated inside the cell. This proper balance of Na^+ and K^+ is accomplished by the action of **transport proteins** located within the cell membrane. **Figure 11** shows how these transport proteins work to pump Na^+ outside and K^+ inside of the cell. The conduction of nerve signals and contraction of muscles depend on a proper balance of electrolytes. If protein intake is deficient, we lose our ability to maintain these functions, resulting in potentially fatal changes in the rhythm of the heart. Other consequences of chronically low protein intakes include muscle weakness and spasms, kidney failure, and, if conditions are severe enough, death.

Proteins Help Maintain Acid–Base Balance

The body's cellular processes result in the constant production of acids and bases. These substances are transported in the blood to be excreted through the kidneys and the lungs. The human body maintains very tight control over the **pH,** or the

edema A disorder in which fluids build up in the tissue spaces of the body, causing fluid imbalances and a swollen appearance.

transport proteins Protein molecules that help transport substances throughout the body and across cell membranes.

pH Stands for percentage of hydrogen. It is a measure of the acidity—or level of hydrogen—of any solution, including human blood.

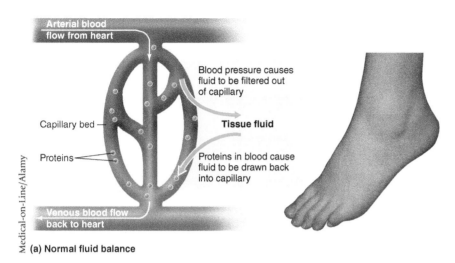

(a) Normal fluid balance

Arterial blood flow from heart

Blood pressure causes fluid to be filtered out of capillary

Tissue fluid

Proteins in blood cause fluid to be drawn back into capillary

Capillary bed

Proteins

Venous blood flow back to heart

Medical-on-Line/Alamy

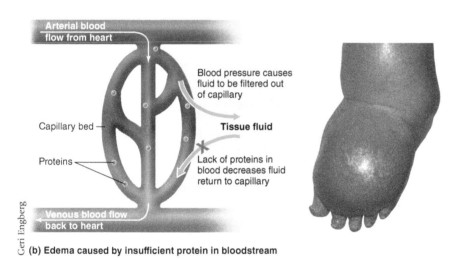

(b) Edema caused by insufficient protein in bloodstream

Arterial blood flow from heart

Blood pressure causes fluid to be filtered out of capillary

Tissue fluid

Lack of proteins in blood decreases fluid return to capillary

Capillary bed

Proteins

Venous blood flow back to heart

Geri Engberg

Figure 10 The role of proteins in maintaining fluid balance. The heartbeat exerts pressure that continually pushes fluids in the bloodstream through the arterial walls and out into the tissue spaces. By the time blood reaches the veins, the pressure of the heartbeat has greatly decreased. In this environment, proteins in the blood are able to draw fluids out of the tissues and back into the bloodstream. **(a)** This healthy (non-swollen) tissue suggests that body fluids in the bloodstream and in the tissue spaces are in balance. **(b)** When the level of proteins in the blood is insufficient to draw fluids out of the tissues, edema can result. This foot with edema is swollen due to fluid imbalance.

acid–base balance, of the blood. The body goes into a state called **acidosis** when the blood becomes too acidic. **Alkalosis** results if the blood becomes too basic (alkaline). Both acidosis and alkalosis can be caused by respiratory or metabolic problems. Acidosis and alkalosis can cause coma and death by denaturing body proteins.

Proteins are excellent **buffers,** meaning that they help maintain proper acid–base balance. Acids contain hydrogen ions, which are positively charged. The side chains of proteins have negative charges that attract the hydrogen ions and neutralize their detrimental effects on the body. Proteins can release the hydrogen ions when the blood becomes too basic. By buffering acids and bases, proteins maintain acid–base balance and blood pH.

Proteins Help Maintain a Strong Immune System

Antibodies are special proteins that are critical components of the immune system. When a foreign substance attacks the body, the immune system produces antibodies to defend against it. Bacteria, viruses, toxins, and allergens (substances that cause allergic reactions) are examples of antigens that can trigger antibody production. (An *antigen* is any substance—but typically a protein—that our bodies recognize as foreign and that triggers an immune response.)

acidosis A disorder in which the blood becomes acidic; that is, the level of hydrogen in the blood is excessive. It can be caused by respiratory or metabolic problems.

alkalosis A disorder in which the blood becomes basic; that is, the level of hydrogen in the blood is deficient. It can be caused by respiratory or metabolic problems.

buffers Proteins that help maintain proper acid–base balance by attaching to, or releasing, hydrogen ions as conditions change in the body.

antibodies Defensive proteins of the immune system. Their production is prompted by the presence of bacteria, viruses, toxins, allergens, and so on.

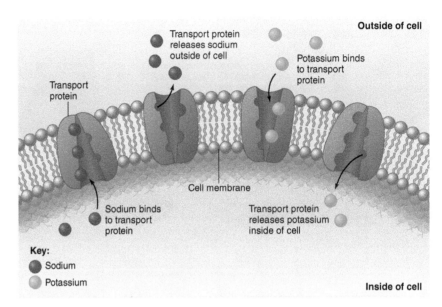

Figure 11 Transport proteins help maintain electrolyte balance. Transport proteins in the cell membrane pick up potassium and sodium and transport them across the cell membrane.

Each antibody is designed to destroy one specific invader. When that substance invades the body, antibodies are produced to attack and destroy the specific antigen. Once antibodies have been made, the body "remembers" this process and can respond more quickly the next time that particular invader appears. *Immunity* refers to the development of the molecular memory to produce antibodies quickly upon subsequent invasions.

Adequate protein is necessary to support the increased production of antibodies that occurs in response to a cold, the flu, or an allergic reaction. If we do not consume enough protein, our resistance to illnesses and disease is weakened. On the other hand, eating more protein than we need does not improve immune function.

Proteins Serve as an Energy Source

The body's primary energy sources are carbohydrate and fat. Remember that both carbohydrate and fat have specialized storage forms that can be used for energy—glycogen for carbohydrate and triglycerides for fat. Proteins do not have a specialized storage form for energy. This means that, when proteins need to be used for energy, they are taken from the blood and body tissues, such as the liver and skeletal muscle. In healthy people, proteins contribute very little to energy needs. Because we are efficient at recycling amino acids, protein needs are relatively low as compared to needs for carbohydrate and fat.

To use proteins for energy, the liver removes the amine group from the amino acids in a process called **deamination.** The nitrogen bonds with hydrogen, creating ammonia, which is quickly converted to *urea*. The urea is then transported to the kidneys, where it is excreted in the urine. The remaining fragments of the amino acid contain carbon, hydrogen, and oxygen. The body can use these fragments to generate energy or to build carbohydrates. Certain amino acids can be converted into glucose via gluconeogenesis. This is a critical process during times of low carbohydrate intake or starvation. Fat cannot be converted into glucose, but body proteins can be broken down and converted into glucose to provide needed energy to the brain.

To protect the proteins in our body tissues, it is important that we regularly eat an adequate amount of carbohydrate and fat to provide energy. We also need to con-

deamination The process by which an amine group is removed from an amino acid. The nitrogen is then transported to the kidneys for excretion in the urine, while the carbon and other components are metabolized for energy or used to make other compounds.

sume enough dietary protein to perform the required work without using up the proteins that already are playing an active role in our bodies. Unfortunately, our bodies cannot store excess dietary protein. As a consequence, eating too much protein results in the removal and excretion of the nitrogen in the urine and the use of the remaining components for energy. Any remaining components not used for energy can be converted and stored as body fat.

RECAP Proteins serve many important functions, including (1) enabling the growth, repair, and maintenance of body tissues; (2) acting as enzymes and hormones; (3) maintaining fluid and electrolyte balance; (4) maintaining acid–base balance; (5) making antibodies, which strengthen our immune system; and (6) providing energy when carbohydrate and fat intake are inadequate. Proteins function best when we also consume adequate amounts of carbohydrate and fat.

How Do Our Bodies Break Down Proteins?

Our bodies do not directly use proteins from the diet to make the proteins we need. Dietary proteins are first digested and broken into smaller particles, such as amino acids, dipeptides, and tripeptides, so that they can be absorbed and transported to the cells. In this section, we will review how proteins are digested and absorbed. As you read about each step in this process, refer to **Figure 12** for a visual tour through the digestive system.

Stomach Acids and Enzymes Break Proteins into Short Polypeptides

Virtually no enzymatic digestion of proteins occurs in the mouth. As shown in step 1 in Figure 12, proteins in food are chewed, crushed, and moistened with saliva to ease swallowing and to increase the surface area of the protein for more efficient digestion. There is no further digestive action on proteins in the mouth.

When proteins reach the stomach, *hydrochloric acid* denatures the protein strands (Figure 12, step 2). It also converts the inactive enzyme *pepsinogen* into its active form, **pepsin.** Although pepsin is itself a protein, it is not denatured by the acid in the stomach because it has evolved to work optimally in an acidic environment. The hormone *gastrin* controls both the production of hydrochloric acid and the release of pepsin; thinking about food or actually chewing food stimulates the gastrin-producing cells located in the stomach. Pepsin begins breaking proteins into single amino acids and shorter polypeptides; these amino acids and polypeptides then travel to the small intestine for further digestion and absorption.

Enzymes in the Small Intestine Break Polypeptides into Single Amino Acids

As the polypeptides reach the small intestine, the pancreas and the small intestine secrete enzymes that digest them into oligopeptides, tripeptides, dipeptides, and single amino acids (Figure 12, step 3). The enzymes that digest proteins in the small intestine are called **proteases.**

The cells in the wall of the small intestine then absorb the single amino acids, dipeptides, and tripeptides. Enzymes in the intestinal cells break the dipeptides and tripeptides into single amino acids. The amino acids are then transported via the portal vein into the liver. Once in the liver, amino acids may be converted to glucose or fat, combined to build new proteins, used for energy, or released into the bloodstream and transported to other cells as needed (Figure 12, step 4).

pepsin An enzyme in the stomach that begins the breakdown of proteins into shorter polypeptide chains and single amino acids.

proteases Enzymes that continue the breakdown of polypeptides in the small intestine.

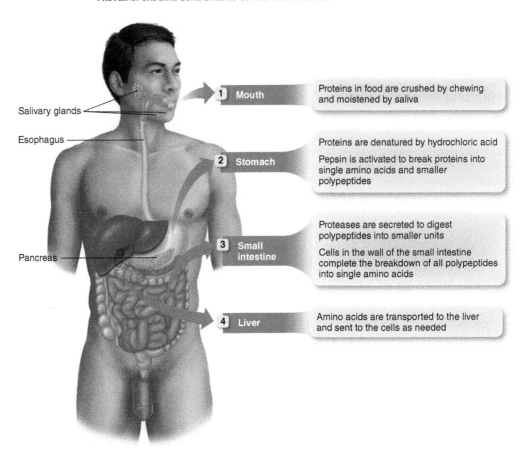

1. **Mouth** — Proteins in food are crushed by chewing and moistened by saliva

2. **Stomach** — Proteins are denatured by hydrochloric acid

Pepsin is activated to break proteins into single amino acids and smaller polypeptides

3. **Small intestine** — Proteases are secreted to digest polypeptides into smaller units

Cells in the wall of the small intestine complete the breakdown of all polypeptides into single amino acids

4. **Liver** — Amino acids are transported to the liver and sent to the cells as needed

Salivary glands

Esophagus

Pancreas

Figure 12 The process of protein digestion.

Ian O'Leary/Dorling Kindersley

 Meats are highly digestible sources of dietary protein.

The cells of the small intestine have different sites that specialize in transporting certain types of amino acids, dipeptides, and tripeptides. This fact has implications for users of amino acid supplements. When very large doses of single amino acids are taken on an empty stomach, they typically compete for the same absorption sites. This competition can block the absorption of other amino acids, causing an imbalance of amino acids and leading to various amino acid deficiencies. Some people believe that this is why it is not beneficial to consume individual amino acid supplements. In reality, people rarely take very large doses of single amino acids on an empty stomach. The primary reason people should not take single amino acids is that the amount taken is usually so small that they don't have any beneficial effect.

Protein Digestibility Affects Protein Quality

Earlier in this chapter, we discussed how various protein sources differ in quality of protein. The quantity of essential amino acids in a protein determines its quality: higher-protein-quality foods are those that contain more of the essential amino acids in sufficient quantities needed to build proteins, and lower-quality-protein foods contain fewer essential amino acids. Another factor in protein quality is *digestibility,* or how well our bodies can digest a protein. Animal protein sources, such as meat and dairy products, are highly digestible, as are many soy products; we can absorb more than 90% of the amino acids in these protein sources. Legumes are also highly digestible (about 70% to 80%). Grains and many vegetable proteins are less digestible, ranging from 60% to 90%.

RECAP In the stomach, hydrochloric acid denatures proteins and converts pepsinogen to pepsin; pepsin breaks proteins into smaller polypeptides and individual amino acids. In the small intestine, proteases break polypeptides into smaller fragments and single amino acids. The cells in the wall of the small intestine break the smaller peptide fragments into single amino acids, which are then transported to the liver for distribution to our cells. Protein digestibility as well as provision of essential amino acids influence protein quality.

How Much Protein Should We Eat?

Consuming adequate protein is a major concern of many people. In fact, one of the most common concerns among active people and athletes is that their diets are deficient in protein (see the Nutrition Myth or Fact? box below for a discussion of this topic). This concern about dietary protein is generally unnecessary, as we can easily consume the protein our bodies need by eating an adequate and varied diet.

Nitrogen Balance Is a Method Used to Determine Protein Needs

A highly specialized *nitrogen balance* procedure is used to determine a person's protein needs. Nitrogen is excreted through the body's processes of recycling or using proteins; thus, the balance can be used to estimate whether protein intake is adequate to meet protein needs.

Typically performed only in experimental laboratories, the nitrogen balance procedure involves measuring both nitrogen intake and nitrogen excretion over a 2-week

NUTRITION MYTH OR FACT?
Do Athletes Need More Protein than Inactive People?

At one time, it was believed that the Recommended Dietary Allowance (RDA) for protein, which is 0.8 g per kg body weight, was sufficient for both inactive people and athletes. Recent studies, however, show that athletes' protein needs are higher.

Why do athletes need more protein? Regular exercise increases the transport of oxygen to body tissues, requiring changes in the oxygen-carrying capacity of the blood. To carry more oxygen, we need to produce more of the protein that carries oxygen in the blood (i.e., hemoglobin). During intense exercise, we use a small amount of protein directly for energy. We also use protein to make glucose to maintain adequate blood glucose levels and to prevent hypoglycemia (low blood sugar) during exercise. Regular exercise stimulates tissue growth and causes tissue damage, which must be repaired by additional proteins. Strength athletes (such as bodybuilders and weightlifters) need 1.8 to 2 times more protein than

➥ Some athletes who persistently diet are at risk for low protein intake.
AP Photos

the current RDA, and endurance athletes (such as distance runners and triathletes) need 1.5 to 1.75 times more protein than the current RDA. Later in this chapter, we will calculate the protein needs for inactive and active people.

If you're active, does this mean you should add more protein to your diet? Not necessarily. Contrary to popular belief, most Americans, including inactive people *and* athletes, already consume more than twice the RDA for protein. For healthy individuals, evidence does not support eating more than two times the RDA for protein to increase strength, build muscle, or improve athletic performance. In fact, eating more protein as food or supplements or taking individual amino acid supplements does not cause muscles to become bigger or stronger. Only regular strength training can achieve these goals. By eating a balanced diet and consuming a variety of foods, both inactive and active people can easily meet their protein requirements.

period. A standardized diet, the nitrogen content of which has been measured and recorded, is fed to the study participant. The person is required to consume all of the foods provided. Because the majority of nitrogen is excreted in the urine and feces, laboratory technicians directly measure the nitrogen content of the subject's urine and fecal samples. Small amounts of nitrogen are excreted in the skin, hair, and body fluids such as mucus and semen, but, because of the complexity of collecting nitrogen excreted via these routes, the measurements are estimated. Then, technicians add the estimated nitrogen losses to the nitrogen measured in the subject's urine and feces. Nitrogen balance is then calculated as the difference between nitrogen intake and nitrogen excretion.

People who consume more nitrogen than is excreted are considered to be in positive nitrogen balance (Figure 13). This state indicates that the body is retaining or

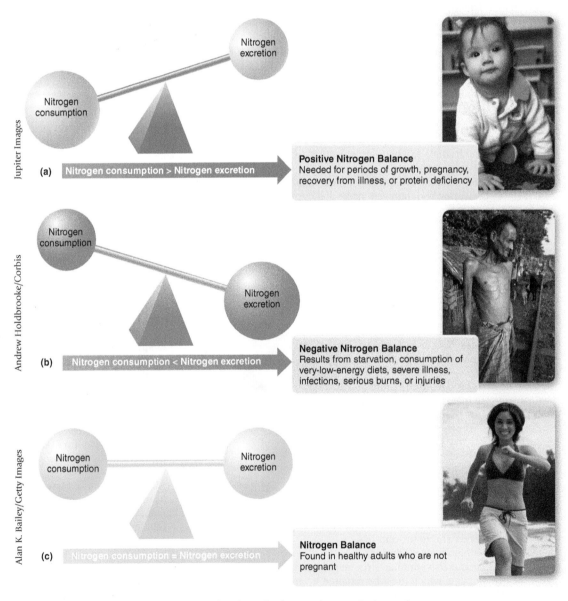

Figure 13 Nitrogen balance describes the relationship between how much nitrogen (or protein) we consume and excrete each day. **(a)** Positive nitrogen balance occurs when nitrogen consumption is greater than excretion. **(b)** Negative nitrogen balance occurs when nitrogen consumption is less than excretion. **(c)** Nitrogen balance is maintained when nitrogen consumption equals excretion.

adding protein, and it occurs during periods of growth, pregnancy, or recovery from illness or a protein deficiency. People who excrete more nitrogen than they consume are in negative nitrogen balance. This situation indicates that the body is losing protein, and it occurs during starvation or when people are consuming very-low-energy diets. This is because, when energy intake is too low to meet energy demands over a prolonged period of time, the body metabolizes body proteins for energy. The nitrogen from these proteins is excreted in the urine and feces. Negative nitrogen balance also occurs during severe illness, infections, high fever, serious burns, or injuries that cause significant blood loss. People in these situations require increased dietary protein. A person is in nitrogen balance when nitrogen intake equals nitrogen excretion. This indicates that protein intake is sufficient to cover protein needs. Healthy adults who are not pregnant are in nitrogen balance.

TABLE 2	Recommended Protein Intakes
Group	Protein Intake (grams per kilogram* body weight per day)
Most adults[†]	0.8
Nonvegetarian endurance athletes[‡]	1.2 to 1.4
Nonvegetarian strength athletes[‡]	1.2 to 1.7
Vegetarian endurance athletes[‡]	1.3 to 1.5
Vegetarian strength athletes[‡]	1.3 to 1.8

*To convert body weight to kilograms, divide weight in pounds by 2.2.
Weight (lb)/2.2 = Weight (kg)
Weight (kg) × protein recommendation (g/kg body weight/day) = protein intake (g/day)
†Data from Food and Nutrition Board, Institute of Medicine. 2002. *Dietary Reference Intakes for Energy, Carbohydrate, Fiber, Fat, Fatty Acids, Cholesterol, Protein, and Amino Acids (Macronutrients)*, pp. 465–608. Washington, DC: National Academies Press.
‡Data from American College of Sports Medicine, American Dietetic Association, and Dietitians of Canada. 2009. Joint Position Statement. Nutrition and athletic performance. *Med. Sci. Sports Exerc.* 41(3):709–731.

Recommended Dietary Allowance for Protein

How much protein should we eat? The RDA for sedentary people is 0.8 g per kg body weight per day. The recommended percentage of energy that should come from protein is 10% to 35% of total energy intake. Protein needs are higher for children, adolescents, and pregnant/lactating women because more protein is needed during times of growth and development. Protein needs can also be higher for active people and for vegetarians.

Table 2 lists the daily recommendations for protein for a variety of lifestyles. How can we convert this recommendation into total grams of protein for the day? In the You Do the Math box, let's calculate Theo's RDA for protein.

Is it possible for Theo to eat this much protein each day? It may surprise you to discover that most Americans eat 1.5 to 2 times the RDA for protein without any effort!

YOU DO THE MATH
Calculating Your Protein Needs

Theo wants to know how much protein he needs each day. During the off-season, he works out three times a week at a gym and practices basketball with friends every Friday night. He is not a vegetarian. Although Theo exercises regularly, he does not qualify as an endurance athlete or as a strength athlete. At this level of physical activity, Theo's RDA for protein probably ranges from the RDA of 0.8 up to 1.0 g per kg body weight per day. To calculate the total number of grams of protein Theo should eat each day:

1. Convert Theo's weight from pounds to kilograms. Theo presently weighs 200 pounds. To convert this value to kilograms, divide by 2.2:

    200 pounds ÷ 2.2 pounds/kg = 91 kg

2. Multiply Theo's weight in kilograms by his RDA for protein:

    91 kg × 0.8 g/kg = 72.8 grams of protein per day

    91 kg × 1.0 g/kg = 91 grams of protein per day

What happens during basketball season, when Theo practices or has games 5 or 6 days a week? This will probably raise his protein needs to approximately 1.0 to 1.2 g per kg body weight per day. How much more protein should he eat?

    91 kg × 1.2 g/kg = 109.2 grams of protein per day

Now calculate your recommended protein intake based on your activity level.

Most Americans Meet or Exceed the RDA for Protein

Surveys indicate that Americans eat 15–17% of their total daily energy intake as protein.[3-5] In these studies, women reported eating about 65 to 70 g of protein each day, whereas men consumed 88 to 110 g per day. Putting these values into perspective, let's assume that the average man weighs 75 kg (165 pounds) and the average woman weighs 65 kg (143 pounds). Their protein requirements (assuming they are not athletes or vegetarians) are 60 g and 52 g per day, respectively. As you can see, most adults in the United States appear to have no problems meeting their protein needs each day.

What are the typical protein intakes of active people? Research indicates that the self-reported intake of athletes participating in a variety of sports can well exceed current recommendations.[6] For instance, the protein intake for some female distance runners is 1.2 g per kg of body weight per day, accounting for 15% of their total daily energy intake. In addition, some male bodybuilders consume 3 g per kg of body weight per day, accounting for almost 38% of their total daily intake! However, there are certain groups of athletes who are at risk for low protein intakes. Athletes who consume inadequate energy and limit food choices, such as some distance runners, figure skaters, female gymnasts, and wrestlers who are dieting, are all at risk for low protein intakes. Unlike people who consume adequate energy, individuals who are restricting their total energy intake (kilocalories) need to pay close attention to their protein intake.

Protein: Much More Than Meat!

Table 3 compares the protein content of a variety of foods. Although some people think that the only good sources of protein are meats (beef, pork, poultry, seafood), many other foods are rich in proteins. These include dairy products (milk, cheese, yogurt, etc.), eggs, legumes (including soy products), whole grains, and nuts. Fruits and many vegetables are not particularly high in protein; however, these foods provide fiber and many vitamins and minerals and are excellent sources of carbohydrates. Thus, eating them can help provide the carbohydrates and energy you need, so that your body can use proteins for building and maintaining tissues.

After reviewing Table 3, you might be wondering how much protein you typically eat. See the What About You? feature box to find out.

Amino Acid Supplements: Necessity or Waste?

"Amino acid supplements—you can't gain without them!" This is just one of the headlines found in bodybuilding magazines and Internet sites touting amino acid supplements as the key to achieving power, strength, and performance "perfection." Many athletes who read these claims believe that taking amino acid supplements will boost their energy during performance, replace proteins metabolized for energy during exercise, enhance muscle growth and strength, and hasten recovery from intense training or injury. Should you believe the hype?

As noted earlier in this chapter, we use very little protein for energy during exercise, and most Americans already consume more than twice the RDA for protein. Consuming adequate energy and up to two times the RDA for protein in the diet is more than enough to support either strength or endurance exercise training and performance. What about the claims related to muscle-building? Although some research has shown that intravenous infusions of various amino acids in the laboratory can stimulate certain hormones that enhance the building of muscle, there is little evidence that taking individual amino acids or protein supplements orally can build muscle or improve strength.[6] Since these supplements are relatively expensive, getting enough protein via your diet alone will put a lot less strain on your wallet!

TABLE 3	Protein Content of Commonly Consumed Foods				
Food	Serving Size	Protein (g)	Food	Serving Size	Protein (g)
Beef:			*Beans:*		
Ground, lean, baked (15% fat)	3 oz	22	Refried	1/2 cup	7
Prime rib, broiled (1/8-in. fat)	3 oz	18	Kidney, red	1/2 cup	7.7
Top sirloin, broiled (1/8-in. fat)	3 oz	23	Black	1/2 cup	7
Poultry:			*Nuts:*		
Chicken breast, broiled, no skin (bone removed)	1/2 breast	29	Peanuts, dry roasted	1 oz	6.7
Chicken thigh, bone and skin removed	1 thigh	13.5	Peanut butter, creamy	2 tbsp.	8
Turkey breast, roasted, Louis Rich	3 oz	15	Almonds, blanched	1 oz	6
Seafood:			*Cereals, Grains, and Breads:*		
Cod, cooked	3 oz	19	Oatmeal, quick instant	1 cup	5.4
Salmon, Chinook, baked	3 oz	22	Cheerios	1 cup	3
Shrimp, steamed	3 oz	18	Grape-Nuts	1/2 cup	6
Tuna, in water, drained	3 oz	22	Raisin Bran	1 cup	5
Pork:			Brown rice, cooked	1 cup	5
Pork loin chop, broiled	3 oz	25	Whole-wheat bread	1 slice	2.7
Ham, roasted, lean	3 oz	20	Bagel, 3 1/2 -in.-diameter	1 each	7
Dairy:			*Vegetables:*		
Whole milk (3.3% fat)	8 fl. oz	7.9	Carrots, raw (7.5 × 1 1/8 in.)	1 each	0.7
1% milk	8 fl. oz	8.5	Broccoli, raw, chopped	1 cup	2.6
Skim milk	8 fl. oz	8.8	Collards, cooked from frozen	1 cup	5
Low-fat, plain yogurt	8 fl. oz	13	Spinach, raw	1 cup	0.9
American cheese, processed	1 oz	6			
Cottage cheese, low-fat (2%)	1 cup	27			
Soy Products:					
Tofu	3.3 oz	7			
Tempeh, cooked	3.3 oz	18			
Soy milk beverage	1 cup	7			

Data from Values obtained from U.S. Department of Agriculture, Agricultural Research Service. 2009. USDA National Nutrient Database for Standard Reference, Release 22. Nutrient Data Laboratory Home Page, www.ars.usda.gov/ba/bhnrc/ndl.

Legumes

Legumes include foods such as soybeans, kidney beans, pinto beans, black beans, garbanzo beans (chickpeas), lentils, green peas, black-eyed peas, and lima beans. Would you be surprised to learn that the quality of the protein in some of these legumes is almost equal to that of meat? It's true! The quality of soybean protein is almost identical to that of meat and is available as soy milk, tofu, textured vegetable protein, and tempeh, a firm cake that is made by cooking and fermenting whole soybeans. The protein quality of other legumes is also relatively high. In addition to being excellent sources of protein, legumes are high in fiber, iron, calcium, and many of the B-vitamins. They are also low in saturated fat and cholesterol. Eating legumes regularly, including foods made from soybeans, may help reduce the risk for heart disease by lowering blood cholesterol levels. Diets high in legumes and soy products are also associated with lower rates of some cancers. Legumes are not nutritionally complete, however, as they do not contain vitamins B_{12}, C, or A. They're also deficient in methionine, an essential amino acid; however, combining them with grains, nuts, or seeds gives you a complete protein.

Considering their nutrient profile, satiety value, and good taste, it's no wonder that many experts consider legumes an almost perfect food. From main dishes to snacks, here are some simple ways to add legumes to your daily diet.

Nuts

Nuts are another healthful high-protein food. In the past, the high fat and energy content of nuts was assumed to be harmful, and people were advised to eat nuts only

The quality of the protein in some legumes is almost equal to that of meat.

Ranald MacKechnie/Dorling Kindersley

179

What About You?

How Much Protein Do You Eat?

One way to find out if your diet contains enough protein is to keep a food diary. Record everything you eat and drink for at least 3 days, and the grams of protein each item provides. To determine the grams of protein, for packaged foods, use the Nutrition Facts Panel, and make sure to adjust for the serving size you actually consume. For products without labels, check Table 3, or use the diet analysis tools that accompany this text. There is also a U.S. Department of Agriculture website that lists the energy and nutrient content of thousands of foods (go to www.ars.usda.gov/ba/bhnrc/ndl).

Below is an example, using Theo's food choices for 1 day. Do you think he's meeting his protein needs?

As calculated in the You Do the Math box, Theo's RDA is 72.8 to 91 g of protein. He is consuming 2 1/2 to 3 times that amount! You can see that he does not need to use amino acid or protein supplements, since he has more than adequate amounts of protein to build lean tissue. Now calculate your own protein intake. Are you getting enough protein each day?

Foods Consumed	Protein Content (g)
Breakfast:	
Brewed coffee (2 cups) with 2 tbsp. cream	1
1 large bagel (5-in.-diameter)	10
Low-fat cream cheese (1.5 oz)	4.5
Mid-morning snack:	
Cola beverage (32 fl. oz)	0
Low-fat strawberry yogurt (1 cup)	10
Snackwells Apple Cinnamon Bars (2)	2
Lunch:	
Ham and cheese sandwich:	
Whole-wheat bread (2 slices)	4
Mayonnaise (1.5 tbsp.)	1
Lean ham (4 oz)	24
Swiss cheese (2 oz)	16
Iceberg lettuce (2 leaves)	0.5
Sliced tomato (3 slices)	0.5
Banana (1 large)	1
Triscuit crackers (20 crackers)	7
Bottled water (20 fl. oz)	0

Foods Consumed	Protein Content (g)
Afternoon snack:	
Dry roasted peanuts (1 oz)	7
2% low-fat milk (1 cup)	8
Dinner:	
Cheeseburger:	
Broiled ground beef (1/2 lb cooked)	64
American cheese (1 oz)	6
Seeded bun (1 large)	6
Ketchup (2 tbsp.)	1
Mustard (1 tbsp.)	1
Shredded lettuce (1/2 cup)	0.5
Sliced tomato (3 slices)	0.5
French fries (2- to 3-in. strips; 30 fries)	6
Baked beans (2 cups)	28
2% low-fat milk (1 cup)	8
Evening snack:	
Chocolate chip cookies (4 3-in.-diameter cookies)	3
2% low-fat milk (1 cup)	8
Total Protein Intake for the Day:	**228.5 g**

occasionally and in very small amounts. The results from recent epidemiological studies have helped to substantially change the way nutrition experts view nuts. These studies show that consuming about 2 to 5 oz of nuts per week significantly reduces people's risk for cardiovascular disease.[7–9] Although the exact mechanism for the reduction in cardiovascular disease risk with increased nut intake is not known, nuts contain many nutrients and other substances that are associated with health benefits, including fiber, unsaturated fats, potassium, folate, and plant sterols that inhibit cholesterol absorption.

"New" Foods

A new source of non-meat protein that is available on the market is *quorn*, a protein product derived from fermented fungus. It is mixed with a variety of other foods to produce various types of meat substitutes. Other "new" foods high in protein include some very ancient grains! For instance, you may have heard of pastas and other products made with quinoa (pronounced keen-wah), a plant so essential to the diet of the ancient Incas that they considered it sacred. No wonder: quinoa, cooked much like rice, provides 8 g of protein in a 1-cup serving. It's highly digestible and unlike many more familiar grains, provides all nine essential amino acids. A similar grain, called amaranth, also provides complete protein. Teff, millet, and sorghum are grains long cultivated in Africa as rich sources of protein. They are now widely available in the United States. Although these three grains are low in the essential amino acid lysine, combining them with legumes produces a complete-protein meal.

With such a wide variety of protein sources to choose from, it's easy to eat right all day! See the Eating Right All Day feature for some simple high-protein menu choices that are low in saturated fat and high in nutrients and phytochemicals.

QUICK TIPS

Adding Legumes to Your Daily Diet

Breakfast

✓ Instead of cereal, eggs, or a muffin, microwave a frozen bean burrito for a quick, portable breakfast.

✓ Make your pancakes with soy milk, or pour soy milk on your cereal.

✓ If you normally have a side of bacon, ham, or sausage with your eggs, have a side of black beans instead.

Lunch and Dinner

✓ Try a sandwich made with hummus (a garbanzo bean spread), cucumbers, tomato, avocado, and/or lettuce on whole-wheat bread or in a whole-wheat pocket.

✓ Use deli "meats" made with soy in your sandwich. Also try soy hot dogs, burgers, and "chicken" nuggets.

✓ Add garbanzo beans, kidney beans, or fresh peas to tossed salads, or make a three-bean salad with kidney beans, green beans, and garbanzo beans.

✓ Make a side dish using legumes such as peas with pearl onions, or succotash (lima beans, corn, and tomatoes), or home-made chili with kidney beans and tofu instead of meat.

✓ Make black bean soup, lentil soup, pea soup, minestrone soup, or a batch of dal (a type of yellow lentil used in Indian cuisine) and serve over brown rice. Top with plain yogurt, a traditional accompaniment in many Asian cuisines.

✓ Use soy "crumbles" in any recipe calling for ground beef.

✓ Make burritos with black or pinto beans instead of shredded meat.

✓ To stir-fried vegetables, add cubes of tofu or strips of tempeh.

✓ Make a "meatloaf" using cooked, mashed lentils instead of ground beef.

✓ For fast food at home, keep canned beans on hand. Serve over rice with a salad for a complete and hearty meal.

Snacks

✓ Instead of potato chips or pretzels, try one of the new bean chips.

✓ Dip fresh vegetables in bean dip.

✓ Serve hummus on wedges of pita bread.

✓ Add roasted soy "nuts" to your trail mix.

✓ Keep frozen tofu desserts, such as tofu ice cream, in your freezer.

RECAP The RDA for protein for most nonpregnant, nonlactating, nonvegetarian adults is 0.8 g per kg body weight. Children, pregnant women, nursing mothers, vegetarians, and active people need slightly more. Most people who eat enough kilocalories and carbohydrates have no problem meeting their RDA for protein. Good sources of protein include meats, eggs, dairy products, legumes, whole grains, and nuts.

Can a Vegetarian Diet Provide Adequate Protein?

Vegetarianism is the practice of restricting the diet to food substances of plant origin, including vegetables, fruits, grains, and nuts. As stated in the introduction, approximately 6 to 8 million adults in the United States are vegetarians; of these, about 2 to

vegetarianism The practice of restricting the diet to food substances of plant origin, including vegetables, fruits, grains, and nuts.

Eating Right All Day

Breakfast
Whole-grain cereal with soymilk instead of a doughnut!

Lunch
Veggie burger instead of a ground beef burger!

Dinner
Stir fry chicken instead of fried chicken!

Snack
Raw veggies with lowfat dip instead of nachos!

Barbara Petrick/Dreamstime

Stockstudios/Shutterstock

Lauri Patterson/iStockphoto

Elena Elisseeva/Dreamstime

3 million are vegans, people who do not eat any kind of animal product, including dairy foods and eggs.[1] Many vegetarians are college students; moving away from home and taking responsibility for one's eating habits appears to influence some young adults to try vegetarianism as a lifestyle choice.

Types of Vegetarian Diets

There are almost as many types of vegetarian diets as there are vegetarians. Some people who consider themselves vegetarians regularly eat poultry and fish. Others avoid the flesh of animals but consume eggs, milk, and cheese liberally. Still others strictly avoid all products of animal origin, including milk and eggs, and even by-products such as candies and puddings made with gelatin. A type of "vegetarian" diet receiving significant media attention recently is the *flexitarian* diet: Flexitarians are considered semivegetarians who eat mostly plant foods, eggs, and dairy but occasionally eat red meat, poultry, and/or fish.

Table 4 identifies the various types of vegetarian diets, ranging from the most inclusive to the most restrictive. Notice that, the more restrictive the diet, the more challenging it becomes to achieve an adequate protein intake.

Why Do People Become Vegetarians?

When discussing vegetarianism, one of the most often asked questions is why people would make this food choice. The most common responses are included here.

Religious, Ethical, and Food-Safety Reasons

◀ Soy products are a good source of dietary protein.

Some make the choice for religious or spiritual reasons. Several religions prohibit or restrict the consumption of animal flesh; however, generalizations can be misleading. For example, while certain sects within Hinduism forbid the consumption of meat, perusing the menu at any Indian restaurant will reveal that many other Hindus regularly consume small quantities of meat, poultry, and fish. Many Buddhists are vegetarians, as are some Christians, including Seventh-Day Adventists.

Many vegetarians are guided by their personal philosophy to choose vegetarianism. These people feel that it is morally and ethically wrong to consume animals and any products from animals (such as dairy or egg products) because they view the practices in the modern animal industries as inhumane. They may consume milk and eggs but choose to purchase them only from family farms where animals are treated humanely.

There is also a great deal of concern about meat handling practices, as contaminated meat has found its way into our food supply. For example, several outbreaks of

TABLE 4   Terms and Definitions of a Vegetarian Diet

Type of Diet	Foods Consumed	Comments
Semivegetarian (also called partial vegetarian or flexitarian)	Vegetables, grains, nuts, fruits, legumes; sometimes seafood, poultry, eggs, and dairy products	Typically excludes or limit red meat; may also avoid other meats
Pescovegetarian	Similar to semivegetarian but excludes poultry	*Pesco* means "fish," the only animal source of protein in this diet
Lacto-ovo-vegetarian	Vegetables, grains, nuts, fruits, legumes, dairy products (*lacto*) and eggs (*ovo*)	Excludes animal flesh and seafood
Lacto-vegetarian	Similar to lacto-ovo-vegetarian but excludes eggs	Relies on milk and cheese for animal sources of protein
Ovovegetarian	Vegetables, grains, nuts, fruits, legumes, and eggs	Excludes dairy, flesh, and seafood products
Vegan (also called strict vegetarian)	Only plant-based foods (vegetables, grains, nuts, seeds, fruits, legumes)	May not provide adequate vitamin B_{12}, zinc, iron, or calcium
Macrobiotic diet	Vegan-type of diet; becomes progressively more strict until almost all foods are eliminated; at the extreme, only brown rice and small amounts of water or herbal tea are consumed	Taken to the extreme, can cause malnutrition and death
Fruitarian	Only raw or dried fruit, seeds, nuts, honey, and vegetable oil	Very restrictive diet; deficient in protein, calcium, zinc, iron, vitamin B_{12}, riboflavin, and other nutrients

severe illness, sometimes resulting in permanent disability and even death, have been traced to hamburgers served at fast-food restaurants, as well as ground beef sold in markets and consumed at home. A concern surrounding beef that has taken Europe by storm is the outbreak of *mad cow disease*.

Ecological Benefits

Many people choose vegetarianism because of their concerns about the effect of meat industries on the global environment. Due to the high demand for meat in developed nations, meat production has evolved from small family farming operations to the larger system of agribusiness. Critics point to the environmental costs of agribusiness, including massive uses of water and grain to feed animals, methane gases and other wastes produced by animals themselves, and increased land use to support livestock. For an in-depth discussion of this complex and often emotionally charged topic, see the Nutrition Debate box, Meat Consumption and Global Warming: Tofu to the Rescue? later in this chapter.

Health Benefits

Still others practice vegetarianism because of its health benefits. Research over several years has consistently shown that a varied and balanced vegetarian diet can reduce the risk for many chronic diseases. Its health benefits include the following:[10]

Banana Stock/Alamy

⬆ People who follow certain sects of Hinduism refrain from eating meat.

- Reduced intake of fat and total energy, which reduces the risk for obesity. This may in turn lower a person's risk for type 2 diabetes.
- Lower blood pressure, which may be due to a higher intake of fruits and vegetables. People who eat vegetarian diets tend to be nonsmokers, drink little or no alcohol, and exercise more regularly, which are also factors known to reduce blood pressure and help maintain a healthy body weight.
- Reduced risk for heart disease, which may be due to lower saturated fat intake and a higher consumption of *antioxidants* that are found in plant-based foods. Antioxidants are substances that can protect our cells from damage. They are abundant in fruits and vegetables.
- Fewer digestive problems such as constipation and diverticular disease, perhaps due to the higher fiber content of vegetarian diets. Diverticular disease,

occurs when the wall of the bowel (large intestine) pouches and becomes inflamed.

- Reduced risk for some cancers. Research shows that vegetarians may have lower rates of cancer, particularly colon cancer.[10] Many components of a vegetarian diet might contribute to reducing cancer risks, including higher fiber and antioxidant intakes, lower dietary fat intake, lower consumption of **carcinogens** (cancer-causing agents) that are formed when cooking meat, and higher consumption of soy protein, which may have anticancer properties.[10]
- Reduced risk for kidney disease, kidney stones, and gallstones. The lower protein contents of vegetarian diets, plus the higher intake of legumes and vegetable proteins (such as soy), may be protective against these conditions.

What Are the Challenges of a Vegetarian Diet?

Although a vegetarian diet can be healthful, it also presents many challenges. Limiting the consumption of flesh and dairy products introduces the potential for inadequate intakes of certain nutrients, especially for people consuming a vegan, macrobiotic, or fruitarian diet. Table 5 lists the nutrients that can be deficient in a vegan-type diet plan and describes good non-animal sources that can provide these nutrients. Vegetarians who consume dairy and/or egg products obtain these nutrients more easily.

Research indicates that a sign of disordered eating in some college females is the switch to a vegetarian diet.[11] Instead of eating a healthy variety of non-animal foods, people struggling with this problem may use vegetarianism as an excuse to restrict many foods from their diets.

Can a vegetarian diet provide enough protein? Because high-quality non-meat protein sources are quite easy to obtain in developed countries, a well-balanced vegetarian diet can provide adequate protein. In fact, the American Dietetic Association and Dietitians of Canada endorse an appropriately planned vegetarian diet as healthful, nutritionally adequate, and beneficial in reducing and preventing various diseases.[10] As you can see, the emphasis is on a *balanced* and *adequate* vegetarian diet; thus, it is important for vegetarians to consume soy products, eat complementary proteins, and obtain enough energy from other macronutrients to spare protein from being used as an energy source. Although the digestibility of a vegetarian diet is potentially lower than that of an animal-based diet, there is no separate protein recommendation for vegetarians who consume complementary plant proteins.[12]

Shutterstock

⬆ A well-balanced vegetarian diet can provide adequate protein and other nutrients.

carcinogens Cancer-causing agents, such as certain pesticides, industrial chemicals, and pollutants.

TABLE 5	Nutrients of Concern in a Vegan Diet	
Nutrient	**Functions**	**Non-Meat/Non-Dairy Food Sources**
Vitamin B$_{12}$	Assists with DNA synthesis; protection and growth of nerve fibers	Vitamin B$_{12}$–fortified cereals, yeast, soy products, and other meat analogs; vitamin B$_{12}$ supplements
Vitamin D	Promotes bone growth	Vitamin D–fortified cereals, margarines, and soy products; adequate exposure to sunlight; supplementation may be necessary for those who do not get adequate exposure to sunlight
Riboflavin (vitamin B$_2$)	Promotes release of energy; supports normal vision and skin health	Whole and enriched grains, green leafy vegetables, mushrooms, beans, nuts, and seeds
Iron	Assists with oxygen transport; involved in making amino acids and hormones	Whole-grain products, prune juice, dried fruits, beans, nuts, seeds, and leafy vegetables (such as spinach)
Calcium	Maintains bone health; assists with muscle contraction, blood pressure, and nerve transmission	Fortified soy milk and tofu, almonds, dry beans, leafy vegetables, calcium-fortified juices, and fortified breakfast cereals
Zinc	Assists with DNA and RNA synthesis, immune function, and growth	Whole-grain products, wheat germ, beans, nuts, and seeds

"No way would I ever become a vegetarian! The only way to build up your muscles is to eat meat. I was reading in a bodybuilding magazine last week about some guy who doesn't eat anything from animals, not even milk or eggs, and he looked pretty buff—but I don't believe it. They can do anything to photos these days. Besides, after a game I just crave red meat. If I don't have it, I feel sort of like my batteries don't get recharged. It's just not practical for a competitive athlete to go without meat."

What two claims does Theo make here about the role of red meat in his diet? Do you think these claims are valid? Why or why not? Without trying to convert Theo to vegetarianism, what facts might you offer him about the nature of plant and animal proteins?

Stockbyte/Getty Images

Using the Vegetarian Food Guide Pyramid

A Vegetarian Food Guide Pyramid based on the USDA MyPyramid is illustrated in **Figure 14**. Vegetarians can use this pyramid to design a healthful diet that contains all of the necessary nutrients.

For example, to meet their needs for protein and calcium, lacto-vegetarians can consume low-fat or nonfat dairy products. Vegans and ovovegetarians can consume calcium-fortified soy milk or one of the many protein bars now fortified with calcium.

In addition to protein and calcium, vegans need to pay special attention to consuming food high in vitamins D, B_{12}, and riboflavin (B_2) and the minerals zinc and

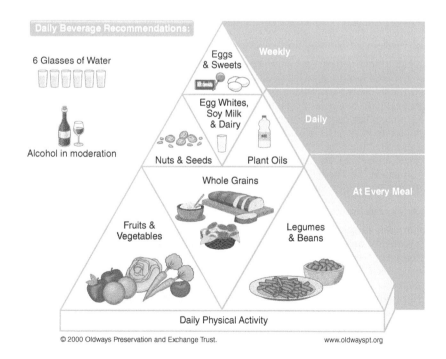

Figure 14 The Vegetarian Food Guide Pyramid. This pyramid guides general food choices at each meal, daily, and weekly.

© 2000 Oldways Preservation and Exchange Trust.   www.oldwayspt.org

Dorling Kindersley

Vegetarians should eat 5 servings of beans, nuts, seeds, eggs, or meat substitutes daily.

iron. Supplementation of these micronutrients may be necessary for certain individuals if they cannot consume adequate amounts in their diet.

RECAP A balanced vegetarian diet may reduce the risk for obesity, type 2 diabetes, heart disease, digestive problems, some cancers, kidney disease, kidney stones, and gallstones. Whereas varied vegetarian diets can provide enough protein, vegetarians who consume no animal products need to make sure they consume adequate plant sources of protein and supplement their diet with good sources of vitamin B_{12}, vitamin D, riboflavin, iron, calcium, and zinc.

What Health Problems Are Related to Protein Intake?

Consuming too much protein can cause significant health problems. In addition, consuming inadequate protein can result in severe illness and death. Typically, this occurs when people do not consume enough total kilocalories, but a diet deficient specifically in protein can have similar effects.

Too Much Dietary Protein Can Be Harmful

Excessive protein intake may increase the risk for health problems. Three health conditions that have received particular attention are heart disease, bone loss, and kidney disease.

High Protein Intake Is Associated with High Cholesterol

Animal sources of protein are typically high in saturated fat and cholesterol. Thus, high-protein diets composed of predominantly animal sources are associated with unhealthful blood lipid profiles. One study showed that people with heart disease improved their health when they ate a diet that was high in whole grains, fruits, and vegetables and met the RDA for protein.[13] However, some of the people in this study chose to eat a high-protein diet, and their risk factors worsened. In addition, vegetarians have been shown to have a greatly reduced risk for heart disease.[14,15]

High Protein Intake May Contribute to Bone Loss

Some nutritionists have been concerned that high-protein diets might increase calcium excretion and lead to bone loss. Animal products contain more of the sulfur amino acids (methionine and cysteine), and metabolizing these amino acids makes the blood more acidic. To buffer the acids, the body pulls calcium from bone. Although eating more protein can cause you to excrete more calcium, it is very controversial whether high protein intakes actually cause bone loss. We do know that eating too little protein causes bone loss, which increases the risk for fractures and osteoporosis. Higher intakes of animal and soy protein have been shown to protect bone in middle-aged and older women.[16,17] There does not appear to be enough direct evidence at this time to show that higher protein intakes cause bone loss in healthy people.

High Protein Intake Can Increase the Risk for Kidney Disease

A third risk associated with high protein intakes is kidney disease. People with kidney problems are advised to eat a low-protein diet because a high-protein diet can increase the risk of acquiring kidney disease in people who are susceptible. People with diabetes have higher rates of kidney disease and may benefit from a lower-protein diet.[18] The American Diabetes Association states that people with diabetes have a higher protein need than people without diabetes, but a protein intake of 15–20% of total energy is adequate to meet these increased protein needs.[19] This level of protein intake is deemed safe for people with diabetes who have normal renal function. There is no evidence, however, that eating more protein causes kidney disease in healthy people who are not susceptible to this condition. In fact, one study found that athletes consuming up to 2.8 g of protein per kg body weight per day experienced no unhealthy changes in kidney function.[20] Experts agree that eating no more than 2 g of protein per kg body weight each day is safe for healthy people.

It is important for people who consume a lot of protein to drink more water. This is because eating more protein increases protein metabolism and urea production. As mentioned earlier, urea is a waste product that forms when nitrogen is removed during amino acid metabolism. Adequate fluid is needed to flush excess urea from the kidneys. This is particularly important for athletes, who need more fluid to counterbalance higher sweat losses.

Protein-Energy Malnutrition Can Lead to Debility and Death

When a person consumes too little protein and energy, the result is **protein–energy malnutrition** (also called *protein–calorie malnutrition*). Two diseases that can follow are marasmus and kwashiorkor (Figure 15).

Marasmus Results from Grossly Inadequate Energy Intakes

Marasmus is a disease that results from grossly inadequate intakes of protein, energy, and other nutrients. Essentially, people with marasmus slowly starve to death. It is most common in young children (6 to 18 months of age) living in impoverished conditions who are severely undernourished. For example, the children may be fed diluted cereal drinks that are inadequate in energy, protein, and most nutrients. People suffering from marasmus have the look of "skin and bones" as their body fat and tissues are wasting. The consequences of marasmus include the following:

- Wasting and weakening of muscles, including the heart muscle
- Stunted brain development and learning impairment
- Depressed metabolism and little insulation from body fat, causing a dangerously low body temperature
- Stunted physical growth and development
- Deterioration of the intestinal lining, which further inhibits the absorption of nutrients

protein–energy malnutrition A disorder caused by inadequate consumption of protein. It is characterized by severe wasting.

marasmus A form of protein–energy malnutrition that results from grossly inadequate intakes of protein, energy, and other nutrients.

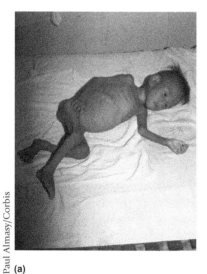
(a)

(b)

Paul Almasy/Corbis

AP Photos

🔺 **Figure 15** Two forms of protein–energy malnutrition are **(a)** marasmus and **(b)** kwashiorkor.

- *Anemia* (abnormally low levels of hemoglobin in the blood)
- Severely weakened immune system
- Fluid and electrolyte imbalances

If marasmus is left untreated, death from dehydration, heart failure, or infection will result. Treating marasmus involves carefully correcting fluid and electrolyte imbalances. Protein and carbohydrates are provided once the body's condition has stabilized. Fat is introduced much later, as the protein levels in the blood must improve to the point at which the body can use them to carry fat, so that it can be safely metabolized by the body.

Kwashiorkor Results from a Low-Protein Diet

Kwashiorkor often occurs in developing countries where infants are weaned early due to the arrival of a subsequent baby. This deficiency disease is typically seen in young children (1 to 3 years of age) who no longer drink breast milk. Instead, they often are fed a low-protein, starchy cereal. Unlike marasmus, kwashiorkor often develops quickly and causes the person to look swollen, particularly in the belly. This is because the low protein content of the blood is inadequate to keep fluids from seeping into the tissue spaces. These are other symptoms of kwashiorkor:

- Some weight loss and muscle wasting, with some retention of body fat
- Retarded growth and development; less severe than that seen with marasmus
- Edema, which results in extreme distention of the belly and is caused by fluid and electrolyte imbalances
- Fatty degeneration of the liver
- Loss of appetite, sadness, irritability, apathy
- Development of sores and other skin problems; skin pigmentation changes
- Dry, brittle hair that changes color, straightens, and falls out easily

Kwashiorkor can be reversed if adequate protein and energy are given in time. Because of their severely weakened immune systems, many individuals with kwashiorkor die from diseases they contract in their weakened state. Of those who are treated, many return home to the same impoverished conditions, only to develop this deficiency once again.

Many people think that only children in developing countries suffer from these diseases. However, protein–energy malnutrition occurs in all countries and affects both children and adults. In the United States, poor people living in inner cities and isolated rural areas are especially affected. Others at risk include the elderly, the homeless, people with eating disorders, those addicted to alcohol and other drugs, and individuals with wasting diseases, such as AIDS or cancer.

kwashiorkor A form of protein–energy malnutrition that is typically seen in developing countries in infants and toddlers who are weaned early because of the birth of a subsequent child. Denied breast milk, they are fed a cereal diet that provides adequate energy but inadequate protein.

RECAP Eating too much protein may increase your risk for heart disease and kidney disease if you are already at risk for these diseases. Protein-energy malnutrition can lead to marasmus and kwashiorkor. These diseases primarily affect impoverished children in developing nations. However, residents of developed countries are also at risk, especially the elderly, the homeless, people struggling with substance abuse, and people with AIDS, cancer, and other wasting diseases.

Nutrition DEBATE
Meat Consumption and Global Warming: Tofu to the Rescue?

Which causes more greenhouse gas emissions: livestock production or traffic? The answer may surprise you: according to the United Nations Food and Agriculture Organization (FAO), livestock production generates more of the gases responsible for global warming—18%—than transportation.[21] The FAO estimates that livestock production accounts for

- 9% of all carbon dioxide (CO_2) production from human activity
- 37% of all human-induced methane
- 64% of ammonia
- 65% of human-related production of nitrous oxide

How does this compare to emissions generated from the production of plant foods? Researchers at the University of Chicago concluded that an adult consuming an average daily number of Calories from a typical mixed American diet causes the emission of 1,485 kg of greenhouse gases *above* the emission associated with consuming the same number of Calories from plant sources.[22]

Livestock production is also a major source of land degradation, using 30% of the earth's land surface for pasture or feed production. Aggressive deforestation, which has long been linked to global warming, has cleared about 70% of former forests in the Amazon for grazing.[21] In addition, the production of feed crops for livestock uses 33% of global arable land. Livestock's presence in vast tracts of land and its demand for feed crops also have contributed significantly to a reduction in biodiversity and decline in ecosystems.[21]

It is also estimated that in the United States it takes 430 gallons of water to produce 1 lb of pork. This is in contrast with the 151 gallons of wa-

ter it takes to produce 1 lb of wheat. Animal waste, antibiotics, hormones, and fertilizers and pesticides used on feed crops can run off into neighboring streams, rivers, and lakes and into nearby irrigation fields used to produce crops for human consumption.

Considering the damage that livestock production wreaks on the environment, should you adopt a vegetarian—or semivegetarian—diet? The world's leading authority on global warming thinks you should. In 2008,

Glowimages/Getty Images

(a)

Kevin Schafer/Danita Delimont Photography
(b)

⬆ Livestock production (a) and aggressive deforestation (b) both contribute to greenhouse emissions.

Dr. Rajendra Pachauri, chair of the United Nations Intergovernmental Panel on Climate Change, which earned a joint share of the Nobel Peace Prize in 2007, released a statement calling upon individuals to have 1 meat-free day a week and to progressively reduce their meat consumption even further.[23] Pachauri noted that reducing meat consumption is an action that anyone can take immediately, and one that can have a significant impact on global warming in a short period of time.

But not everyone agrees. In response to many of the claims of environmental degradation from livestock production, meat industry organizations have published information in defense of their practices. A 2003 fact sheet from the National Cattlemen's Beef Association states:[24]

- Waste produced by cattle is minor, with about 2.5% of the total methane production in the U.S. coming from domestic livestock.
- Less than 1% of the total 2001 beef supply in the United States was imported from rain forest countries, and the largest fast-food chains have policies prohibiting the purchase of beef from these countries.
- Livestock production accounts for only 11% of the total amount of water used in the United States each year.

If people were to significantly reduce their consumption of meat, it might be possible to return to small family farming, which is more environmentally friendly. When animals are raised on smaller farms and/or allowed to range freely, they consume grass, crop wastes, and scraps recycled from the kitchen, which efficiently utilizes unused food sources.

Chapter Review

Test Yourself ANSWERS

1. False. Although protein can be used for energy in certain circumstances, fats and carbohydrates are the primary sources of energy for our bodies.

2. False. Vegetarian diets can meet and even exceed an individual's protein needs, assuming that adequate energy-yielding macronutrients, a variety of protein sources, and complementary protein sources are consumed.

3. True. Most people in the United States consume 1.5 to 2 times more protein than they need.

Find the Quack

Colby works out at a public gym three times a week, trying to gain muscle mass. One afternoon, as he is leaving the workout room to head for the showers, he is approached by a friendly looking young man he has never seen at the gym before. Introducing himself as Russ, a new member of the gym, the man compliments Colby on his workout. Colby can't help noticing Russ's extremely muscular physique, and so when he offers to tell Colby all about how he, too, can build muscle fast, Colby agrees to talk with him. Here is what Russ tells him:

* "Protein shakes are the secret to gaining muscle."
* "Bodybuilding causes microscopic tears in the muscle tissue, which have to be repaired with protein. This process of tearing down and rebuilding is increasing Colby's protein requirement so much that he cannot get the amount of protein he needs from foods alone."
* "Russ tells Colby that bodybuilders need to eat at least a gram of protein per pound of body weight per day. He says this means that Colby needs to eat a minimum of 150 g of protein every day and asks him how much protein he is currently consuming. Colby answers that he eats a sandwich with meat or poultry for lunch most days and usually has meat at dinner. Russ raises his eyebrows. "That's all?" he asks. "You're only getting maybe 50 g of protein a day! How do you expect to build muscle on that?"
* "Russ then tells Colby that he must start drinking protein shakes three times a day, in the morning and as a mid-afternoon and evening snack. He also insists that, in addition to three shakes, Colby drink a protein shake after every workout. He says that, after a workout, the mus-

cles get totally depleted of their protein stores and need to have them replenished. Then he assures Colby that every scoop of the protein powder used for one shake will provide 25 g of pure protein with no fat and no carbohydrates."

When Colby asks how much the protein powder costs, Russ hands him a brochure. "Visit my website and register as a first-time buyer and you can order all you want for half-price! It's a lot less expensive than eating five or six steaks a day, and a lot more convenient, too!"

1. Russ claims that bodybuilders need to consume at least a gram of protein per pound of body weight per day. Does this assertion sound correct to you?

2. Colby weighs 150 pounds and works out intensely with weights three times a week. Refer to the You Do the Math box of this chapter. How much protein does Colby actually need to consume each day? Do you think that he is only consuming about 50 g of protein a day, as Russ claims? (If you need a hint, return to the What About You? feature earlier in this chapter.)

3. Do our muscles get "totally depleted of their protein stores" after an intensive workout, as Russ claims? Explain your answer.

4. Is Colby at risk for any health problems if he begins to consume 150 g or more of protein every day, as Russ suggests?

Answers can be found on the companion website, at www.pearsonhighered.com/thompsonmanore.

 **NutriTools** Check out the companion website at www.pearsonhighered.com/thompsonmanore, or use MyNutritionLab.com, to access interactive animations, including:

* Know Your Protein Sources
* Digestion and Absorption: Protein

Review Questions

1. The process of combining peanut butter and whole-wheat bread to make a complete protein is called
   a. deamination.
   b. vegetarianism.
   c. transamination.
   d. mutual supplementation.

2. Which of the following meals is typical of a vegan diet?
   a. Rice, pinto beans, acorn squash, soy butter, and almond milk
   b. Veggie dog, bun, and a banana blended with yogurt
   c. Brown rice and green tea
   d. Egg salad on whole-wheat toast, broccoli, carrot sticks, and soy milk

3. The substance that breaks down polypeptides in the small intestine is called
   a. hydrochloric acid.
   b. pepsin.
   c. protease.
   d. ketones.

4. The portion of an amino acid that contains nitrogen is called the
   a. side chain.
   b. amine group.
   c. acid group.
   d. nitrate cluster.

5. Proteins contain
   a. carbon, oxygen, and nitrogen.
   b. oxygen and hydrogen.
   c. carbon, oxygen, hydrogen, and nitrogen.
   d. carbon, oxygen, and hydrogen.

6. True or false? After leaving the small intestine, amino acids are transported to the liver for distribution throughout the body.

7. True or false? When a protein is denatured, its shape is lost but its function is retained.

8. True or false? All hormones are proteins.

9. True or false? Buffers help the body maintain its fluids in proper balance.

10. True or false? Athletes typically require about three times as much protein as nonactive people.

Answers to Review Questions can be found at the back of this text, and additional essay questions and answers are located on the companion website at www.pearsonhighered.com/thompsonmanore.

Web Resources

www.eatright.org
American Dietetic Association

Search for vegetarian diets to learn how to plan healthful meat-free meals.

www.aphis.usda.gov
Animal and Plant Health Inspection Service

Select "Hot Issues" or search for "Bovine Spongiform Encephalopathy (BSE)" to learn more about mad cow disease.

www.vrg.org
The Vegetarian Resource Group

Obtain vegetarian and vegan news, recipes, information, and additional links.

www.beef.org
National Cattlemen's Beef Association

An industry website that provides information about beef production.

www.cdc.gov
Centers for Disease Control and Prevention

Click on "A–Z Index" to learn more about *E. coli* and mad cow disease.

www.who.int/nut/en
World Health Organization Nutrition

Visit this site to find out more about the worldwide magnitude of protein–energy malnutrition and the diseases that can result from inadequate intakes of protein, energy-yielding carbohydrates and fats, and various additional nutrients.

www.nlm.nih.gov/medlineplus
MEDLINE Plus Health Information

Search for "sickle cell anemia" and "cystic fibrosis" to obtain additional resources and the latest news about these inherited diseases.

References

1. Bennett, J., and C. Lewis. 2001. Very Vegetarian. Nashville: Rutledge Hill Press.
2. Vegetarian Resource Group. 2009. Vegetarian Journal Available online at www.vrg.org/press/2009poll.htm.
3. McDowell, M. A., R. R. Briefel, K. Alaimo, A. M. Bischof, C. R. Caughman, M. D. Carroll, C. M. Lona, and C. L. Johnson. 1994. Energy and macronutrient intakes of persons ages 2 months and over in the United States: Third National Health and Nutrition Examination Survey, Phase I 1988-1991. Adv. Data 255:1-24.
4. Tillotson, J. L., G. E. Bartsch, D. Gorder, G. A. Grandits, and J. Stamler. 1997. Food group and nutrient intakes at baseline in the Multiple Risk Factor Intervention Trial. Am. J. Clin. Nutr. 65(suppl.):228S-257S.
5. Smit, E., J. Nieto, C. J. Crespo, and P. Mitchell. 1999. Estimates of animal and plant protein intake in US adults: results from the Third National Health and Nutrition Examination Survey, 1988-1991. J. Am. Diet. Assoc. 99:813-820.
6. Manore, M. M, N. L. Meyer, and J. Thompson. 2009. Sport Nutrition for Health and Performance. 2nd Edition. Champaign, IL: Human Kinetics.
7. Fraser, G. E., J. Sabaté, W. L. Beeson, and M. Strahan. 1992. A possible protective effect of nut consumption on risk of coronary heart disease. Arch. Intern. Med. 152:1416-1424.
8. Hu, F. B., M. J. Stampfer, J. E. Manson, E. B. Rimm, G. A. Colditz, B. A. Rosner, F. E. Speizer, C. H. Hennekens, and W. C.Willett. 1998. Frequent nut consumption and risk of coronary heart disease in women: Prospective cohort study. BMJ 317: 1341-1345.
9. Albert, C. M., J. M. Gaziano, W. C.Willett, J. E. Mason, and C. H. Hennekens. 2002. Nut consumption and decreased risk of sudden cardiac death in the Physicians' Health Study. Arch. Intern. Med. 162:1382-1387.
10. American Dietetic Association and Dietitians of Canada. 2003. Position of the American Dietetic Association and Dietitians of Canada: Vegetarian diets. J. Am. Diet. Assoc. 103(6):748-765.
11. Klopp, S. A., C. J. Heiss, and H. S. Smith. 2003. Self-reported vegetarianism may be a marker for college women at risk for disordered eating. J. Am. Diet. Assoc. 103(6):745-747.
12. Institute of Medicine, Food and Nutrition Board. 2002. Dietary Reference Intakes for Energy, Carbohydrate, Fiber, Fat, Fatty Acids, Cholesterol, Protein, and Amino Acids (Macronutrients). Washington, DC: National Academies Press.
13. Fleming, R. M. 2000. The effect of high-protein diets on coronary blood flow. Angiology 51:817-826.
14. Leitzmann, C. 2005. Vegetarian diets: what are the advantages? Forum Nutr. 57:147-156.
15. Szeto, Y. T., T. C. Y. Kwok, and I. F. F. Benzie. 2004. Effects of a long-term vegetarian diet on biomarkers of antioxidant status and cardiovascular disease risk. Nutrition 20:863-866.
16. Munger, R. G., J. R. Cerhan, and B. C.-H. Chiu. 1999. Prospective study of dietary protein intake and risk of hip fracture in postmenopausal women. Am. J. Clin. Nutr. 69:147-152.
17. Alekel, D. L., A. St. Germain, C. T. Peterson, K. B. Hanson, J. W. Stewart, and T. Toda. 2000. Isoflavone-rich soy protein isolate attenuates bone loss in the lumbar spine of perimenopausal women. Am. J. Clin. Nutr. 72:844-852.
18. Kontessis, P., I. Bossinakou, L. Sarika, E. Iliopoulou, A. Papantoniou, R. Trevisan, D. Roussi, K. Stipsanelli, S. Grigorakis, and A. Souvatzoglou. 1995. Renal, metabolic, and hormonal responses to proteins of different origin in normotensive, non-proteinuric type 1 diabetic patients. Diabetes Care 18:1233-1240.
19. American Diabetes Association (ADA). 2003. Evidence-based nutrition principles and recommendations for the treatment and prevention of diabetes and related complications. Diabet. Care 26:S51-S61.
20. Poortmans, J. R., and O. Dellalieux. 2000. Do regular high protein diets have potential health risks on kidney function in athletes? Int. J. Sport Nutr. 10:2.
21. Food and Agriculture Organization. 2006. Livestock a major threat to environment: Remedies urgently needed. FAO Newsroom. 29 November. www.fao.org/newsroom/en/news/2006/1000448/index.html.
22. Eshel, G., and P. Martin. 2006. Diet, energy and global warming. Earth Interactions (March) 10:1-17. http://geosci.uchicago.edu/~gidon/papers/nutri/nutri.html.
23. Jowit, J. 2008. UN says eat less meat to curb global warming. The Observer (September 7). www.guardian.co.uk/environment/2008/sep/07/food.foodanddrink.
24. National Cattlemen's Beef Association. 2010. Beef Industry Myths and Facts. http://www.beefusa.org/beefFactoidFighter.aspx.

Answers to Review Questions

Answers to Review Questions 11-15 (essay questions) for this chapter are located on the Companion Website at **www.pearsonhighered.com/thompsonmanore**

1. **d.** mutual supplementation.
2. **a.** Rice, pinto beans, acorn squash, soy butter, and almond milk.
3. **c.** protease.
4. **b.** amine group.
5. **c.** carbon, oxygen, hydrogen, and nitrogen.
6. True.
7. False. Both shape and function are lost when a protein is denatured.
8. False. Some hormones are made from lipids.
9. False. Buffers help the body maintain acid-base balance.
10. False. Depending upon the type of sport, athletes may require the same or up to two times as much protein as nonactive people.

In Depth: Vitamins and Minerals: Micronutrients with Macro Powers

Vitamins and Minerals: Micronutrients with Macro Powers

Tatar/iStockphoto

WANT TO FIND OUT. . .

- **how a few fortunate accidents led to the discovery of micronutrients?**

- **why large doses of certain micronutrients could kill you—and which ones?**

- **whether micronutrient supplements have the same health benefits as nutrients found in whole foods?**

READ ON.

Have you heard the one about the college student on the junk-food diet who developed scurvy, a disease caused by inadequate intake of vitamin C? This "urban legend" seems to circulate on most college campuses every year, but that might be because there's some truth behind it. Away from their families, many college students do adopt diets that are deficient in one or more micronutrients. For instance, some students adopt a vegan diet with insufficient iron, whereas others stop choosing foods rich in calcium and vitamin D. Why is it important to consume adequate levels of the micronutrients, and exactly what constitutes a micronutrient, anyway? This *In Depth* explores the discovery of micronutrients, their classification and naming, and their impact on our health.

Discovering the "Hidden" Nutrients

There are three general classes of nutrients. Fluids provide water, which is essential for our survival and helps regulate many body functions. Macronutrients, which include carbohydrates, fats, and proteins, provide energy; thus, we need to consume them in relatively large amounts. **Micronutrients**, which include vitamins and minerals, are needed in much smaller amounts. They assist body functions such as energy metabolism and the formation and maintenance of healthy cells and tissues.

Much of our knowledge of vitamins and minerals comes from accidental observations of animals and humans. For instance, in the 1890s, a Dutch physician by the name of C. Eijkman noticed that chickens fed polished rice developed paralysis, which could be reversed by feeding them whole-grain rice. Noting the high incidence of beriberi, which results in extensive nerve damage, among hospital patients fed polished rice, he hypothesized that a highly refined diet was the main cause of beriberi. We now know that whole-grain rice, with its nutrient-rich bran layer, contains the vitamin thiamin and that thiamin deficiency results in beriberi. Simi-

larly, in the early 1900s, it was observed that Japanese children living in fishing villages rarely developed a type of blindness common among Japanese children who did not eat fish. Experiments soon showed that cod liver oil, chicken liver, and eel fat prevented the disorder. We now know that each of these foods contains vitamin A, which is essential for healthy vision.

Such observations were followed by years of laboratory research before nutritionists came to fully accept the idea that very small amounts of substances present in food are critical to good health. In 1906, the term *accessory factors* was coined by the English scientist F. G. Hopkins; we now categorize these accessory factors as vitamins and minerals.

How Are Vitamins Classified?

Vitamins are carbon-containing compounds that regulate a wide range of body processes. Of the thirteen vitamins recognized as essential, humans can synthesize only small amounts of vitamins D and K, so we must consume virtually all of the vitamins in our diets. Almost everyone who eats a varied and healthful diet can readily meet his or her vitamin needs from foods alone. The exceptions to this will be discussed shortly.

Fat-Soluble Vitamins

Vitamins A, D, E, and K are **fat-soluble vitamins (Table 1)**. They are found in the fatty portions of foods (butterfat, cod liver oil, corn oil, and so on) and are absorbed along with dietary fat. Fat-containing meats, dairy products, nuts, seeds, vegetable oils, and avocados are all sources of one or more fat-soluble vitamins.

In general, the fat-soluble vitamins are readily stored in the body's

▲ Avocados are a source of fat-soluble vitamins.
Simon Smith/Dorling Kindersley

adipose tissue; thus, we don't need to consume them every single day. While this may simplify day-to-day menu planning, there is also a disadvantage to our ability to store these nutrients. When we consume more of them than we can use, they build up in the adipose tissue, liver, and other tissues and can reach toxic levels. Symptoms of fat-soluble vitamin toxicity, described in Table 1, include damage to our hair, skin, bones, eyes, and nervous system. Overconsumption of vitamin supplements is the most common cause of vitamin toxicity in the United States; rarely do our dietary choices lead to toxicity. Of the four fat-soluble vitamins, vitamins A and D are the most toxic; **megadosing** with ten or more times the recommended intake of either can result in irreversible organ damage and even death.

Even though our bodies can store the fat-soluble vitamins, deficiencies can occur, especially in people who have a disorder that reduces their

---

micronutrients Nutrients needed in the daily diet in relatively small amounts; vitamins and minerals are micronutrients.

vitamins Organic compounds that assist in regulating body processes.

fat-soluble vitamins Vitamins that are not soluble in water but are soluble in fat, including vitamins A, D, E, and K.

megadosing Consuming nutrients in amounts that are ten or more times higher than recommended levels.

▲ Fruits contain many vitamins.
Alexandr Makarov/Shutterstock

TABLE 1   Fat-Soluble Vitamins

Vitamin Name	Primary Functions	Recommended Intake*	Reliable Food Sources	Toxicity/Deficiency Symptoms
A (retinol, retinal, retinoic acid)	Required for ability of eyes to adjust to changes in light Protects color vision Assists cell differentiation Required for sperm production in men and fertilization in women Contributes to healthy bone Contributes to healthy immune system	RDA: Men = 900 µg Women = 700 µg UL = 3,000 µg/day	Preformed retinol: beef and chicken liver, egg yolks, milk Carotenoid precursors: spinach, carrots, mango, apricots, cantaloupe, pumpkin, yams	*Toxicity:* fatigue; bone and joint pain; spontaneous abortion and birth defects of fetuses in pregnant women; nausea and diarrhea; liver damage; nervous system damage; blurred vision; hair loss; skin disorders *Deficiency:* night blindness, xerophthalmia; impaired growth, immunity, and reproductive function
D (cholecalciferol)	Regulates blood calcium levels Maintains bone health Assists cell differentiation	AI (assumes that person does not get adequate sun exposure): Adult aged 19 to 50 = 5 µg/day Adult aged 50 to 70 = 10 µg/day Adult aged >70 = 15 µg/day UL = 50 µg/day	Canned salmon and mackerel, milk, fortified cereals	*Toxicity:* hypercalcemia *Deficiency:* rickets in children; osteomalacia and/or osteoporosis in adults
E (tocopherol)	As a powerful antioxidant, protects cell membranes, polyunsaturated fatty acids, and vitamin A from oxidation Protects white blood cells Enhances immune function Improves absorption of vitamin A	RDA: Men = 15 mg/day Women = 15 mg/day UL = 1,000 mg/day	Sunflower seeds, almonds, vegetable oils, fortified cereals	*Toxicity:* rare *Deficiency:* hemolytic anemia; impairment of nerve, muscle, and immune function
K (phylloquinone, menaquinone, menadione)	Serves as a coenzyme during production of specific proteins that assist in blood coagulation and bone metabolism	AI: Men = 120 µg/day Women = 90 µg/day	Kale, spinach, turnip greens, brussels sprouts	*Toxicity:* none known *Deficiency:* impaired blood clotting; possible effect on bone health

*Abbreviations: RDA, Recommended Dietary Allowance; UL, upper limit; AI, Adequate Intake.

ability to absorb dietary fat. In addition, people who are "fat phobic," or eat very small amounts of dietary fat, are at risk for a deficiency. The consequences of fat-soluble vitamin deficiencies, described in Table 1, include osteoporosis, the loss of night vision, and even death in the most severe cases.

Water-Soluble Vitamins

Vitamin C (ascorbic acid) and the B-complex vitamins (thiamin, riboflavin, niacin, vitamin B_6, vitamin B_{12}, folate, pantothenic acid, and biotin) are all **water-soluble vitamins** (Table 2). They are found in a wide variety of foods, including whole grains, fruits, vegetables, meats, and dairy products. They are easily absorbed through the intestinal tract directly into the bloodstream, where they then travel to target cells.

With the exception of vitamin B_{12}, our bodies do not store large amounts of water-soluble vitamins. Instead, our kidneys filter from our bloodstream any excess amounts and excretes them in urine.

water-soluble vitamins Vitamins that are soluble in water, including vitamin C and the B-complex vitamins.

Paul Prescott/Shutterstock

Water-soluble vitamins can be found in a variety of foods.

TABLE 2 Water-Soluble Vitamins

Vitamin Name	Primary Functions	Recommended Intake*	Reliable Food Sources	Toxicity/Deficiency Symptoms
Thiamin (vitamin B₁)	Required as enzyme cofactor for carbohydrate and amino acid metabolism	RDA: Men = 1.2 mg/day Women = 1.1 mg/day	Pork, fortified cereals, enriched rice and pasta, peas, tuna, legumes	*Toxicity:* none known *Deficiency:* beriberi; fatigue, apathy, decreased memory, confusion, irritability, muscle weakness
Riboflavin (vitamin B₂)	Required as enzyme cofactor for carbohydrate and fat metabolism	RDA: Men = 1.3 mg/day Women = 1.1 mg/day	Beef liver, shrimp, milk and other dairy foods, fortified cereals, enriched breads and grains	*Toxicity:* none known *Deficiency:* ariboflavinosis; swollen mouth and throat; seborrheic dermatitis; anemia
Niacin, nicotinamide, nicotinic acid	Required for carbohydrate and fat metabolism Plays role in DNA replication and repair and cell differentiation	RDA: Men = 16 mg/day Women = 14 mg/day UL = 35 mg/day	Beef liver, most cuts of meat/fish/poultry, fortified cereals, enriched breads and grains, canned tomato products	*Toxicity:* flushing, liver damage, glucose intolerance, blurred vision differentiation *Deficiency:* pellagra; vomiting, constipation, or diarrhea; apathy
Pyridoxine, pyridoxal, pyridoxamine (vitamin B₆)	Required as enzyme cofactor for carbohydrate and amino acid metabolism Assists synthesis of blood cells	RDA: Men and women aged 19 to 50 = 1.3 mg/day Men aged >50 = 1.7 mg/day Women aged >50 = 1.5 mg/day UL = 100 mg/day	Chickpeas (garbanzo beans), most cuts of meat/fish/poultry, fortified cereals, white potatoes	*Toxicity:* nerve damage, skin lesions *Deficiency:* anemia; seborrheic dermatitis; depression, confusion, and convulsions
Folate (folic acid)	Required as enzyme cofactor for amino acid metabolism Required for DNA synthesis Involved in metabolism of homocysteine	RDA: Men = 400 µg/day Women = 400 µg/day UL = 1,000 µg/day	Fortified cereals, enriched breads and grains, spinach, legumes (lentils, chickpeas, pinto beans), greens (spinach, romaine lettuce), liver	*Toxicity:* masks symptoms of vitamin B₁₂ deficiency, specifically signs of nerve damage *Deficiency:* macrocytic anemia; neural tube defects in a developing fetus; elevated homocysteine levels
Cobalamin (vitamin B₁₂)	Assists with formation of blood Required for healthy nervous system function Involved as enzyme cofactor in metabolism of homocysteine	RDA: Men = 2.4 µg/day Women = 2.4 µg/day	Shellfish, all cuts of meat/fish/poultry, milk and other dairy foods, fortified cereals	*Toxicity:* none known *Deficiency:* pernicious anemia; tingling and numbness of extremities; nerve damage; memory loss, disorientation, and dementia
Pantothenic acid	Assists with fat metabolism	AI: Men = 5 mg/day Women = 5 mg/day	Meat/fish/poultry, shiitake mushrooms, fortified cereals, egg yolk	*Toxicity:* none known *Deficiency:* rare
Biotin	Involved as enzyme cofactor in carbohydrate, fat, and protein metabolism	RDA: Men = 30 µg/day Women = 30 µg/day	Nuts, egg yolk	*Toxicity:* none known *Deficiency:* rare
Ascorbic acid (vitamin C)	Antioxidant in extracellular fluid and lungs Regenerates oxidized vitamin E Assists with collagen synthesis Enhances immune function Assists in synthesis of hormones, neurotransmitters, and DNA Enhances iron absorption	RDA: Men = 90 mg/day Women = 75 mg/day Smokers = 35 mg more per day than RDA UL = 2,000 mg	Sweet peppers, citrus fruits and juices, broccoli, strawberries, kiwi	*Toxicity:* nausea and diarrhea, nosebleeds, increased oxidative damage, increased formation of kidney stones in people with kidney disease *Deficiency:* scurvy; bone pain and fractures, depression, and anemia

*Abbreviations: RDA, Recommended Dietary Allowance; UL, upper limit; AI, Adequate Intake.

Because we do not store large amounts of these vitamins in our tissues, toxicity is rare. When it does occur, however, it is often from the overuse of high-potency vitamin supplements. Toxicity can cause nerve damage and skin lesions.

Since most water-soluble vitamins are not stored in large amounts, they need to be consumed on a daily or weekly basis. Deficiency symptoms, including diseases or syndromes, can arise fairly quickly, especially during fetal development and in growing infants and children. The signs of water-soluble vitamin deficiency vary widely and are identified in Table 2.

Same Vitamin, Different Names and Forms

Food and supplement labels, magazine articles, and even nutrition textbooks such as this often use simplified alphabetic (A, D, E, K) names for the fat-soluble vitamins. The letters reflect their order of discovery: vitamin A was discovered in 1916, whereas vitamin K was not isolated until 1939. These lay terms, however, are more appropriately viewed as "umbrellas" that unify a small cluster of chemically related compounds. For example, the term *vitamin A* refers to the specific compounds retinol, retinal, and retinoic acid. Similarly, *vitamin E* occurs naturally in eight forms, known as tocopherols, of which the primary form is alpha-tocopherol. Compounds with

vitamin D activity include cholecalciferol and ergocalciferol, and the *vitamin K* "umbrella" includes phylloquinone and menaquinone. As you can see, most of the individual compounds making up a fat-soluble vitamin cluster have similar chemical designations (such as tocopherols and calciferols). Table 1 lists both the alphabetic and chemical terms for the fat-soluble vitamins.

Similarly, there are both alphabetic and chemical designations for water-soluble vitamins. In some cases, such as *vitamin C* and *ascorbic acid*, you may be familiar with both terms. But few people would recognize *cobalamin* as designating the same micronutrient as *vitamin B_{12}*. Some of the water-soluble vitamins, such as niacin and vitamin B_6, mimic the "umbrella" clustering seen with vitamins A, E, D, and K: the term *vitamin B_6* includes pyridoxal, pyridoxine, and pyridoxamine. If you read any of these three terms on a supplement label, you'll know it refers to vitamin B_6.

Some vitamins exist in only one form. For example, thiamin is the only chemical compound known as *vitamin B_1*. There are no other related chemical compounds. Table 2 lists both the alphabetic and chemical terms for the water-soluble vitamins.

How Are Minerals Classified?

Minerals are naturally occurring inorganic (non-carbon-containing) substances such as calcium, iron, and zinc. All minerals are elements; that is, they are already in the simplest chemical form possible and are not digested or broken down prior to absorption. Furthermore, unlike vitamins, they cannot be synthesized in the laboratory or by any plant or animal, including humans. Minerals are the same wherever they are found, whether in soil, a car part, or the human body. The minerals in our foods ultimately come from the environment; for example, the selenium in soil and water is taken up into plants

Barbara Helgason/Dreamstime

Plants absorb minerals from soil and water.

and then incorporated into the animals that eat the plants. Whether humans eat the plant foods directly or eat the animal products, all of the minerals in our food supply originate from Mother Earth!

Major Minerals

Major minerals are those that are required in amounts of at least 100 mg per day. In addition, these minerals are found in the human body in amounts of 5 g (5,000 mg) or higher. There are seven major minerals: sodium, potassium, phosphorus, chloride, calcium, magnesium, and sulfur. Table 3 summarizes the primary functions, recommended intakes, food sources, and toxicity/deficiency symptoms of these minerals.

Trace Minerals

Trace minerals are those we need to consume in amounts of less than 100 mg per day. They are found in the human body in amounts of less than 5 g (5,000 mg). Currently, the Dietary Reference Intake (DRI) Committee recognizes eight trace minerals as essential for human health: selenium, fluoride, iodine,

---

minerals Inorganic substances that are not broken down during digestion or absorption; they assist in regulating body processes.

major minerals Minerals that must be consumed in amounts of 100 mg/day or more and that are present in the body at the level of 5 g or more.

trace minerals Minerals that must be consumed in amounts of less than 100 mg/day and that are present in the body at the level of less than 5 g.

TABLE 3 Major Minerals

Mineral Name	Primary Functions	Recommended Intake*	Reliable Food Sources	Toxicity/Deficiency Symptoms
Sodium	Fluid balance Acid–base balance Transmission of nerve impulses Muscle contraction	AI: Adults = 1.5 g/day (1,500 mg/day)	Table salt, pickles, most canned soups, snack foods, cured luncheon meats, canned tomato products	*Toxicity:* water retention, high blood pressure, loss of calcium *Deficiency:* muscle cramps, dizziness, fatigue, nausea, vomiting, mental confusion
Potassium	Fluid balance Transmission of nerve impulses Muscle contraction	AI: Adults = 4.7 g/day (4,700 mg/day)	Most fresh fruits and vegetables: potatoes, bananas, tomato juice, orange juice, melons	*Toxicity:* muscle weakness, vomiting, irregular heartbeat *Deficiency:* muscle weakness, paralysis, mental confusion, irregular heartbeat
Phosphorus	Fluid balance Bone formation Component of ATP, which provides energy for our bodies	RDA: Adults = 700 mg/day	Milk/cheese/yogurt, soy milk and tofu, legumes (lentils, black beans), nuts (almonds, peanuts and peanut butter), poultry	*Toxicity:* muscle spasms, convulsions, low blood calcium *Deficiency:* muscle weakness, muscle damage, bone pain, dizziness
Chloride	Fluid balance Transmission of nerve impulses Component of stomach acid (HCl) Antibacterial	AI: Adults = 2.3 g/day (2,300 mg/day)	Table salt	*Toxicity:* none known *Deficiency:* dangerous blood acid–base imbalances, irregular heartbeat
Calcium	Primary component of bone Acid–base balance Transmission of nerve impulses Muscle contraction	AI: Adults aged 19 to 50 = 1,000 mg/day Adults aged >50 = 1,200 mg/day UL = 2,500 mg/day	Milk/yogurt/cheese (best-absorbed form of calcium), sardines, collard greens and spinach, calcium-fortified juices	*Toxicity:* mineral imbalances, shock, kidney failure, fatigue, mental confusion *Deficiency:* osteoporosis, convulsions, heart failure
Magnesium	Component of bone Muscle contraction Assists more than 300 enzyme systems	RDA: Men aged 19 to 30 = 400 mg/day Men aged >30 = 420 mg/day Women aged 19 to 30 = 310 mg/day Women aged >30 = 320 mg/day UL = 350 mg/day	Greens (spinach, kale, collard greens), whole grains, seeds, nuts, legumes (navy and black beans)	*Toxicity:* none known *Deficiency:* low blood calcium, muscle spasms or seizures, nausea, weakness, increased risk for chronic diseases, such as heart disease, hypertension, osteoporosis, and type 2 diabetes
Sulfur	Component of certain B-vitamins and amino acids Acid–base balance Detoxification in liver	No DRI	Protein-rich foods	*Toxicity:* none known *Deficiency:* none known

*Abbreviations: RDA, Recommended Dietary Allowance; UL, upper limit; AI, Adequate Intake; DRI, Dietary Reference Intake.

chromium, manganese, iron, zinc, and copper.[1] Table 4 identifies the primary functions, recommended intakes, food sources, and toxicity/deficiency symptoms of these minerals.

Same Mineral, Different Forms

Unlike most vitamins, which can be identified by either alphabetic designations or the more complicated chemical terms, minerals are known by one name only. Iron, calcium, sodium, and all other minerals are simply referred to by their chemical name. That said, minerals do often exist within different chemical compounds; for example, a supplement label might identify calcium as calcium lactate, calcium gluconate, or calcium citrate. These different chemical compounds, while all containing the same elemental mineral, may differ in their ability to be absorbed by the body.

How Do Our Bodies Use Micronutrients?

What is the truth behind the claim "You are what you eat"? We found out that the body has to change food in order to use it. This is also true for foods containing vitamins and minerals, because the micronutrients found in foods and supplements are not always in a

TABLE 4   Trace Minerals

Mineral Name	Primary Functions	Recommended Intake*	Reliable Food Sources	Toxicity/Deficiency Symptoms
Selenium	Required for carbohydrate and fat metabolism	RDA: Adults = 55 µg/day UL = 400 µg/day	Nuts, shellfish, meat/fish/poultry, whole grains	*Toxicity:* brittle hair and nails, skin rashes, nausea and vomiting, weakness, liver disease *Deficiency:* specific forms of heart disease and arthritis, impaired immune function, muscle pain and wasting, depression, hostility
Fluoride	Development and maintenance of healthy teeth and bones	RDA: Men = 4 mg/day Women = 3 mg/day UL: 2.2 mg/day for children aged 4 to 8; children aged >8 = 10 mg/day	Fish, seafood, legumes, whole grains, drinking water (variable)	*Toxicity:* fluorosis of teeth and bones *Deficiency:* dental caries, low bone density
Iodine	Synthesis of thyroid hormones Temperature regulation Reproduction and growth	RDA: Adults = 150 µg/day UL = 1,100 µg/day	Iodized salt, saltwater seafood	*Toxicity:* goiter *Deficiency:* goiter, hypothyroidism, cretinism in infant of mother who is iodine deficient
Chromium	Glucose transport Metabolism of DNA and RNA Immune function and growth	AI: Men aged 19 to 50 = 35 µg/day Men aged >50 = 30 µg/day Women aged 19 to 50 = 25 µg/day Women aged >50 = 20 µg/day	Whole grains, brewer's yeast	*Toxicity:* none known *Deficiency:* elevated blood glucose and blood lipids, damage to brain and nervous system
Manganese	Assists many enzyme systems Synthesis of protein found in bone and cartilage	AI: Men = 2.3 mg/day Women = 1.8 mg/day UL = 11 mg/day for adults	Whole grains, nuts, leafy vegetables, tea	*Toxicity:* impairment of neuromuscular system *Deficiency:* impaired growth and reproductive function, reduced bone density, impaired glucose and lipid metabolism, skin rash
Iron	Component of hemoglobin in blood cells Component of myoglobin in muscle cells Assists many enzyme systems	RDA: Adult men = 8 mg/day Women aged 19 to 50 = 18 mg/day Women aged >50 = 8 mg/day	Meat/fish/poultry (best-absorbed form of iron), fortified cereals, legumes, spinach	*Toxicity:* nausea, vomiting, and diarrhea; dizziness, confusion; rapid heartbeat, organ damage, death *Deficiency:* iron-deficiency microcytic (small red blood cells), hypochromic anemia
Zinc	Assists more than 100 enzyme systems Immune system function Growth and sexual maturation Gene regulation	RDA: Men 11 = mg/day Women = 8 mg/day UL = 40 mg/day	Meat/fish/poultry (best-absorbed form of zinc), fortified cereals, legumes	*Toxicity:* nausea, vomiting, and diarrhea; headaches, depressed immune function, reduced absorption of copper *Deficiency:* growth retardation, delayed sexual maturation, eye and skin lesions, hair loss, increased incidence of illness and infection
Copper	Assists many enzyme systems Iron transport	RDA: Adults = 900 µg/day UL = 10 mg/day	Shellfish, organ meats, nuts, legumes	*Toxicity:* nausea, vomiting, and diarrhea; liver damage *Deficiency:* anemia, reduced levels of white blood cells, osteoporosis in infants and growing children

*Abbreviations: RDA, Recommended Dietary Allowance; UL, upper limit; AI, Adequate Intake.

Minerals help maintain healthy skin and nails.

Foods high in oxalic acid, such as rhubarb, can decrease zinc and iron absorption.

chemical form that can be used by our cells. This discussion will highlight some of the ways in which our bodies modify the food forms of vitamins and minerals in order to maximize their absorption and utilization.

What We Eat Differs from What We Absorb

The most healthful diet is of no value to our bodies unless the nutrients can be absorbed and transported to the cells that need them. Unlike carbohydrates, fats, and proteins, which are efficiently absorbed (85–99% of what is eaten makes it into the blood), some micronutrients are so poorly absorbed that only 3% to 10% of what is eaten ever arrives in the bloodstream.

The absorption of many vitamins and minerals depends on their chemical form. Dietary iron, for example, can be in the form of **heme iron** (found only in meats, fish, and poultry) or **non-heme iron** (found in plant and animal foods, as well as iron-fortified foods and supplements). Healthy adults absorb about 25% of heme iron but as little as 3% to 5% of non-heme iron.

In addition, the presence of other factors within the same food influences mineral absorption. For example, approximately 30% to 45% of the calcium found in milk and dairy prod-

ucts is absorbed, but the calcium in spinach, Swiss chard, seeds, and nuts is absorbed at a much lower rate because factors in these foods bind the calcium and prevent its absorption. Non-heme iron, zinc, vitamin E, and vitamin B_6 are other micronutrients whose absorption can be reduced by various binding factors in foods.

The absorption of many vitamins and minerals is also influenced by other foods within the meal. For example, the fat-soluble vitamins are much better absorbed when the meal contains some dietary fat. Calcium absorption is increased by the presence of lactose, found in milk, and non-heme iron absorption can be doubled if the meal includes vitamin C–rich foods, such as red peppers, oranges, or tomatoes. On the other hand, high-fiber foods, such as whole grains, and foods high in oxalic acid, such as tea, spinach, and rhubarb, can decrease the absorption of zinc and iron. It may seem an impossible task to correctly balance your food choices to optimize micronutrient absorption, but the best approach, as always, is to eat a variety of healthful foods every day.

What We Eat Differs from What Our Cells Use

Many vitamins undergo one or more chemical transformations after they are eaten and absorbed into our bodies. For example, before they can go to work for our bodies, the B-complex vitamins must combine with other substances. For thiamin and vitamin B_6, a phosphate group is added. Vitamin D is another example: before cells can use it, the food form of vitamin D must have two hydroxyl (-OH) groups added to its structure. These combinations activate the vitamin; because they don't occur randomly, but only when the compound is needed, they help the body maintain control over its metabolic pathways.

While the basic nature of minerals does not, of course, change, they can undergo minor modifications that change their atomic structure. Iron

(Fe) may alternate between Fe^{2+} (ferrous) and Fe^{3+} (ferric); copper (Cu) may exist as Cu^{1+} or Cu^{2+}. These are just two examples of how micronutrients can be modified from one form to another to help the body make the best use of dietary nutrients.

Controversies in Micronutrient Metabolism

The science of nutrition continues to evolve, and our current understanding of vitamins and minerals will no doubt change over the next several years or decades. While some people interpret the term *controversy* as negative, nutrition controversies are exciting developments, proof of new information, and a sign of continued growth in the field.

heme iron Iron that is part of the proteins hemoglobin and myoglobin; found only in animal-based foods, such as meat, fish, and poultry.

non-heme iron Iron that is not part of hemoglobin or myoglobin; found in both animal-based and plant-based foods.

NUTRI-CASE LIZ

"I used to have dinner in the dorm cafeteria, but not anymore. It's too tempting to see everybody eating all that fattening food and then topping it off with a big dessert. . . . My weight would balloon up in a week if I ate like that! So instead I stay in my dorm room and have a bowl of cereal with skim milk. The cereal box says it provides a full day's supply of all the vitamins and minerals, so I know it's nutritious. And when I eat cereal for dinner, it doesn't matter if I didn't eat all the right things earlier in the day!"

What do you think of Liz's "cereal suppers"? If the cereal provides 100% of the DRI for all vitamins and minerals, then is Liz correct that it doesn't matter what else she eats during the day? If not, why not? What factors besides the percentage of DRI does Liz need to consider?

Rubberball/Getty Images

Are Supplements Healthful Sources of Micronutrients?

Are the micronutrients in supplements any better or worse than those in foods? Do our bodies use the nutrients from these two sources any differently? These are issues that nutrition scientists and consumers continue to discuss.

The availability, or "usefulness," of micronutrients in foods depends in part on the food itself. The iron and calcium in spinach are poorly absorbed, whereas the iron in beef and the calcium in milk are absorbed efficiently. Because of these and other differences in the availability of micronutrients from different sources, it is difficult to generalize about the usefulness of supplements. Nevertheless, we can say a few things about this issue:

- In general, it is much easier to develop a toxic overload of nutrients from supplements than it is from foods. It is very difficult, if not impossible, to develop a vitamin or mineral toxicity through diet (food) alone.
- Some micronutrients consumed as supplements appear to be harmful to the health of certain consumers. Recent research has shown that the use of high-potency supplements of vitamins A, C, and E may actually increase rates of death.[2]

Earlier, it had been shown that high-potency beta-carotene supplements increased death rates among male smokers. Alcoholics are more susceptible to the potentially toxic effects of vitamin A supplements and should avoid their use unless specifically prescribed by a healthcare provider. There is also some evidence that high intake of vitamin A increases risk for osteoporosis and hip fracture in older adults.[3]

Nancy R. Cohen/Getty Images

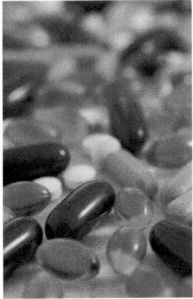

Thousands of supplements are marketed to consumers.

- Most minerals are better absorbed from animal food sources than they are from supplements, except calcium citrate-malate, used in calcium-fortified juices.
- Enriching a low-nutrient food with a few vitamins and/or minerals does not turn it into a healthful food. For example, soda fortified with micronutrients is still basically soda.
- Eating a variety of healthful foods provides you with many more nutrients, phytochemicals, and other dietary factors than supplements alone. Nutritionists are not even sure they have identified all the essential nutrients; the list of essential micronutrients may, in the future, expand. Supplements provide only those nutrients that the manufacturer puts in; foods provide nutrients that have been identified as well as yet-unknown factors.
- Foods often provide a balance of micronutrients and other factors that work in concert with one another. The whole food is more healthful than its isolated individual nutrients, providing benefits not always seen with purified supplements or highly refined, highly enriched food products.[4]
- A healthful diet, built from a wide variety of foods, offers social, emotional, and other benefits that are absent from supplements. Humans eat food, not nutrients.

In certain populations, micronutrient supplements can play an important role in promoting good health. These include pregnant women, children with poor eating habits, and people with certain illnesses.

Can Micronutrients Really Prevent or Treat Disease?

Nutritionists and other healthcare professionals clearly accept the role that dietary fat plays in the prevention and treatment of coronary heart disease. The relationship between total carbohydrate intake and the management of diabetes is also firmly established. Less clear, however, are the links between individual vitamins and minerals and certain chronic diseases.

A number of research studies have suggested, but not proven, links between the following vitamins and disease states. In each case, adequate intake of the nutrient has been associated with lower disease risk.

- Vitamin C and cataracts
- Vitamin D and colon cancer
- Vitamin E and complications of diabetes
- Vitamin K and osteoporosis

Other studies have examined relationships between minerals and chronic diseases. Again, in each case, the nutrient seems to be protective against the disease listed.

- Calcium and high blood pressure (hypertension)
- Chromium and type 2 diabetes in older adults
- Magnesium and muscle wasting (sarcopenia) in older adults
- Selenium and certain types of cancer

As consumers, it is important to critically evaluate any claims that are made regarding the protective or disease-preventing ability of a specific vitamin or mineral. Supplements that provide megadoses of micronutrients are potentially harmful, and vitamin/mineral therapies should never replace more traditional, proven methods of disease treatment. Current, reputable information can provide updates as the research into micronutrients continues.

Do More Essential Micronutrients Exist?

Nutrition researchers continue to explore the potential of a variety of substances to qualify as essential micronutrients. Vitamin-like factors, such as carnitine, and trace minerals, such as boron, nickel, and silicon, seem to have beneficial roles in human health, yet additional information is needed in order to fully define their metabolic roles. Until more research is done, we cannot classify such substances as essential micronutrients.

Another subject of controversy is the question "What is the appropriate intake of each micronutrient?" Contemporary research suggests that the answer to this question is to be found in each individual's genetic profile. The science of *nutrigenomics* blends the study of human nutrition with that of genetics. It is becoming clear that some individuals, for example, require much higher intakes of folate in order to achieve optimal health. Researchers have identified a specific genetic variation in a subset of the population that increases their need for dietary folate.[5] Future studies may identify other examples of how a person's genetic profile influences his or her individual need for vitamins and minerals.

The DRI Committees rely on Adequate Intake (AI) guidelines to suggest appropriate nutrient intake levels when research has not clearly defined an Estimated Average Requirement (EAR). As the science of nutrition continues to evolve, the next 50 years will be an exciting time for micronutrient research. Who knows? Within a few decades, we all might have personalized micronutrient prescriptions matched to our gender, age, and DNA!

Check out the companion website at www.pearsonhighered.com/thompson manore, or use MyNutritionLab, to access interactive animations including:

- Know Your Calcium Food Sources
- Know Your Iron Food Sources
- Let's Go to Lunch (for fat-soluble vitamins, water-soluble vitamins, and minerals)
- Vitamin or Mineral?

Web Resources

www.fda.gov
U.S. Food and Drug Administration

Select "Food" and then "Dietary Supplements" on the menu for information on how to evaluate dietary supplements.

www.ars.usda.gov/ba/bhnrc/ndl
Nutrient Data Laboratory Home Page

Click on "Search" and then type "Nutrients Lists" to find information on food sources of selected vitamins and minerals.

www.nal.usda.gov/fnic
The Food and Nutrition Information Center

Click on "Dietary Supplements" to obtain information on vitamin and mineral supplements.

www.dietary-supplements.info.nih.gov
Office of Dietary Supplements

This site provides summaries of current research results and helpful information about the use of dietary supplements.

www.lpi.oregonstate.edu
Linus Pauling Institute of Oregon State University

This site provides up-to-date information on vitamins and minerals that promote health and lower disease risk.

References

1. Institute of Medicine, Food and Nutrition Board. 2001. Dietary Reference Intakes for Vitamin A, Vitamin K, Arsenic, Boron, Chromium, Copper, Iodine, Iron, Manganese, Molybdenum, Nickel, Silicon, Vanadium, and Zinc. Washington, DC: National Academy Press.

2. Bjelakovic, G., D. Nikolova, L. L. Gluud, R. G. Simonetti, and C. Gluud. 2007. Mortality in randomized trials of antioxidant supplements for primary and secondary prevention. *J. Am. Med. Assoc.* 297:842–857.

3. Penniston, K. L., and S. A. Tanumihardjo. 2006. The acute and chronic toxic effects of vitamin A. *Am. J. Clin. Nutr.* 83:191–201.

4. Pollan, M. 2007. The age of nutritionism. *The New York Times Magazine*, January 28.

5. Stover, P. J. 2006. Influence of human genetic variation on nutritional requirements. *Am. J. Clin. Nutr.* 83:436S–443S.

Nutrients Involved in Fluid and Electrolyte Balance

From Chapter 7 of *Nutrition: An Applied Approach*, Third Edition. Janice Thompson, Melinda Manore. Copyright © 2012 by Pearson Education, Inc. Published by Pearson Benjamin Cummings. All rights reserved.

Nutrients Involved in Fluid and Electrolyte Balance

CHAPTER OBJECTIVES

After reading this chapter you will be able to:

1. Identify four nutrients that function as electrolytes in our body.

2. List three functions of water in our body.

3. Describe how electrolytes assist in the regulation of healthful fluid balance.

4. Discuss the physical changes that trigger our thirst mechanism.

5. Describe the sources of fluid intake and output in our body.

6. Compare and contrast hypernatremia and hyponatremia.

Test Yourself

1. (T) (F) Caffeine is a powerful diuretic, causing the body to lose excessive fluid in the urine.

2. (T) (F) Sodium is an unhealthful nutrient, and we should avoid consuming it in our diet.

3. (T) (F) Drinking until we are no longer thirsty always ensures that we are properly hydrated.

Test Yourself answers can be found at the end of the chapter.

In April of 2002, Cynthia Lucero, a healthy 28-year-old woman who had just completed her doctoral dissertation, was running the Boston Marathon. Although not a professional athlete, Cynthia was running in her second marathon, and in the words of her coach, she had been "diligent" in her training. While her parents, who had traveled from Ecuador, waited at the finish line, friends in the crowd watched as Cynthia steadily completed mile after mile, drinking large amounts of fluid as she progressed through the course. They described her as looking strong as she jogged up Heartbreak Hill, about 6 miles from the finish. But then she began to falter. One of her friends ran to her side and asked if she was okay. Cynthia replied that she felt dehydrated and rubber-legged; then she fell to the pavement. She was rushed to nearby Brigham and Women's Hospital, but by the time she got there, she was in an irreversible coma. The official cause of her death was hyponatremia, commonly called "low blood sodium." According to a study involving the 488 runners in that 2002 Boston Marathon, 13% had hyponatremia by the end of the race.[1] Hyponatremia continues to cause illness and death in runners, triathletes, and even hikers.

What is hyponatremia, and how does it differ from dehydration? Are you at risk for either condition? Do sport beverages offer any protection against these types of fluid imbalances? If at the start of football practice on a hot, humid afternoon, a friend confided to you that he had been on a drinking binge the night before, what would you say to him? Would you urge him to tell his coach, and if so, why?

In this chapter, we'll explore the role of fluids and electrolytes in keeping the body properly hydrated and maintaining the functions of nerves and muscles. Immediately following this chapter, we take an *In Depth* look at some disorders that occur when fluids and electrolytes are out of balance.

What Are Fluids and Electrolytes, and What Are Their Functions?

Of course, you know that orange juice, blood, and shampoo are all fluids, but what makes them so? A **fluid** is characterized by its ability to move freely, adapting to the shape of the container that holds it. This might not seem very important, but as you'll learn in this chapter, the fluid composition of your cells and tissues is critical to your body's ability to function.

Body Fluid Is the Liquid Portion of Our Cells and Tissues

Between 50% and 70% of a healthy adult's body weight is fluid. When we cut a finger, we can see some of this fluid dripping out as blood, but the fluid in the bloodstream can't account for such a large percentage. So where is all this fluid hiding?

About two-thirds of an adult's body fluid is held within the walls of cells and is therefore called **intracellular fluid** **(Figure 1a)**. Every cell in our body contains fluid. When our cells lose their fluid, they quickly shrink and die. On the other hand, when cells take in too much fluid, they swell and burst apart. This is why appropriate fluid balance—which we'll discuss throughout this chapter—is so critical to life.

The remaining third of body fluid is referred to as **extracellular fluid** because it flows outside our cells (Figure 1a). There are two types of extracellular fluid:

1. *Tissue fluid* (sometimes called *interstitial fluid*) flows between the cells that make up a particular tissue or organ, such as muscle fibers or the liver (Figure 1b). Other extracellular fluids, such as cerebrospinal fluid, mucus, and synovial fluid within joints, are also considered tissue fluid.
2. *Intravascular fluid* is found within blood and lymphatic vessels. Plasma is the fluid portion of blood that transports red blood cells through blood vessels. Plasma also contains proteins that are too large to leak out of blood vessels into the surrounding tissue fluid. Protein concentration plays a major role in regulating the movement of fluids into and out of the bloodstream (Figure 1c).

Not every tissue in our body contains the same amount of fluid. Lean tissues, such as muscle, are more than 70% fluid by weight, whereas fat tissue is only between 10% and 20% fluid. This is not surprising, considering the water-repellant nature of lipids.

Body fluid levels also vary according to gender and age. Compared to females, males have more lean tissue and thus a higher percentage of body weight as fluid. The amount of body fluid as a percentage of total weight decreases with age. About 75% of an infant's body weight is water, whereas the total body water of an elderly person is generally less than 50% of body weight. This decrease in total body water is the result of the loss of lean tissue that typically occurs as people age.

Body Fluid Is Composed of Water and Salts Called Electrolytes

Water is made up of molecules consisting of two hydrogen atoms bound to one oxygen atom (H_2O). You might think that pure water would be healthful, but we would

Arthur Tilley/Getty Images

As we age, our body water content decreases: approximately 75% of an infant's body weight is composed of water, while an elderly adult's body weight is only 50% water (or less).

fluid A substance composed of molecules that move past one another freely. Fluids are characterized by their ability to conform to the shape of whatever container holds them.

intracellular fluid The fluid held at any given time within the walls of the body's cells.

extracellular fluid The fluid outside the body's cells, either in the body's tissues or as the liquid portion of blood, called *plasma*.

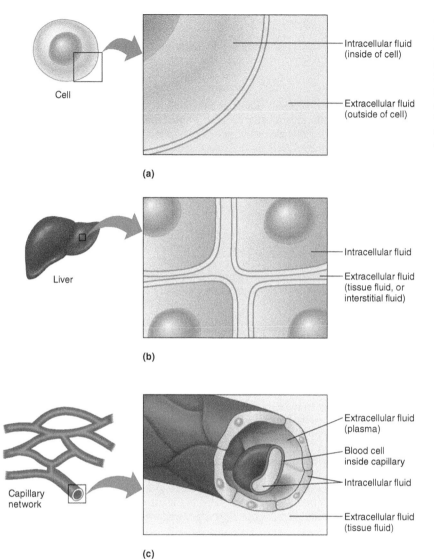

Cell

(a)

Intracellular fluid (inside of cell)

Extracellular fluid (outside of cell)

Liver

(b)

Intracellular fluid

Extracellular fluid (tissue fluid, or interstitial fluid)

Capillary network

(c)

Extracellular fluid (plasma)

Blood cell inside capillary

Intracellular fluid

Extracellular fluid (tissue fluid)

◄ **Figure 1** The components of body fluid. **(a)** Intracellular fluid is contained inside the cells that make up our body tissues. **(b)** Extracellular fluid is external to cells. Tissue fluid is external to tissue cells. **(c)** Another form of extracellular fluid is intravascular fluid—that is, fluid contained within vessels. Plasma is the fluid in blood vessels and is external to blood cells.

quickly die if our cell and tissue fluids contained only pure water. Instead, within the body fluids are a variety of dissolved substances (called *solutes*) critical to life. These include four major minerals: sodium, potassium, chloride, and phosphorus. We consume these minerals in compounds called *salts,* including table salt, which is made of sodium and chloride.

These mineral salts are called **electrolytes,** because when they dissolve in water, the two component minerals separate and form charged particles called **ions,** which are capable of carrying an electrical current. The electrical charge, which can be positive or negative, is the "spark" that stimulates nerves and causes muscles to contract, making electrolytes critical to body functioning.

Of the four major minerals just mentioned, sodium (Na^+) and potassium (K^+) are positively charged, whereas chloride (Cl^{2-}) and phosphorus (in the form of hydrogen phosphate, or HPO_4^{2-}) are negatively charged. In the intracellular fluid, potassium and phosphate predominate. In the extracellular fluid, sodium and chloride predominate. There is a slight difference in electrical charge on either side of the cell's membrane that is needed in order for the cell to perform its normal functions.

electrolyte A substance that disassociates in solution into positively and negatively charged ions and is thus capable of carrying an electrical current.

ion An electrically charged particle, either positively or negatively charged.

Fluids Serve Many Critical Functions

Water not only quenches our thirst; it also performs a number of functions that are critical to sustain life.

Fluids Dissolve and Transport Substances

Water is an excellent **solvent**; that is, it's capable of dissolving a wide variety of substances. Since blood is mostly water, it's able to transport a variety of solutes—such as amino acids, glucose, water-soluble vitamins, minerals, and medications—to body cells. In contrast, fats do not dissolve in water. To overcome this chemical incompatibility, lipids and fat-soluble vitamins are either attached to or surrounded by water-soluble proteins, so that they, too, can be transported in the blood to the cells.

Fluids Account for Blood Volume

Blood volume is the amount of fluid in blood; thus, appropriate fluid levels are essential to maintaining healthful blood volume. When blood volume rises inappropriately, blood pressure increases; when blood volume decreases inappropriately, blood pressure decreases. High blood pressure is an important risk factor for heart disease and stroke. In contrast, low blood pressure can cause people to feel tired, confused, or dizzy.

Fluids Help Maintain Body Temperature

Just as overheating is disastrous to a car engine, a high internal temperature can cause our body to stop functioning. Fluids are vital to the body's ability to maintain its temperature within a safe range. Two factors account for the ability of fluids to keep us cool. First, water has a relatively high capacity for heat: in other words, it takes a lot of energy to raise its temperature. Since the body contains a lot of water, only prolonged exposure to high heat can increase body temperature.

Second, body fluids are our primary coolant. When heat needs to be released from the body, there is an increase in the flow of blood from the warm body core to the vessels lying just under the skin. This action transports heat from the body core out to the periphery, where it can be released from the skin. At the same time, sweat glands secrete more sweat from the skin. As this sweat evaporates off of the skin's surface, heat is released and the skin and underlying blood are cooled **(Figure 2)**. This cooler blood flows back to the body's core and reduces internal body temperature.

A hiker must consume adequate amounts of water to prevent heat illness in hot and dry environments. Jupiterimages/Thinkstock

solvent A substance that is capable of mixing with and breaking apart a variety of compounds. Water is an excellent solvent.

blood volume The amount of fluid in blood.

Figure 2 Evaporative cooling occurs when heat is transported from the body core through the bloodstream to the surface of the skin. The water evaporates into the air and carries away heat. This cools the blood, which circulates back to the body core, reducing body temperature.

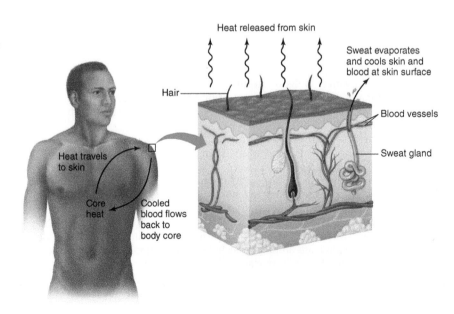

Fluids Protect and Lubricate Our Tissues

Water is a major part of the fluids that protect and lubricate tissues. The cerebrospinal fluid that surrounds the brain and spinal cord protects them from damage, and a fetus in a mother's womb is protected by amniotic fluid. Synovial fluid lubricates joints, and tears cleanse and lubricate the eyes. Saliva moistens the food we eat and the mucus lining the walls of the GI tract eases the movement of food through the stomach and intestines. Finally, pleural fluid covering the lungs allows their friction-free expansion and retraction within the chest cavity.

RECAP Our body fluids consists of water plus a variety of dissolved substances, including electrically charged minerals called electrolytes. Water serves many important functions in our bodies, including dissolving and transporting substances, accounting for blood volume, regulating body temperature, and protecting and lubricating body tissues.

Electrolytes Support Many Body Functions

Now that you know why fluid is so essential to the body's functioning, we're ready to explore the critical roles of the electrolytes.

Electrolytes Help Regulate Fluid Balance

Cell membranes are *permeable* to water, meaning water flows easily through them. Cells cannot voluntarily regulate this flow of water and thus have no active control over the balance of fluid between the intracellular and extracellular environments. In contrast, cell membranes are *not* freely permeable to electrolytes. Sodium, potassium, and the other electrolytes stay where they are, either inside or outside a cell, unless they are actively transported across the cell membrane by special transport proteins. So how do electrolytes help cells maintain their fluid balance? To answer this question, a short review of chemistry is needed.

Imagine that you have a special filter with the same properties as cell membranes; in other words, this filter is freely permeable to water but not permeable to electrolytes. Now imagine that you insert this filter into a glass of pure distilled water to divide the glass into two separate chambers (Figure 3a). Of course, the water levels on both sides of the filter would be identical, because the filter is freely permeable to water. Now imagine that you add a teaspoon of salt (which contains the electrolytes

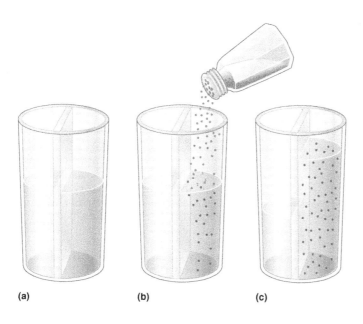

Figure 3 Osmosis. (a) A filter that is freely permeable to water is placed in a glass of pure water. (b) Salt is added to only one side of the glass. (c) Drawn by the high concentration of electrolytes, pure water flows to the "salt water" side of the filter. This flow of water into the concentrated solution will continue until the concentration of electrolytes on both sides of the membrane is equal.

(a)   (b)   (c)

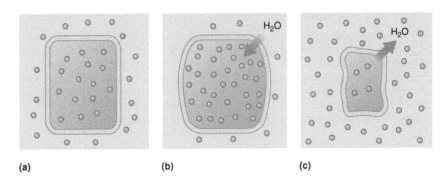

(a) (b) (c)

Figure 4 The health of our body's cells depends on maintaining the proper balance of fluids and electrolytes on both sides of the cell membrane. **(a)** The concentration of electrolytes is the same on both sides of the cell membrane. **(b)** The concentration of electrolytes is much greater inside the cell, drawing water into the cell and making it swell. **(c)** The concentration of electrolytes is much greater outside the cell, drawing water out of the cell and making it shrink.

sodium and chloride) to the water on only one side of the filter (Figure 3b). Immediately, you would see the water on the "pure water" side of the glass begin to flow through the filter to the "salt water" side of the glass (Figure 3c). Why would this movement of water occur? It is because water always moves from areas where solutes, such as sodium and chloride, are low in concentration to areas where they are high in concentration. To put it another way, solutes *attract* water toward areas where they are more concentrated. This movement of water toward solutes, called **osmosis,** continues until the concentration of solutes is equal on both sides of the cell membrane.

Osmosis provides the body a mechanism for controlling the movement of fluid into and out of cells. Cells can regulate the balance of fluids between their internal and extracellular environments by using special transport proteins to actively pump electrolytes across their membranes. The health of the body's cells depends on maintaining an appropriate balance of fluid and electrolytes between the intracellular and extracellular environments **(Figure 4a)**. If the concentration of electrolytes is much higher inside cells as compared to outside, water will flow into the cells in such large amounts that the cells can burst (Figure 4b). On the other hand, if the extracellular environment contains too high a concentration of electrolytes, water flows out of the cells, and they can dry up (Figure 4c).

Electrolytes Enable Our Nerves to Respond to Stimuli

In addition to their role in maintaining fluid balance, electrolytes are critical in allowing our nerves to respond to stimuli. Nerve impulses are initiated at the membrane of a nerve cell in response to a stimulus—for example, the touch of a hand or the clanging of a bell. Stimuli prompt changes in membranes that allow an influx of sodium into the nerve cell, causing the cell to become slightly less negatively charged. This is called *depolarization*. If enough sodium enters the cell, an electrical impulse is generated along the cell membrane **(Figure 5)**. Once this impulse has been transmitted, the cell membrane returns to its normal electrical state through the release of potassium to the outside of the cell. This return to the initial electrical state is termed *repolarization*. Thus, both sodium and potassium play critical roles in ensuring that nerve impulses are generated, transmitted, and completed.

Electrolytes Signal Our Muscles to Contract

Muscles contract in response to a series of complex physiological changes that will not be described in detail here. Simply stated, muscle contraction occurs in response to stimulation of nerve cells. As described previously, sodium and potassium play a key role in the generation of nerve impulses, or electrical signals. When a muscle fiber is stimulated by an electrical signal, changes occur in the cell membrane that lead to an increased flow of calcium into the muscle from the extracellular space. This movement of calcium into the muscle provides the stimulus for muscle contraction. The muscles relax after a contraction once the electrical signal is complete and calcium has been pumped out of the muscle cell.

Certain illnesses can threaten the delicate balance of fluid inside and outside the cells and impair the function of nerves and muscles. You may have heard of someone

osmosis The movement of water (or any solvent) through a semipermeable membrane from an area where solutes are less concentrated to areas where solutes are highly concentrated.

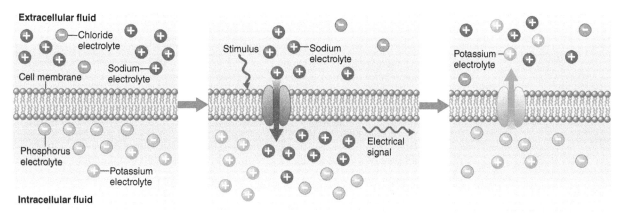

(a) Resting state **(b) Depolarization** **(c) Repolarization**

Figure 5 The role of electrolytes in conduction of a nerve impulse. **(a)** In the resting state, the intracellular fluid has slightly more electrolytes with a negative charge. **(b)** A stimulus causes changes to occur that prompt the influx of sodium into the interior of the cell. Sodium has a positive charge, so when this happens, the charge inside the cell becomes slightly positive. This is called depolarization. If enough sodium enters the cell, an electrical signal is transmitted to adjacent regions of the cell membrane. **(c)** Release of potassium to the exterior of the cell allows the first portion of the membrane almost immediately to return to the resting state. This is called repolarization.

being hospitalized because of excessive diarrhea and/or vomiting. When this happens, the body loses a great deal of fluid from the intestinal tract and extracellular environment. This large fluid loss causes the extracellular electrolyte concentration to become very high. In response, a great deal of intracellular fluid flows out of the cells (see Figure 4c). This imbalance in fluid and electrolytes changes the flow of electrical impulses through the nerve and muscle cells of the heart, causing an irregular heart rate, which can eventually lead to death if left untreated. Food poisoning and eating disorders involving repeated vomiting and diarrhea can also result in death from life-threatening fluid and electrolyte imbalances.

RECAP Electrolytes help regulate fluid balance by controlling the movement of fluid into and out of cells. Electrolytes, specifically sodium and potassium, play a key role in generating nerve impulses in response to stimuli. Calcium is an electrolyte that stimulates muscle contraction.

How Does Our Body Maintain Fluid Balance?

The proper balance of fluid is maintained in the body by a series of mechanisms that prompt us to drink and retain fluid when we are dehydrated and to excrete fluid as urine when we consume more than we need.

Our Thirst Mechanism Prompts Us to Drink Fluids

Imagine that, at lunch, you ate a ham sandwich and a bag of salted potato chips. Now it's almost time for your afternoon seminar to end and you are very thirsty. The last 5 minutes of class are a torment, and when the instructor ends the session you dash to the nearest drinking fountain. What prompted you to suddenly feel so thirsty?

The body's command center for fluid intake is in the hypothalamus, part of the forebrain. A cluster of cells in the hypothalamus triggers hunger. Similarly, a group of hypothalamic cells, collectively referred to as the **thirst mechanism,** causes you to consciously desire fluids. The thirst mechanism prompts us to feel thirsty whenever it is stimulated by the following:

- An increased concentration of salt and other dissolved substances in our blood. Remember that ham sandwich and those potato chips? Both these foods are salty, and eating them increased the blood's sodium concentration.
- A reduction in blood volume and blood pressure. This can occur when fluids are lost because of profuse sweating, blood loss, vomiting, or diarrhea or simply when fluid intake is too low.
- Dryness in the tissues of the mouth and throat. Tissue dryness reflects a lower amount of fluid in the bloodstream, which causes a reduced production of saliva.

Once the hypothalamus detects such changes, it stimulates the release of a hormone that signals the kidneys to reduce urine flow and return more water to the bloodstream. The kidneys also secrete an enzyme that triggers blood vessels throughout the body to constrict, helping it retain water. Water is drawn out of the salivary glands in an attempt to further dilute the concentration of blood solutes; this causes the mouth and throat to become even drier. Together, these mechanisms prevent a further loss of body fluid and help the body avoid dehydration.

Although the thirst mechanism can trigger an increase in fluid intake, this mechanism alone is not always sufficient: people tend to drink until they are no longer thirsty, but the amount of fluid they consume may not be enough to achieve fluid balance. This is particularly true when body water is lost rapidly, such as during intense exercise in the heat. Because the thirst mechanism has some limitations, it is important to drink regularly throughout the day and not wait to drink until you become thirsty, especially if you are active.

We Gain Fluids by Consuming Beverages and Foods and Through Metabolism

We obtain the fluid we need each day from three primary sources: beverages, foods, and the body's production of metabolic water. Of course, you know that beverages are mostly water, but it isn't as easy to see the water content in the foods we eat. For example, iceberg lettuce is almost 99% water, and even almonds contain a small amount of water (Figure 6).

Metabolic water is the water formed from the body's metabolic reactions. This water contributes about 10–14% of the water the body needs each day.

We Lose Fluids Through Urine, Sweat, Evaporation, Exhalation, and Feces

We can perceive—or sense—water loss through urine output and sweating, so we refer to this as **sensible water loss.** Most of the water we consume is excreted through the kidneys in the form of urine. When we consume more water than we need, the kidneys process and excrete the excess in the form of dilute urine.

The second type of sensible water loss is via sweat. Our sweat glands produce more sweat during exercise or when we are is in a hot environment. The evaporation of sweat from the skin releases heat, which cools the skin and reduces the body's core temperature.

Water is continuously evaporated from the skin, even when a person is not visibly sweating, and water is continuously exhaled from the lungs during breathing. Water loss through these routes is known as **insensible water loss,** as we do not perceive it. Under normal resting conditions, insensible water loss is less than 1 liter (L) of fluid each day; during heavy exercise or in hot weather, a person can lose up to 2 L of water per hour from insensible water loss.

Under normal conditions, only about 150 to 200 ml of water is lost each day in feces. The gastrointestinal tract typically absorbs much of the fluid that passes through it each day.

Jill Chen/iStockphoto

◀ Fruits and vegetables are delicious sources of water.

thirst mechanism A cluster of nerve cells in the hypothalamus that stimulate our conscious desire to drink fluids in response to an increase in the concentration of salt in our blood or a decrease in blood pressure and blood volume.

metabolic water The water formed as a by-product of our body's metabolic reactions.

sensible water loss Water loss that is noticed by a person, such as through urine output and visible sweating.

insensible water loss The loss of water not noticeable by a person, such as through evaporation from the skin and exhalation from the lungs during breathing.

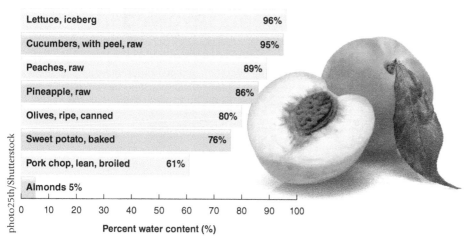

Food	Percent water content (%)
Lettuce, iceberg	96%
Cucumbers, with peel, raw	95%
Peaches, raw	89%
Pineapple, raw	86%
Olives, ripe, canned	80%
Sweet potato, baked	76%
Pork chop, lean, broiled	61%
Almonds	5%

photo25th/Shutterstock

⬆ **Figure 6** Water content of different foods. Much of your daily water intake comes from the foods you eat.
Data from U.S. Department of Agriculture, Agricultural Research Service. 2009. USDA Nutrient Database for Standard Reference, Release 22. Nutrient Data Laboratory Home Page. www.ars.usda.gov/ba/bhnrc/ndl.

In addition to these five avenues of regular fluid loss, certain situations can cause a significant loss of fluid from our body:

- Illnesses that involve fever, coughing, vomiting, diarrhea, and a runny nose significantly increase fluid loss. For instance, when someone suffers from extreme diarrhea, water loss via bowel elimination alone can be as high as several liters per day. This is one reason that doctors advise people to drink plenty of fluids when they are ill.
- Traumatic injury, internal bleeding, blood donation, and surgery also increase loss of fluid because of the blood loss involved.
- Exercise increases fluid loss via sweat and respiration; although urine production typically decreases during exercise, fluid losses increase through the skin and lungs.
- Certain environmental conditions increase fluid loss. One of these is low humidity, such as in a desert or an airplane. When the water content of the environment is low, water from the body more easily evaporates into the surrounding dry air. High altitudes increase fluid loss, because we breathe faster to compensate for the lower oxygen pressure. This results in greater fluid loss via the lungs. Hot and cold environments also increase fluid loss. We've mentioned sensible losses from sweating in the heat, but cold temperatures can trigger hormonal changes that also increase fluid loss.
- Pregnancy increases fluid loss for the mother because fluids are continually diverted to the fetus and amniotic fluid.
- Breastfeeding requires a tremendous increase in fluid intake to make up for the loss of fluid as breast milk.
- Consumption of **diuretics**—substances that increase fluid loss via the urine—can result in dangerously excessive fluid loss. Diuretics include certain prescription medications, alcohol, and many over-the-counter weight-loss remedies. In the past, it was believed that caffeine acted as a diuretic, but recent research suggests that caffeinated drinks do not significantly influence fluid status in healthy adults.

⬆ Drinking beverages that contain alcohol causes an increase in water loss, because alcohol is a diuretic.

Stockbyte/Getty Images

RECAP A healthy fluid level is maintained by balancing intake and excretion. The primary sources of fluids are water and other beverages, foods, and the production of metabolic water in the body. Fluid losses occur through urination, sweating, the feces, exhalation from the lungs, and insensible evaporation from the skin.

diuretic A substance that increases fluid loss via the urine. Common diuretics include alcohol, some prescription medications, and many over-the-counter weight-loss pills.

A Profile of Nutrients Involved in Hydration and Neuromuscular Function

The nutrients involved in maintaining hydration and neuromuscular function are water and the minerals sodium, potassium, chloride, and phosphorus (Table 1). These minerals are classified as *major minerals*, as the body needs more than 100 mg of each per day.

Calcium and magnesium also function as electrolytes and influence our body's fluid balance and neuromuscular function.

Water

Water is essential for life. Although we can live weeks without food, we can survive only a few days without water, depending on the environmental temperature. The human body does not have the capacity to store water, so we must continuously replace the water lost each day.

How Much Water Should We Drink?

Our need for water varies greatly, depending on our age, body size, health status, physical activity level, and exposure to environmental conditions. It is important to pay attention to how much our need for water changes under various conditions, so that we can avoid dehydration.

Fluid requirements are very individualized. For example, a highly active male athlete training in a hot environment may require up to 10 liters (L) of fluid per day to maintain a healthy fluid balance, while an inactive, petite woman who lives in a mild climate and works in a temperature-controlled office building may only require about 3 L of fluid per day.

The DRI for adult men aged 19 to 50 years is 3.7 L of total water per day. This includes approximately 3.0 L (13 cups) as beverages, including water. The DRI for adult women aged 19 to 50 years is 2.7 L of total water per day, including about 2.2 L (9 cups) as beverages.[2]

Figure 7 shows the amount and sources of water intake and output for a woman expending 2,500 kcal per day. Based on current recommendations, this woman needs about 3,000 ml (3 L) of fluid per day. As shown,

- Water from metabolism provides 300 ml of water.
- The foods she eats provide her with an additional 500 ml of water each day.
- The beverages she drinks provide the remainder of the water she needs, which is equal to 2,200 ml.

An 8-oz glass of fluid is equal to 240 ml. In this example, the woman would need to drink nine glasses of fluid to meet her needs. You may have read or heard that drinking eight glasses of fluid each day is recommended for most people. Remember, however, that this recommendation is a general guideline. You may need to drink a different amount to meet your individual fluid needs.

Corbis

⬥ Vigorous exercise causes significant water loss, which must be replenished to optimize performance and health.

TABLE 1 Overview of Nutrients Involved in Hydration and Neuromuscular Function	
To see the full profile of nutrients involved in hydration and neuromusclar function, see *In Depth*, Vitamins and Minerals: Micronutrients with Macro Powers.	
Nutrient	**Recommended Intake**
Sodium	1.5 g/day*
Potassium	4.7 g/day*
Chloride	2.3 g/day*
Phosphorus	700 mg/day†
*Adequate Intake (AI). †Recommended Dietary Allowance (RDA).	

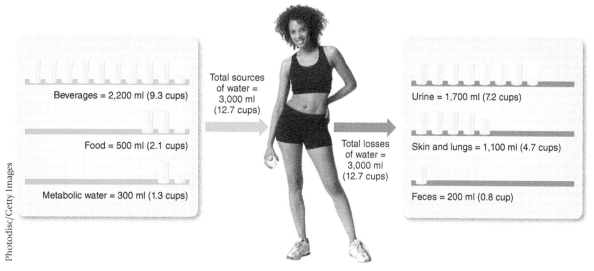

Beverages = 2,200 ml (9.3 cups)

Food = 500 ml (2.1 cups)

Metabolic water = 300 ml (1.3 cups)

Total sources
of water =
3,000 ml
(12.7 cups)

Total losses
of water =
3,000 ml
(12.7 cups)

Urine = 1,700 ml (7.2 cups)

Skin and lungs = 1,100 ml (4.7 cups)

Feces = 200 ml (0.8 cup)

Photodisc/Getty Images

◆ Figure 7 Amount and sources of water intake and output for a woman expending 2,500 kcal/day.

Athletes and other people who are active, especially those working in very hot environments, may require more fluid than the current recommendations. The amount of sweat lost during exercise is very individualized and depends on body size, exercise intensity, level of personal fitness, environmental temperature, and humidity. A recent study reported that professional football players lose almost 7 liters of sweat per day when practicing in a hot, humid environment.[3] Thus, these individuals need to drink more to replace the fluid they lose. Sodium is the major electrolyte lost in sweat; some potassium and small amounts of minerals such as iron and calcium are also lost in sweat.

Because of their high fluid and electrolyte losses during exercise, some athletes drink sports beverages instead of plain water to help them maintain fluid balance. Recently, sports beverages have also become popular with recreationally active people and non-athletes. Is it really necessary for people to consume these beverages if they are not highly active? See the Nutrition Debate on sports beverages later in this chapter to learn whether they are right for recreationally active people and non-athletes.

Sources of Drinking Water

Millions of Americans routinely consume the tap water found in homes and public places, which generally comes from two sources: surface water and groundwater. *Surface water* comes from lakes, rivers, and reservoirs. *Groundwater* comes from underground rock formations called *aquifers*. Many people who live in rural areas depend on groundwater pumped from a well as their water source. The most common chemical used to treat and purify public water supplies is *chlorine*, which is effective in killing many microorganisms. Water treatment plants also routinely check water supplies for hazardous chemicals, minerals, and other contaminants. Because of these efforts, the United States has one of the safest water systems in the world.

The Environmental Protection Agency (EPA) sets and monitors the standards for public water systems. Local water regulatory agencies, such as cities and counties, must provide an annual report on specific water contaminants to all households served by that agency. The EPA does not monitor water from private wells, but it publishes recommendations for well owners to help them maintain a safe water supply. For more information on drinking water safety, go to the EPA website (see Web Resources at the end of this chapter).

Over the past 20 years, there has been a major shift away from the use of tap water to the consumption of bottled water. Americans now drink about 9 billion gallons of bottled water each year.[4] The meteoric rise in bottled water production and consumption is most likely due to the convenience of drinking bottled water, the health messages related to drinking more water, and the public's fears related to the safety of tap water. Recent environmental concerns related to the disposal of water bottles has, however, slowed the use of bottled water.

The Food and Drug Administration (FDA) is responsible for the regulation of bottled water. As with tap water, bottled water is taken from either surface water or groundwater sources. But it is often treated and filtered differently. Although this treatment may make bottled water taste better than tap water, it doesn't necessarily make it any safer to drink. Also, although some types of bottled water contain more minerals than tap water, there are no other additional nutritional benefits of drinking bottled water. For more information on bottled water, go to www.bottledwater.org.

How pure is your favorite bottled water? Follow the steps in the What About You? box on to find out!

Many types of bottled water are available in the United States. Carbonated water (seltzer water) contains carbon dioxide gas that either occurs naturally or is added to the water. Mineral waters contain various levels of minerals and offer a unique taste. Some brands, however, contain high amounts of sodium and should be avoided by people who are trying to reduce their sodium intake. Distilled water is mineral-free but has a "flat" taste.

HOT TOPIC

Can Fluids Make You Fat?

Until about 50 years ago, beverage choices were limited. But the introduction of a new, cheap sweetener derived from corn, *high-fructose corn syrup*, caused soda and other sweetened beverages to flood the market. Today, Americans take in approximately 21% of their calories from beverages, mostly in the form of sweetened soft drinks and fruit juices. Recently, sweetened bottled waters, bottled teas, and specialty coffee drinks have contributed to the problem: a coffee mocha at one national chain of cafes provides 350 calories, which is 17.5% of an average adult's total daily calorie needs.

It's not surprising, then, that many (although not all!) researchers believe that calories from such beverages have contributed significantly to the rise in caloric intake among Americans since the late 1970s. That's because beverages with a high calorie content appear to do little to curb appetite, so people may not compensate for the extra calories they drink by eating less.[5]

What Happens If We Drink Too Much Water?

Drinking too much water and becoming overhydrated is very rare, but it can occur. Certain illnesses can cause excessive reabsorption, or retention, of water by the kidneys. When this occurs, overhydration and dilution of blood sodium result. As described in the chapter-opening story, marathon runners and other endurance athletes can overhydrate and dangerously dilute their blood sodium concentration. This condition, called *hyponatremia,* is discussed in more detail shortly.

What Happens If We Don't Drink Enough Water?

Dehydration results when we do not drink enough water or are unable to retain the water we consume. It is one of the leading causes of death around the world. Dehydration is generally due to some form of illness or gastrointestinal infection that causes diarrhea and vomiting.

Network Productions/The Image Works

Numerous varieties of drinking water are available to consumers.

What About You?

How Pure Is Your Favorite Bottled Water?

The next time you reach for a bottle of water, check the label. To find out how pure it is, consider the following factors:

1. Find out where it comes from. If no location is identified, even a bottle labeled "spring water" may actually contain tap water with minerals added to improve the taste. What you're looking for are the words "Bottled at the source." Water that comes from a protected groundwater source is less likely to have contaminants, such as disease-causing microbes. If the label doesn't identify the water's source, it should at least provide contact information, such as a phone number or website of the bottled water company, so that you can track down the source.

2. Find out how the water in the bottle has been treated. There are several ways of treating water, but what you're looking for is either of the following two methods, which have been proven to be effective against the most common waterborne disease-causing microorganisms:

➤ *Micron filtration* is a process whereby water is filtered through screens with various-sized microscopic holes. High-quality micron filtration can eliminate most chemical contaminants and microbes.

➤ *Reverse osmosis* is a process often referred to as *ultra-filtration* because it uses a membrane with microscopic openings that allow water to pass through but not larger compounds. Reverse osmosis membranes also utilize electrical charges to reject harmful chemicals.

If the label on your bottle of water says that the water was purified using any of the following methods, you might want to consider switching brands: filtered, carbon-filtered, particle-filtered, ozonated or ozone-treated, ultraviolet light, ion exchange, or deionized. These methods have not been proven to be effective against the most common water-borne disease-causing microorganisms.

3. Check the nutrient content on the label. Ideally, water should be high in magnesium (at least 20 mg per 8 fl. oz serving) and calcium but low in sodium (less than 5 mg per 8 fl. oz serving). Avoid bottled waters with sweeteners, as their "empty calories" can contribute significantly to your energy intake. These products are often promoted as healthful beverage choices, with names including words such as *vitamins, herbs, nature,* and *life,* but they are essentially "liquid candy." Check the Nutrition Facts Panel and don't be fooled!

Kristin Piljay

➡ Can you tell where the water in each bottle comes from?

NUTRI-CASE JUDY

"I've heard about how important it is to drink at least 8 cups of fluid a day. At first that seemed like an awful lot, but after keeping track of what I drank yesterday, I figured I'm good. I had a mug of coffee when I first got up, a can of soda on my way to work, a coffee mocha on my morning break, another soda with lunch, and a bottle of Gatorade in the afternoon. On my way home, I stopped to pick up a pizza, and they were offering a free 22-ounce bottle of soda, so I went for it. I'm not sure what all that adds up to, but I know it's more than 8 cups. It's not as hard as I thought to get enough fluid!"

What do you think of the nutritional quality of Judy's fluid choices? If one 8-ounce serving of soda provides about 100 kcal, and a can is 12 ounces, how many Calories did Judy consume just from her soft drinks? And what about that coffee mocha? Given what you've learned about Judy so far in this text, could you suggest some other beverages that might be smarter choices for her?

George Doyle & Ciaran Griffin/Stockbyte/Getty Images

RECAP Fluid intake needs are highly variable and depend on body size, age, physical activity, health status, and environmental conditions. Drinking too much water can lead to overhydration and dilution of blood sodium. Drinking too little water leads to dehydration, one of the leading causes of death around the world.

Sodium

Over the last 20 years, researchers have linked high sodium intake to an increased risk for high blood pressure among some groups of individuals. Because of this link, many people have come to believe that sodium is harmful to the body. This oversimplification, however, is just not true: sodium is a valuable nutrient that is essential for survival.

Functions of Sodium

Sodium has a variety of functions. As discussed earlier in this chapter, it is the major positively charged electrolyte in the extracellular fluid. Its exchange with potassium across cell membranes allows cells to maintain proper fluid balance, blood pressure, and acid–base balance.

Sodium also assists with the transmission of nerve signals and aids in muscle contraction. To review, the release of sodium from inside to outside the cell stimulates the spread of nerve signals within nervous tissue. The stimulation of muscles by nerve impulses provides the impetus for muscle contraction.

How Much Sodium Should We Consume?

The AI for sodium is listed in Table 1. Most people in the United States consume two to four times the AI daily. Several health organizations recommend a daily sodium intake of no more than 2.3 g per day. The 2005 Dietary Guidelines for Americans specifically recommend that African Americans (who have a higher risk of hypertension, especially when consuming too much sodium) and all persons who already have hypertension limit their daily sodium intake to no more than 1.5 g.[6]

Beyond Table Salt: Sneaky Sources of Sodium

Sodium is found naturally in many whole foods, but most dietary sodium comes from processed foods and restaurant foods, which typically contain large amounts of added sodium. Try to guess which of the following foods contains the most sodium: 1 cup of tomato juice, 1 oz of potato chips, or 4 saltine crackers. Now look at Table 2

Andrea Skjold/Shutterstock

◆ Many popular snack foods are high in sodium.

TABLE 2	High-Sodium Foods and Lower-Sodium Alternatives			
High-Sodium Food	Sodium (mg)	Lower-Sodium Food	Sodium (mg)
Dill pickle (1 large, 4 in.)	1,731	Low-sodium dill pickle (1 large, 4 in.)	23
Ham, cured, roasted (3 oz)	1,023	Pork, loin roast (3 oz)	54
Turkey pastrami (3 oz)	915	Roasted turkey, cooked (3 oz)	54
Tomato juice, regular (1 cup)	877	Tomato juice, lower sodium (1 cup)	24
Macaroni and cheese (1 cup)	800	Spanish rice (1 cup)	5
Ramen noodle soup (chicken flavor) (1 package [85 g])	1,960	Ramen noodle soup made with sodium-free chicken bouillon (1 cup)	0
Teriyaki chicken (1 cup)	3,210	Stir-fried pork/rice/vegetables (1 cup)	575
Tomato sauce, canned (1/2 cup)	741	Fresh tomato (1 medium)	11
Creamed corn, canned (1 cup)	730	Cooked corn, fresh (1 cup)	28
Tomato soup, canned (1 cup)	695	Lower-sodium tomato soup, canned (1 cup)	480
Potato chips, salted (1 oz)	168	Baked potato, unsalted (1 medium)	14
Saltine crackers (4 crackers)	156	Saltine crackers, unsalted (4 crackers)	100

Data from U.S. Department of Agriculture. 2009. USDA Nutrient Database for Standard Reference, Release 22. Nutrient Data Laboratory Home Page. www.ars.usda.gov/ba/bhnrc/ndl.

to find the answer. This table shows foods that are high in sodium and gives lower-sodium alternatives. Are you surprised to find out that, of all of these food items, the tomato juice has the most sodium?

Because sodium is so abundant, it's easy to overdo it. To help you eat right all day, see the menu choices low in sodium. Each of these choices would be appropriate on the DASH diet. See the Quick Tips feature on the next page for ways to reduce your sodium intake.[7]

Eating Right All Day

Breakfast
Whole-grain waffle with jam instead of a ham & cheese omlette!

Lunch
Spinach salad instead of canned spinach!

Dinner
Veggie pizza instead of pepperoni!

Snack
Unsalted almonds instead of corn chips!

iStockphoto

Lorraine Kourafas/Shutterstock

barbaradudzinska/shutterstock

FotografiaBasica/iStockphoto

What Happens If We Consume Too Much Sodium?

High blood pressure is typically more common in people who consume high-sodium diets. This strong relationship between high-sodium diets and high blood pressure has prompted many health organizations to recommend lower sodium intakes; however, the question of whether high-sodium diets actually cause high blood pressure is a matter of considerable debate. Consuming excess sodium can cause an increased urinary excretion of calcium in some people, which in turn may increase their risk for bone loss. The relationship between sodium intake and bone health is also controversial; however, a number of recent studies suggest that a reduction in sodium intake improves bone status, particularly in older adults.[8]

Hypernatremia refers to an abnormally high blood sodium concentration. Although theoretically it could be caused by a rapid intake of high amounts of sodium—for instance, if a shipwrecked sailor resorted to drinking seawater—consuming too much sodium does not usually cause hypernatremia in a healthy person, as the kidneys are able to excrete excess sodium in the urine. But people with congestive heart failure or kidney disease are not able to excrete sodium effectively, making them more prone to the condition. Hypernatremia is dangerous because it causes an abnormally high blood volume, again, by pulling water from the intracellular environment to dilute the sodium in the extracellular tissue spaces and vessels. This leads to edema (swelling) of tissues and elevation of blood pressure to unhealthy levels.

What Happens If We Don't Consume Enough Sodium?

Because the dietary intake of sodium is so high among Americans, deficiencies of sodium are extremely rare, except in individuals who sweat heavily or consume little or no sodium in the diet. Nevertheless, certain conditions can cause dangerously low blood sodium levels.

Rachel Weill/Foodpix/Jupiter Images

Condiments can add sodium to your diet.

hypernatremia A condition in which blood sodium levels are dangerously high.

QUICK TIPS

Reducing the Sodium in Your Diet

✓ Put away the salt shaker—keep it off the table and train your taste buds to prefer foods with less salt.

✓ Follow the DASH diet plan, which is high in fruits, vegetables, whole grains, and lean protein foods. The more you include fresh, whole foods in your diet, the less sodium you will be eating.

✓ Look for the words *low sodium* when buying processed foods. Use the Nutrition Facts Panel to find foods that contain 5% or less of the daily value for sodium or less than 200 mg per serving.

✓ Look for *hidden* salt content on food labels; for example, both monosodium glutamate and sodium benzoate are forms of sodium.

✓ Compare the labels of various name brands of the same food, since products can vary greatly in their sodium content.

✓ Choose fresh or frozen vegetables (without added sauces), as they are usually much lower in sodium than canned vegetables. Alternatively, choose salt-free canned vegetables.

✓ Stay away from prepared stews, canned and dried soups, gravies, and pasta sauces, as well as packaged pasta, rice, and potato dishes that are high in sodium.

✓ Choose low-sodium versions of pickles, olives, three-bean salad, and salad dressings.

✓ Choose low-sodium versions of cheese, smoked meats and fish, and nuts.

✓ Snack on fruits and vegetables instead of salty snack foods. If you do buy pretzels, chips, and other snack items, choose low-sodium versions.

✓ When cooking, experiment with commercial salt substitutes, herbs, spices, lemon juice, and possibly cooking wine to flavor your food. Products that end in the word *salt*, such as garlic salt or celery salt, are high in sodium and should be avoided.

✓ Rinse canned legumes, such as black, navy, garbanzo, or kidney beans, with cold water to lower the sodium content before heating and consuming them.

✓ Reduce the amounts of condiments you use. Condiments such as ketchup, mustard, pickle relish, and soy sauce can add a considerable amount of sodium to your foods. Again, check the labels of these items.

✓ When eating out, look for entrées labeled "heart healthy" or "lower in sodium"; if nutrition information is provided, compare foods to select those with lower amounts of sodium.

✓ Check the labels on your medications. Many medications, including aspirin, are high in sodium.

✓ Check the labels of the beverages you consume as well; fluids are often a "hidden" source of dietary sodium.

Hyponatremia, or abnormally low blood sodium levels, can occur in people engaged in strenuous physical activity who drink large volumes of water and fail to replace sodium. This was the case with Cynthia Lucero in our chapter-opening story, and it is discussed further in the accompanying Nutrition Myth or Fact? box. Severe diarrhea, vomiting, or excessive prolonged sweating can also cause hyponatremia. Symptoms include headaches, dizziness, fatigue, nausea, vomiting, and muscle cramps. If hyponatremia is left untreated, it can lead to seizures, coma, and death. Treatment for hyponatremia includes replacement of the lost minerals by consuming liquids and foods high in sodium and other minerals. It may be necessary to administer electrolyte-rich solutions intravenously if the person has lost consciousness or is not able to consume beverages and foods by mouth.

Potassium

As we discussed previously, potassium is the major positively charged electrolyte in the intracellular fluid. It is a major constituent of all living cells and is found in both plants and animals.

Functions of Potassium

Potassium and sodium work together to maintain proper fluid balance and regulate the transmission of nerve impulses and the contraction of muscles. And in contrast to a high-sodium diet, a diet high in potassium actually helps maintain a lower blood pressure.

How Much Potassium Should We Consume?

Potassium is found in abundance in many fresh foods, especially fresh fruits and vegetables. Processed foods generally have less potassium than fresh foods.

The AI for potassium is listed in Table 1. According to a recent report, fewer than 10% of American adults consume the recommended amount of potassium.[9] By avoiding processed foods and eating more fresh fruits, vegetables, legumes, whole grains, and dairy foods, you'll increase your potassium intake and decrease your sodium intake, achieving a more healthful diet.

hyponatremia A condition in which blood sodium levels are dangerously low.

NUTRITION MYTH OR FACT?
Can Fluids Provide Too Much of a Good Thing?

At the beginning of this chapter, we described the death of marathon runner Cynthia Lucero. Her case is only one of several that have gained attention in recent years. How can seemingly healthy, highly fit individuals competing in marathons collapse and even die during or shortly after a race? One common challenge these athletes face is that of maintaining a proper balance of fluid and electrolytes throughout the race.

It is well known that people participating in distance events, such as marathons (26.2 miles), need to drink enough fluid to stay hydrated. But what hasn't been recognized until recently is that some runners, especially novice runners, can drink *too much* water and other fluids and develop hyponatremia, or abnormally low blood sodium levels.

A recent scientific review of what is now termed "exercise-associated hyponatremia," or EAH, found that major risk factors included longer race times, a slow pace of running, and intake of large amounts of water or other

Consuming too much water can deplete blood sodium levels.

fluids during the race.[10] The researchers speculate that less experienced athletes run more slowly, increasing the total time that they are competing; at the same time, they consume very large amounts of fluids, including water, to avoid dehydration. The longer these individuals run, the more fluids they drink and the more diluted their blood sodium levels become. Many hyponatremic runners need to be hospitalized in order to prevent life-threatening complications.

A study of long-distance triathletes (competing in swimming, cycling, and running) found that about 18% of these athletes suffered from hyponatremia.[11] Thus, individuals competing in various long-distance events or activities are at risk for this disorder.

Hyponatremia is a dangerous and potentially fatal condition. Moderating total fluid intake during marathons and other long-distance activities and developing a personal plan of action with your healthcare provider can help prevent it.

Sources of Potassium: Potatoes, Bananas, and More

As more and more people rely on processed foods, their sodium intake increases and their potassium intake decreases. Many researchers think that this sodium–potassium imbalance is a major factor contributing to the increased incidence of hypertension in the United States. Thus, fresh foods, particularly fresh fruits and vegetables, should be included in every meal. **Figure 8** identifies foods that are high in potassium. See the Quick Tips on the next page on how to increase your dietary potassium.

What Happens If We Consume Too Much Potassium?

People with healthy kidneys are able to excrete excess potassium effectively. However, people with kidney disease are not able to regulate their blood potassium levels. **Hyperkalemia,** or high blood potassium levels, occurs when potassium is not excreted efficiently from the body. Because of potassium's role in cardiac muscle contraction, severe hyperkalemia can alter the normal rhythm of the heart, resulting in heart attack and death. People with kidney failure must monitor their potassium intake very carefully to prevent complications from hyperkalemia. Individuals at risk for hyperkalemia should avoid consuming salt substitutes, as these products are high in potassium.

Tomato juice is an excellent source of potassium. Make sure you choose the low-sodium variety!

hyperkalemia A condition in which blood potassium levels are dangerously high.

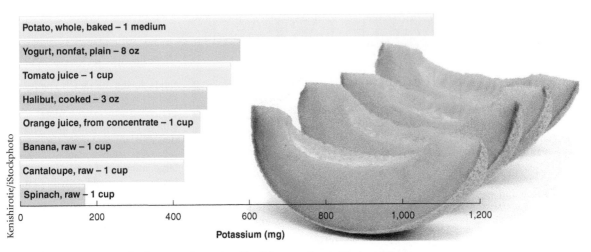

Figure 8 Common food sources of potassium. The AI for potassium is 4.7 g (or 4,700 mg) per day.

Data from U.S. Department of Agriculture, Agricultural Research Service. 2009. USDA Nutrient Database for Standard Reference, Release 22. Nutrient Data Laboratory Home Page. www.ars.usda.gov/ba/bhnrc/ndl.

QUICK TIPS

Increasing Your Potassium Intake

✓ Avoid processed foods that are high in sodium and low in potassium. Check the Nutrition Facts Panel of the food before you buy it!

✓ For breakfast, look for cereals containing bran and/or wheat germ.

✓ Sprinkle wheat germ on yogurt and top with banana slices.

✓ Add wheat germ to baked goods, such as homemade pancakes and muffins.

✓ Drink milk! If you don't like milk, try one of the new drinkable yogurts. Many brands of soy milk are also good sources of potassium.

✓ Make a smoothie by blending ice cubes and low-fat vanilla ice cream or yogurt with a banana.

✓ Pack a can of low-sodium vegetable or tomato juice in your lunch in place of a soft drink.

✓ Serve avocado or bean dip with veggie slices.

✓ Replace the meat in your sandwich with thin slices of avocado or marinated tofu.

✓ Replace the meat in tacos and burritos with black or pinto beans.

✓ For a healthful alternative to french fries, toss slices of sweet potato in olive oil, place on a cookie sheet, and oven bake at 400° for 10–15 minutes.

✓ Toss a banana, some dried apricots, or a bag of sunflower seeds into your lunch bag.

✓ Make a fruit salad with apricots, bananas, cantaloupe, honeydew melon, mango, or papaya.

✓ Bake and enjoy a fresh pumpkin pie!

What Happens If We Don't Consume Enough Potassium?

Because potassium is widespread in many foods, a dietary potassium deficiency is rare. However, potassium deficiency is not uncommon among people who have serious medical disorders. Kidney disease, a complication of poorly controlled diabetes known as diabetic acidosis, and other illnesses can lead to potassium deficiency.

In addition, people with high blood pressure who are prescribed diuretic medications are at risk for potassium deficiency. Diuretics promote the excretion of fluid as urine through the kidneys and some also increase the excretion of potassium. People who are taking diuretic medications should have their blood potassium monitored regularly and should eat foods that are high in potassium to prevent **hypokalemia,** or low blood potassium levels. This is not a universal recommendation, however, because some diuretics are specially formulated to spare potassium; therefore, people taking this type of diuretic should not increase their dietary potassium above recommended levels.

Extreme dehydration, vomiting, and diarrhea can also cause hypokalemia. People who abuse alcohol or laxatives are also at risk for hypokalemia. Symptoms include

hypokalemia A condition in which blood potassium levels are dangerously low.

confusion, loss of appetite, and muscle weakness. Severe cases of hypokalemia result in fatal changes in heart rate; many deaths attributed to extreme dehydration or eating disorders are caused by abnormal heart rhythms due to hypokalemia.

Chloride

Chloride should not be confused with *chlorine*, which is a poisonous gas used to kill bacteria and other germs in our water supply. Chloride is a negatively charged ion that is obtained almost exclusively in our diet from sodium chloride, or table salt.

Functions of Chloride

Coupled with sodium in the extracellular fluid, chloride assists with the maintenance of fluid balance. Chloride is also a part of hydrochloric acid (HCl) in the stomach, which aids in preparing food for further digestion. Chloride works with the white blood cells of our body during an immune response to help kill bacteria, and it assists in the transmission of nerve impulses.

How Much Chloride Should We Consume?

The AI for chloride is listed in Table 1. Our primary dietary source of chloride is salt in our foods. Chloride is also found in some fruits and vegetables.

Since virtually all dietary chloride is in the form of sodium chloride, consuming excess amounts of this mineral over a prolonged period leads to hypertension in salt-sensitive individuals. There is no other known toxicity symptom for chloride.[2]

Because of the relatively high dietary salt intake in the United States, most people consume more than enough chloride. Even when a person consumes a low-sodium diet, chloride intake is usually adequate. A chloride deficiency can occur, however, during conditions of severe dehydration and frequent vomiting. For example, it can develop in people with eating disorders who regularly vomit to rid their bodies of unwanted calories.

Foodcollection/Getty Images

◆ Almost all chloride is consumed through table salt.

Phosphorus

Phosphorus is the major intracellular negatively charged electrolyte. In the body, phosphorus is most commonly found in the form of phosphate, PO_4^{2-}. Phosphorus is an essential constituent of all cells and is found in both plants and animals.

Functions of Phosphorus

Phosphorus works with potassium inside cells to maintain proper fluid balance. It also plays a critical role in bone formation, as it is a part of the mineral complex of bone. In fact, about 85% of our body's phosphorus is stored in our bones.

As a primary component of adenosine triphosphate (ATP), phosphorus plays a key role in creating energy for our body. It also helps regulate many biochemical reactions by activating and deactivating enzymes. Phosphorus is a part of deoxyribonucleic acid (DNA) and ribonucleic acid (RNA), and it is a component in cell membranes (as phospholipids) and lipoproteins.

How Much Phosphorus Should We Consume?

The RDA for phosphorus is listed in Table 1. The average U.S. adult consumes about twice this amount each day; thus, phosphorus deficiencies are rare. Phosphorus is widespread in many foods and is found in high amounts in foods that contain protein. Milk, meats, and eggs are good sources. **Figure 9** shows the phosphorus content of various foods.

It is important to note that phosphorus from animal sources is absorbed more readily than that from plant sources. The phosphorus in plant foods such as beans,

Fotogiunta/Shutterstock

◆ Milk is a good source of phosphorus.

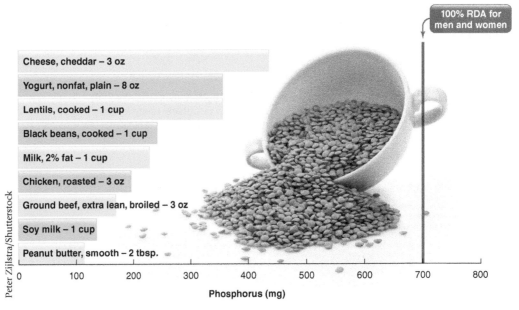

Peter Zijlstra/Shutterstock

Figure 9 Common food sources of phosphorus. The RDA for phosphorus is 700 mg/day.
Data from U.S. Department of Agriculture, Agricultural Research Service. 2009. USDA Nutrient Database for Standard Reference, Release 22.
Nutrient Data Laboratory Home Page. www.ars.usda.gov/ba/bhnrc/ndl.

cereals, and nuts is found in the form of **phytic acid,** a plant storage form of phosphorus. Our body does not produce enzymes that can break down phytic acid, but we are still able to absorb up to 50% of the phosphorus found in plant foods because other foods and the bacteria in our large intestine can break down phytic acid. Soft drinks are another common source of phosphorus in our diet, and the heavy consumption of soft drinks may be detrimental to bone health.

People suffering from kidney disease and people taking too many vitamin D supplements or too many phosphorus-containing antacids can suffer from high blood phosphorus levels. Severely high levels of blood phosphorus cause muscle spasms and convulsions.

As mentioned previously, deficiencies of phosphorus are rare. People who may suffer from low blood phosphorus levels include premature infants, elderly people with poor diets, and people who abuse alcohol. People with vitamin D deficiency, those with hyperparathyroidism (oversecretion of parathyroid hormone), and those who overuse antacids that bind with phosphorus may also have low blood phosphorus levels.

RECAP The four electrolytes critical for hydration and neuromuscular function are sodium, potassium, chloride, and phosphorus. Most Americans consume too much sodium and often get too little potassium; intakes of chloride and phosphorus are almost always adequate but not excessive. Electrolyte imbalances can result in heart failure, seizures, and death.

phytic acid The form of phosphorus stored in plants.

Nutrition DEBATE

Sports Beverages: Help or Hype?

Once considered specialty items used exclusively by elite athletes, sports beverages have become popular everyday beverage choices for both active and nonactive people. This surge in popularity leads us to ask three important questions:

- Do these beverages benefit highly active athletes?
- Do these beverages benefit recreationally active people?
- Do non-athletes need to consume sports beverages?

The first question is relatively easy to answer. Sports beverages were originally developed to meet the unique fluid, electrolyte, and carbohydrate needs of competitive athletes. Highly active people need to replenish both fluids and electrolytes to avoid either dehydration or hyponatremia. For example, endurance athletes are able to exercise longer, maintain a higher intensity, and improve performance times when they drink a sports beverage during exercise.[12] The carbohydrates in sports beverages may also help athletes consume more energy than they could by eating solid foods and water alone. Some competitive athletes train for 6 to 8 hours each day on a regular basis: it's virtually impossible to consume enough solid foods to support this level of exercise.

Do recreationally active people need to consume sports beverages? Most probably do not, but if they exercise for periods longer than 1 hour, they can benefit from consuming the carbo-

hydrate and electrolytes in sports beverages during exercise. Any person who exercises in high temperatures also will benefit from the fluid and electrolyte replacement benefits of sports beverages.[13]

If you're active, how do you know whether you should consume a sports beverage? The answer depends on the duration and intensity of exercise, the environmental conditions, and your unique characteristics. Here are some situations in which drinking a sports beverage is appropriate:[12]

- During exercise or physical work in high heat and/or high humidity or if you have recently experienced diarrhea or vomiting
- During exercise at high altitude and in cold environments; these conditions increase fluid and electrolyte losses
- After exercise for rapid rehydration or between exercise bouts, such as between multiple soccer matches during a tournament
- During long-duration exercise when blood glucose levels get low; sports beverages may be needed to maintain

Tobias Titz/Getty Images

→ Sports beverages were originally designed to meet the needs of competitive athletes.

energy levels and to provide the fluid necessary to prevent dehydration

- During exercise sessions if you have poor glycogen stores prior to exercise or are not well fed prior to exercise

Interestingly, sports beverages have become very popular with people who do little or no regular exercise. Are there any benefits or negative consequences for inactive or lightly active people who regularly consume these drinks? There does not appear to be any evidence that people who do not exercise derive any benefits from consuming sports beverages. Even if these individuals live in a hot environment, they should be able to replenish the fluid and electrolytes they lose during sweating by drinking water and other beverages and eating a normal diet.

One common negative consequence when inactive people drink sports beverages is weight gain, contributing to obesity. As an example, drinking 12 fl. oz (1.5 cups) of Gatorade adds 90 kcal to a person's daily energy intake. Many inactive people consume two to three times this amount each day, adding 180 to 270 kcal to their diet. With obesity rates at an all-time high, it is important that we attempt to consume only the foods and beverages necessary to support our health. Sports beverages are not designed to be consumed by inactive people, and they do not contribute to the overall health of inactive or lightly active people.

Chapter Review

Test Yourself ANSWERS

1. False. Recent research suggests that caffeine intake has virtually no effect on fluid balance.

2. False. Sodium is a nutrient necessary for health, but we should not consume more than recommended amounts.

3. False. Our thirst mechanism signals that we need to replenish fluids, but it is not sufficient to ensure that we are completely hydrated.

Find the Quack

Libby is shopping for groceries with her 10-year-old daughter, Jen. When they turn into the beverage aisle, Jen exclaims over a colorful display offering a free hot-pink Frisbee with the purchase of a six-pack of a new vitamin-fortified sparkling water. The poster above the display shows a family in a park playing Frisbee together while drinking or holding a bottle of the new water. A banner above the photograph proclaims "Part of Your Healthy Life!"

"Mom, can we get some?" Jen asks.

Libby reads the product packaging, which describes the beverage as follows:

- "Lightly carbonated delicious sparkling water!"
- "All natural flavor and color!"
- "Packed with vitamins!"
- "A 12-oz serving of the water contains 10% of the Daily Value (DV) for vitamins E, B_6, B_{12}, and niacin."
- "No other vitamins or minerals are listed."
- "A serving contains 128 calories and 32 g of carbohydrate."
- "The product is sweetened with high-fructose corn syrup."
- "The cost is $4.99 per six-pack."

Libby can't decide whether to give in and buy the water or not. "I don't know, honey," she tells her daughter. "It looks healthy, but $4.99 seems like a lot to pay for a Frisbee and some vitamins!"

1. The product packaging claims that the beverage is "Packed with vitamins!" Evaluate this statement by checking out the label of a multivitamin supplement either at home or at a market. How many vitamins does it contain, and at what percentage of the DV? Which provides more nutrients: the fortified water or a glass of plain water plus a multivitamin tablet? Calculate the difference in cost per serving.

2. It's summer, and Jen plays children's soccer two mornings a week on an unshaded field. Would Libby be smarter to purchase a sports beverage, such as Gatorade, for her daughter to drink during her soccer matches or this new vitamin-fortified water, or should she give Jen plain water to drink? Explain. (Hint: See the Nutrition Debate on the previous page.)

3. Check out the nutrition information on a carton of milk. Which contains the greater variety of nutrients, and at what cost: the fortified water or the milk?

4. The vitamin-fortified water is sweetened with high-fructose corn syrup and contains 128 calories per serving. This is about equivalent to a can of grape soda. The promoters characterize the beverage as "Part of Your Healthy Life." Do you agree or disagree? Why?

Answers can be found on the companion website, at www.pearsonhighered.com/thompsonmanore.

 NutriTools Check out the companion website at www.pearsonhighered.com/thompsonmanore, or use MyNutritionLab.com, to access interactive animations, including:

- Nutrient Functionality

Review Questions

1. Which of the following is a characteristic of potassium?
   a. It is the major positively charged electrolyte in the extracellular fluid.
   b. It can be found in fresh fruits and vegetables.
   c. It is a critical component of the mineral complex of bone.
   d. It is the major negatively charged electrolyte in the extracellular fluid.

2. Which of the following people probably has the greatest percentage of his or her weight as body fluid?
   a. A female adult who is slightly overweight and vomits nightly after eating dinner.
   b. An elderly male of average weight who has low blood pressure.
   c. An overweight football player who has just completed a practice session in high heat.
   d. A healthy infant of average weight.

3. Plasma is one example of
   a. extracellular fluid.
   b. intracellular fluid.
   c. tissue fluid.
   d. metabolic water.

4. Which of the following is true of the cell membrane?
   a. It is freely permeable to all electrolytes.
   b. It is freely permeable to water and all solutes.
   c. It is freely permeable only to fats.
   d. It is freely permeable to water but not to solutes.

5. We lose fluids through
   a. sweat.
   b. breath.
   c. feces.
   d. all of the above.

6. True or false? Drinking lots of water throughout a marathon will prevent fluid imbalances.

7. True or false? A decreased concentration of electrolytes in our blood stimulates the thirst mechanism.

8. True or false? Hypernatremia commonly occurs when we are dehydrated.

9. True or false? Absence of thirst is a reliable indicator of adequate hydration.

10. True or false? Conditions that increase fluid loss include constipation, blood transfusions, and high humidity.

Answers to Review Questions can be found at the back of this text, and additional essay questions and answers are located on the companion website at www.pearsonhighered.com/ thompsonmanore.

Web Resources

www.epa.gov/OW
U.S. Environmental Protection Agency: Water

Go to the EPA's water website for more information about drinking water quality, standards, and safety.

www.bottledwater.org
International Bottled Water Association

Find current information about bottled water from this trade association, which represents the bottled water industry.

www.mayoclinic.com
MayoClinic.com

Search for "hyponatremia" to learn more about this potentially fatal condition.

www.nih.gov
The National Institutes of Health (NIH)

Search this site to learn more about the Dietary Approaches to Stop Hypertension (DASH) diet.

www.nephrologychannel.com/electrolytes
Nephrologychannel.com: Electrolyte Imbalances

Visit this website to learn more about hyponatremia, hypernatremia, hypokalemia, and hyperkalemia.

www.wqa.org
Water Quality Association (WQA)

The website for the WQA, a trade association for the water treatment industry, lists recent news affecting municipal water supplies, home water testing, and water quality.

References

1. Almond, C. S. D., A. Y. Shin, E. B. Fortescue, R. C. Mannix, D. Wypij, B. A. Binstadt, C. N. Duncan, D. P. Olson, A. E. Salerno, J. W. Newburger, and D. S. Greenes. 2005. Hyponatremia among runners in the Boston Marathon. *N. Engl. J. Med.* 352:1150–1156.
2. Institute of Medicine. 2004. Dietary Reference Intakes for Water, Potassium, Sodium, Chloride, and Sulfate. Washington, DC: National Academies Press.
3. Godek, S. F., A. R. Bartolozzi, R. Burkholder, E. Sugarman, and C. Peduzzi. 2008. Sweat rates and fluid turnover in professional football players: a comparison of national football league linemen and backs. *J. Athletic Training* 43:184–189.
4. Smith, T. 2008. Bottled water consumption continues to rise worldwide. TimesDaily.com. Available at http://www.timesdaily.com/article/20081020/ARTICLES/810200321?Title=Bottled-water-consumption-continues-to-rise-worldwide.
5. Brody, J. 2007. You are also what you drink. *New York Times*, Personal Health; March 27, 2007, Section F.
6. U.S. Department of Health and Human Services (USDHHS) and U.S. Department of Agriculture (USDA). 2005. Dietary Guidelines for Americans, 2005. 6th ed. Washington, DC: U.S. Government Printing Office. Available at www.healthierus.gov/dietaryguidelines.
7. The University of Maine Cooperative Extension. 2007. Sodium content of your food. http://www.umext.maine.edu/onlinepubs/htmpubs/4059.htm.
8. Frassetto, L. A., R. C. Morris, D. E. Sellmeyer, and A. Sebastian. 2008. Adverse effects of sodium chloride on bone in the aging human population resulting from habitual consumption of typical American diets. *J. Nutr.* 138:419S–422S.
9. McGill, C. R., V. L. Fulgoni, D. DiRienzo, P. J. Huth, A. C. Kurilich, and G. D. Miller. 2008. Contributions of dairy products to dietary potassium intake in the United States population. *J. Am. College Nutr.* 27:44–50.
10. Hew-Butler, T., J. C. Ayus, C. Kipps, R. J. Maughan, S. Mettler, W. H. Meeuwisse, A. J. Page, S. A. Reid, N. J. Rehrer, W. O. Roberts, I. R. Rogers, M. H. Rosner, A. J. Siegel, D. B. Speedy, K. J. Stuempfle, J. G. Verbalis, L. B. Weschler, and P. Wharam. 2008. Statement of the second international exercise-associated hyponatremia consensus development conference, New Zealand, 2007. *Clin. J. Sport Med.* 18:111–121.
11. Speedy, D. B., T. D. Noakes, I. R. Rogers, J. M. Thompson, R. G. Campbell, J. A. Kuttner, D. R. Boswell, S. Wright, and M. Hamlin. 1999. Hyponatremia in ultradistance triathletes. *Med. Sci. Sports Exerc.* 31:809–815.
12. Manore, M., N. L. Meyer, and J. Thompson. 2009. Sport Nutrition for Health and Performance, 2nd ed. Champaign, IL: Human Kinetics (117).
13. Sawka, M. N., L. M. Burke, E. R. Eichner, R. J. Maughan, S. J. Montain, and N. S. Stachenfeld. 2007. American College of Sports Medicine Position Stand: Exercise and fluid replacement. *Med. Sci. Sports Exer.* 39:377–390.

Answers to Review Questions

Answers to Review Questions 11-15 (essay questions) for this chapter are located on the Companion Website at **www.pearsonhighered.com/thompsonmanore**

1. **b.** It can be found in fresh fruits and vegetables.
2. **d.** A healthy infant of average weight.
3. **a.** extracellular fluid.
4. **d.** It is freely permeable to water but impermeable to solutes.
5. **d.** all of the above.
6. False. In addition to water, the body needs electrolytes, such as sodium and potassium, to prevent fluid imbalances during long-distance events such as a marathon. As purified water contains no electrolytes, this would not be the ideal beverage to prevent fluid imbalances during a marathon.
7. False. Our thirst mechanism is triggered by an increase in the concentration of electrolytes in our blood.
8. False. Hypernatremia is commonly caused by a rapid intake of high amounts of sodium.
9. False. Quenching our thirst does not guarantee adequate hydration. Urine that is clear or light yellow in color is one indicator of adequate hydration.
10. False. These conditions are associated with decreased fluid loss or an increase in body fluid. Diarrhea, blood loss, and low humidity are conditions that increase fluid loss.

Nutrients Involved in Antioxidant Function

From Chapter 8 of *Nutrition: An Applied Approach*, Third Edition. Janice Thompson, Melinda Manore. Copyright © 2012 by Pearson Education, Inc. Published by Pearson Benjamin Cummings. All rights reserved.

Nutrients Involved in Antioxidant Function

CHAPTER OBJECTIVES

After reading this chapter you will be able to:

1. Define the term *free radicals* and explain how they can damage cells.

2. Define the term *antioxidant enzyme systems* and identify the minerals involved in these systems.

3. Discuss the interrelated roles of vitamins E and C in protecting cells from oxidative damage.

4. Explain how vitamin C helps maintain bone, skin, tendons, and other tissues.

5. Describe the relationship between beta-carotene and vitamin A.

6. Discuss the role of vitamin A in vision.

Kelly Cline/iStockphoto

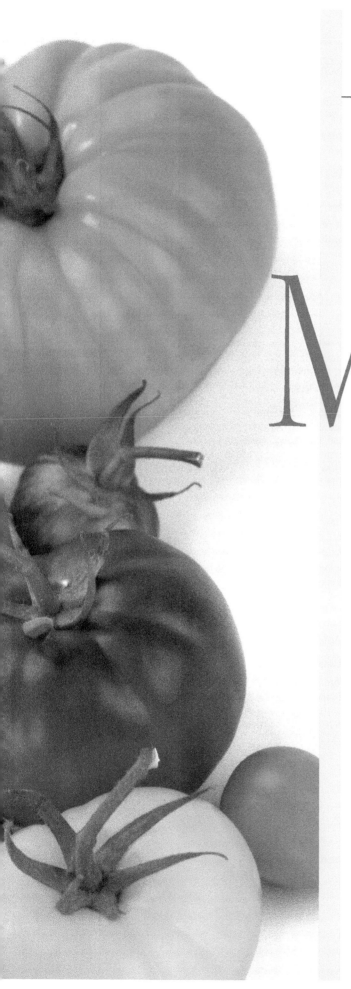

M ika, a first-year student at a university hundreds of miles from home, just opened another care package from her mom. As usual, it contained an assortment of healthful snacks, a box of chamomile tea, and several types of supplements: echinacea extract to ward off colds, powdered papaya for good digestion, and antioxidant vitamins. "Wow, Mika!" her roommate laughed. "Can you let your mom know I'm available for adoption?"

"I guess she just wants me to stay healthy," Mika sighed. She wondered what her mother would think if she ever found out how much junk food Mika had been eating since she'd started college, or that she'd been binge-drinking most weekends, or that she'd been smoking since high school. "Still," Mika reminded herself, "at least I take the vitamins she sends."

What do you think of Mika's current lifestyle? Can a poor diet, binge-drinking, and smoking cause cancer or other health problems, and can the use of dietary supplements provide some protection? What are antioxidant vitamins, and why do you think Mika's mom included a bottle of these in her care package? If your health food store were promoting an antioxidant supplement, would you buy it?

It isn't easy to sort fact from fiction when it comes to antioxidants—especially when they're in the form of supplements. Internet ads and articles in fitness and health magazines tout their benefits, yet some researchers claim that antioxidant supplements don't protect us from diseases and in some cases may even be harmful. In this chapter, you'll learn what antioxidants are and how they work in the body. We'll discuss how antioxidants consumed in foods protect cells from damage that can lead to cancer and cardiovascular disease, and how consuming antioxidants in supplements may work against us. And as we profile each antioxidant nutrient, we'll identify additional roles it plays in protecting and maintaining our health.

What Are Antioxidants, and How Does Our Body Use Them?

Antioxidants are compounds that protect our cells from the damage caused by oxidation. *Anti* means "against," and antioxidants work *against,* or *prevent,* oxidation. Before we can go further in our discussion of antioxidants, we need to learn what oxidation is and how it damages cells.

Oxidation Is a Chemical Reaction in Which Atoms Lose Electrons

A review of some basic chemistry will help you understand the process of oxidation. Our body is made up of atoms, tiny units of matter that cannot be broken down by natural means. Hydrogen, carbon, and iron are unique because their atoms are unique. Every atom of carbon, for example, is identical to every other atom of carbon, whether it is present in coal or in cheese. We also said that atoms join together to form molecules, such as saccharides and amino acids, which are the smallest *physical units* of a substance. Some molecules, such as hydrogen gas (H_2), contain only one type of atom—in this case, hydrogen. Most molecules, however, are *compounds*—they contain two or more different types of atoms (such as water, H_2O). Our body is constantly breaking down compounds of food, water, and air into their component atoms, then rearranging these freed atoms to build the different substances our body needs.

Atoms Are Composed of Particles

We just said that atoms cannot be broken down by natural means, but during the 20th century, physicists learned how to split atoms into their components, which they called *particles*. As you can see in **Figure 1**, this research revealed that all atoms have a central core, called a **nucleus,** which is positively charged. Orbiting around this nucleus at close to the speed of light are one or more **electrons,** which are negatively charged. The opposite attraction between the positive nucleus and the negative electrons keeps an atom together by making the atom stable, so that its electrons remain with it and do not veer off toward other atoms.

During Metabolism, Atoms Exchange Electrons

The process by which our body breaks down and builds up molecules is called *metabolism*. During metabolism, atoms may lose electrons **(Figure 2a)**. We call this loss of electrons **oxidation,** because it is fueled by oxygen. Atoms are capable of gaining electrons during metabolism as well. We call

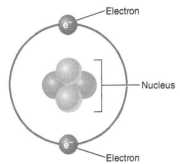

▲ **Figure 1** An atom consists of a central nucleus and orbiting electrons. The nucleus exerts a positive charge, which keeps the negatively charged electrons in its vicinity. Notice that this atom has an even number of electrons in orbit around the nucleus. This pairing of electrons results in the atom being chemically stable.

antioxidant A compound that has the ability to prevent or repair the damage caused by oxidation.

nucleus The positively charged, central core of an atom. It is made up of two types of particles—protons and neutrons—bound tightly together. The nucleus of an atom contains essentially all of its atomic mass.

electron A negatively charged particle orbiting the nucleus of an atom.

oxidation A chemical reaction in which molecules of a substance are broken down into their component atoms. During oxidation, the atoms involved lose electrons.

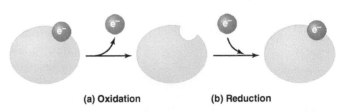

(a) Oxidation   **(b) Reduction**

▲ **Figure 2** The exchange reaction. Exchange reactions consist of two parts. **(a)** During oxidation, atoms *lose* electrons. **(b)** In the second part of the reaction, atoms *gain* electrons, which is called reduction.

this process *reduction* (Figure 2b). This loss and gain of electrons typically results in an even exchange of electrons. Scientists call this loss and gain of electrons an *exchange reaction.*

Oxidation Sometimes Results in the Formation of Free Radicals

Stable atoms have an even number of electrons orbiting in pairs at successive distances (called *shells* or *rings*) from the nucleus. When a stable atom loses an electron during oxidation, it is left with an odd number of electrons in its outermost shell. In other words, it now has an *unpaired electron.* In most exchange reactions, unpaired electrons immediately pair up with other unpaired electrons, making newly stabilized atoms, but in some cases, atoms with unpaired electrons in their outermost shell remain unpaired. Such atoms are highly unstable and are called **free radicals.**

Free radicals are formed as a normal by-product of many of our body's fundamental physiologic processes. Still, excessive production of free radicals can cause serious damage to our cells and other body components. Let's look at the most common way they arise. Our body uses oxygen and hydrogen to generate the energy (ATP) it needs (**Figure 3**). We are constantly inhaling air into our body, thereby providing the oxygen needed to fuel this reaction. At the same time, we generate the necessary hydrogen as a result of digesting food. As shown in **Figure 4**, occasionally during metabolism, oxygen accepts a single electron that was released during this process. When it does so, the oxygen atom becomes an unstable free radical because of the added unpaired electron.

Free radicals are also formed from other physiologic processes, such as when the immune system produces inflammation to fight allergens or infections. Other factors

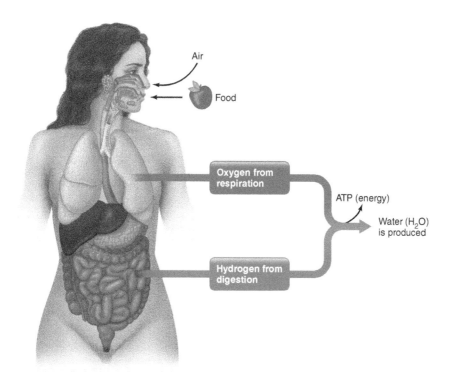

Figure 3 Oxygen (O) enters our body when we inhale air. Hydrogen (H) is released through the process of metabolizing food. As a result of exchange reactions during metabolism, electrons are freed to contribute to the production of the energy molecule ATP in body cells. The hydrogen and oxygen then recombine to form water (H_2O).

free radical A highly unstable atom with an unpaired electron in its outermost shell.

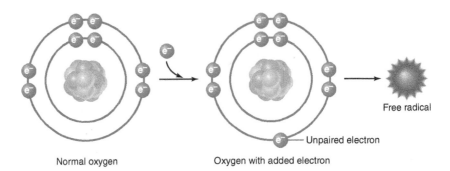

Normal oxygen

Oxygen with added electron

Unpaired electron

Free radical

Figure 4 Normally, an oxygen atom contains eight electrons. Occasionally, oxygen will accept an unpaired electron during the oxidation process. This acceptance of a single electron causes oxygen to become an unstable atom called a free radical.

that cause free radical formation include exposure to air pollution, ultraviolet (UV) rays from the sun, other types of radiation, tobacco smoke, industrial chemicals, and asbestos. Continual exposure to these factors leads to uncontrollable free radical formation, cell damage, and disease, as discussed next.

Free Radicals Can Destabilize Other Molecules and Damage Our Cells

Why are we concerned with the formation of free radicals? Simply put, it is because of their destabilizing power. If you were to think of paired electrons as a married couple, a free radical would be an extremely seductive outsider. Its unpaired electron exerts a powerful attraction toward all stable atoms and molecules around it. In an attempt to stabilize itself, a free radical will "steal" an electron from these stable neighbors, in turn generating more unstable free radicals. This is a dangerous chain reaction, since the free radicals generated can damage or destroy our cells.

One of the most significant sites of free radical damage is the cell membrane. As shown in **Figure 5a**, free radicals that form within the phospholipid bilayer of cell membranes steal electrons from the stable lipid heads. Lipids are insoluble in water, so a stable line-up of lipid heads allows cell membranes to keep water out. When these lipid heads are destroyed, the cell membrane can no longer repel water. With the cell membrane's integrity lost, its ability to regulate the movement of fluids and nutrients into and out of the cell is also lost. This loss of cell integrity causes damage to the cell and to all systems affected by the cell.

Other sites of free radical damage include low-density lipoproteins (LDLs), cell proteins, and DNA. Damage to LDLs and cell proteins disrupts the transport of substances into and out of cells and alters cell function, whereas defective DNA results in faulty protein synthesis. These changes can also cause harmful changes (mutations) in cells or prompt cells to die prematurely. Free radicals also promote blood vessel inflammation and the formation of clots, both of which are risk factors for cardiovascular disease. Not surprisingly, many diseases are linked with free radical production, including cancer, heart disease, type 2 diabetes, arthritis, cataracts, and kidney, Alzheimer's, and Parkinson's diseases.

Antioxidants Work by Stabilizing Free Radicals or Opposing Oxidation

How does our body fight free radicals and repair the damage they cause? These actions are performed by antioxidant vitamins, minerals, and phytochemicals and other compounds. These antioxidants perform their role in three ways:

1. Antioxidant vitamins work independently by donating their electrons or hydrogen atoms to free radicals to stabilize them and reduce the damage caused by oxidation (Figure 5b).

Walter Bibikow/Alamy

Exposure to pollution from car exhaust and industrial waste increases our production of free radicals.

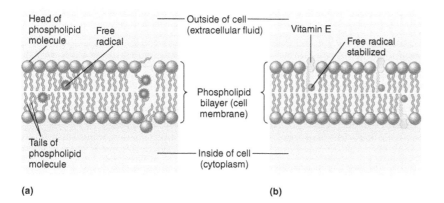

(a)

(b)

Figure 5 **(a)** The formation of free radicals in the lipid portion of our cell membranes can cause a dangerous chain reaction that damages the integrity of the membrane and can cause cell death. **(b)** Vitamin E is stored in the lipid portion of our cell membranes. By donating an electron to free radicals, it protects the lipid molecules in our cell membranes from themselves being oxidized and stops the chain reaction of oxidative damage.

2. Antioxidant minerals, including selenium, copper, iron, zinc, and manganese, act as **cofactors,** substances required to activate enzymes so that they can do their work. These minerals function within complex *antioxidant enzyme systems* that convert free radicals to less damaging substances that are excreted by our body. They also work to break down fatty acids that have become oxidized, thereby destroying the free radicals associated with them. Antioxidant enzyme systems also make more vitamin antioxidants available to fight other free radicals. Examples of these antioxidant enzyme systems are superoxide dismutase, catalase, and glutathione peroxidase.

3. Other compounds, such as beta-carotene and other phytochemicals, help stabilize free radicals and prevent damage to cells and tissues.

In summary, free radical formation is generally kept safely under control by certain vitamins, minerals working within antioxidant enzyme systems, and phytochemicals. Next, we take a look at the specific vitamins and minerals involved.

RECAP An atom is an infinitely small and unique unit of matter having a nucleus and orbiting electrons. Atoms join together to form molecules. During metabolism, molecules break apart and their atoms gain, lose, or exchange electrons; loss of electrons is called oxidation. Free radicals are highly unstable atoms with an unpaired electron in their outermost shell. A normal by-product of oxidation reactions, they can damage our LDLs, cell proteins, and DNA and are associated with many diseases. Antioxidant vitamins and phytochemicals donate electrons or hydrogen atoms to free radicals to stabilize them and reduce oxidative damage. Antioxidant minerals are part of antioxidant enzyme systems that convert free radicals to less damaging substances.

TABLE 1 Nutrients Involved in Antioxidant Function	
Nutrient	**Recommended Intake**
Vitamin E (fat soluble)	RDA: Women and men = 15 mg alpha-tocopheral
Vitamin C (water soluble)	RDA: Women = 75 mg Men = 90 mg Smokers = 35 mg more per day than RDA
Beta-carotene (fat-soluble provitamin for vitamin A)	None at this time
Vitamin A (fat soluble)	RDA: Women: 700 µg Men: 900 µg
Selenium (trace mineral)	RDA: Women and men = 55 µg

A Profile of Nutrients That Function as Antioxidants

Our body cannot form antioxidants spontaneously. Instead, we must consume them in our diet. Nutrients that appear to have antioxidant properties or are part of our protective antioxidant enzyme systems include vitamins E, C, and A; beta-carotene (a phytochemical that is a precursor to vitamin A); and the mineral selenium (Table 1). The minerals copper, iron, zinc, and manganese play a peripheral role in fighting oxidation and are only mentioned in this chapter. Let's review each of these nutrients now and learn more about their functions in the body.

cofactor A mineral or other substance that is needed to allow enzymes to function properly.

237

Vitamin E

Vitamin E is one of the fat-soluble vitamins; thus, dietary fats carry it from our intestines through the lymphatic system and eventually transport it to our cells. As you remember, our body stores the fat-soluble vitamins: about 90% of the vitamin E in our body is stored in our adipose tissue. The remaining vitamin E is found in cell membranes.

Vitamin E is actually two separate families of compounds, *tocotrienols* and **tocopherols.** None of the different tocotrienol compounds appear to play an active role in our body. The four tocopherol compounds—alpha, beta, gamma, and delta—are the biologically active forms. Of these, the most active, or potent, vitamin E compound found in food and supplements is *alpha-tocopherol.* The RDA for vitamin E is expressed as milligrams of alpha-tocopherol equivalents per day (mg α-tocopherol/day). Food labels and vitamin and mineral supplements may express vitamin E in units of alpha-tocopherol equivalents (α-TE), milligrams, or International Units (IU). For conversion purposes,

- One α-TE is equal to 1 mg of active vitamin E.
- In supplements containing natural sources of vitamin E, 1 IU is equal to 0.67 mg α-TE.
- In supplements containing synthetic sources of vitamin E, 1 IU is equal to 0.45 mg α-TE.

Functions of Vitamin E

The primary function of vitamin E is as an antioxidant: it donates an electron to free radicals, stabilizing them and preventing them from destabilizing other molecules. Once vitamin E is oxidized, it is either excreted from the body or recycled back into active vitamin E through the help of other antioxidant nutrients, such as vitamin C.

Because vitamin E is prevalent in our adipose tissues and cell membranes, its action specifically protects polyunsaturated fatty acids (PUFAs) and other fatty components of our cells and cell membranes from being oxidized (Figure 5b). Vitamin E also protects our LDLs from being oxidized, thereby lowering our risk for heart disease. In addition to protecting our PUFAs and LDLs, vitamin E protects the membranes of our red blood cells from oxidation and plays a critical role in protecting the cells of our lungs, which are constantly exposed to oxygen and the potentially damaging effects of oxidation. Vitamin E's role in protecting PUFAs and other fatty components also explains why it is added to many oil-based foods and skincare products—by preventing oxidation in these products, it reduces rancidity and spoilage.

Vitamin E serves many other roles essential to human health. It is critical for normal fetal and early childhood development of nerves and muscles, as well as for maintenance of their functions. It protects white blood cells and other components of our immune system, thereby helping the body defend against illness and disease. It also improves the absorption of vitamin A if the dietary intake of vitamin A is low.

How Much Vitamin E Should We Consume?

Considering the importance of vitamin E to our health, you might think that you need to consume a huge amount daily. In fact, the RDA is modest: 15 mg alpha-tocopherol per day (see Table 1).[1] The tolerable upper intake level (UL) is 1,000 mg alpha-tocopherol per day. Remember that one of the primary roles of vitamin E is to protect PUFAs from oxidation. Thus, our need for vitamin E increases as we eat more oils and other foods that contain PUFAs. Fortunately, these foods also contain vitamin E, so we typically consume enough vitamin E within them to protect their PUFAs from oxidation.

Vitamin E: The Vegetarian Vitamin

Vitamin E is widespread in foods from plant sources **(Figure 6)**. Much of the vitamin E that we consume comes from products such as spreads, salad dressings, and mayonnaise made from vegetable oils, including safflower oil, sunflower oil, canola oil,

Valentyn Volkov/Shutterstock

⬆ Vegetable oils, nuts, and seeds are good sources of vitamin E.

tocopherol The active form of vitamin E in our body.

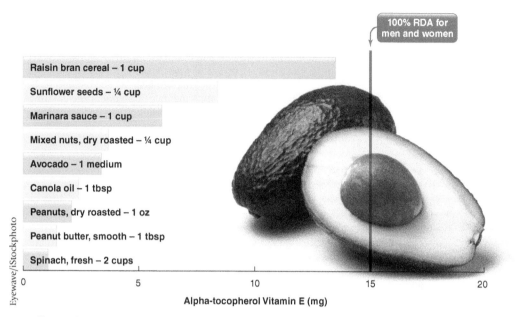

100% RDA for men and women

Raisin bran cereal – 1 cup

Sunflower seeds – ¼ cup

Marinara sauce – 1 cup

Mixed nuts, dry roasted – ¼ cup

Avocado – 1 medium

Canola oil – 1 tbsp

Peanuts, dry roasted – 1 oz

Peanut butter, smooth – 1 tbsp

Spinach, fresh – 2 cups

0   5   10   15   20

Alpha-tocopherol Vitamin E (mg)

Eyewave/iStockphoto

Figure 6 Common food sources of vitamin E. The RDA for vitamin E is 15 mg alpha-tocopherol per day for men and women.

Data from U.S. Department of Agriculture, Agricultural Research Service, 2009. USDA Nutrient Database for Standard Reference, Release 22. Nutrient Data Laboratory Home Page, www.ars.usda.gov/ba/bhnrc/ndl.

and soybean oil. Nuts, seeds, soybeans, and some vegetables—including spinach, broccoli, and avocados—also contribute vitamin E to our diet. Although no single fruit or vegetable contains very high amounts of vitamin E, eating the recommended amounts of fruits and vegetables each day will help ensure adequate intake of this nutrient. Cereals are often fortified with vitamin E, and other grain products contribute modest amounts to our diet. Animal and dairy products are poor sources.

Vitamin E is destroyed by exposure to oxygen, metals, ultraviolet light, and heat. Although raw (uncooked) vegetable oils contain vitamin E, heating these oils destroys vitamin E. Thus, fried foods contain little vitamin E. This includes most fast foods. See the Quick Tips above for increasing your intake of vitamin E.

QUICK TIPS

Eating More Vitamin E

✓ Eat cereals high in vitamin E for breakfast or as a snack.

✓ Add sunflower seeds to salads and trail mixes, or just have them as a snack.

✓ Add sliced almonds to salads, granola, and trail mixes to boost vitamin E intake.

✓ Pack a peanut butter sandwich for lunch.

✓ Eat veggies throughout the day—for snacks, for sides, and in main dishes.

✓ When dressing a salad, use vitamin E–rich oils, such as sunflower, safflower, or canola.

✓ Enjoy some fresh, homemade guacamole: mash a ripe avocado with a squeeze of lime juice and a sprinkle of garlic salt.

What Happens If We Consume Too Much Vitamin E?

Until recently, standard supplemental doses (one to eighteen times the RDA) of vitamin E were not associated with any adverse health effects. However, a 2005 study found that, among adults 55 years of age or older with vascular disease or diabetes, a daily intake of 268 mg of vitamin E per day (about eighteen times the RDA) for approximately 7 years resulted in a significant increase in heart failure.[2] However, these results have not been confirmed by additional research studies. At this time, it is unclear whether these adverse effects are an anomaly or if high supplemental doses of vitamin E may be harmful for certain individuals.

Some individuals report side effects such as nausea, intestinal distress, and diarrhea with vitamin E supplementation. In addition, certain medications interact negatively with vitamin E. The most important of these are the *anticoagulants*, substances that stop blood from clotting excessively. Aspirin is an anticoagulant, as is the prescription drug Coumadin. Vitamin E supplements can augment the action of these substances, causing uncontrollable bleeding. In addition, new evidence suggests that, in some people, long-term use of standard vitamin E supplements may cause hemorrhaging in the brain, leading to a type of stroke called *hemorrhagic stroke*.[3]

What Happens If We Don't Consume Enough Vitamin E?

True vitamin E deficiencies are uncommon in humans. This is primarily because vitamin E is fat soluble, so we typically store adequate amounts in our fatty tissues, even when our current dietary intake is low. Vitamin E deficiencies are usually a result of diseases that cause malabsorption of fat. However, results from the NHANES III survey show that the dietary intake of vitamin E of 27–41% of Americans is low enough that, although these individuals probably don't have a true deficiency, they may have suboptimal blood levels of vitamin E, putting them at increased risk for cardiovascular disease.[4]

Despite the rarity of true vitamin E deficiencies, they do occur. One vitamin E deficiency symptom is *erythrocyte hemolysis,* or the rupturing (*lysis*) of red blood cells (*erythrocytes*). The rupturing of our red blood cells leads to *anemia,* a condition in which our red blood cells cannot carry and transport enough oxygen to our tissues, leading to fatigue, weakness, and a diminished ability to perform physical and mental work. Other symptoms of vitamin E deficiency include loss of muscle coordination and reflexes, leading to impairments in vision, speech, and movement. Vitamin E deficiency can also impair immune function, especially when body stores of the mineral selenium are low.

RECAP Vitamin E protects our cell membranes from oxidation, enhances immune function, and improves our absorption of vitamin A if dietary intake is low. The RDA for vitamin E is 15 mg alpha-tocopherol per day for men and women. Vitamin E is found primarily in vegetable oils and nuts. Toxicity is uncommon, but taking very high doses can cause excessive bleeding. A genuine deficiency is rare, but symptoms include anemia and impaired vision, speech, and movement.

Vitamin C

Vitamin C is a water-soluble vitamin. We must therefore consume it on a regular basis, as any excess is excreted (primarily in our urine) rather than stored. There are two active forms of vitamin C: ascorbic acid and dehydroascorbic acid. Interestingly, most animals can make their own vitamin C from glucose. Humans and guinea pigs are two groups that cannot synthesize their own vitamin C and must consume it in the diet.

Functions of Vitamin C

Vitamin C is probably most well known for its role in preventing scurvy, a disease that ravaged sailors on long sea voyages centuries ago. In fact, the name *ascorbic acid* is derived from the combined Latin terms *a* (meaning "without") and *scorbic* (meaning "having scurvy"). Scurvy was characterized by bleeding tissues, especially of the gums, and is thought to have caused more than half of the deaths that occurred at sea. During these long voyages, the crew ate all of the fruits and vegetables early in the trip, then had only grain and animal products available until they reached land to resupply. In 1740 in England, Dr. James Lind discovered that citrus fruits can prevent

Dorling Kindersley

◄ Raw almonds are an appetizing way to help meet your vitamin E needs.

◄ Many fruits, such as these yellow tomatoes, are high in vitamin C.

scurvy. This is due to their high vitamin C content. Fifty years after the discovery of the link between citrus fruits and scurvy prevention, the British Navy finally required all ships to provide daily lemon juice rations for each sailor to prevent the onset of scurvy. A century later, sailors were given lime juice rations, earning them the nickname "limeys." It wasn't until 1930 that vitamin C was discovered and identified as a nutrient.

One reason that vitamin C prevents scurvy is that it assists in the synthesis of **collagen**. Collagen, a protein, is a critical component of all connective tissues in the body, including bone, teeth, skin, tendons, and blood vessels. Collagen assists in preventing bruises, and it ensures proper wound healing, as it is a part of scar tissue and a component of the tissue that mends broken bones. Without adequate vitamin C, the body cannot form collagen, and tissue hemorrhage, or bleeding, occurs. Vitamin C may also be involved in the synthesis of other components of connective tissues, such as elastin and bone matrix.

Eating Right All Day

Breakfast
Grapefruit juice instead of sweetened coffee!

Paul Blundell/Alamy

Lunch
Vegetable soup instead of chicken noodle!

Foodfolio/Alamy

Dinner
Spring rolls instead of sweet & sour pork!

Le Do/iStockphoto

Snack
Grapes instead of M&Ms!

Stock Foundry/Alamy

In addition to connective tissues, vitamin C assists in the synthesis of DNA, bile, neurotransmitters (such as serotonin, which helps regulate mood), and carnitine, which transports long-chain fatty acids from the cytosol into the mitochondria for energy production. Vitamin C also helps ensure that appropriate levels of thyroxine, a hormone produced by the thyroid gland, are produced to support basal metabolic rate and to maintain body temperature. Other hormones that are synthesized with assistance from vitamin C include epinephrine, norepinephrine, and steroid hormones.

Vitamin C also acts as an antioxidant. Because it is water soluble, it is an important antioxidant in the extracellular fluid. Like vitamin E, it donates electrons to free radicals, thus preventing the damage of cells and tissues. It also protects LDL-cholesterol from oxidation, which may reduce the risk for cardiovascular disease. Vitamin C acts as an important antioxidant in the lungs, helping protect us from the damage caused by ozone and cigarette smoke.[5] Vitamin C also regenerates vitamin E after it has been oxidized by donating an electron. This enables vitamin E to continue to protect our cell membranes and other tissues. It also enhances immune function by protecting white blood cells from the oxidative damage that occurs in response to fighting illness and infection. But contrary to popular belief, it is not a miracle cure (see the Nutrition Myth or Fact? box on vitamin C, next page). In the stomach, vitamin C reduces the formation of *nitrosamines*, cancer-causing agents found in foods such as cured and processed meats.

collagen A protein found in all the connective tissues in our body.

NUTRITION MYTH OR FACT?

Can Vitamin C Prevent the Common Cold?

What do you do when you feel a cold coming on? If you are like many people, you drink a lot of orange juice or take vitamin C supplements to ward it off. Do these tactics really help prevent a cold?

It is well known that vitamin C is important for a healthy immune system. A deficiency of vitamin C can seriously weaken the immune cells' ability to detect and destroy invading microbes, increasing susceptibility to many diseases and illnesses—including the common cold. Many people have taken vitamin C supplements to prevent the common cold, basing their behavior on its actions of enhancing our immune function. Interestingly, scientific studies do not support this action. A recent review of many of the studies of vitamin C and the common cold found that people taking vitamin C regularly in an attempt to ward off the common cold experienced as many colds as people who took a placebo. However, the *duration* of their colds was reduced—by 8% in adults and 13.6% in children.[6] Timing appeared to be important, though: taking vitamin C after the onset of cold symptoms did not reduce either the duration or the severity of the cold. Interestingly, taking vitamin C supplements regularly did reduce the number of colds experienced in marathon runners, skiers, and soldiers participating in exercises done under extreme environmental conditions.

The amount of vitamin C taken in these studies was at least 200 mg per day, with many using doses as high as 4,000 mg per day (more than forty times the RDA), with no harmful effects noted in those studies that reported adverse events.

In summary, it appears that, for most people, taking vitamin C supplements regularly will not prevent colds but may reduce their duration. Consuming a healthful diet that includes excellent sources of vitamin C will also help you maintain a strong immune system. Taking vitamin C after the onset of cold symptoms does not appear to help, so next time you feel a cold coming on, you may want to think twice before taking extra vitamin C.

Vitamin C also enhances the absorption of iron. It is recommended that people with low iron stores consume vitamin C–rich foods along with iron sources to improve absorption of the iron. For people with high iron stores, however, this practice can be dangerous and lead to iron toxicity.

Steve Gorton/Dorling Kindersley

How Much Vitamin C Should We Consume?

Although popular opinion suggests that our need for vitamin C is quite high, we really require amounts that are easily obtained when we eat the recommended amounts of fruits and vegetables daily. The RDA for vitamin C is 90 mg per day for men and 75 mg per day for women (see Table 1).[1] The Tolerable Upper Intake Level (UL) is 2,000 mg per day for adults. Smoking increases a person's need for vitamin C; thus, the RDA for smokers is 35 mg more per day than for nonsmokers. This equals 125 mg per day for men and 110 mg per day for women. Other situations that may increase the need for vitamin C include healing from a traumatic injury, surgery, or burns and the use of oral contraceptives among women; there is no consensus on how much extra vitamin C is needed in these circumstances.

Vitamin C: Citrus and More

Fruits and vegetables are the best sources of vitamin C. Because heat and oxygen destroy vitamin C, fresh sources of these foods have the highest content. Cooking foods, especially boiling them, leaches their vitamin C, which is then lost when we strain them. The forms of cooking that are least likely to compromise the vitamin C content of foods are steaming, microwaving, and stir-frying.

As indicated in **Figure 7**, many fruits and vegetables are high in vitamin C. Citrus fruits (such as oranges, lemons, and limes), potatoes, strawberries, tomatoes, kiwi fruit, broccoli, spinach and other leafy greens, cabbage, green and red peppers, and cauliflower are excellent sources of vitamin C. Fortified beverages and cereals

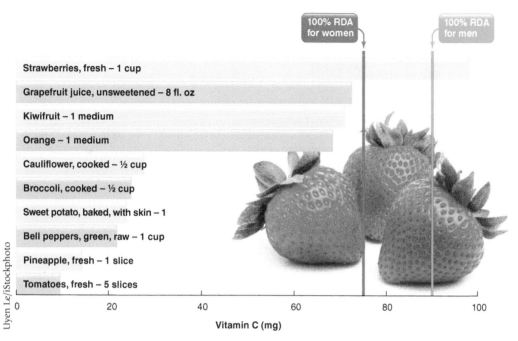

Figure 7 Common food sources of vitamin C. The RDA for vitamin C is 90 mg/day for men and 75 mg/day for women.

Data from U.S. Department of Agriculture, Agricultural Research Service, 2009. USDA Nutrient Database for Standard Reference, Release 22. Nutrient Data Laboratory Home Page, www.ars.usda.gov/ba/bhnrc/ndl.

QUICK TIPS

Selecting Foods High in Vitamin C

✓ Mix strawberries, kiwi fruit, cantaloupe, and oranges for a tasty fruit salad loaded with vitamin C.

✓ Include tomatoes on salads, wraps, and sandwiches for more vitamin C.

✓ Make your own fresh-squeezed orange or grapefruit juice!

✓ Add your favorite vitamin C–rich fruits, such as strawberries, to smoothies.

✓ Buy ready-to-eat vegetables, such as baby carrots and cherry tomatoes, and toss some in a zip-lock bag to take to school or work.

✓ Put a few slices of romaine lettuce on your sandwich.

✓ Throw a small container of orange slices, fresh pineapple chunks, or berries into your backpack for an afternoon snack.

✓ Store some juice boxes in your freezer to pack with your lunch. They'll thaw slowly, keeping the rest of your lunch cool, and many brands contain a full day's supply of vitamin C in just 6 oz.

✓ Enjoy raw bell peppers with low-fat dip for a crunchy snack.

✓ Serve reduced-salt corn chips with fresh salsa.

✓ Make gazpacho! In a blender, combine 1–3 cups of tomato juice, chunks of green pepper and red onion, a cucumber with seeds removed (no need to peel), the juice of one lime, a garlic clove, a splash each of red-wine vinegar and olive oil, a half teaspoon each of basil and cumin, and salt and pepper to taste. Seed and dice two to three fresh tomatoes and add to blended ingredients. Chill for several hours and serve cold, topped with a dollop of plain yogurt.

Philip Wilkins/Dorling Kindersley

Fresh vegetables are good sources of vitamin C and beta-carotene.

are also good sources. Dairy foods, meats, and nonfortified cereals and grains provide little or no vitamin C. With such a wide variety of foods to choose from, it's easy to eat right all day! See Eating Right All Day for some simple menu choices that are high in vitamin C. In addition, the following are some tips for increasing your intake of vitamin C.

What Happens If We Consume Too Much Vitamin C?

Because vitamin C is water soluble, we usually excrete any excess. Consuming excess amounts in food sources does not lead to toxicity, and only supplements can lead to toxic doses. Taking a **megadose** of vitamin C is not fatally harmful. However, side effects of doses exceeding 2,000 mg/day for a prolonged period include nausea, diarrhea, nosebleeds, and abdominal cramps.

There are rare instances in which consuming even moderately excessive doses of vitamin C can be harmful. As mentioned earlier, vitamin C enhances the absorption of iron. This action is beneficial to people who need to increase iron absorption. It can be harmful, however, to people with a disease called *hemochromatosis*, which causes an excess accumulation of iron in the body. Such iron toxicity can damage our tissues and lead to a heart attack. In people who have preexisting kidney disease, taking excess vitamin C can lead to the formation of kidney stones. This does not appear to occur in healthy individuals.

Critics of vitamin C supplementation claim that taking the supplemental form of the vitamin is "unbalanced" nutrition and leads vitamin C to act as a prooxidant. A **prooxidant,** as you might guess, is a nutrient that promotes oxidation. It does this by pushing the balance of exchange reactions toward oxidation, which promotes the production of free radicals. Although the results of a few studies suggest that vitamin C acts as a prooxidant, these studies were found to be flawed or irrelevant for humans. At the present time, there appears to be no strong scientific evidence that vitamin C, from either food or dietary supplements, acts as a prooxidant in humans.

What Happens If We Don't Consume Enough Vitamin C?

Vitamin C deficiencies are rare in developed countries but can occur in developing countries. Scurvy is the most common vitamin C–deficiency disease. The symptoms of scurvy appear after about 1 month of a vitamin C–deficient diet and include bleeding gums **(Figure 8)**, loose teeth, wounds that fail to heal, swollen ankles and wrists, bone pain and fractures, diarrhea, weakness, and depression. Anemia can also result from vitamin C deficiency. The people most at risk are those who eat few fruits and vegetables, including impoverished or homebound individuals, and people who abuse alcohol and drugs.

Medical-on-Line/Alamy

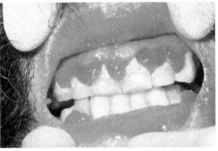

 Figure 8 Bleeding gums are one symptom of scurvy, the most common vitamin C–deficiency disease.

megadose A dose of a nutrient that is 10 or more times greater than the recommended amount.

prooxidant A nutrient that promotes oxidation and oxidative cell and tissue damage.

NUTRI-CASE HANNAH

"Since I started college in September, I've had one cold after another. I guess it's being around so many different people every day, plus all the stress. Then a few weeks ago I found this cool orange-tasting vitamin C powder at the health food outlet on campus, and I started mixing it into my orange juice every morning. I guess it's working, because I haven't had a cold since I started using it, but this morning I woke up with stomach cramps and

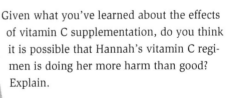

diarrhea, so now I guess I have to worry about a stomach flu. I wish there was a vitamin C powder for that!"

Given what you've learned about the effects of vitamin C supplementation, do you think it is possible that Hannah's vitamin C regimen is doing her more harm than good? Explain.

PhotoDisc/Getty Images

RECAP Vitamin C scavenges free radicals and regenerates vitamin E after it has been oxidized. It also assists in the synthesis of collagen, hormones, neurotransmitters, and DNA. Vitamin C also enhances iron absorption. The RDA for vitamin C is 90 mg per day for men and 75 mg per day for women. Many fruits and vegetables are high in vitamin C, and our requirements are modest. Toxicity is uncommon; symptoms include nausea, diarrhea, and nosebleeds. Deficiency can result in scurvy or anemia.

Beta-Carotene

Although beta-carotene is not considered an essential nutrient, it is a *provitamin* found in many fruits and vegetables. **Provitamins** are inactive forms of vitamins that the body cannot use until they are converted to their active form. Our body converts beta-carotene to the active form of vitamin A, or *retinol*; thus, beta-carotene is a precursor of retinol. It takes two units of beta-carotene to make one unit of active vitamin A. Not surprisingly, nutritionists express the units of beta-carotene in a food as Retinol Activity Equivalents, or RAE. This measurement tells us how much active vitamin A is available to the body after it has converted the beta-carotene in the food.

Beta-carotene is classified as a **carotenoid,** a class of phytochemicals. As you might guess from their name, carotenoids are a group of plant pigments that are the basis for the orange, red, and deep yellow colors of many fruits and vegetables, including carrots. (Even dark-green leafy vegetables contain plenty of carotenoids, but the green pigment, chlorophyll, masks their color!) Although there are more than 600 carotenoids found in nature, only about 50 are in the typical human diet. The six most common carotenoids found in human blood are alpha-carotene, beta-carotene, beta-cryptoxanthin, lutein, lycopene, and zeaxanthin. Of these, the body can convert only alpha-carotene, beta-carotene, and beta-cryptoxanthin to retinol. These are referred to as *provitamin A carotenoids*. We are just beginning to learn more about how carotenoids function in our body and how they may affect our health.

Functions of Beta-Carotene

Beta-carotene and some other carotenoids are recognized to have antioxidant properties. Like vitamin E, they are fat soluble and fight the harmful effects of oxidation in the lipid portions of our cell membranes and in our LDLs; however, compared to vitamin E, beta-carotene is a relatively weak antioxidant. In fact, other carotenoids, such as lycopene and lutein, may be stronger antioxidants.

Carotenoids play other important roles in our body. Specifically, they

- Enhance our immune system and boost our ability to fight illness and disease.
- Protect our skin from the damage caused by the sun's ultraviolet rays.
- Protect our eyes from damage, preventing or delaying age-related vision impairment.

Carotenoids are also associated with a decreased risk for certain types of cancer.

How Much Beta-Carotene Should We Consume?

Nutritional scientists do not consider beta-carotene and other carotenoids to be essential nutrients, as they play no known essential roles in our body and are not associated with any deficiency symptoms. Thus, no RDA for these compounds has been established. It has been suggested that consuming 6 to 10 mg of beta-carotene per day from food sources can increase the beta-carotene levels in our blood to amounts that may reduce our risks for some diseases, such as cancer and heart disease.[7] Supplements containing beta-carotene have become very popular,

provitamin An inactive form of a vitamin that the body can convert to an active form. An example is beta-carotene.

carotenoid A fat-soluble plant pigment that the body stores in the liver and adipose tissues. The body is able to convert certain carotenoids to vitamin A.

→ Foods that are high in carotenoids are easy to recognize by their bright colors.
Corbis

and supplementation studies have prescribed doses of 15 to 30 mg of beta-carotene. Refer to the Nutrition Debate later in this chapter to learn more about how antioxidant supplementation, including beta-carotene, may affect your risk for cancer and cardiovascular disease.

Beta-Carotene: Beyond Carrots

Not only carrots, but most vegetables—and fruits—that are red, orange, yellow, or deep green are high in beta-carotene and other carotenoids, such as lutein and lycopene. Tomatoes, sweet potatoes, leafy greens (such as kale and spinach), apricots, cantaloupe, and pumpkin are good sources. Eating the recommended amounts of fruits and vegetables each day ensures an adequate intake of carotenoids. Because of its color, beta-carotene is used as a natural coloring agent for many foods, including margarine, yellow cheddar cheese, cereal, cake mixes, gelatins, and soft drinks. However, these foods are not significant sources of beta-carotene. **Figure 9** identifies common foods that are high in beta-carotene.

We generally absorb only between 20% and 40% of the carotenoids present in the foods we eat. In contrast to vitamins E and C, carotenoids are absorbed better from cooked foods. Carotenoids are bound in the cells of plants, and the process of lightly cooking these plants breaks chemical bonds and can rupture cell walls, which humans don't digest. These actions result in more of the carotenoids being released from the plant. For instance, 1 cup of raw carrots contains approximately 10 mg of beta-carotene, whereas the same amount of cooked carrots contains approximately 13 mg.[8] The following are some tips for increasing your intake of beta-carotene.

What Happens If We Consume Too Much Beta-Carotene?

Consuming large amounts of beta-carotene or other carotenoids in foods does not appear to cause toxic symptoms. However, your skin can turn yellow or orange if you consume large amounts of foods that are high in beta-carotene. This condition is referred to as *carotenosis* or *carotenoderma*, and it appears to be both reversible and harmless. Taking beta-carotene supplements is not generally recommended, because we can get adequate amounts of this nutrient by eating more fruits and vegetables, and supplements may be harmful in certain populations.

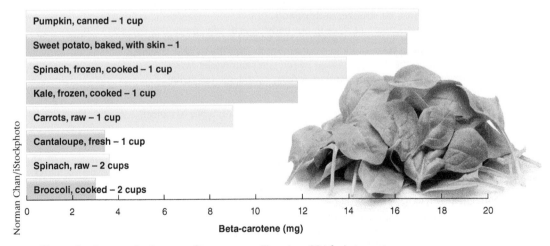

Pumpkin, canned – 1 cup
Sweet potato, baked, with skin – 1
Spinach, frozen, cooked – 1 cup
Kale, frozen, cooked – 1 cup
Carrots, raw – 1 cup
Cantaloupe, fresh – 1 cup
Spinach, raw – 2 cups
Broccoli, cooked – 2 cups

Beta-carotene (mg)

Norman Chan/iStockphoto

→ **Figure 9** Common food sources of beta-carotene. There is no RDA for beta-carotene.

Data from U.S. Department of Agriculture, Agricultural Research Service. USDA—NCC Carotenoid Database for U.S. Foods, 2009. USDA Nutrient Database for Standard Reference, Release 22. Nutrient Data Laboratory Home Page, www.ars.usda.gov/ba/bhnrc/ndl.

Boosting Your Beta-Carotene

✓ Start your day with an orange, grapefruit, a pear, a banana, an apple, or a slice of cantaloupe. All are good sources of beta-carotene.

✓ Pack a zip-lock bag of carrot slices or dried apricots in your lunch.

✓ Instead of french fries, think orange! Slice raw sweet potatoes, toss the slices in olive or canola oil, and bake.

✓ Add veggies to homemade pizza.

✓ Add shredded carrots to cake and muffin batters.

✓ Taking dessert to a potluck? Make a pumpkin pie! It's easy if you use canned pumpkin and follow the recipe on the can.

✓ Go green, too! The next time you have a salad, go for the dark-green leafy vegetables instead of iceberg lettuce.

✓ Add raw spinach or other green leafy vegetables to wraps and sandwiches.

What Happens If We Don't Consume Enough Beta-Carotene?

There are no known deficiency symptoms of beta-carotene or other carotenoids apart from beta-carotene's function as a precursor for vitamin A.

RECAP Beta-carotene is a carotenoid and a provitamin of vitamin A. It protects the lipid portions of cell membranes and LDL-cholesterol from oxidative damage. It also enhances immune function and protects vision. There is no RDA for beta-carotene. Orange, red, and deep green fruits and vegetables are good sources of beta-carotene. There are no known toxicity or deficiency symptoms, but yellowing of the skin can occur if too much beta-carotene is consumed.

Vitamin A: Much More than an Antioxidant Nutrient

As early as AD 30, the Roman writer Aulus Cornelius Celsus described in his medical encyclopedia, *De Medicina*, a condition called night blindness and recommended as a cure the consumption of liver. We now know that night blindness is due to a deficiency of vitamin A, a fat-soluble vitamin stored primarily in the liver of animals. When we consume vitamin A, we store 90% in our liver, and the remainder in our adipose tissue, kidneys, and lungs. Because fat-soluble vitamins cannot dissolve in our blood, they require proteins that can bind with and transport them through the bloodstream to target tissues and cells. *Retinol-binding protein* is one such carrier protein for vitamin A. Retinol-binding protein carries one form of vitamin A, retinol, from the liver to the cells that require it.

There are three active forms of vitamin A in our body: **retinol** is the alcohol form, **retinal** is the aldehyde form, and **retinoic acid** is the acid form. These three forms are collectively referred to as the *retinoids* (Figure 10). Of the three, retinol has the starring role in maintaining our body's physiologic functions. Remember from the previous section that beta-carotene is a precursor to vitamin A. When we eat foods that contain beta-carotene, it is converted to retinol in the wall of our small intestine.

The unit of expression for vitamin A is Retinol Activity Equivalents (RAE). You may still see the expression Retinol Equivalents (RE) or International Units (IU) for vitamin A on food labels and dietary supplements. The conversions to RAE from

retinol An active, alcohol form of vitamin A that plays an important role in healthy vision and immune function.

retinal An active, aldehyde form of vitamin A that plays an important role in healthy vision and immune function.

retinoic acid An active, acid form of vitamin A that plays an important role in cell growth and immune function.

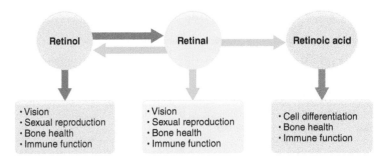

Figure 10 The three active forms of vitamin A in our body are retinol, retinal, and retinoic acid. Retinol and retinal can be converted interchangeably; retinoic acid is formed from retinal, and this process is irreversible. Each form of vitamin A contributes to many of our bodily processes.

Eating plenty of fruits and vegetables can help prevent vitamin A deficiency.

retina The delicate, light-sensitive membrane lining the inner eyeball and connected to the optic nerve. It contains retinal.

rhodopsin A light-sensitive pigment found in the rod cells that is formed by retinal and opsin.

various forms of retinol are 1 RAE = 1 microgram (µg) retinol, 12 µg beta-carotene, 24 µg alpha-carotene or beta-cryptoxanthin, 1 RE, and 3.3 IU.

Functions of Vitamin A

The known functions of vitamin A are numerous, and researchers speculate that many are still to be discovered.

Vitamin A May Act as an Antioxidant   Limited research indicates that vitamin A may act as an antioxidant.[9-11] Like vitamins E and C, it appears to scavenge free radicals and protect our LDLs from oxidation. As you might expect, adequate vitamin A levels in the blood are associated with lower risks for some forms of cancer and heart disease. However, the role of vitamin A as an antioxidant is not strongly established and is still under investigation.

Vitamin A Is Essential to Sight   A critical role of vitamin A in our body is certainly in the maintenance of healthy vision. Specifically, vitamin A affects our sight in two ways: it enables us to react to changes in the brightness of light, and it enables us to distinguish between various wavelengths of light—in other words, to see different colors. Let's take a closer look at this process.

Light enters our eyes through the cornea, travels through the lens, and then hits the **retina,** which is a delicate membrane lining the back of the inner eyeball (**Figure 11**). You might already have guessed how *retinal* got its name: it is found in—and is integral to—the retina. In the retina, retinal combines with a protein called *opsin* to form **rhodopsin,** a light-sensitive pigment. Rhodopsin is found in the *rod cells*, which are cells that react to dim light and interpret black-and-white images.

When light hits the retina, a reaction occurs in which rhodopsin is split into retinal and opsin. This causes the rod cells to lose their color. It also causes both retinal and opsin to change shape. These changes in turn result in the transmission of a signal to the brain that is interpreted as a black-and-white image. This process goes on continually, allowing our eyes to adjust continuously to subtle changes in our surroundings or in the level of light. Most of the retinal is recycled and combines with opsin to form rhodopsin again. However, some of the retinal is lost with each cycle and must be replaced by retinol from the bloodstream. At the same time, the *cone cells* of the retina, which are effective only in bright light, use retinal to interpret different wavelengths of light as different colors.

In summary, our abilities to adjust to dim light, recover from a bright flash of light, and see in color are all critically dependent on adequate levels of retinal in our eyes.

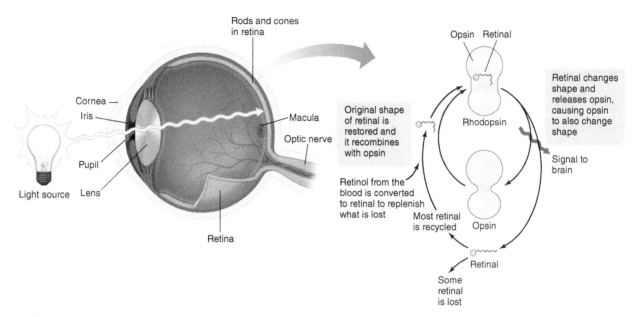

Figure 11 Vitamin A is necessary to maintain healthy vision. Light enters the eye through the cornea, travels through the lens, and hits the retina located in the back of the eye. In the rod cells of the retina, retinal is combined with opsin to form rhodopsin. As light hits the rod cells, they lose color, and the components of rhodopsin, retinal and opsin, split and change shape. These changes cause transmission of a signal to the brain that allows us to see.

Vitamin A Contributes to Cell Differentiation   Another important role of vitamin A is its contribution to **cell differentiation,** the process by which immature cells develop into highly specialized cells that perform unique functions. Obviously, this process is critical to the development of healthy organs and effectively functioning body systems. For example, specialized cells lining the trachea and bronchi, intestines, stomach, bladder, cornea of the eye, and other organs produce mucus, which lubricates the tissue and helps us propel substances out of our body tissues (for example, when we cough up secretions or empty our bladder). When vitamin A levels are insufficient, these cells fail to differentiate appropriately, and we lose these functions. Vitamin A is also critical to the differentiation of specialized immune cells called *T-lymphocytes,* or *T-cells,* which fight infections. You can now see why vitamin A deficiency can lead to infections and other disorders of the lungs and respiratory tract, urinary tract, vagina, and eyes.

Other Functions of Vitamin A   Vitamin A is involved in reproduction. Although its exact role is unclear, it appears necessary for sperm production in men and for fertilization to occur in women. It also contributes to healthy bone growth by assisting in breaking down old bone, so that new, longer, and stronger bone can develop. As a result of a vitamin A deficiency, children suffer from stunted growth and wasting. Finally, two popular treatments for acne contain derivatives of vitamin A.

How Much Vitamin A Should We Consume?

Vitamin A toxicity can occur readily because it is a fat-soluble vitamin, so it is important to consume only the amount recommended for your gender and age range. The RDA for vitamin A is 900 µg per day for men and 700 µg per day for women (see Table 1).[12] The UL is 3,000 µg per day of preformed vitamin A in men and women (including those pregnant and lactating).

Dorling Kindersley

Liver, carrots, and cantaloupe all contain vitamin A.

cell differentiation The process by which immature, undifferentiated stem cells develop into highly specialized functional cells of discrete organs and tissues.

The most common sources of dietary pre-formed vitamin A are animal foods, such as beef liver, chicken liver, eggs, and whole-fat dairy products. Vitamin A is also found in fortified reduced-fat milks, margarine, and some breakfast cereals (Figure 12). The other sources of the vitamin A we consume are foods high in beta-carotene and other carotenoids that can be converted to vitamin A. As discussed earlier in this chapter, dark-green, orange, and deep-yellow fruits and vegetables are good sources of beta-carotene, and thus of vitamin A. Carrots, spinach, mango, cantaloupe, and tomato juice are excellent sources of vitamin A because they contain beta-carotene.

What Happens If We Consume Too Much Vitamin A?

Vitamin A is highly toxic, and toxicity symptoms develop after consuming only three to four times the RDA. Toxicity rarely results from food sources; however, vitamin A supplementation is known to have caused severe illness and even death. In pregnant women, it can cause serious birth defects and spontaneous abortion. Other toxicity symptoms include fatigue, loss of appetite, blurred vision, hair loss, skin disorders, bone and joint pain, abdominal pain, nausea, diarrhea, and damage to the liver and nervous system. If caught in time, many of these symptoms are reversible once vitamin A supplementation is stopped. However, permanent damage can occur to the liver, eyes, and other organs.

What Happens If We Don't Consume Enough Vitamin A?

Night blindness and color blindness can result from vitamin A deficiency. Night blindness is characterized by an inability to adjust to dim light, as well as the failure to regain sight quickly after a bright flash of light (Figure 13). How severe a problem is night blindness? Although less common among people of developed nations, vitamin A deficiency is a severe public health concern in developing nations. According to the World Health Organization, approximately 250 million preschool children suffer from vitamin A deficiency.[14] Of the children affected, 250,000 to 500,000 become permanently blinded every year. At least half of these children will die within 1 year of losing their sight. Death is due to infections and illnesses, including measles and diarrhea, that are easily treated in wealthier countries. Vitamin A deficiency is also a tragedy for pregnant women in these countries. These women suffer from night blindness, are more likely to transmit HIV to their child if HIV-positive, and run a greater risk for maternal mortality.

night blindness A vitamin A deficiency disorder that results in loss of the ability to see in dim light.

HOT TOPIC

Acne and Vitamin A—Is There a Link?

Search the Internet and you'll find plenty of sites claiming a direct link between vitamin A deficiency and acne, and insisting that vitamin A supplements can successfully treat acne. Should you believe the hype?

In 2006, a study reported an association between low blood levels of vitamin A and the presence of acne: the more severe the acne, the lower the levels of vitamin A.[13] Although these findings may seem suggestive, this study was conducted with a very small number of participants who were not randomly selected. Also, plasma levels of vitamin A were assessed to indicate vitamin A status; however, the Institute of Medicine[12] states that plasma levels of vitamin A are not necessarily an indicator of vitamin A status. To date, these results have not been replicated by other researchers, and there appears to be no evidence that vitamin A deficiency causes acne.

Interestingly, two effective treatments for acne are synthetic derivatives of vitamin A. Retin-A, or tretinoin, is a treatment applied to the skin. Accutane, or isotretinoin, is taken orally. These medications should be used carefully and only under the supervision of a licensed physician.

Contrary to what you might read on the Internet, vitamin A itself has no effect on acne; thus, vitamin A supplements are not recommended in its treatment.

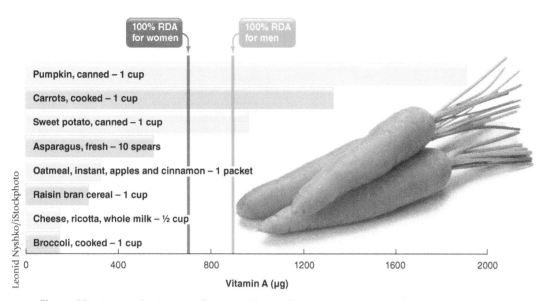

Leonid Nyshko/iStockphoto

🔺 **Figure 12** Common food sources of vitamin A. The RDA for vitamin A is 900 μg/day for men and 700 μg/day for women.

Data from U.S. Department of Agriculture, Agricultural Research Service, 2009. USDA Nutrient Database for Standard Reference, Release 22. Nutrient Data Laboratory Home Page, www.ars.usda.gov/ba/bhnrc/ndl.

(a) Normal night vision

Poor night vision

Kristin Piljay

(b) Normal light adjustment

Slow light adjustment

🔺 **Figure 13** A deficiency of vitamin A can result in night blindness. This condition results in **(a)** diminished side vision and overall poor night vision and **(b)** difficulty in adjusting from bright light to dim light.

If vitamin A deficiency progresses, it can result in irreversible blindness due to hardening of the cornea (the transparent membrane covering the front of the eye), a condition called *xerophthalmia*. The prefix of this word, *xero-*, comes from a Greek word meaning "dry." Lack of vitamin A causes the cells of the cornea to lose their ability to produce mucus, causing the eye to become very dry. This leaves the cornea susceptible to damage, infection, and hardening. Once the cornea hardens in this way, the resulting blindness is irreversible. This is why it is critical to catch vitamin A deficiency in its early stages and treat it either with the regular consumption of fruits and vegetables that contain beta-carotene or with vitamin A supplementation.

Other deficiency symptoms include impaired immunity, increased risk for illness and infections, reproductive system disorders, and failure of normal growth. Individuals who are at risk for vitamin A deficiency include elderly people with poor diets, newborn or premature infants (due to low liver stores of vitamin A), young children with inadequate vegetable and fruit intakes, and alcoholics. Any condition that results in fat malabsorption can also lead to vitamin A deficiency. Children with cystic fibrosis; individuals with Crohn's disease, celiac disease, or diseases of the liver, pancreas, or gallbladder; and people who consume large amounts of the fat substitute Olestra are at risk for vitamin A deficiency.

RECAP The role of vitamin A as an antioxidant is still under investigation. Vitamin A is critical for maintaining our vision. It is also necessary for cell differentiation, reproduction, and growth. The RDA for vitamin A is 900 µg per day for men and 700 µg per day for women. Animal liver, dairy products, and eggs are good animal sources of vitamin A; fruits and vegetables are high in beta-carotene, which our body uses to synthesize vitamin A. Supplementation can be dangerous, as toxicity is reached at levels of only three to four times the RDA. Toxicity symptoms include birth defects, spontaneous abortion, blurred vision, and liver damage. Deficiency symptoms include night blindness, impaired immune function, and growth failure.

Selenium

Selenium is a trace mineral, and it is found in varying amounts in soil and thus in the food grown there. Keep in mind that, although we need only minute amounts of trace minerals, they are just as important to our health as the major minerals.

Functions of Selenium

It is only recently that we have learned about the critical role of selenium as a nutrient in human health. In 1979, Chinese scientists reported an association between a heart disorder called **Keshan disease** and selenium deficiency. This disease occurs in children in the Keshan province of China, where the soil is depleted of selenium. The scientists found that Keshan disease can be prevented with selenium supplementation.

The selenium in our body is contained in amino acids. Two amino acid derivatives contain most of the selenium in our body: *selenomethionine* is the storage form for selenium, while *selenocysteine* is the active form of selenium. Selenium is a critical component of the glutathione peroxidase antioxidant enzyme system mentioned earlier. Thus, selenium helps spare vitamin E and prevents oxidative damage to our cell membranes.

Like vitamin C, selenium is needed for the production of thyroxine, or thyroid hormone. By this action, selenium is involved in the maintenance of our basal metabolism and body temperature. Selenium appears to play a role in immune function, and poor selenium status is associated with higher rates of some forms of cancer.

Keshan disease A heart disorder caused by selenium deficiency. It was first identified in children in the Keshan province of China.

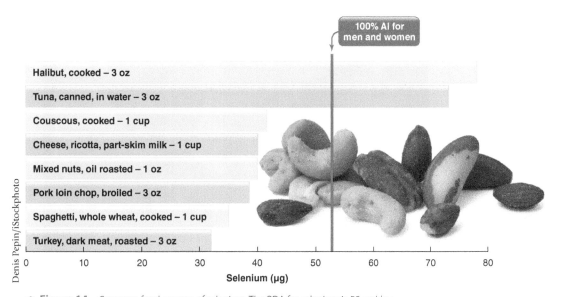

100% AI for
men and women

Halibut, cooked – 3 oz

Tuna, canned, in water – 3 oz

Couscous, cooked – 1 cup

Cheese, ricotta, part-skim milk – 1 cup

Mixed nuts, oil roasted – 1 oz

Pork loin chop, broiled – 3 oz

Spaghetti, whole wheat, cooked – 1 cup

Turkey, dark meat, roasted – 3 oz

Denis Pepin/iStockphoto

Selenium (µg)

Figure 14 Common food sources of selenium. The RDA for selenium is 55 µg/day.

Data from U.S. Department of Agriculture, Agricultural Research Service, 2009. USDA Nutrient Database for Standard Reference, Release 22.
Nutrient Data Laboratory Home Page, www.ars.usda.gov/ba/bhnrc/ndl.

How Much Selenium Should We Consume?

The content of selenium in foods is highly variable. As it is a trace mineral, we need only minute amounts to maintain health. The RDA for selenium is 55 µg per day for both men and women (see Table 1).[1] The UL is 400 µg per day.

Selenium is present in both animal and plant food sources but in variable amounts. Because it is stored in the tissues of animals, selenium is found in reliably consistent amounts in animal foods. Organ meats, such as liver and kidneys, as well as pork and seafood, are particularly good sources (Figure 14).

In contrast, the amount of selenium in plants is dependent on the selenium content of the soil in which the plant is grown. Many companies marketing selenium supplements warn that the agricultural soils in the United States are depleted of selenium and inform us that we need to take selenium supplements. In reality, the selenium content of soil varies greatly across North America, and because we obtain our food from a variety of geographic locations, few people in the United States suffer from selenium deficiency. This is especially true for people who eat even small quantities of meat or seafood.

What Happens If We Consume Too Much Selenium?

Selenium toxicity does not result from eating foods high in selenium. However, supplementation can cause toxicity. Toxicity symptoms include brittle hair and nails that can eventually break and fall off. Other symptoms include skin rashes, vomiting, nausea, weakness, and liver disease.

What Happens If We Don't Consume Enough Selenium?

As discussed previously, selenium deficiency is associated with a form of heart disease called Keshan disease. Selenium deficiency does not cause the disease, but selenium is necessary to help the immune system effectively fight the virus that causes the disease. Another deficiency disease is *Kashin-Beck disease*, a deforming arthritis also found in selenium-depleted areas in China and Tibet (Figure 15).

Dorling Kindersley

Wheat is a rich source of selenium.

Miranda Mimi Kuo

Figure 15 Selenium deficiency can lead to deforming arthritis called Kashin-Beck disease.

Other deficiency symptoms include impaired immune responses, increased risk for viral infections, infertility, depression, hostility, impaired cognitive function, and muscle pain and wasting. Deficiencies of both selenium and iodine in pregnant women can cause a form of *cretinism* in the infant.

Copper, Iron, Zinc, and Manganese Assist in Antioxidant Function

As discussed earlier, there are numerous antioxidant enzyme systems in our body. Copper, zinc, and manganese are cofactors for the superoxide dismutase antioxidant enzyme system. Iron is a part of the structure of catalase. In addition to their role in protecting against oxidative damage, these minerals play major roles in the optimal functioning of many other enzymes in our body. Copper, iron, and zinc help us maintain the health of our blood, and manganese is an important cofactor in carbohydrate metabolism.

RECAP Selenium is part of the glutathione peroxidase antioxidant enzyme system. It indirectly spares vitamin E from oxidative damage, and it assists with immune function and the production of thyroid hormone. Organ meats, pork, and seafood are good sources of selenium, as are nuts, wheat, and rice. The selenium content of plants is dependent on the amount of selenium in the soil in which they are grown. Toxicity symptoms include brittle hair and nails, vomiting, nausea, and liver cirrhosis. Deficiency symptoms and side effects include Keshan disease, Kashin-Beck disease, impaired immune function, infertility, and muscle wasting. Copper, zinc, and manganese are cofactors for the superoxide dismutase antioxidant enzyme system. Iron is a cofactor for the catalase antioxidant enzyme. These minerals play critical roles in blood health and energy metabolism.

Nutrition DEBATE

Antioxidants: Food or Supplements?

As you have learned in this chapter, antioxidant nutrients play an important role in reducing free radical damage, which can in turn reduce the risk for chronic diseases such as cancer and cardiovascular disease (CVD). Despite this, research studies on the effects of antioxidant supplements on risks for cancer and CVD show inconsistent results.

The results of the Alpha-Tocopherol Beta-Carotene (ATBC) Cancer Prevention Study and the Beta-Carotene and Retinol Efficacy Trial (CARET) were particularly surprising.[15,16] The ATBC Cancer Prevention Study was conducted in Finland from 1985 to 1993 with the purpose of determining the effects of beta-carotene and vitamin E supplements on the rates of lung cancer and other forms of cancer among male smokers between the ages of 50 and 69 years. Almost 30,000 men participated in the study for an average of 6 years. The participants were given daily a beta-carotene supplement, a vitamin E supplement, a supplement containing both, or a placebo.

Contrary to expectations, the male smokers who took beta-carotene supplements experienced an *increased* number of deaths during the study. More men in this group died of lung cancer, and there were higher rates of prostate and stomach cancers. Also, more men died of CVD. This negative effect appeared to be particularly strong in men who had a higher alcohol intake.

CARET began as a pilot study in the United States in 1985 and included more than 18,000 men and women who were smokers, former smokers, or workers who had been exposed to asbestos. The participants were randomly assigned to take daily supplements of beta-carotene and retinol (vitamin A) or a placebo. After a 4-year follow-up

period, the incidence of lung cancer was 28% higher among those taking the beta-carotene and retinol supplement. This significant finding, in addition to the results from the ATBC Cancer Prevention Study, prompted researchers to end the CARET study early and recommend that participants discontinue the supplements.[16]

The reasons that beta-carotene increased lung cancer risk in this population are not clear. However, the results of this study suggest that, for certain people, supplementation with beta-carotene may be harmful.

As with the research conducted on cancer, the studies of antioxidants and CVD show inconsistent results. Two large-scale surveys conducted in the United States show that men and women who eat more fruits and vegetables have a significantly reduced risk of CVD.[17,18] And in the ATBC Can-

The flavonoids in black tea might reduce the risk for CVD.
Ukrphoto/Dreamstime

cer Prevention Study, vitamin E was found to lower the number of deaths due to heart disease. However, it had no overall effect on the risk for stroke.[19] In another study, vitamin E had no impact on the risk for CVD in people at high risk for heart attack and stroke.[2] And recently, other large intervention studies conducted in the United States have shown no reductions in major cardiovascular events in men and women taking vitamins E or C.[3,20] Thus, there is growing evidence that antioxidant supplements do not reduce our risk for CVD.

Why might foods high in antioxidants be beneficial in reducing our risks for cancer and CVD, whereas supplements are not? It is important to note that other compounds (besides antioxidants) found in fruits, vegetables, and whole grains can reduce our risk for cancer and CVD. Here are just a few examples: dietary fiber has been shown to reduce the risk for colon and rectal cancers, decrease blood pressure, lower total cholesterol levels, and improve blood glucose and insulin levels. Folate, a B-vitamin found in fortified cereals, green leafy vegetables, and some other plant foods, is known to reduce blood levels of the amino acid homocysteine, and a high concentration of homocysteine is a known risk factor for CVD. Flavonoids are a group of phytochemicals found in many plant foods, including black tea. A recent study has shown that individuals who drank more than three cups of black tea per day had a lower rate of heart attacks than non–tea drinkers.[21] Thus, it appears that any number of nutrients and other components in fruits, vegetables, and whole-grain foods may be protective against cancer and CVD. As you can see, there is still much to learn about how people respond to foods high in antioxidant nutrients as compared to antioxidant supplementation.

Chapter Review

1. True. Free radicals are highly unstable atoms that can destabilize neighboring atoms or molecules and harm our cells; however, they are produced as a normal by-product of human physiology.

2. False. Overall, the research on vitamin C and colds does not show strong evidence that taking vitamin C supplements reduces our risk of suffering from the common cold.

3. True. Carrots are an excellent source of beta-carotene, a precursor for vitamin A, which helps maintain good vision.

Find the Quack

When Bruce and Tina got married, they assumed they'd have no problem becoming parents. But 2 years later, they're still trying. So when Tina comes home from a doctor's appointment and tells Bruce she has some bad news, he doesn't know what to expect. "Bruce," she says, "I know you're not going to like this, but the doctor says you should quit smoking. She says that smoking reduces your sperm count and could be one reason we haven't conceived. And besides, your own doctor has tried to get you to quit because of your high blood pressure." Bruce feels his spirits sink. It's true he has hypertension, and his dad died of a heart attack at age 45. But he's tried to quit smoking before, and the withdrawal symptoms have always been more than he could handle.

That evening he goes onto the Internet and searches under "smoking" and "withdrawal symptoms." He finds a website promoting a supplement called "Quit Calm" that sounds promising, offering relief from the anxiety, sleeplessness, and cravings of nicotine withdrawal. Here's what the site states:

- "Quit Calm offers an all-natural blend of herbs that work together to decrease cravings, eliminate your anxiety, promote your sleep, heal your respiratory tissues, and purge harmful toxins from your body."
- "Ingredients include licorice root, peppermint, ginger, and slippery elm in a proprietary blend that soothes the body's tissues as they recover from nicotine addiction."

- "Independent studies have confirmed the beneficial effects of our patented formula."
- "Take one capsule three times a day 30 minutes before meals."
- "If you order now, a 30-day supply (90 capsules) costs just $29.99. Why wait? Think of all the money you'll be saving by not smoking, and order today!"

1. Bruce finds the statement "Independent studies have confirmed the beneficial effects of our patented formula" reassuring. Do you? Why or why not?

2. Look up licorice root in the "Herbs at a Glance" section of the website of the National Center for Complementary and Alternative Medicine (http://nccam.nih.gov). Would you recommend that Bruce take a supplement containing licorice root? Why or why not?

3. Comment on the advertisement's final bullet urging consumers to "think of all the money you'll be saving by not smoking, and order today!"

4. Instead of a supplements website, where online might Bruce have found reliable help in his quest to quit smoking? What other resources should he consult?

Answers can be found on the companion website, at www.pearsonhighered.com/thompsonmanore.

 **NutriTools** Check out the companion website at www.pearsonhighered.com/thompsonmanore, or use MyNutritionLab.com, to access interactive animations, including:

- Nutrient Functionality

Review Questions

1. Which of the following is a characteristic of vitamin E?
   a. It enhances the absorption of iron.
   b. It can be manufactured from beta-carotene.
   c. It is a critical component of the glutathione peroxidase system.
   d. It is destroyed by exposure to high heat.

2. Oxidation is best described as a process in which
   a. radiation causes a mutation in a cell's DNA.
   b. an atom loses an electron.
   c. an element loses an atom of oxygen.
   d. a compound loses a molecule of water.

3. Which of the following disorders is linked with the production of free radicals?
   a. cardiovascular disease
   b. carotenosis
   c. ulcers
   d. malaria

4. Which of the following function as a cofactor in antioxidant enzyme systems?
   a. iron
   b. zinc
   c. copper
   d. all of the above

5. Taking daily doses of three to four times the RDA of which of the following nutrients may cause death?
   a. vitamin A
   b. vitamin C
   c. vitamin E
   d. selenium

6. True or false? Tocopherol is the biologically active form of vitamin E in our body.

7. True or false? Free radical formation can occur as a result of normal cellular metabolism.

8. True or false? Vitamin C helps regenerate vitamin A.

9. True or false? Reliable food sources of selenium include beef liver, pork, and seafood.

10. True or false? Pregnant women are advised to consume plenty of beef liver.

Answers to Review Questions can be found at the back of this text, and additional essay questions and answers are located on the companion website at www.pearsonhighered.com/thompsonmanore.

Web Resources

www.who.int
World Health Organization (WHO)

Search for "vitamin A deficiency" to find out more about vitamin A deficiency around the world.

www.cfsan.fda.gov
U.S. Food and Drug Administration (FDA)

This site provides information on how to make informed decisions and evaluate information related to dietary supplements.

www.nal.usda.gov/fnic
The Food and Nutrition Information Center (FNIC)

Click on the Dietary Supplements button to obtain information on vitamin and mineral supplements, including consumer reports and industry regulations.

www.dietary-supplements.info.nih.gov
Office of Dietary Supplements

Go to this site to obtain current research results and reliable information about dietary supplements.

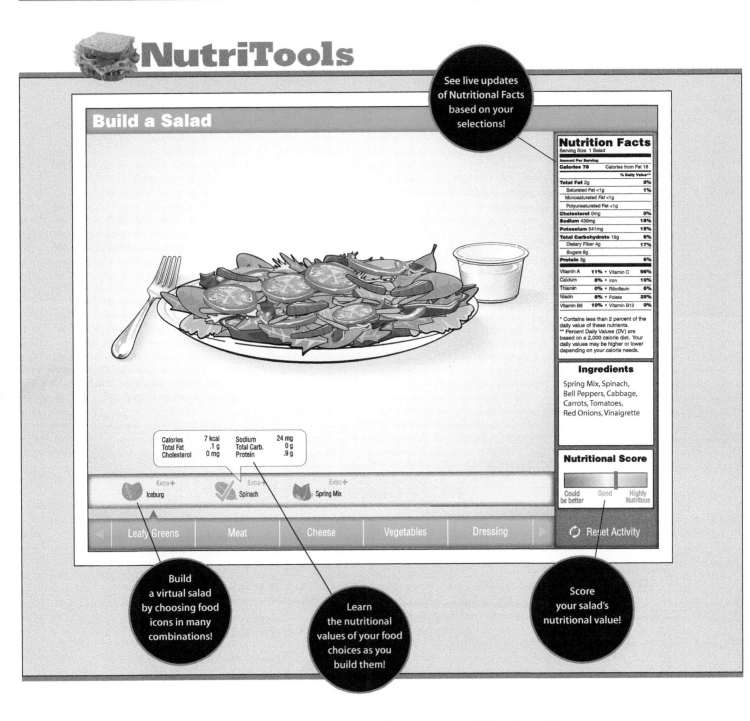

NutriTools

Build a Salad

See live updates of Nutritional Facts based on your selections!

Nutrition Facts
Serving Size 1 Salad

Amount Per Serving	
Calories 75	Calories from Fat 18

	% Daily Value**
Total Fat 2g	3%
Saturated Fat <1g	1%
Monosaturated Fat <1g	
Polyunsaturated Fat <1g	
Cholesterol 0mg	0%
Sodium 430mg	18%
Potassium 541mg	15%
Total Carbohydrate 19g	6%
Dietary Fiber 4g	17%
Sugars 8g	
Protein 3g	6%

Vitamin A	11%	Vitamin C	98%
Calcium	8%	Iron	10%
Thiamin	0%	Riboflavin	6%
Niacin	8%	Folate	25%
Vitamin B6	10%	Vitamin B12	0%

* Contains less than 2 percent of the daily value of these nutrients.
** Percent Daily Values (DV) are based on a 2,000 calorie diet. Your daily values may be higher or lower depending on your calorie needs.

Ingredients

Spring Mix, Spinach, Bell Peppers, Cabbage, Carrots, Tomatoes, Red Onions, Vinaigrette

Nutritional Score

Could be better — Good — Highly Nutritous

Calories	7 kcal	Sodium	24 mg
Total Fat	.1 g	Total Carb.	0 g
Cholesterol	0 mg	Protein	.9 g

Extra+ Iceburg   Extra+ Spinach   Extra+ Spring Mix

Leafy Greens | Meat | Cheese | Vegetables | Dressing

↻ Reset Activity

Build a virtual salad by choosing food icons in many combinations!

Learn the nutritional values of your food choices as you build them!

Score your salad's nutritional value!

To build your salad, just visit www.pearsonhighered.com/thompsonmanore **or** www.mynutritionlab.com

After building your salad, you should be able to answer these questions:

1. What are some of the best vegetables to select for a highly nutritious salad?
2. How do the types of greens selected for your salad affect its nutritional score?
3. Are your salad toppings making your salad too high in fat? How do you know?
4. Do the kcalories in your salad make it a side dish or a full meal?
5. Which nutrient guidelines are the most challenging in building your salad?

References

1. Institute of Medicine. Food and Nutrition Board. 2000. Dietary Reference Intakes for Vitamin C, Vitamin E, Selenium and Carotenoids. Washington, DC: National Academy Press.

2. The HOPE and HOPE-TOO Trial Investigators. 2005. Effects of long-term vitamin E supplementation on cardiovascular events and cancer. A randomized controlled trial. *JAMA* 293:1338–1347.

3. Sesso, H. D., J. E. Buring, W. G. Christen, T. Kurth, C. Belanger, J. MacFadyn, V. Bubes, J. E. Manson, R. J. Glynn, and J. M. Gaziano. 2008. Vitamins E and C in the prevention of cardiovascular disease in men: The Physicians' Health Study II randomized controlled trial. *JAMA* 300(18):2123–2133.

4. Ford, E. S., and A. Sowell. 1999. Serum alpha-tocopherol status in the United States population: findings from the Third National Health and Nutrition Examination Survey. *Am. J. Epidemiol.* 150(3):290–300.

5. Yeomans, V. C., J. Linseisen, and G. Wolfram. 2005. Interactive effects of polyphenols, tocopherol, and ascorbic acid on the Cu2+-mediated oxidative modification of human low density lipoproteins. *Eur. J. Nutr.* 44(7): 422–428.

6. Hemilä, H., E. Chalker, B. Treacy, and B. Douglas. 2007. Vitamin C for preventing and treating the common cold. Cochrane Database of Systematic Reviews. Issue 3. Art. No. CD000980. DOI: 10.1002/14651858.CD000980.pub3.

7. Burri, B. J. 1997. Beta-carotene and human health: a review of current research. *Nutr. Res.* 17:547–580.

8. U.S. Department of Agriculture (USDA), Agricultural Research Service. 2009. USDA National Nutrient Database for Standard Reference, Release 22. Available at http://www.ars.usda.gov/ba/bhnrc/ndl.

9. Larsson, S., L. Bergkvist, I. Näslund, J. Rutegård, and A. Wolk. 2007. Vitamin A, retinol, and carotenoids and the risk of gastric cancer: a prospective cohort study. *Am. J. Clin. Nutr.* 85:497–503.

10. Livrea, M. A., L. Tesoriere, A. Bongiorno, A. M. Pintaudi, M. Ciaccio, and A. Riccio. 1995. Contribution of vitamin A to the oxidation resistance of human low density lipoproteins. *Free Radic. Biol. Med.* 18:401–409.

11. Gutteridge, J. M. C., and B. Halliwell. 1994. Antioxidants in Nutrition, Health, and Disease. Oxford, UK: Oxford University Press.

12. Institute of Medicine. Food and Nutrition Board. 2001. Dietary Reference Intakes for Vitamin A, Vitamin K, Arsenic, Boron, Chromium, Copper, Iodine, Iron, Manganese, Molybdenum, Nickel, Silicon, Vanadium, and Zinc. Washington, DC: National Academy Press.

13. El-akawi, Z., N. Abdel-Latif, and K. Abdul-Razzak. 2006. Does the plasma level of vitamins A and E affect acne condition? *Clin. Experimen. Dermatol.* 31:430–434.

14. World Health Organization (WHO). 2009. Micronutrient deficiencies. Vitamin A deficiency. Available at http://www.who.int/nutrition/topics/vad/en/.

15. Albanes, D., O. P. Heinonen, J. K. Huttunen, P. R. Taylor, J. Virtamo, B. K. Edwards, J. Haapakoski, M. Rautalahti, A. M. Hartman, J. Palmgren, and P. Greenwald. 1995. Effects of alpha-tocopherol and beta-carotene supplements on cancer incidence in the Alpha-Tocopherol Beta-Carotene Cancer Prevention Study. *Am. J. Clin. Nutr.* 62(suppl.):1427S–1430S.

16. Omenn, G. S., G. E. Goodman, M. D. Thornquist, J. Balmes, M. R. Cullen, A. Glass, J. P. Keogh, F. L. Meyskens, B. Valanis, J. H. Williams, S. Barnhart, and S. Hammar. 1996. Effects of a combination of beta carotene and vitamin A on lung cancer and cardiovascular disease. *New Engl. J. Med.* 334:1150–1155.

17. Joshipura, K. J., F. B. Hu, J. E. Manson, M. J. Stampfer, E. B. Rimm, F. E. Speizer, G. Colditz, A. Ascherio, B. Rosner, D. Spiegelman, and W. C. Willett. 2001. The effect of fruit and vegetable intake on risk for coronary heart disease. *Ann. Intern. Med.* 134:1106–1114.

18. Liu, S., I.-M. Lee, U. Ajani, S. R. Cole, J. E. Buring, and J. E. Manson. 2001. Intake of vegetables rich in carotenoids and risk of coronary heart disease in men: The Physicians' Health Study. *Intl. J. Epidemiol.* 30:130–135.

19. The Alpha-Tocopherol, Beta-Carotene Cancer Prevention Study Group (The ATBC Study Group). 1994. The effect of vitamin E and beta carotene on the incidence of lung cancer and other cancers in male smokers. *N. Engl. J. Med.* 330:1029–1035.

20. Lee, I. M., N. R. Cook, J. M. Gaziano, D. Gordon, P. M. Ridker, J. E. Manson, C. H. Hennekens, and J. E. Buring. 2005. Vitamin E in the primary prevention of cardiovascular disease and cancer: The Women's Health Study: A randomized controlled trial. *JAMA* 294(1):56–65.

21. Geleijnse, J. M., L. J. Launer, D. A. M. van der Kuip, A. Hofman, and J. C. M. Witteman. 2002. Inverse association of tea and flavonoid intakes with incident myocardial infarction: The Rotterdam Study. *Am. J. Clin. Nutr.* 75:880–886.

Answers to Review Questions

Answers to Review Questions 11-15 (essay questions) for this chapter are located on the Companion Website at **www.pearsonhighered.com/thompsonmanore**

1. **d.** It is destroyed by exposure to high heat.
2. **b.** an atom loses an electron.
3. **a.** cardiovascular disease.
4. **d.** all of the above.
5. **a.** vitamin A.
6. True.
7. True.
8. False. Vitamin C helps regenerate vitamin E.
9. True.
10. False. Pregnant women should not consume beef liver very often, as it can lead to vitamin A toxicity and potentially serious birth defects.

Nutrients Involved in Bone Health

From Chapter 9 of *Nutrition: An Applied Approach*, Third Edition. Janice Thompson, Melinda Manore. Copyright © 2012 by Pearson Education, Inc. Published by Pearson Benjamin Cummings. All rights reserved.

Nutrients Involved in Bone Health

Diane Diederich/iStockphoto

CHAPTER OBJECTIVES

After reading this chapter you will be able to:

1. Describe the differences between cortical bone and trabecular bone.

2. Discuss the processes of bone growth, modeling, and remodeling.

3. List two vitamins and three minerals that play important roles in maintaining bone health.

4. Identify foods that are good sources of calcium.

5. Describe how vitamin D assists in regulating blood calcium levels.

6. Discuss three potential reasons that consumption of soft drinks may be detrimental to bone health.

Test Yourself

1. (T) (F) Very few foods—except milk, yogurt, and cheese—provide calcium.

2. (T) (F) We are capable of making vitamin D within our body by using energy obtained from exposure to sunlight.

3. (T) (F) Drinking lots of milk can help you lose weight.

Test Yourself answers can be found at the end of the chapter.

I n northern Maine, hockey is the local sport. So what's a poster of NBA star Chris Paul—who plays for the New Orleans Hornets—doing on the cafeteria walls in local schools? Paul is one of many athletes participating in the new "Body by Milk" ad campaign by the Milk Processor Education Program to teach kids about the benefits of drinking milk. On the campaign's TV commercials and website, Paul tells kids that the protein in milk helps build strong muscles and the calcium helps build strong bones.

Is the campaign working? Americans are consuming only about 1.8 cups of dairy (including milk, yogurt, ice cream, and cheese) per day, far short of the recommended 2–3 cups. In addition, the consumption of milk, specifically, plummeted from 31 gallons per person per year in 1970 to 21 gallons in 2005, likely because of competition from soft drinks, bottled waters, and specialty juices, coffees, and teas.[1] This concerns healthcare professionals, because milk is a convenient source of a form of calcium that's easily absorbed by the body, and calcium is required for kids and teens to build dense, compact bones. What's more, milk is fortified with vitamin D and is a good source of phosphorus, two more nutrients critical to bone health.

Still, milk is hardly the only food source of these nutrients. What other foods build bone? And how does bone grow—and break down? We begin this chapter with a quick look at the components and activities of bone tissue. Then we discuss the nutrients, dietary choices, and other lifestyle factors that play a critical role in maintaining bone health.

How Does Our Body Maintain Bone Health?

Contrary to what most people think, our skeleton is not an inactive collection of bones that simply holds our body together. Bones are living organs that contain several tissues, including two types of bone tissue, cartilage, and connective tissue. Nerves and blood vessels run within channels in bone tissue, supporting its activities. Bones have many important functions in our body, some of which might surprise you (Table 1). For instance, did you know that most of your blood cells are formed deep within your bones?

Given the importance of bones, it is critical that we maintain their health. Bone health is achieved through complex interactions among nutrients, hormones, and environmental factors. To better understand these interactions, we first need to learn about how bone structure and the constant activity of bone tissue influence bone health throughout our lifetime.

The Composition of Bone Provides Strength and Flexibility

We tend to think of bones as totally rigid, but if they were, how could we twist and jump our way through a basketball game or even carry an armload of books up a flight of stairs? Our bones need to be both strong and flexible, so that they can resist the compression, stretching, and twisting that occur throughout our daily activities. Fortunately, the composition of bone is ideally suited for its complex job: about 65% of bone tissue is made up of an assortment of minerals (mostly calcium and phosphorus) that provide hardness, but the remaining 35% is a mixture of organic substances that provide strength, durability, and flexibility. The most important of these substances is a fibrous protein called **collagen.** You might be surprised to learn that collagen fibers are actually stronger than steel fibers of similar size! Within our bones, the minerals form tiny crystals (called *hydroxyapatite*) that cluster around the collagen fibers. This design enables bones to bear our weight while responding to our demands for movement.

If you examine a bone very closely, you will notice two distinct types of tissue (Figure 1): cortical bone and trabecular bone. **Cortical bone,** which is also called **compact bone,** is very dense. It constitutes approximately 80% of our skeleton. The outer surface of all bones is cortical; plus, many small bones of the body, such as the bones of the wrists, hands, and feet, are made entirely of cortical bone. Although cortical bone looks solid to the naked eye, it actually contains many microscopic openings, which serve as passageways for blood vessels and nerves.

In contrast, **trabecular bone** makes up only 20% of our skeleton. It is found within the ends of the long bones (such as the bones of the arms and legs), the

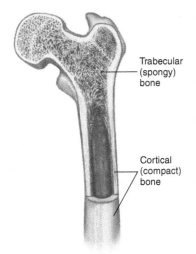

Figure 1 The structure of bone. Notice the difference in density between the trabecular (spongy) bone and the cortical (compact) bone.

collagen A protein that forms strong fibers in bone and connective tissue.

cortical bone (compact bone) A dense bone tissue that makes up the outer surface of all bones as well as the entirety of most small bones of the body.

trabecular bone (spongy bone) A porous bone tissue that makes up only 20% of our skeleton and is found within the ends of the long bones, inside the spinal vertebrae, inside the flat bones (sternum, ribs, and most bones of the skull), and inside the bones of the pelvis.

TABLE 1	Functions of Bone in the Human Body
Functions Related to Structure and Support	**Functions Related to Metabolic Processes**
Bones provide physical support for organs and body segments. Bones protect vital organs; for example, the rib cage protects the lungs, the skull protects the brain, and the vertebrae of the spine protect the spinal cord. Bones work with muscles and tendons to allow movement—muscles attach to bones via tendons, and their contraction produces movement at the body's joints.	Bone tissue acts as a storage reservoir for many minerals, including calcium, phosphorus, and fluoride. The body draws upon such deposits when these minerals are needed for various body processes; however, this can reduce bone mass. Most blood cells are produced in the bone marrow.

spinal vertebrae, the sternum (breastbone), the ribs, most bones of the skull, and the pelvis. Trabecular bone is sometimes referred to as **spongy bone** because to the naked eye it looks like a sponge, with cavities and no clear organization. The microscope reveals that trabecular bone is, in fact, aligned in a precise network of columns that protects the bone from stress. You can think of trabecular bone as the scaffolding inside the bone that supports the outer cortical bone.

Cortical and trabecular bone also differ in their rate of turnover—that is, in how quickly the bone tissue is broken down and replenished. Trabecular bone has a faster turnover rate than cortical bone. This makes trabecular bone more sensitive to changes in hormones and nutritional deficiencies. It also accounts for the much higher rate of age-related fractures in the spine and pelvis (including the hip)—both of which contain a significant amount of trabecular bone. Let's investigate how bone turnover influences bone health.

The Constant Activity of Bone Tissue Promotes Bone Health

Our bones develop through a series of three processes: bone growth, bone modeling, and bone remodeling (Figure 2). Bone growth and modeling begin during the early months of fetal life, when our skeleton is forming, and continue until early adulthood. Bone remodeling predominates during adulthood; this process helps us maintain a healthy skeleton as we age.

Bone Growth and Modeling Determine the Size and Shape of Our Bones

Through the process of *bone growth,* the size of our bones increases. The first period of rapid bone growth is from birth to age 2, but growth continues in spurts throughout childhood and into adolescence. Most girls reach their adult height by age 14, and boys generally reach adult height by age 17.[1] In the later decades of life, some loss in height usually occurs because of decreased bone density in the spine.

Bone modeling is the process by which the shape of our bones is determined, from the round "pebble" bones that make up our wrists, to the uniquely shaped bones of our face, to the long bones of our arms and legs. Even after bones stop growing in length, they can still increase in thickness if they are stressed by engaging in repetitive exercise, such as weight training, or by being overweight or obese.

Although the size and shape of our bones do not change significantly after puberty, our **bone density,** or the compactness of our bones, continues to develop into early adulthood. *Peak bone density* is the point at which our bones are strongest because they are at their highest density. The following factors are associated with a lower peak bone density:[2-4]

- late pubertal age in boys and late onset of menstruation in girls
- inadequate calcium intake
- low body weight
- physical inactivity during adolescence.

About 90% of a woman's bone density has been built by 17 years of age, whereas the majority of a man's has been built by his twenties. However, male or female,

bone density The degree of compactness of bone tissue, reflecting the strength of the bones. *Peak bone density* is the point at which a bone is strongest.

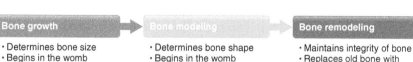

Bone growth	Bone modeling	Bone remodeling
• Determines bone size • Begins in the womb • Continues until early adulthood	• Determines bone shape • Begins in the womb • Continues until early adulthood	• Maintains integrity of bone • Replaces old bone with new bone to maintain mineral balance • Involves bone resorption and formation • Occurs predominantly during adulthood

◀ **Figure 2** Bone develops through three processes: bone growth, bone modeling, and bone remodeling.

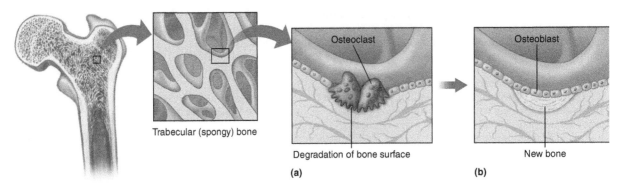

Trabecular (spongy) bone

Osteoclast

Degradation of bone surface

(a)

Osteoblast

New bone

(b)

Figure 3 Bone remodeling involves resorption and formation. **(a)** Osteoclasts erode the bone surface by degrading its components, including calcium, other minerals, and collagen; these components are then transported to the bloodstream. **(b)** Osteoblasts work to build new bone by filling the pit formed by the resorption process with new bone.

before we reach the age of 30 years, our bodies have reached peak bone mass, and we can no longer significantly add to our bone density. In our thirties, our bone density remains relatively stable, but by age 40, it has begun its irreversible decline.

Bone Remodeling Maintains a Balance Between Breakdown and Repair

Although our bones cannot increase their peak density after our twenties, bone tissue still remains very active throughout adulthood, balancing the breakdown of older bone tissue and the formation of new bone tissue. This bone recycling process is called **remodeling.** Remodeling is also used to repair fractures and to strengthen bone regions that are exposed to higher physical stress. The process of remodeling involves two steps: resorption and formation.

Bone is broken down through a process referred to as **resorption** (Figure 3a). During resorption, cells called **osteoclasts** erode the bone surface by secreting enzymes and acids that dig grooves into the bone matrix. Their ruffled surface also acts somewhat like a scrubbing brush to assist in the erosion process. One of the primary reasons the body regularly breaks down bone is to release calcium into the bloodstream. As discussed in more detail later in this chapter, calcium is critical for many physiologic processes, and bone is an important calcium reservoir. The body also breaks down bone that is fractured and needs to be repaired. Resorption at the injury site smooths the rough edges created by the break. Bone may also be broken down in areas away from the fracture site to obtain the minerals that are needed to repair the damage. Regardless of the reason, once bone is broken down, the resulting products are transported into the bloodstream and used for various body functions.

New bone is formed through the action of cells called **osteoblasts,** or "bone builders" (see Figure 3b). These cells work to synthesize new bone matrix by laying down the collagen-containing organic component of bone. Within this substance, the hydroxyapatite crystallizes and packs together to create new bone where it is needed.

In young, healthy adults, the processes of bone resorption and formation are equal, so that just as much bone is broken down as is built, maintaining bone mass. Around 40 years of age, bone resorption begins to occur more rapidly than bone formation, and this imbalance results in an overall loss in bone density. Because this affects the vertebrae of the spine, we also tend to lose height as we age. As we will discuss shortly, achieving a high peak bone mass through proper nutrition and exercise when we are young provides us with a stronger skeleton before the loss of bone begins. It can therefore reduce our risk for *osteoporosis,* a disorder characterized by low-density bones that fracture easily.

remodeling The two-step process by which bone tissue is recycled; includes the breakdown of existing bone and the formation of new bone.

resorption The process by which the surface of bone is broken down by cells called osteoclasts.

osteoclasts Cells that erode the surface of bones by secreting enzymes and acids that dig grooves into the bone matrix.

osteoblasts Cells that prompt the formation of new bone matrix by laying down the collagen-containing component of bone, which is then mineralized.

RECAP Bones are organs that contain metabolically active tissues composed primarily of minerals and a fibrous protein called collagen. Of the two types of bone, cortical bone is more dense; trabecular bone is more porous. Trabecular bone is also more sensitive to hormonal and nutritional factors and turns over more rapidly than cortical bone. The three types of bone activity are growth, modeling, and remodeling. Bones reach their peak bone mass by the late teenage years into the twenties; bone mass begins to decline around age 40.

How Do We Assess Bone Health?

Over the past 40 years, technological advancements have led to the development of a number of affordable methods for measuring bone health. **Dual energy x-ray absorptiometry (DXA or DEXA)** is considered the most accurate assessment tool for measuring bone density. This method can measure the density of the bone mass over the entire body. Software is also available that provides an estimation of percentage body fat.

The DXA procedure is simple, painless, and noninvasive, and it is considered to be of minimal risk. It takes just 15 to 30 minutes to complete. The person participating in the test remains fully clothed but must remove all jewelry and other metal objects. The participant lies quietly on a table, and bone density is assessed through the use of a very low level of x-ray (Figure 4).

DXA is a very important tool in determining a person's risk for osteoporosis. It generates a bone density score, which is compared to the average peak bone density of a healthy 30-year-old. Doctors use this comparison, which is known as a **T-score,** to assess the risk for fracture and determine whether the person has osteoporosis. If bone density is normal, the T-score ranges between +1 and –1 of the value for a healthy 30-year-old. A negative T-score between –1 and –2.5 indicates low bone mass and an increased risk for fractures. If the T-score is more negative than –2.5, the person has osteoporosis.

dual energy x-ray absorptiometry (DXA or DEXA) Currently, the most accurate tool for measuring bone density.

T-score A comparison of an individual's bone density to the average peak bone density of a 30-year-old healthy adult.

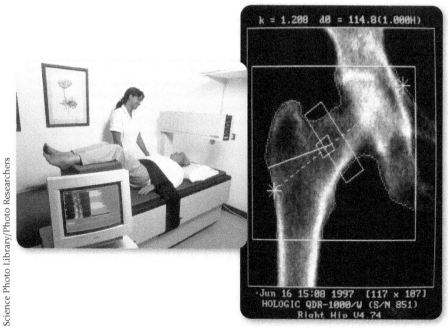

Science Photo Library/Photo Researchers

Pascal Alix/Photo Researchers

k = 1.208 d0 = 114.8(1.000H)

·Jun 16 15:08 1997 [117 x 107]
HOLOGIC QDR-1000/W (S/N 851)
Right Hip V4.74

◆ **Figure 4** Dual energy x-ray absorptiometry is a safe and simple procedure that assesses bone density.

DXA tests are generally recommended for postmenopausal women because they are at highest risk for osteoporosis and fracture. Men and younger women may also be recommended for a DXA test if they have significant risk factors for osteoporosis.

Other technologies have been developed to measure bone density. These use ultrasound or different forms of x-ray technology to measure the density of bone in the heel or another more peripheral part of the body. These technologies are frequently used at health fairs because the machines are portable and provide scores faster than the traditional DXA.

RECAP Dual energy x-ray absorptiometry (DXA or DEXA) is the gold standard measurement of bone mass. It is a simple, painless, and minimal-risk procedure. The result of a DXA is a T-score, which is a comparison of a person's bone density with that of a healthy 30-year-old. A T-score between +1 and –1 is normal; a score between –1 and –2.5 indicates poor bone density; and a score more negative than –2.5 indicates osteoporosis.

Richard Ross/Getty Images

One major role of calcium is to form and maintain bones and teeth.

parathyroid hormone (PTH) A hormone secreted by the parathyroid gland when blood calcium levels fall. Also known as parathormone, it increases blood calcium levels by stimulating the activation of vitamin D, increasing reabsorption of calcium from the kidneys, and stimulating osteoclasts to break down bone, which releases more calcium into the bloodstream.

calcitonin A hormone secreted by the thyroid gland when blood calcium levels are too high. Calcitonin inhibits the actions of vitamin D, preventing reabsorption of calcium in the kidneys, limiting calcium absorption in the small intestine, and inhibiting the osteoclasts from breaking down bone.

A Profile of Nutrients That Maintain Bone Health

Calcium is the most recognized nutrient associated with bone health; however, vitamins D and K, phosphorus, magnesium, and fluoride are also essential for strong bones, and the roles of other vitamins, minerals, and phytochemicals are currently being researched.

Calcium

The major minerals are those required in our diet in amounts greater than 100 mg per day. Calcium is by far the most abundant major mineral in our body, constituting about 2% of our entire body weight! Not surprisingly, it plays many critical roles in maintaining overall function and health.

Functions of Calcium

One of the primary functions of calcium is to provide structure to our bones and teeth. About 99% of the calcium found in our body is stored in the hydroxyapatite crystals built up on the collagen foundation of bone. As noted earlier, the combination of crystals and collagen provides both the characteristic hardness of bone and the flexibility needed to support various activities.

The remaining 1% of calcium in our body is found in the blood and soft tissues. Calcium is alkaline, or basic, and plays a critical role in assisting with acid–base balance. We cannot survive for long if our blood calcium level rises above or falls below a very narrow range; therefore, our body maintains the appropriate blood calcium level at all costs.

Figure 5 illustrates how various organ systems and hormones work together to maintain blood calcium levels. When blood calcium levels fall (Figure 5a), the parathyroid glands are stimulated to produce **parathyroid hormone (PTH).** Also known as parathormone, PTH stimulates the activation of vitamin D. Together, PTH and vitamin D stimulate the kidneys to reabsorb calcium from the bloodstream. They also stimulate osteoclasts to break down bone, releasing more calcium into the bloodstream. In addition, vitamin D increases the absorption of calcium from the intestines. Through these three mechanisms, blood calcium levels increase.

When blood calcium levels are too high, the thyroid gland secretes a hormone called **calcitonin,** which inhibits the actions of vitamin D (Figure 5b). Thus, calcitonin prevents the reabsorption of calcium in the kidneys, limits calcium absorption in the intestines, and inhibits the osteoclasts from breaking down bone.

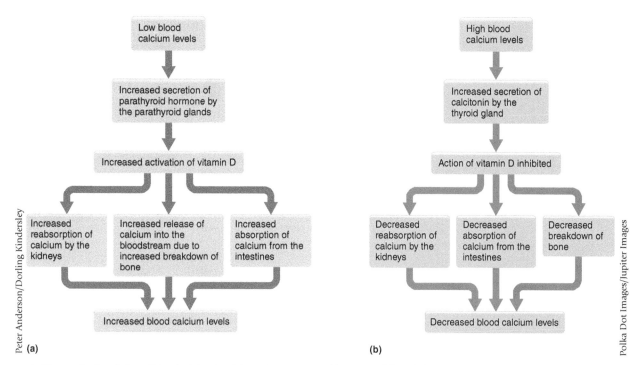

Peter Anderson/Dorling Kindersley

Polka Dot Images/Jupiter Images

Figure 5 Regulation of blood calcium levels by various organs and hormones. **(a)** Low blood calcium levels stimulate the production of parathyroid hormone and activation of vitamin D, which in turn cause an increase in blood calcium levels. **(b)** High blood calcium levels stimulate the secretion of calcitonin, which in turn causes a decrease in blood calcium levels.

As just noted, the body must maintain blood calcium levels within a very narrow range. Thus, when an individual does not consume or absorb enough calcium from the diet, osteoclasts erode bone, so that calcium can be released into the blood. To maintain healthy bone density, we need to consume and absorb enough calcium to balance the calcium taken from our bones.

Calcium is also critical for the normal transmission of nerve impulses. Calcium flows into nerve cells and stimulates the release of molecules called neurotransmitters, which transfer the nerve impulses from one nerve cell (neuron) to another. Without adequate calcium, our nerves' ability to transmit messages is inhibited. Not surprisingly, when blood calcium levels fall dangerously low, a person can experience convulsions.

A fourth role of calcium is to assist in muscle contraction, which is initiated when calcium flows into muscle cells. Conversely, muscles relax when calcium is pumped back outside of muscle cells. If calcium levels are inadequate, normal muscle contraction and relaxation are inhibited, and the person may suffer from twitching and spasms. This is referred to as **calcium tetany.** High levels of blood calcium can cause **calcium rigor,** an inability of muscles to relax, which leads to a hardening or stiffening of the muscles. These problems affect the function not only of skeletal muscles but also of heart muscle and can cause heart failure.

Other functions of calcium include the maintenance of healthy blood pressure, the initiation of blood clotting, and the regulation of various hormones and enzymes.

How Much Calcium Should We Consume?

There are no RDA values for calcium. The Adequate Intake (AI) varies according to age and gender. Adult values are listed in Table 2. Values for adults over age 50 are higher (1,200 mg/day), and pre-teens and teens have the highest calcium requirements (1,300 mg/day). Many people of all ages fail to consume enough calcium to maintain bone health.

calcium tetany A condition in which muscles experience twitching and spasms as a result of inadequate blood calcium levels.

calcium rigor A failure of muscles to relax, which leads to a hardening or stiffening of the muscles; caused by high levels of blood calcium.

TABLE 2 Overview of Nutrients Essential to Bone Health

To see the full profile of nutrients essential to bone health, turn to *In Depth,* Vitamins and Minerals: Micronutrients with Macro Powers.

Nutrient	Recommended Intake
Calcium (major mineral)	Adequate Intake (AI): Women and men aged 19 to 50 years = 1,000 mg/day Women and men aged >50 years = 1,200 mg/day
Vitamin D (fat-soluble vitamin)	AI:* Women and men aged 19 to 50 years = 5 μg/day Women and men aged 50 to 70 years = 10 μg/day Women and men aged >70 years = 15 μg/day
Vitamin K (fat-soluble vitamin)	AI: Women: 90 μg/day Men: 120 μg/day
Phosphorus (major mineral)	Recommended Dietary Allowance (RDA): Women and men = 700 mg/day
Magnesium (major mineral)	RDA: Women aged 19 to 30 years = 310 mg/day Women aged >30 years = 320 mg/day Men aged 19 to 30 years = 400 mg/day Men aged >30 years = 420 mg/day
Fluoride (trace mineral)	AI: Women: 3 mg/day Men: 4 mg/day

*Based on the assumption that a person does not get adequate sun exposure.

A nutrient's **bioavailability** is the degree to which our body can absorb and use that nutrient. The bioavailability of calcium depends in part on our age and our calcium need. For example, infants, children, and adolescents can absorb more than 60% of the calcium they consume, as calcium needs are very high during these stages of life. In addition, pregnant and lactating women can absorb about 50% of dietary calcium. In contrast, healthy young adults absorb only about 30% of the calcium consumed in the diet. When our calcium needs are high, our body can generally increase its absorption of calcium from the small intestine. Although older adults have a high need for calcium, the ability to absorb calcium diminishes as we age and can be as low as 25%. These variations in bioavailability and absorption capacity were taken into account when calcium recommendations were determined.

The bioavailability of calcium also depends on how much calcium we consume throughout the day or at any one time. When our diet is generally high in calcium, absorption of calcium is reduced. In addition, our body cannot absorb more than 500 mg of calcium at any one time, and as the amount of calcium in a single meal or supplement increases up, the fraction that we absorb decreases down. This explains why it is critical to consume calcium-rich foods throughout the day rather than relying on a single, high-dose supplement. Conversely, when dietary intake of calcium is low, the absorption of calcium is increased.

Dietary factors can also affect our absorption of calcium. Binding factors, such as phytates and oxalates, occur naturally in some calcium-rich seeds, nuts, grains, and vegetables, such as spinach and swiss chard. Such factors bind to the calcium in these foods and prevent its absorption from the small intestine. Additionally, consuming calcium with iron, zinc, magnesium, or phosphorus can interfere with the absorption and utilization of all these minerals. Despite these potential interactions, the Institute of Medicine has concluded that there is not sufficient evidence to suggest that these interactions cause deficiencies of calcium or other minerals in healthy individuals.[5]

Finally, because vitamin D is necessary for the absorption of calcium, a lack of vitamin D severely limits the bioavailability of calcium. We'll discuss this and other contributions of vitamin D to bone health shortly.

Foods Rich in Calcium: Dairy, Greens, and More

Dairy products are among the most common sources of calcium in the U.S. diet. Skim milk, low-fat cheeses, and nonfat yogurt are nutritious sources of calcium (**Figure 6**).

Dave King/Dorling Kindersley

Although spinach contains high levels of calcium, binding factors in the plant prevent much of its absorption.

bioavailability The degree to which our body can absorb and utilize any given nutrient.

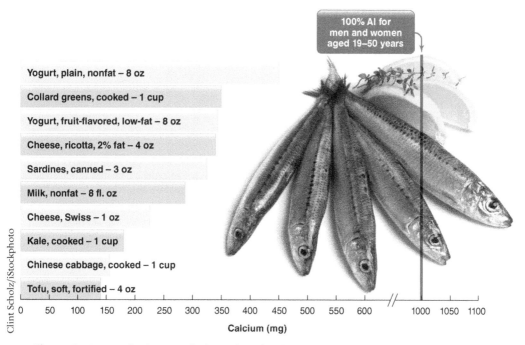

100% AI for men and women aged 19–50 years

Yogurt, plain, nonfat – 8 oz

Collard greens, cooked – 1 cup

Yogurt, fruit-flavored, low-fat – 8 oz

Cheese, ricotta, 2% fat – 4 oz

Sardines, canned – 3 oz

Milk, nonfat – 8 fl. oz

Cheese, Swiss – 1 oz

Kale, cooked – 1 cup

Chinese cabbage, cooked – 1 cup

Tofu, soft, fortified – 4 oz

0   50   100   150   200   250   300   350   400   450   500   550   600   //   1000   1050   1100

Calcium (mg)

Clint Scholz/iStockphoto

Figure 6 Common food sources of calcium. The AI for adult men and women aged 19 to 50 years is 1,000 mg of calcium per day. For men and women older than 50 years of age, the AI increases to 1,200 mg of calcium per day.

Data from U.S. Department of Agriculture, Agricultural Research Service. 2009. USDA Nutrient Database for Standard Reference, Release 22. Nutrient Data Laboratory Home Page. www.ars.usda.gov/ba/bhnrc/ndl.

Ice cream, regular cheese, and whole milk also contain a relatively high amount of calcium, but these foods should be eaten in moderation because of their high fat and energy content. Cottage cheese is one dairy product that is a relatively poor source of calcium, as the processing of this food removes a great deal of the calcium. One cup of low-fat cottage cheese contains approximately 150 mg of calcium, while the same serving of low-fat milk contains almost 300 mg. However calcium-fortified cottage cheese contains 400 mg of calcium.

Other good sources of calcium are green leafy vegetables, such as kale, collard greens, turnip greens, broccoli, cauliflower, green cabbage, brussels sprouts, and Chinese cabbage (bok choy). The bioavailability of the calcium in these vegetables is relatively high compared to spinach, as these vegetables contain low levels of oxalates. Many packaged foods are now available fortified with calcium. For example, you can buy calcium-fortified orange juice, soy milk, rice milk, and tofu processed with calcium. Some dairies have even boosted the amount of calcium in their brand of milk!

Figure 7 illustrates serving sizes of various calcium-rich foods that contain the same amount of calcium as one glass (8 fl. oz) of skim milk. As you can see from this figure, a wide variety of foods can be consumed each day to contribute to an adequate calcium intake. When you are selecting foods that are good sources of calcium, it is important to remember that we do not absorb 100% of the calcium contained in foods.[6,7] For example, although a serving of milk contains approximately 300 mg of calcium, our body does not actually absorb this entire amount. To learn more about how calcium absorption rates vary for select foods, see the Nutrition Label Activity.

In general, meats and fish are not good sources of calcium. An exception is canned fish with bones (for example, sardines or salmon),

Kale is a good source of calcium.

6 cups
lima beans
1,255 kcal

5.4 oz plain,
nonfat yogurt
86 kcal

1.4 oz Swiss
cheese
151 kcal

8 fl. oz
nonfat milk
306 mg Ca
83 kcal

2.8 oz canned
sardines
165 kcal

9 oz tofu, soft,
with calcium
165 kcal

7/8 cup cooked
collard greens
(from frozen)
54 kcal

◆ **Figure 7** Serving sizes and energy content of various foods that contain the same amount of calcium as an 8-fl. oz glass of skim milk.

hypercalcemia A condition marked by an abnormally high concentration of calcium in the blood.

QUICK TIPS

Capitalizing on Calcium

✓ At the grocery store, stock up on calcium-fortified juice, soy milk, and rice milk. Look for single-serving portable "juice boxes" with calcium-fortified juice, milk, or chocolate milk.

✓ Purchase breakfast cereals and breads that are fortified with calcium.

✓ For quick snacks, purchase single-serving cups of yogurt, individually wrapped "cheese sticks," or calcium-fortified protein bars.

✓ Keep on hand shredded parmesan or any other hard cheese, and sprinkle it on hot soups, chili, salads, pasta, and other dishes.

✓ In any recipe, replace sour cream or mayonnaise with nonfat plain yogurt.

✓ Add nonfat dry milk powder to hot cereals, soups, chili, recipes for baked goods, coffee, and hot cocoa. One-third of a cup of nonfat dry milk powder provides the same amount of calcium as a whole cup of nonfat milk.

✓ Make a yogurt smoothie by blending nonfat plain or flavored yogurt with fresh or frozen fruit.

✓ At your favorite cafe, instead of black coffee, order a skim milk latte. Instead of black tea, order a cup of chai—spiced Indian tea brewed with milk.

✓ At home, brew a cup of strong coffee; then add half a cup of warm milk for a café au lait.

✓ When eating out, order skim milk instead of a soft drink with your meal.

✓ If you do not consume enough dietary calcium, consider taking a calcium supplement. Refer to the **In Depth** on osteoporosis following this chapter to learn how to choose a calcium supplement that is right for you.

providing you eat the bones. Fruits (except dried figs) and nonfortified grain products are also poor sources of calcium.

Although many foods in the U.S. diet are good sources of calcium, many Americans do not have adequate intakes because they consume very few dairy-based foods and calcium-rich vegetables. At particular risk are women and young girls. For example, a large national survey conducted by the U.S. Department of Agriculture found that teenage girls consume less than 60% of the recommended amount of calcium.[1]

A variety of quick, simple tools are available on the Internet to help you determine your daily calcium intake. Most of these tools are designed to provide you with an estimated calcium intake score based on the types and amounts of calcium-rich foods you consume. See the Web Resources at the end of this chapter. In addition, following the tips shown above can add more calcium to your bone bank.

As you can see, it's easy to increase your calcium intake by making smart menu choices throughout the day. Eating Right All Day shows menu choices high in calcium. Notice that these are also low in fat and calories.

What Happens If We Consume Too Much Calcium?

In general, consuming too much calcium from foods does not lead to significant toxicity symptoms in healthy individuals. Much of the excess calcium we consume is excreted in the feces. However, an excessive intake of calcium from supplements can lead to health problems.[8] One concern with consuming too much calcium is that it can lead to various mineral imbalances because, as we mentioned earlier, calcium interferes with the absorption of other minerals, including iron, zinc, and magnesium. In some people, the formation of kidney stones is associated with high intakes of calcium, oxalates, protein, and vegetable fiber.[9] However, more studies need to be done to determine whether high intakes of calcium actually cause kidney stones.

Various diseases and metabolic disorders can alter our ability to regulate blood calcium. **Hypercalcemia** is a condition in which our blood calcium levels reach abnormally high concentrations. Hypercalcemia can be caused by cancer and by the overproduction of parathyroid hormone (PTH). As we noted earlier, PTH stimulates osteoclasts to break down bone and release more calcium into the bloodstream. Symptoms of hypercalcemia include fatigue, loss of appetite, constipation, and mental confusion, and it can lead to coma and possibly death. Hypercalcemia can also result in an accumulation of calcium deposits in the soft tissues, such as the liver and kidneys, causing failure of these organs.

What Happens If We Don't Consume Enough Calcium?

There are no short-term symptoms associated with consuming too little calcium. Even when we do not consume enough dietary calcium, our body continues to tightly regulate blood calcium levels by taking the calcium from bone. A long-term repercussion of inadequate calcium intake is osteoporosis. This disease is discussed **In Depth** immediately following this chapter.

Hypocalcemia is an abnormally low level of calcium in the blood. Hypocalcemia does not result from consuming too little dietary calcium, but is caused by various diseases, including kidney disease, vitamin D deficiency, and diseases that inhibit the production of PTH. Symptoms of hypocalcemia include muscle spasms and convulsions.

Eating Right All Day

Breakfast
Skim-milk chai tea instead of a cola!

Heike Brauer/Dreamstime

Lunch
Bean & cheese burrito instead of a beef burrito!

SoFood/Alamy

Dinner
Pasta with broccoli and grated cheese instead of meat sauce!

Igor Dutina/Shutterstock

Snack
Nonfat fruit yogurt instead of Oreos!

Alejandro Rivera/iStockphoto

RECAP Calcium is the most abundant mineral in the human body and a significant component of our bones. Calcium is necessary for normal nerve and muscle function. Blood calcium is maintained within a very narrow range, and bone calcium is used to maintain normal blood calcium if dietary intake is inadequate. The AI for calcium is highest for pre-teens and teens. Dairy products, canned fish with bones, and some green leafy vegetables are good sources of calcium. The most common long-term effect of inadequate calcium consumption is osteoporosis.

Vitamin D

Vitamin D is like other fat-soluble vitamins in that we store excess amounts in our liver and adipose tissue. But vitamin D is different from other nutrients in two ways. First, vitamin D does not always need to come from the diet. This is because our body can synthesize vitamin D using energy from exposure to sunlight. However, when we do not get enough sunlight, we must consume vitamin D in our diet. Second, in addition to being a nutrient, vitamin D is considered a *hormone* because it is made in one part of the body, yet it regulates various activities in other parts of the body.

hypocalcemia A condition characterized by an abnormally low concentration of calcium in the blood.

Figure 8 illustrates how our body makes vitamin D by converting a cholesterol compound in our skin to the active form of vitamin D that we need to function properly. When the ultraviolet rays of the sun hit our skin, they react with 7-dehydrocholesterol. This cholesterol compound is converted into a precursor of vitamin D, cholecalciferol, which is also called provitamin D_3. This inactive form is then converted to calcidiol in the liver. Calcidiol travels to the kidneys, where it is converted into **calcitriol**, which is considered the primary active form of vitamin D in our body. Calcitriol then circulates to various parts of the body, performing its many functions.

Functions of Vitamin D

Vitamin D, PTH, and calcitonin all work together continuously to regulate blood calcium levels, which in turn maintains bone health. They do this by regulating the absorption of calcium and phosphorus from the small intestine, causing more to be absorbed when our needs for them are higher and less when our needs are lower. They also decrease or increase blood calcium levels by signaling the kidneys to excrete more or less calcium in our urine. Finally, vitamin D works with PTH to stimulate osteoclasts to break down bone when calcium is needed elsewhere in the body.

Vitamin D is also necessary for the normal calcification of bone; this means it assists the process by which minerals, such as calcium and phosphorus, are crystallized. Vitamin D may also play a role in decreasing the formation of some cancerous tumors, as it can prevent certain types of cells from growing out of control. Like vitamin A, vitamin D appears to play a role in cell differentiation in various tissues.

How Much Vitamin D Should We Consume?

As for calcium, there is no RDA for vitamin D. The AI is based on the assumption that an individual does not get adequate sun exposure (see Table 2). If your exposure to the sun is adequate, then you do not need to consume any vitamin D in your diet. But how do you know whether you are getting enough sun?

Of the many factors that affect your ability to synthesize vitamin D from sunlight, latitude and time of year are the most significant (**Table 3**). Individuals living in very sunny climates relatively close to the equator, such as the southern United States and Mexico, may synthesize enough vitamin D from the sun to meet their needs throughout the year—as long as they spend time outdoors. However, vitamin D synthesis from the sun is not possible during most of the winter months for people living in places located at a latitude of more than 40°N or more than 40°S. This is because at these latitudes in winter the sun never rises high enough in the sky to provide the direct sunlight needed. The 40°N latitude runs like a belt across the United States from northern Pennsylvania in the east to northern California in the west (**Figure 9**). In addition, entire countries, such as Canada and the United Kingdom, are affected, as are

HOT TOPIC

Can Eating Dairy Foods Help You Lose Weight?

A 2004 research study suggested that a weight-loss diet high in calcium-rich foods may help people lose more weight than if they reduce their energy intake but do not consume enough dietary calcium.[10] This research led to a major advertising campaign by the dairy industry, called the "3-A-Day" campaign. This campaign encourages people who want to lose weight to eat at least 3 servings of dairy foods per day, as study participants who ate calcium-rich foods experienced significantly more weight loss than those who consumed calcium supplements. Interestingly, a 2005 study failed to replicate these findings.[11]

Now the United States Department of Agriculture is conducting its own research into this topic. The study will attempt to determine whether eating various amounts of low-fat dairy foods as part of daily meals and snacks can enhance weight and fat loss in obese adults.[12] We may not know the results of this study for a few more years. Until then, the question of whether eating foods high in dietary calcium can enhance weight loss remains unanswered.

calcitriol The primary active form of vitamin D in the body.

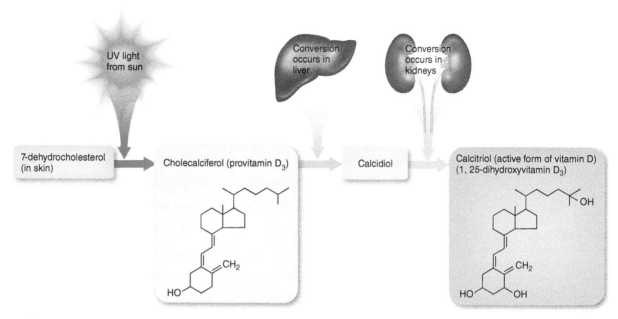

Figure 8 The process of converting sunlight into vitamin D in our skin. When the ultraviolet rays of the sun hit our skin, they react with 7-dehydrocholesterol. This compound is converted to cholecalciferol, an inactive form of vitamin D also called provitamin D$_3$. Cholecalciferol is then converted to calcidiol in the liver. Calcidiol travels to the kidneys, where it is converted into calcitriol, which is considered the primary active form of vitamin D in our body.

countries in the far southern hemisphere. Thus, many people around the world need to consume vitamin D in their diets, particularly during the winter months.

Other factors influencing vitamin D synthesis are time of day, skin color, age, and obesity status:

- More vitamin D can be synthesized when the sun's rays are strongest, generally between 9 AM and 3 PM. Vitamin D synthesis is severely limited or may be non-existent on overcast days.
- Darker skin contains more melanin pigment, which reduces the penetration of sunlight. Thus, people with dark skin have a more difficult time synthesizing vitamin D from the sun than do light-skinned people.

TABLE 3   Factors Affecting Sunlight-Mediated Synthesis of Vitamin D in the Skin

Factors That Enhance Synthesis of Vitamin D	Factors That Inhibit Synthesis of Vitamin D
Season—Most vitamin D is produced during summer months, particularly June and July	Season—Exposure in winter months (October through February) results in little or no vitamin D production
Latitude—Locations closer to the equator get more sunlight throughout the year	Latitude—Locations that are more north of 40°N and more south than 40°S get inadequate sun
Time of day—Generally, between the hours of 9:00 AM and 3:00 PM (dependent on latitude and time of year)	Time of day—Early morning, late afternoon, and evening hours
Age—Younger	Age—Older, due to reduced skin thickness with age
Limited or no use of sunscreen	Use of sunscreen with SPF 8 or greater
Sunny weather	Cloudy weather
Exposed skin	Protective clothing
Lighter skin pigmentation	Darker skin pigmentation
	Obesity—May negatively affect metabolism and storage of vitamin D
	Glass and plastics—Windows and other barriers made of glass or plastic (such as Plexiglas) block the sun's rays

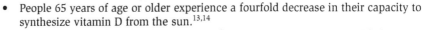
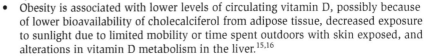

Figure 9 This map illustrates the geographical location of 40° latitude in the United States. In southern cities below 40° latitude, such as Los Angeles, Austin, and Miami, the sunlight is strong enough to allow for vitamin D synthesis throughout the year. In northern cities above 40° latitude, such as Seattle, Chicago, and Boston, the sunlight is too weak from about mid-October to mid-March to allow for adequate vitamin D synthesis.

Peter Turnley/Corbis

Vitamin D synthesis from the sun is not possible during most of the winter months for people living in high latitudes. Therefore, many people need to consume vitamin D in their diet, particularly during the winter.

- People 65 years of age or older experience a fourfold decrease in their capacity to synthesize vitamin D from the sun.[13,14]
- Obesity is associated with lower levels of circulating vitamin D, possibly because of lower bioavailability of cholecalciferol from adipose tissue, decreased exposure to sunlight due to limited mobility or time spent outdoors with skin exposed, and alterations in vitamin D metabolism in the liver.[15,16]

Wearing protective clothing and sunscreen (with an SPF greater than 8) limits sun exposure, so it is suggested that we expose our hands, face, and arms to the sun two or three times per week for a period of time that is one-third to one-half of the amount needed to get sunburned.[17] This means that, if you normally sunburn in 1 hour, you should expose yourself to the sun for 20 to 30 minutes two or three times per week to synthesize adequate amounts of vitamin D. Again, this guideline does not apply to people living in more northern climates during the winter months; they can get enough vitamin D only by consuming it in their diet.

Recent evidence suggests that the current AI for vitamin D is not sufficient to maintain optimal bone health and reduce the risks for diseases such as cancer; the controversy surrounding the current recommendations for vitamin D are discussed in more detail in the Nutrition Debate at the end of this chapter. What about you? Do you think you're getting enough vitamin D each day? To find out, take the quiz in the What About You? box in this chapter.

Vitamin D: Fish, Fortified Foods, Supplements, or Sunlight

There are many forms of vitamin D, but only two can be converted into calcitriol. Vitamin D_2, also called *ergocalciferol*, is found exclusively in plant foods, whereas vitamin D_3, or *cholecalciferol*, is found in animal foods. Recall that cholecalciferol is also the form of vitamin D we synthesize from the sun.

Most foods naturally contain very little vitamin D. The few exceptions are cod liver oil and fatty fish (such as salmon, mackerel, and sardines), foods that few Americans consume in adequate amounts. Eggs, butter, some margarines, and liver also provide small amounts of vitamin D, but we would have to eat very large amounts to consume enough vitamin D.

What About You?

Are You Getting Enough Vitamin D?

After reading this section, you may wonder whether you're getting enough vitamin D to keep your tissues healthy and strong. Take the following simple quiz to find out. For each question, circle either Yes or No:

I live south of 40° latitude (see Figure 10) and expose my bare arms and face to sunlight (without sunscreen) for at least a few minutes two or three times per week all year.	Yes/No
I consume a multivitamin supplement or vitamin D supplement that provides at least 5 μg or 200 IU per day.	Yes/No
I consume a diet high in fatty fish, fortified milk, and/or fortified cereals that provides at least 5 μg or 200 IU per day.	Yes/No

If you answered No to all three of these questions, you are at high risk for vitamin D deficiency. You are probably getting enough vitamin D if you answered Yes to at least one of them. However, notice that, if you rely on sun exposure for your vitamin D, you must make sure that you expose your bare skin to sunlight for an adequate length of time. What's adequate varies for each person: the darker your skin tone, the more time you need in the sun. A general guideline is to expose your skin for a period of time that is one-third to one-half the amount of time in which you would get sunburned. This means that, if you normally sunburn in 1 hour, you should get 30 minutes of sun two or three times a week. Expose your skin when the sun is high in the sky (generally between the hours of 9 AM and 3 PM). Put on sunscreen only *after* your skin has had its daily dose of sunlight.[18–20]

Remember: if you live in the northern United States or Canada, you cannot get adequate sun exposure to synthesize vitamin D from approximately October through February, no matter how long you expose your bare skin to the sun. So, if you are not regularly consuming fortified foods, fatty fish, or cod liver oil, you need to supplement vitamin D during those months.

Thus, the primary source of vitamin D in the diet is from fortified foods such as milk (Figure 10). In the United States, milk is fortified with 10 μg of vitamin D per quart. Because earlier studies examining the actual vitamin D content of fortified milk found that the amount of vitamin D varied widely, the USDA now monitors dairies to make sure they meet the mandated vitamin D fortification guidelines.

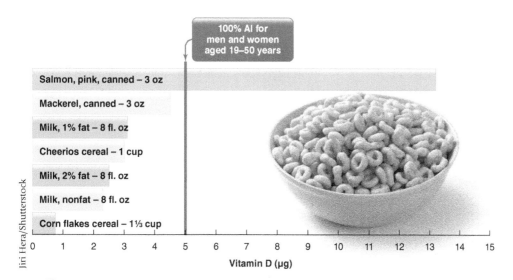

Jiri Hera/Shutterstock

Figure 10 Common food sources of vitamin D. For men and women aged 19 to 50 years, the AI for vitamin D is 5 μg per day. The AI for vitamin D for men and women aged 50 to 70 years is 10 μg per day, and the AI increases to 15 μg per day for adults over the age of 70 years.

Data from U.S. Department of Agriculture, Agricultural Research Service. 2009. USDA Nutrient Database for Standard Reference, Release 22. Nutrient Data Laboratory Home Page. www.ars.usda.gov/ba/bhnrc/ndl.

Dorling Kindersley

Certain fortified cereals, fortified soy and rice milks, and even some brands of fortified orange juice also provide vitamin D. Since plants naturally contain very little vitamin D, vegans need to obtain their vitamin D from these kinds of fortified foods, from sun exposure, or from supplements. When reading the labels of fortified foods and supplements, you will see the amount of vitamin D expressed in units of either μg or IU. For conversion purposes, 1 μg of vitamin D is equal to 40 IU of vitamin D.

What Happens If We Consume Too Much Vitamin D?

We cannot get too much vitamin D from sun exposure, as our skin has the ability to limit its production. As just noted, foods contain little natural vitamin D. Thus, the only way we can consume too much vitamin D is through supplementation.

◄ Fatty fish contain vitamin D.

NUTRITION LABEL ACTIVITY
How Much Calcium Am I Really Consuming?

As you have learned in this chapter, we do not absorb 100% of the calcium contained in foods. This is particularly true for individuals who eat lots of foods high in fiber, oxalates, and phytates, such as whole grains and certain vegetables. So if you want to design an eating plan that contains adequate calcium, it's important to understand how the rate of calcium absorption differs for the foods you include.

Unfortunately, the absorption rate of calcium has not been determined for most foods. However, estimates have been established for some common foods that are considered good sources of calcium. The following table shows some of these foods, their calcium content per serving, the calcium absorption rate, and the estimated amount of calcium absorbed from each food.

As you can see from this table, many dairy products have a similar calcium absorption rate, just over 30%. Interestingly, many green leafy vegetables have a higher absorption rate of around 60%; however, because many times a serving of these foods contains less calcium than dairy foods, you would have to eat more vegetables to get the same calcium as you would from a standard serving of dairy foods. Note the relatively low calcium absorption rate for spinach, even though it contains a relatively high amount of calcium. This is due to the high levels of oxalates in spinach, which bind with calcium and reduce its bioavailability.

Remember that the DRIs for calcium take these differences in absorption rate into account. Thus, the 300 mg of calcium in a glass of milk counts as 300 mg toward your daily calcium goal. In general, you can trust that dairy products such as milk and yogurt (but not cottage cheese) are good, absorbable sources of calcium, as are most dark green leafy vegetables. Other dietary sources of calcium with good absorption rates are calcium-fortified orange juice, soy milk and rice milk, tofu processed with calcium, and fortified breakfast cereals, such as Total.[6] Armed with this knowledge, you will be better able to select foods that can optimize your calcium intake and support bone health.

Food	Serving Size	Calcium per Serving (mg)*	Absorption Rate (%)[†]	Estimated Amount of Calcium Absorbed (mg)
Yogurt, plain skim milk	8 fl. oz	452	32	145
Milk, skim	1 cup	306	32	98
Milk, 2%	1 cup	285	32	91
Kale, frozen, cooked	1 cup	179	59	106
Turnip greens, boiled	1 cup	197	52	103
Broccoli, frozen, chopped, cooked	1 cup	61	61	37
Cauliflower, boiled	1 cup	20	69	14
Spinach, frozen, cooked	1 cup	291	5	14

*Data from U.S. Department of Agriculture, Agricultural Research Service. 2009. USDA National Nutrient Database for Standard Reference, Release 22. www.ars.usda.gov/ba/bhnrc/ndl.
[†]Data from Weaver, C. M., W. R. Proulx, and R. Heaney. 1999. Choices for achieving adequate dietary calcium with a vegetarian diet. *Am. J. Clin. Nutr.* 70(suppl.):543S–548S; Weaver, C. M., and K. L. Plawecki. 1994. Dietary calcium: adequacy of a vegetarian diet. *Am. J. Clin. Nutr.* 59(suppl.):1238S–1241S.

Consuming too much vitamin D causes hypercalcemia, or high blood calcium concentrations. As discussed in the section on calcium, symptoms of hypercalcemia include weakness, loss of appetite, constipation, mental confusion, vomiting, excessive urine output, and extreme thirst. Hypercalcemia also leads to the formation of calcium deposits in soft tissues, such as the kidneys, liver, and heart. In addition, toxic levels of vitamin D lead to increased bone loss because calcium is then pulled from the bones and excreted more readily from the kidneys.

What Happens If We Don't Consume Enough Vitamin D?

The primary deficiency associated with inadequate vitamin D is loss of bone mass. In fact, when vitamin D levels are inadequate, our small intestine can absorb only 10–15% of the calcium we consume. Vitamin D deficiencies occur most often in individuals who have diseases that cause intestinal malabsorption of fat and thus the fat-soluble vitamins. People with liver disease, kidney disease, Crohn's disease, celiac disease, cystic fibrosis, or Whipple's disease may suffer from vitamin D deficiency and require supplements.

Vitamin D–deficiency disease in children, called **rickets,** is caused by inadequate mineralization or demineralization of the skeleton. The classic sign of rickets is deformity of the skeleton, such as bowed legs and knocked knees **(Figure 11)**. However, severe cases can be fatal. Rickets is not common in the United States because of the fortification of milk products with vitamin D, but children with illnesses that cause fat malabsorption or who drink no milk and get limited sun exposure are at increased risk. A recent review of reported cases of rickets among children in the United States found that approximately 83% were African American and that 95% had been breast-fed.[21,22] Breast milk contains very little vitamin D, and fewer than 5% of the breast-fed children were reported to have received vitamin D supplementation. Thus, rickets appears to occur more commonly in children with darker skin (their need for adequate sun exposure is higher than that of light-skinned children) and in breast-fed children who do not receive adequate vitamin D supplementation. In addition, rickets is still a significant nutritional problem for children outside of the United States.

Vitamin D–deficiency disease in adults is called **osteomalacia,** a term meaning "soft bones." With osteomalacia, bones become weak and prone to fractures.

Vitamin D deficiencies have recently been found to be more common among American adults than previously thought. This may be partly due to jobs and lifestyle choices that keep people indoors for most of the day. Not surprisingly, the population at greatest risk is older institutionalized individuals who get little or no sun exposure.

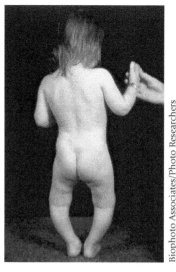

Biophoto Associates/Photo Researchers

▲ **Figure 11** A vitamin D deficiency causes a bone-deforming disease in children called rickets.

rickets A vitamin D–deficiency disease in children. Signs include deformities of the skeleton, such as bowed legs and knocked knees. Severe rickets can be fatal.

osteomalacia A vitamin D–deficiency disease in adults, in which bones become weak and prone to fractures.

NUTRI-CASE THEO

"The health center here on campus is running a study on vitamin D levels among students, and the instructor in my nutrition class invited everybody to participate. I don't think I need to be worried about it, though, 'cause I exercise outdoors a lot—at least, whenever Wisconsin weather allows it! It's true I don't drink much milk, and I hate fish, but otherwise I eat right, and besides, I'm a guy, so I don't have to worry about my bone density."

Should Theo have his vitamin D levels checked? Why or why not? Before you answer, take another look back at the information in this section. Also, consider Theo's assertion that because he is male he doesn't have to worry about his bone density. Is he right? And is calcium regulation the only significant role of vitamin D?

Stockbyte/Getty Images

Various medications can also alter the metabolism and activity of vitamin D. For instance, glucocorticoids, which are medications used to reduce inflammation, can cause bone loss by inhibiting our ability to absorb calcium through the actions of vitamin D. Antiseizure medications, such as phenobarbital and Dilantin, alter vitamin D metabolism. Thus, people who are taking such medications may need to increase their vitamin D intake.

RECAP Vitamin D is a fat-soluble vitamin and a hormone. It can be made in the skin using energy from sunlight. Vitamin D regulates blood calcium levels and maintains bone health. Foods contain little vitamin D, with fortified milk being the primary source. Vitamin D toxicity causes hypercalcemia. Vitamin D deficiency can result in osteoporosis; rickets is vitamin D deficiency in children, whereas osteomalacia is vitamin D deficiency in adults.

Philip Dowell/Dorling Kindersley

Vitamin K

Vitamin K, a fat-soluble vitamin stored primarily in the liver, is actually a family of compounds known as quinones. *Phylloquinone*, which is the primary dietary form of vitamin K, is also the form found in plants; *menaquinone* is the animal form of vitamin K produced by bacteria in the large intestine.

The primary function of vitamin K is to assist in the production of *prothrombin*, a protein that plays a critical role in blood clotting. Vitamin K also assists in the production of *osteocalcin*, a protein associated with bone turnover.

We can obtain vitamin K from our diet, and we absorb the vitamin K produced by bacteria in our large intestine. These two sources usually provide adequate amounts of this nutrient to maintain health, and there is no RDA or UL for vitamin K. AI recommendations are listed in Table 2.

Only a few foods contribute substantially to our dietary intake of vitamin K. Green leafy vegetables, including kale, spinach, collard greens, turnip greens, and lettuce, are good sources, as are broccoli, brussels sprouts, and cabbage. Vegetable oils, such as soybean oil and canola oil, are also good sources. **Figure 12** identifies the amount of vitamin K in micrograms per serving for these foods.

Based on our current knowledge, for healthy individuals there appear to be no side effects associated with consuming large amounts of vitamin K.[23] This appears to be true for both supplements and food sources.

Vitamin K deficiency is associated with a reduced ability to form blood clots, leading to excessive bleeding; however, primary vitamin K deficiency is rare in humans. People with diseases that cause malabsorption of fat, such as celiac disease, Crohn's disease, and cystic fibrosis, can suffer secondarily from a deficiency of vitamin K. Newborns are typically given an injection of vitamin K at birth, as they lack the intestinal bacteria necessary to produce this nutrient.

The impact of vitamin K deficiency on bone health is controversial. A recent study of vitamin K intake and a risk for hip fractures found that women who consumed the least amount of vitamin K had a higher risk for bone fractures than women who consumed relatively more vitamin K. Despite the results of this study, there is not enough scientific evidence to support the contention that vitamin K deficiency leads to osteoporosis.[23] In fact, there is no significant impact on overall bone density in people who take anticoagulant medications that result in a relative state of vitamin K deficiency.

Dorling Kindersley

⬥ Green leafy vegetables, including brussels sprouts and turnip greens, are good sources of vitamin K.

RECAP Vitamin K is a fat-soluble vitamin and coenzyme that is important for blood clotting and bone metabolism. We obtain vitamin K largely from bacteria in our large intestine. Green leafy vegetables and vegetable oils contain vitamin K. There are no known toxicity symptoms for vitamin K in healthy individuals. Although rare, Vitamin K deficiency is rare and may lead to excessive bleeding.

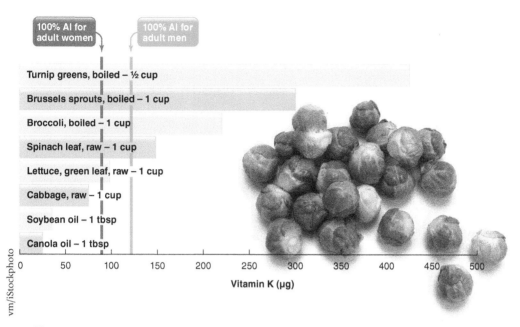

100% AI for adult women

100% AI for adult men

Turnip greens, boiled – ½ cup

Brussels sprouts, boiled – 1 cup

Broccoli, boiled – 1 cup

Spinach leaf, raw – 1 cup

Lettuce, green leaf, raw – 1 cup

Cabbage, raw – 1 cup

Soybean oil – 1 tbsp

Canola oil – 1 tbsp

0   50   100   150   200   250   300   350   400   450   500

Vitamin K (μg)

vm/iStockphoto

Figure 12 Common food sources of vitamin K. The AIs for adult men and women are 120 μg per day and 90 μg per day, respectively.

Data from U.S. Department of Agriculture, Agricultural Research Service. 2009. USDA Nutrient Database for Standard Reference, Release 22. Nutrient Data Laboratory Home Page. www.ars.usda.gov/ba/bhnrc/ndl.

Phosphorus

Phosphorus is the major intracellular negatively charged electrolyte. In our body, phosphorus is most commonly found combined with oxygen in the form of phosphate (PO_4^{3-}). Phosphorus is an essential constituent of all cells and is found in both plants and animals.

Functions of Phosphorus

Phosphorus plays a critical role in bone formation, as it is a part of the mineral complex of bone. As discussed earlier in this chapter, calcium and phosphorus crystallize to form hydroxyapatite crystals, which provide the hardness of bone. About 85% of our body's phosphorus is stored in our bones, with the rest stored in soft tissues, such as muscles and organs.

The role of phosphorus is to maintain proper fluid balance. Phosphorus also helps activate and deactivate enzymes, and it is a component of lipoproteins, cell membranes, DNA and RNA, and several energy molecules, including adenosine triphosphate (ATP).

How Much Phosphorus Should We Consume?

The RDA for phosphorus is listed in Table 2. In general, phosphorus is widespread in many foods and is found in high amounts in foods that contain protein. Milk, meats, and eggs are good sources.

Phosphorus is also found in many processed foods as a food additive, where it enhances smoothness, binding, and moisture retention. Moreover, in the form of phosphoric acid, it is added to soft drinks to give them a sharper, or more tart, flavor and to slow the growth of molds and bacteria. Our society has increased its consumption

Catherine Ledner/Getty Images

⬆ Phosphorus, in the form of phosphoric acid, is a major component of soft drinks.

of processed foods and soft drinks substantially over the past 30 years, resulting in an estimated 10–15% increase in phosphorus consumption.[5]

Nutrition and medical professionals have become increasingly concerned that heavy consumption of soft drinks may be detrimental to bone health. Studies have shown that consuming soft drinks is associated with reduced bone mass or an increased risk for fractures in both youth and adults.[24-26] Researchers have proposed three theories to explain why the consumption of soft drinks may be detrimental to bone health:

- Consuming soft drinks in place of calcium-containing beverages, such as milk, leads to a deficient intake of calcium.
- The phosphoric acid content of soft drinks causes an increased loss of calcium because calcium is drawn from bone into the blood to neutralize the excess acid.
- The caffeine found in many soft drinks causes increased calcium loss through the urine.

A recent study evaluating these factors concluded that the most likely explanation for the link between soft drink consumption and poor bone health is the *milk-displacement effect*; that is, soft drinks take the place of milk in our diet, depriving us of calcium and vitamin D.[27]

What Happens If We Consume Too Much Phosphorus?

People with kidney disease and those who take too many vitamin D supplements or too many phosphorus-containing antacids can suffer from high blood phosphorus levels. Severely high levels of blood phosphorus can cause muscle spasms and convulsions.

What Happens If We Don't Consume Enough Phosphorus?

Phosphorus deficiencies are rare but can occur in people who abuse alcohol, in premature infants, and in elderly people with poor diets. People with vitamin D deficiency, people with hyperparathyroidism (oversecretion of parathyroid hormone), and those who overuse antacids that bind with phosphorus may also have low blood phosphorus levels.

RECAP Phosphorus is the major negatively charged electrolyte inside of the cell. It helps maintain fluid balance and bone health. It also assists in regulating chemical reactions, and it is a primary component of ATP, DNA, and RNA. Phosphorus is commonly found in high-protein foods. Excess phosphorus can lead to muscle spasms and convulsions, whereas phosphorus deficiencies are rare.

Magnesium

Magnesium is a major mineral. Our total body magnesium content is approximately 25 g. About 50–60% of our body's magnesium is found in our bones, with the rest located in our soft tissues.

Functions of Magnesium

Spencer Jones/Photodisc/Getty Images

⬆ Trail mix with chocolate chips, nuts, and seeds is one common food source of magnesium.

Magnesium is one of the minerals that make up the structure of bone. It is also important in the regulation of bone and mineral status. Specifically, magnesium influences the formation of hydroxyapatite crystals through its regulation of calcium balance and its interactions with vitamin D and parathyroid hormone.

Magnesium is a critical *cofactor* for more than 300 enzyme systems. A cofactor is a compound that is needed for an enzyme to be active. Magnesium is necessary for the production of ATP, and it plays an important role in DNA and protein synthesis and repair. Magnesium supplementation has been shown to improve insulin sensitivity, and there is epidemiological evidence that a high magnesium intake is associated with a decrease in the risk for colorectal cancer.[28,29] Magnesium supports normal vitamin D metabolism and action and is necessary for normal muscle contraction and blood clotting.

CanuckStock/Shutterstock

Figure 13 Common food sources of magnesium. For adult men 19 to 30 years of age, the RDA for magnesium is 400 mg per day; the RDA increases to 420 mg per day for men 31 years of age and older. For adult women 19 to 30 years of age, the RDA for magnesium is 310 mg per day; this value increases to 320 mg per day for women 31 years of age and older.

Data from U.S. Department of Agriculture, Agricultural Research Service. 2009. USDA Nutrient Database for Standard Reference, Release 22. Nutrient Data Laboratory Home Page. www.ars.usda.gov/ba/bhnrc/ndl.

How Much Magnesium Should We Consume?

As magnesium is found in a wide variety of foods, people who are adequately nourished generally consume enough magnesium in their diet. The RDA for magnesium is identified in Table 2. There is no UL for magnesium for food and water; the UL for magnesium from pharmacologic sources is 350 mg per day.

Magnesium is found in green leafy vegetables, such as spinach. It is also found in whole grains, seeds, and nuts. Other good food sources of magnesium include seafood, beans, and some dairy products. Refined and processed foods are low in magnesium. Figure 13 shows many foods that are good sources of magnesium.

The magnesium content of drinking water varies considerably. The "harder" the water, the higher its content of magnesium. This variability makes it impossible to estimate how much our drinking water may contribute to the magnesium content of our diet.

The ability of the small intestine to absorb magnesium is reduced when one consumes a diet that is extremely high in fiber and phytates, because these substances bind with magnesium. Even though seeds and nuts are relatively high in fiber, they are excellent sources of absorbable magnesium. Overall, our absorption of magnesium should be sufficient if we consume the recommended amount of fiber each day (20–35 g per day). In contrast, higher dietary protein intakes enhance the absorption and retention of magnesium.

What Happens If We Consume Too Much Magnesium?

There are no known toxicity symptoms related to consuming excess magnesium in the diet. The toxicity symptoms that result from pharmacologic overuse of magnesium include diarrhea, nausea, and abdominal cramps. In extreme cases, large doses can result in acid–base imbalances, massive dehydration, cardiac arrest, and death. High blood magnesium levels, or **hypermagnesemia,** occur in individuals with impaired kidney function who consume large amounts of nondietary magnesium, such as antacids. Side effects include the impairment of nerve, muscle, and heart function.

hypermagnesemia A condition marked by an abnormally high concentration of magnesium in the blood.

What Happens If We Don't Consume Enough Magnesium?

Hypomagnesemia, or low blood magnesium, results from magnesium deficiency. This condition may develop secondary to kidney disease, chronic diarrhea, or chronic alcohol abuse. Elderly people seem to be at particularly high risk for low dietary intakes of magnesium because they have a reduced appetite and blunted senses of taste and smell. In addition, the elderly face challenges related to shopping and preparing meals that contain foods high in magnesium, and their ability to absorb magnesium is reduced.

Low blood calcium levels are a side effect of hypomagnesemia. Other symptoms of magnesium deficiency include muscle cramps, spasms or seizures, nausea, weakness, irritability, and confusion. Considering magnesium's role in bone formation, it is not surprising that long-term magnesium deficiency is associated with osteoporosis. Magnesium deficiency is also associated with many other chronic diseases, including heart disease, high blood pressure, and type 2 diabetes.[5]

RECAP Magnesium is a major mineral found in fresh foods, including spinach, nuts, seeds, whole grains, and meats. It is important for bone health, energy production, and muscle function. The RDA for magnesium varies with age and gender. Hypermagnesemia can result in diarrhea, muscle cramps, and cardiac arrest. Hypomagnesemia causes hypocalcemia, muscle cramps, spasms, and weakness. Magnesium deficiencies are also associated with osteoporosis, heart disease, high blood pressure, and type 2 diabetes.

Fluoride

Fluoride. a trace mineral, is the ionic form of the element fluorine. Trace minerals are minerals that our body needs in amounts less than 100 mg per day; the amount of trace minerals in our body is less than 5 g. About 99% of the fluoride in our body is stored in our teeth and bones.

Functions of Fluoride

Fluoride assists in the development and maintenance of our teeth and bones. During the development of both our baby and permanent teeth, fluoride combines with calcium and phosphorus to form *fluorohydroxyapatite*, which is more resistant to destruction by acids and bacteria than is hydroxyapatite. Even after all of our permanent teeth are in, treating them with fluoride, whether at the dentist's office or with fluoridated toothpaste, gives them more protection against dental caries (cavities) than teeth that have not been treated. That's because fluoride enhances tooth mineralization, decreases and reverses tooth demineralization, and inhibits the metabolism of the acid-producing bacteria that cause tooth decay.

Fluoride also stimulates new bone growth, and it is being researched as a potential treatment for osteoporosis, both alone and in combination with other medications.[32-34] While early results are promising, more research needs to be conducted to determine if fluoride is an effective treatment for osteoporosis.[30-33]

How Much Fluoride Should We Consume?

Our need for fluoride is relatively small. The AI for fluoride is listed in Table 2. The UL is 2.2 mg per day for children aged 4 to 8 years; the UL for everyone older than 8 years of age is 10 mg per day.

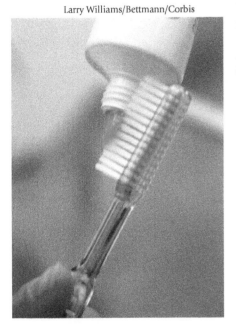

Fluoride is readily available in many communities in the United States through fluoridated water and dental products.

hypomagnesemia A condition characterized by an abnormally low concentration of magnesium in the blood.

Fluoride is readily available in many communities in the United States through fluoridated water and dental products. Fluoride is absorbed directly in the mouth into the teeth and gums, and it can be absorbed from the gastrointestinal tract once it is ingested. In the early 1990s, there was considerable concern that our intake of fluoride was too high due to the consumption of fluoridated water and fluoride-containing toothpastes and mouthwashes; it was speculated that this high intake could be contributing to an increased risk for cancer, bone fractures, kidney and other organ damage, infertility, and Alzheimer's disease. After reviewing the potential health hazards of fluoride, the U.S. Department of Health and Human Services found that there is no reliable scientific evidence available to indicate that fluoride increases our risk for these illnesses.[34]

Figure 14 Consuming too much fluoride causes fluorosis, leading to staining and pitting of the teeth.

National Institute of Dental Research

There are concerns that individuals who consume bottled water exclusively may be getting too little fluoride and increasing their risk for dental caries, as most bottled waters do not contain fluoride. However, these individuals may still consume fluoride through other beverages that contain fluoridated water and through fluoridated dental products. Toothpastes and mouthwashes that contain fluoride are widely marketed and used by the majority of consumers in the United States, and these products can contribute as much if not more fluoride to our diet than fluoridated water. Fluoride supplements are available only by prescription, and they are generally given only to children who do not have access to fluoridated water. Incidentally, tea is a good source of fluoride: one 8-oz cup provides about 20–25% of the AI.

What Happens If We Consume Too Much Fluoride?

Consuming too much fluoride increases the protein content of tooth enamel, resulting in a condition called **fluorosis.** Because increased protein makes the enamel more porous, the teeth become stained and pitted (Figure 14). Teeth seem to be at highest risk for fluorosis during the first 8 years of life, when the permanent teeth are developing. To reduce the risk for fluorosis, children should not swallow oral care products that are meant for topical use only, and children under the age of 6 years should be supervised while using fluoride-containing products.[34] Mild fluorosis generally causes white patches on the teeth, and it has no effect on tooth function. Although moderate and severe fluorosis cause greater discoloration of the teeth, there appears to be no adverse effect on tooth function.[5]

Excess consumption of fluoride can also cause fluorosis of our skeleton. Mild skeletal fluorosis results in an increased bone mass and stiffness and pain in the joints. Moderate and severe skeletal fluorosis can be crippling, but it is extremely rare in the United States, with only five confirmed cases in the last 35 years.[5]

What Happens If We Don't Consume Enough Fluoride?

The primary result of fluoride deficiency is dental caries. Adequate fluoride intake appears necessary at an early age and throughout our adult life to reduce our risk for tooth decay. Inadequate fluoride intake may also be associated with lower bone density, but there is not enough research available to support the widespread use of fluoride to prevent osteoporosis. Studies are being done to determine the role fluoride might play in reducing our risk for osteoporosis and fractures.

RECAP Fluoride is a trace mineral whose primary function is to support the health of teeth and bones. Primary sources of fluoride are fluoridated dental products and fluoridated water. Fluoride toxicity causes fluorosis of the teeth and skeleton, while fluoride deficiency causes an increase in tooth decay.

fluorosis A condition marked by staining and pitting of the teeth; caused by an abnormally high intake of fluoride.

UV SAFETY

THE GLOBAL SOLAR ULTRAVIOLET INDEX

UV INDEX

Be extra careful outdoors!

Lighter skin will burn in minutes without protection.
Avoid exposure from 10:00 to 4:00 and shield skin and eyes.

11+ EXTREME

UV levels are dangerous.

A change in skin color means UV radiation has damaged
your skin. White sand and water increase your UV exposure.

10
9
8

VERY HIGH

Sunburn can happen quickly.

Children are especially sensitive to UV exposure.
Cover up, use sunscreen, and play in the shade.

7
6

HIGH

It may *seem* safe but...

Up to 80% of solar UV radiation can penetrate light cloud
cover. Use UV-blocking sunglasses and protect your skin.

5
4
3

MODERATE

Always protect yourself from the sun.

Even with a low index rating, you can be overexposed. On a sunny
day, snow reflects enough UV radiation to damage eyes and skin.

2
1

LOW

EPA United States
Environmental Protection
Agency

EPA-430-H-04-001
May 2004

The Environmental Protection Agency is just one of many public health agencies that warn Americans about the danger of exposure to even low levels of sun.

Nutrition DEBATE

Vitamin D Deficiency: Why the Surge, and What Can Be Done?

No doubt about it: unless you live at a latitude within 40° of the equator and spend time outdoors without sunscreen, it's tough to get enough vitamin D. That's because, as you learned in this chapter, there are very few natural food sources of vitamin D, and even fortified food sources are limited to milk and a handful of other products. But if meeting the Institute of Medicine's current AI for vitamin D is already posing a challenge to many Americans, why are some researchers calling for an even higher intake recommendation?

Measurements of vitamin D status in a variety of population studies in recent years have led to a growing concern about widespread vitamin D deficiency and its associated diseases, including rickets in children and osteomalacia and osteoporosis in adults. Recent data from the National Health and Examination Survey (NHANES) indicate that, from 1994 to 2004, the prevalence of vitamin D deficiency in U.S. adults almost doubled, with over 90% of people with darker-pigmented skin (African Americans and Latinos) estimated to be vitamin D deficient.[35] In addition, since the Institute of Medicine set its vitamin D recommendations in 1997, new information has been published about vitamin D metabolism and its potential role in reducing the risks for diseases such as type 1 diabetes, some cancers, multiple sclerosis, and meta-

Johner Images/Getty Images

bolic syndrome.[36,37] These discussions have resulted in some nutrition and bone health experts calling for a full review of the recent research on vitamin D and a reevaluation of the current recommendations.[38]

What is contributing to this dramatic increase in vitamin D insufficiency among Americans, and what can we do about it? Researchers have proposed the following three factors:[37,39]

- a downward trend in the consumption of vitamin D–fortified milk products
- a significant increase in sun avoidance and the use of sun protection products
- an increased rate of obesity, as obesity appears to alter the metabolism and storage of vitamin D such that vitamin D deficiency is more likely to occur

To address the first factor, people can increase their intake of vitamin D–fortified milk products; however, it is difficult to meet even the current AI from consumption of milk alone. For instance, children and teens would have to drink a full quart each day to meet the recommendation![40] As a result, the use of vitamin D supplements is gaining wide support. Many healthcare providers now recommend that most children and adolescents who do not or cannot get adequate sun exposure should take a supplement that provides up to 400 IU of vitamin D per day. Whether adults should consume a vitamin D supplement is currently under review by the Food and Nutrition Board, and its decision is expected to be published in the near future. Supplementation with vitamin D is efficient, inexpensive, and effective. Used correctly, it is also very safe. Although vitamin D toxicity is rare, supplementation should be monitored to ensure both a safe and an adequate intake.

What about the second factor—lack of sufficient exposure to sunlight? Responsible, safe exposure to sunlight offers many advantages: it will never lead to vitamin D toxicity, it is easy and virtually cost-free, and sun exposure may offer benefits beyond that of improved vitamin D status.[41] That's why many healthcare professionals advocate moderate sun exposure. They suggest that public health authorities soften the "sun avoidance" campaigns of recent years (see the accompanying figure); they would like to see "well-balanced" recommendations that promote brief (15 minutes or so) periods of sun exposure without sunscreen or sun-blocking clothing two or three times a week, with avoidance of mid-day sun during summer months.[42]

To address the third factor in vitamin D deficiency—obesity—the only solution is to maintain a healthful weight. That means losing weight if you are overweight or obese. By doing so, you'll reduce your risk not only for vitamin D deficiency but also for cardiovascular disease, type 2 diabetes, and many forms of cancer.

Thus, although vitamin D deficiency is becoming a public health issue in the United States, there appear to be a number of strategies you can use to maintain a healthy vitamin D status.

Chapter Review

1. False. There are many good sources of calcium besides milk, yogurt, and cheese, including calcium-fortified juices, soy/rice beverages, and green leafy vegetables, such as kale, broccoli, and collard greens.

2. True. Our body can convert a cholesterol compound in our skin into vitamin D.

3. False. There is no clear, decisive evidence that consuming dairy products high in calcium, such as milk and yogurt, can result in weight loss.

Find the Quack

Wyn just got some bad news: her mom phoned to say that a DXA scan ordered by her physician shows that she has osteoporosis. Wyn decides to go online to see if she can learn more about osteoporosis. When she discovers the importance of calcium and vitamin D, she searches on "calcium supplements." That's when she finds a site promoting "a unique form of calcium from Pacific sea coral." She reads that this form of "coral calcium" is derived from remnants of coral that have broken off from coral reefs and are mined from ocean beds. The manufacturer makes the following claims for coral calcium:

- "Coral calcium is absorbed into the body within 20 minutes, rather than within 6–8 hours, like other calcium supplements."
- "The calcium carbonate in coral calcium is 100% absorbable, whereas the calcium in milk is only 17% absorbable."
- "The most important daily habits people can adopt to preserve their health are to consume coral calcium and get a minimum of 2 hours of sunlight on their face, without sunscreen."
- "Calcium deficiency not only causes osteoporosis but also makes the body acidic and leads to a host of other diseases, including heart disease, multiple sclerosis, and cancer. People who live on the Japanese island of Okinawa

never experience cancer because there is coral calcium in their drinking water, which keeps their body alkaline and cancels out disease-causing acids."

- "Coral calcium is only $19.95 for a 30-day supply."

1. Recall what you have learned about digestion. Do you think it is likely that coral calcium is absorbed into the body within 20 minutes? Why or why not?

2. Do you accept the claim that the calcium in milk is 17% absorbable but the calcium carbonate in coral calcium is 100% absorbable? Why or why not? If necessary, review the information on calcium absorption in this chapter.

3. Comment on the statement "The most important daily habits people can adopt to preserve their health are to consume coral calcium and get a minimum of 2 hours of sunlight on their face, without sunscreen."

4. Comment on the statement that calcium deficiency causes a host of diseases, such as heart disease, multiple sclerosis, and cancer, and that Okinawans "never experience cancer because there is coral calcium in their drinking water, which keeps their body alkaline and cancels out disease-causing acids."

Answers can be found on the companion website, at www.pearsonhighered.com/thompsonmanore.

 **NutriTools** Check out the companion website at www.pearsonhighered.com/thompsonmanore, or use MyNutritionLab.com, to access interactive animations, including:

- Nutrient Functionality

Review Questions

1. Hydroxyapatite crystals are predominantly made up of
   a. calcium and phosphorus.
   b. hydrogen, oxygen, and titanium.
   c. calcium and vitamin D.
   d. calcium and magnesium.

2. On a DXA test, a T-score of +1.0 indicates that the patient
   a. has osteoporosis.
   b. is at greater risk for fractures than an average, healthy 30-year-old.
   c. has normal bone density as compared to an average, healthy 30-year-old.
   d. has slightly lower bone density than an average, healthy person of the same age.

3. Which of the following statements about trabecular bone is true?
   a. It accounts for about 80% of our skeleton.
   b. It forms the core of almost all the bones of our skeleton.
   c. It is also called compact bone.
   d. It provides the scaffolding for cortical bone.

4. Which of the following individuals is most likely to require vitamin D supplements?
   a. a dark-skinned child living and playing outdoors in Hawaii
   b. a fair-skinned construction worker living in Florida
   c. a fair-skinned retired teacher living in a nursing home in Ohio
   d. None of the above individuals is likely to require vitamin D supplements.

5. Calcium is necessary for several body functions, including
   a. demineralization of bone, nerve transmission, and immune responses.
   b. cartilage structure, nerve transmission, and muscle contraction.
   c. structure of bone, nerve, and muscle tissue; immune responses; and muscle contraction.
   d. structure of bone, nerve transmission, and muscle contraction.

6. True or false? The process by which bone is formed through the action of osteoblasts and resorbed through the action of osteoclasts is called remodeling.

7. True or false? The amount of calcium we absorb depends on our age, our calcium intake, the types of calcium-rich foods we eat, and our body's supply of vitamin D.

8. True or false? Our body absorbs vitamin D from sunlight.

9. True or false? Magnesium is a trace mineral.

10. True or false? Fluoride inhibits the reproduction of acid-producing bacteria in the mouth.

Answers to Review Questions can be found at the back of this text, and additional essay questions and answers are located on the companion website at www.pearsonhighered.com/thompsonmanore.

Web Resources

www.dairycouncilofca.org/Tools/CalciumQuiz
Dairy Council of California's Calcium Quiz

Use this online interactive quiz to estimate your calcium intake.

www.nlm.nih.gov/medlineplus
MEDLINE Plus Health Information

Search for rickets or osteomalacia to learn more about these vitamin D–deficiency diseases.

www.ada.org
American Dental Association

Look under "Your Oral Health" to learn more about the fluoridation of community water supplies and the use of fluoride-containing products.

References

1. United States Department of Agriculture, Economic Research Service. 2008. Dietary assessment of major trends in U.S. food consumption, 1970-2005. Economic Information Bulletin No. EIB-33, 1-27. www.ers.usda/Publications/EIB33/. EIB33_ReportSummary.html.

2. Ho, A. Y. Y., and A. W. C. Kung. 2005. Determinants of peak bone mineral density and bone area in young women. *J. Bone Miner. Metab.* 23:470-475.

3. Chevalley, T., R. Rizzoli, D. Hans, S. Ferrari, and J. P. Bonjour. 2005. Interaction between calcium intake and menarcheal age on bone mass gain: an eight-year follow-up study from prepuberty to postmenarche. *J. Clin. Endocrinol. Metab.* 90:44-51.

4. Kindblom, J. M., M. Lorentzon, E. Norjavaara, A. Hellqvist, S. Nilsson, D. Mellström, and C. Ohlsson. 2006. Pubertal timing predicts previous fractures and BMD in young adult men: the GOOD study. *J. Bone Min. Res.* 21:790-795.

5. Institute of Medicine, Food and Nutrition Board. 1997. Dietary Reference Intakes for Calcium, Phosphorus, Magnesium, Vitamin D, and Fluoride. Washington, DC: National Academies Press.

6. Keller, J. L., A. J. Lanou, and N. D. Barnard. 2002. The consumer cost of calcium from food and supplements. *J. Am. Diet. Assoc.* 102:1669-1671.

7. Nusser, S. M., A. L. Carriquiry, K. W. Dodd, and W. A. Fuller. 1996. A semiparametric transformation approach to estimating usual daily intake distributions. *J. Am. Stat. Assoc.* 91:1440-1449.

8. Ross, E. A., N. J. Szabo, and I. R. Tebbett. 2000. Lead content of calcium supplements. *JAMA* 284:1425-1433.

9. Massey, L. K., H. Roman-Smith, and R. A. Sutton. 1993. Effect of dietary oxalate and calcium on urinary oxalate and risk of formation of calcium oxalate kidney stones. *J. Am. Diet. Assoc.* 93:901-906.

10. Zemel, M. B., W. Thompson, A. Milstead, K. Morris, and P. Campbell. 2004. Calcium and dairy acceleration of weight and fat loss during energy restriction in obese adults. *Obes. Res.* 12:582-590.

11. Bowen, J., M. Noakes, and P. M. Clifton. 2005. Effect of calcium and dairy foods in high protein, energy-restricted diets on weight loss and metabolic parameters in overweight adults. *Int. J. Obes.* 29:957-965.

12. United States Department of Agriculture (USDA), Agricultural Research Service. 2007. News and Events. Weight loss study focuses on dairy foods. www.ars.usda.gov/IS/pr/2007/070427.htm.

13. Holick, M. F., L. Y. Matsuoka, and J. Wortsman. 1989. Age, vitamin D, and solar ultraviolet. *Lancet* 2:1104-1105.

14. Need, A. G., H. A. Morris, M. Horowitz, and C. Nordin. 1993. Effects of skin thickness, age, body fat, and sunlight on serum 25-hydroxyvitamin D. *Am. J. Clin. Nutr.* 58:882-885.

15. Florez, H., R. Martinez, W. Chacra, N. Strickman-Stein, and S. Levis. 2007. Outdoor exercise reduces the risk of hypovitaminosis D in the obese. *J. Steroid Biochem. Mol. Biol.* 103:679-681.

16. Holick, M. F. 2005. The vitamin D epidemic and its health consequences. *J. Nutr.* 135:2739S-2748S.

17. Holick, M. F. 1994. McCollum Award Lecture, 1994: Vitamin D: new horizons for the 21st century. *Am. J. Clin. Nutr.* 60:619-630.

18. Lim, H. W., B. A. Gilchrist, K. D. Cooper, H. A. Bischoff-Ferrari, D. S. Rigel, W. H. Cyr, S. Miller, V. A. DeLeo, T. K. Lee, C. A. Demko, M. A. Weinstock, A. Young, L. S. Edwards, T. M. Johnson, and S. P. Stone. 2005. Sunlight, tanning booths, and vitamin D. *J. Am. Acad. Dermatol.* 52:868-876.

19. Heaney, R. P. 2005. The vitamin D requirement in health and disease. *J. Steroid Biochem. Molec. Biol.* 97:13-19.

20. Heaney, R. P. 2007. The case for improving vitamin D status. *J. Steroid Biochem. Molec. Biol.* 103:635-641.

21. Holick, M. F. 2006. Resurrection of vitamin D deficiency and rickets. *J. Clin. Invest.* 116:2062-2072.

22. Weisberg, P., K. S. Scanlon, R. Li, and M. E. Cogswell. 2004. Nutritional rickets among children in the United States: review of cases reported between 1986 and 2003. *Am. J. Clin. Nutr.* 80(suppl.):1697S-1705S.

23. Institute of Medicine, Food and Nutrition Board. 2002. Dietary Reference Intakes for Vitamin A, Vitamin K, Arsenic, Boron, Chromium, Copper, Iodine, Iron, Manganese, Molybdenum, Nickel, Silicon, Vanadium, and Zinc. Washington, DC: National Academies Press.

24. Wyshak, G., R. E. Frisch, T. E. Albright, N. L. Albright, I. Schiff, and J. Witschi. 1989. Nonalcoholic carbonated beverage consumption and bone fractures among women former college athletes. *J. Orthop. Res.* 7:91-99.

25. Wyshak, G., and R. E. Frisch. 1994. Carbonated beverages, dietary calcium, the dietary calcium/phosphorus ratio, and bone fractures in girls and boys. *J. Adolesc. Health* 15:210-215.

26. Wyshak, G. 2000. Teenaged girls, carbonated beverage consumption, and bone fractures. *Arch. Pediatr. Adolesc. Med.* 154:610-613.

27. Heaney, R. P., and K. Rafferty. 2001. Carbonated beverages and urinary calcium excretion. *Am. J. Clin. Nutr.* 74:343-347.

28. Paolisso G., S. Sgambato, A. Gambardella, G. Pizza, P. Tesauro, M. Varricchio, and F. D'Onofrio. 1992. Daily magnesium supplements improve glucose handling in elderly subjects. *Am. J. Clin. Nutr.* 55:1161-1167.

29. Larsson, S. C., L. Bergkvist, and A. Wolk. 2005. Magnesium intake in relation to risk of colorectal cancer in women. *JAMA* 293:86-89.

30. Pak, C. Y., K. Sakhaee, B. Adams-Huet, V. Piziak, R. D. Peterson, and J. R. Poindexter. 1995. Treatment of postmenopausal osteoporosis with slow-release sodium fluoride. Final report of a randomized controlled trial. *Ann. Int. Med.* 123:401-408.

31. Reginster, J. Y., D. Felsenberg, I. Pavo, J. Stepan, J. Payer, H. Resch, C. C. Glüer, D. Mühlenbacher, D. Quail, H. Schmitt, and T. Nickelsen. 2003. Effect of raloxifene combined with monofluorophosphate as compared with monofluorophosphate alone in postmenopausal women with low bone mass: a randomized, controlled trial. *Osteoporosis Int.* 14:741-749.

32. Ringe, J. D., A. Dorst, H. Faber, C. Kipshoven, L. C. Rovati, and I. Setnikar. 2005. Efficacy of etidronate and sequential monofluorophosphate in severe postmenopausal osteoporosis: a pilot study. *Rheumatol. Int.* 25:296-300.

33. American Dietetic Association. 2005. Position of the American Dietetic Association: the impact of fluoride on health. *J. Am. Diet. Assoc.* 105:1620-1628.

34. U.S. Department of Health and Human Services. Public Health Service. 1991. Review of Fluoride: Benefits and Risks. Report of the Ad Hoc Subcommittee on Fluoride of the Committee to Coordinate Environmental Health and Related Programs. www.health.gov/environment/ReviewofFluoride/default.htm. (Accessed April 2007.)

35. Ginde, A. A., M. C. Liu, and C. A. Camargo, Jr. 2009. Demographic differences and trends of vitamin D insufficiency in the U.S. population, 1988-2004. *Arch. Intern. Med.* 169:626-632.

36. Weaver, C. M., and J. C. Fleet. 2004. Vitamin D requirements: Current and future. *Am. J. Clin. Nutr.* 80(suppl):1735S-1739S.

37. Adams, J. S. and M. Hewison. 2010. Update on vitamin D. *J. Clin. Endocrinol. Metab.* 95:471-478.

38. Yetley, E. A., B. Brulé, M. C. Cheney, C. D. Davis, K. A. Esslinger, P. W. F. Fischer, K. E. Friedl, L. S. Greene-Finestone, P. M. Guenther, D. M. Klurfeld, M. R. L'Abbe, and K. Y. McMurry. 2009. Dietary reference intakes for vitamin D: Justification for a review of the 1997 values. *Am. J. Clin. Nutr.* 89:719-727.

39. Looker, A. C., C. M. Pfeiffer, D. A. Lacher, R. L. Schleicher, M. F. Picciano, and E. A. Yetley. 2008. Serum 25-hydroxyvitamin D status of the U.S. population: 1988-1994 compared with 2000-2004. *Am. J. Clin. Nutr.* 88:1519-1527.

40. Wolpowitz, D., and B. A. Gilchrest. 2006. The vitamin D questions: how much do we need and how should we get it? *J. Am. Acad. Dermatol.* 54(2):301–317.
41. Lucas, R. M., and A. L. Ponsonby. 2006. Considering the potential benefits as well as adverse effects of sun exposure: Can all the potential benefits be provided by oral vitamin D supplementation? *Prog. Biophys. Molec. Biol.* 92:140–149.

42. Reichrath, J. 2006. The challenge resulting from positive and negative effects of sunlight: How much solar UV exposure is appropriate to balance between risks of vitamin D deficiency and skin cancer? *Prog. Biophys. Molec. Biol.* 92:9–16.

Answers to Review Questions

Answers to Review Questions 11-15 (essay questions) for this chapter are located on the Companion Website at **www.pearsonhighered.com/thompsonmanore**

1. **a.** calcium and phosphorus.
2. **c.** has normal bone density as compared to an average, healthy 30-year-old.
3. **d.** It provides the scaffolding for cortical bone.
4. **c.** a fair-skinned retired teacher living in a nursing home in Ohio
5. **d.** structure of bone, nerve transmission, and muscle contraction.

6. True.
7. True.
8. False. Our body makes vitamin D by converting a cholesterol compound in our skin to the active form of vitamin D that we need to function. We do not absorb vitamin D from sunlight, but when the ultraviolet rays of the sun hit our skin, they react to eventually form calcitriol, which is considered the primary active form of vitamin D in our bodies.
9. False. Magnesium is a major mineral.
10. True.

Nutrients Involved in Energy Metabolism and Blood Health

From Chapter 10 of *Nutrition: An Applied Approach*, Third Edition. Janice Thompson, Melinda Manore. Copyright © 2012 by Pearson Education, Inc. Published by Pearson Benjamin Cummings. All rights reserved.

Nutrients Involved in Energy Metabolism and Blood Health

Donald Erickson/iStockphoto

CHAPTER OBJECTIVES

After reading this chapter you will be able to:

1. Describe how coenzymes enhance the activities of enzymes.

2. Describe the primary functions and food sources for the eight B-vitamins.

3. Explain the importance of adequate folate intake for women of childbearing age.

4. Describe the association between folate, vitamin B_{12}, and vascular disease.

5. Describe the four components of blood.

6. Discuss the role that iron plays in oxygen transport.

7. Distinguish between iron-deficiency anemia, pernicious anemia, and macrocytic anemia.

Test Yourself

1. (T) (F) The B-vitamins are an important source of energy for our body.

2. (T) (F) People consuming a vegan diet are at greater risk for micronutrient deficiencies than are people who eat foods of animal origin.

3. (T) (F) Iron deficiency is the most common nutrient deficiency in the world.

Test Yourself answers can be found at the end of the chapter.

Dr. Leslie Bernstein looked in astonishment at the 80-year-old man in his office. A leading gastroenterologist and professor of medicine at Albert Einstein College of Medicine in New York City, he had admired Pop Katz for years as one of his most healthy patients, a strict vegetarian and athlete who just weeks before had been going on 3-mile runs as if he were 40 years younger. Now he could barely stand. He was confused, cried easily, was wandering away from the house partially clothed, and had lost control of his bladder. Tests showed that he was not suffering from Alzheimer's disease, had not had a stroke, did not have a tumor or an infection, and had no evidence of exposure to pesticides, metals, drugs, or other toxins. Blood tests were normal, except that his red blood cells were slightly enlarged. Bernstein consulted with a neurologist, who diagnosed "rapidly progressive dementia of unknown origin."

Bernstein was unconvinced: "In a matter of weeks, a man who hadn't been sick for 80 years suddenly became demented. 'Holy smoke!' I thought, 'I'm an idiot! The man's been a vegetarian for 38 years. No meat. No fish. No eggs. No milk. He hasn't had any animal protein for decades. He has to be B_{12} deficient!'" Bernstein immediately tested Katz's blood, then gave him an injection of B_{12}. The blood test confirmed Bernstein's hunch: the level of B_{12} in Katz's blood was too low to measure. The morning after his injection, Katz could sit up without help. Within a week of continuing treatment, he could read, play card games, and hold his own in conversations. Unfortunately, the delay in diagnosis left some permanent neurologic damage, including alterations in his personality and an inability to concentrate. Bernstein notes, "A diet free of animal protein can be

PhotoDisc/Getty Images

Vitamins do not provide energy directly, but the B-vitamins help our body create the energy we need from the foods we eat.

healthful and safe, but it should be supplemented periodically with B_{12} by mouth or by injection."[1]

It was not until 1906—when the English biochemist F. G. Hopkins discovered what he called *accessory factors*—that scientists began to appreciate the many critical roles of micronutrients in maintaining human health. Vitamin B_{12}, for instance, was not isolated until 1948! There are several key roles of vitamins and minerals, including regulation of fluids and nerve-impulse transmission, protection against the damage caused by oxidation, and maintenance of healthy bones. In this chapter, we conclude our exploration of the micronutrients with a discussion of two final roles: their contribution to the metabolism of carbohydrates, fats, and proteins and their role in the formation and maintenance of our blood.

How Does Our Body Regulate Energy Metabolism?

The regulation of energy metabolism is a complex process involving numerous biological substances and chemical pathways. Here, we describe how the micronutrients we consume in our diet assist us in generating energy from the carbohydrates, fats, and proteins we eat along with them.

Our Body Requires Vitamins and Minerals to Produce Energy

Although vitamins and minerals do not directly provide energy, we are unable to generate energy from the macronutrients without them. The B-vitamins are particularly important in assisting us with energy metabolism. They include thiamin, riboflavin, vitamin B_6, niacin, folate, vitamin B_{12}, pantothenic acid, and biotin.

The primary role of the B-vitamins is to act as coenzymes. Recall that an *enzyme* is a protein that accelerates the rate of chemical reactions but is not used up or changed during the reaction. A **coenzyme** is a molecule that combines with an enzyme to activate it and help it do its job. **Figure 1** illustrates how coenzymes work.

coenzyme A molecule that combines with an enzyme to activate it and help it do its job.

Figure 1 Coenzymes combine with enzymes to activate them, ensuring that the chemical reactions that depend on these enzymes can occur.

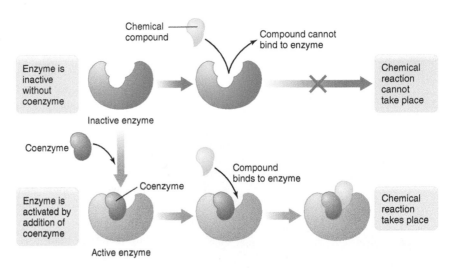

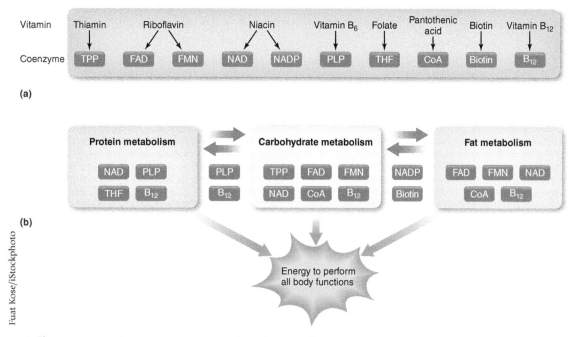

Fuat Kose/iStockphoto

Figure 2 The B-vitamins play many important roles in the reactions involved in energy metabolism. **(a)** B-vitamins and the coenzymes they are a part of. **(b)** This chart illustrates many of the coenzymes essential for various metabolic functions; however, this is only a small sample of the thousands of roles that the B-vitamins serve in our body.

Without coenzymes, we would be unable to produce the energy necessary for sustaining life and supporting daily activities.

Figure 2 provides an overview of how some of the B-vitamins act as coenzymes to promote energy metabolism. For instance, thiamin is part of the coenzyme thiamin pyrophosphate, or TPP, which assists in the breakdown of glucose. Riboflavin is a part of two coenzymes, flavin mononucleotide (FMN) and flavin adenine dinucleotide (FAD), which help break down both glucose and fatty acids. The specific functions of each B-vitamin are described in detail shortly.

Some Micronutrients Assist with Nutrient Transport and Hormone Production

Some micronutrients promote energy metabolism by facilitating the transport of nutrients into the cells. For instance, the mineral chromium helps improve glucose uptake into cells. Other micronutrients assist in the production of hormones that regulate metabolic processes; the mineral iodine, for example, is necessary for the synthesis of thyroid hormones, which regulate our metabolic rate and promote growth and development. The details of these processes and their related nutrients are discussed in the following section.

RECAP Vitamins and minerals are not direct sources of energy, but they help generate energy from carbohydrates, fats, and proteins. Acting as coenzymes, nutrients such as the B-vitamins assist enzymes in metabolizing nutrients to produce energy. Minerals such as chromium and iodine assist with nutrient uptake into the cells and with regulating energy production and cell growth.

A Profile of Nutrients Involved in Energy Metabolism

Thiamin (vitamin B_1), riboflavin (vitamin B_2), niacin (nicotinamide and nicotinic acid), vitamin B_6 (pyridoxine), folate (folic acid), vitamin B_{12} (cobalamin), pantothenic acid, and biotin are the nutrients identified as the B-vitamins. Other nutrients involved in energy metabolism include a vitamin-like substance called choline and the minerals iodine, chromium, manganese, and sulfur. In this section, we discuss the functions, food sources, toxicity, and deficiency symptoms for these vitamins and minerals. For a list of recommended intakes, see Table 1.

TABLE 1   Overview of Nutrients Involved in Energy Metabolism

Nutrient	Recommended Intake
Thiamin (vitamin B_1)	RDA for 19 years and older: Women = 1.1 mg/day Men = 1.2 mg/day
Riboflavin (vitamin B_2)	RDA for 19 years and older: Women = 1.1 mg/day Men = 1.3 mg/day
Niacin (nicotinamide and nicotinic acid)	RDA for 19 years and older: Women = 14 mg/day Men = 16 mg/day
Vitamin B_6 (pyridoxine)	RDA for 19 to 50 years of age: Women and men = 1.3 mg/day RDA for 51 years and older: Women = 1.5 mg/day Men = 1.7 mg/day
Folate (folic acid)	RDA for 19 years and older: Women and men = 400 µg/day
Vitamin B_{12} (cobalamin)	RDA for 19 years and older: Women and men = 2.4 µg/day
Pantothenic acid	AI for 19 years and older: Women and men = 5 mg/day
Biotin	AI for 19 years and older: Women and men = 30 µg/day
Choline	AI for 19 years and older: Women = 425 mg/day Men = 550 mg/day
Iodine	RDA for 19 years and older: Women and men = 150 µg/day
Chromium	RDA for 19 to 50 years of age: Women = 25 µg/day Men = 35 µg/day RDA for 51 years and older: Women = 20 µg/day Men = 30 µg/day
Manganese	AI for 19 years and older: Women = 1.8 mg/day Men = 2.3 mg/day

Thiamin (Vitamin B$_1$)

Thiamin deficiency results in a disease called **beriberi.** The symptoms, which include paralysis of the lower limbs, have been described throughout recorded history. But it was not until the 19th century, when steam-powered mills began removing the outer shell of grains, especially rice, that the disease became widespread, especially in Southeast Asia. At the time, it was thought that milling grain improved the quality of the grain and made it more acceptable to consumers. What wasn't known was that the outer layer of the grain contained the highest concentrations of B-vitamins, especially thiamin.[2] Thus, most of the B-vitamins were being removed and discarded as the grain was milled or the rice polished. In 1885, Dr. Kanehiro Takaki, a Japanese naval surgeon, discovered that he could prevent beriberi by improving the quality of the diets of seamen. Then in 1906, Dr. Christiaan Eijkman, a Dutch physician living in Java, and his colleague, Dr. Gerrit Grijns, described how they could produce beriberi in chickens or pigeons by feeding them polished rice and could cure them by feeding back the rice bran that was removed during polishing.[2,3] In 1911, Polish chemist Casimir Funk was able to isolate the water-soluble nitrogen-containing compound in rice bran that was responsible for the cure. He referred to this compound as a "vital amine" and called it thiamin. Because it was the first B-vitamin discovered, it is designated vitamin B$_1$.[2]

Thiamin is part of the coenzyme thiamin pyrophosphate, or TPP. As a part of TPP, thiamin plays a critical role in the breakdown of glucose for energy and acts as a coenzyme in the metabolism of the essential amino acids leucine, isoleucine, and valine, also referred to as the *branched-chain amino acids*. These amino acids are metabolized primarily in the muscle and can be used to produce glucose if necessary. TPP also assists in producing DNA and RNA and plays a role in the synthesis of *neurotransmitters*, chemicals important in the transmission of messages throughout the nervous system.

Good food sources of thiamin include enriched cereals and grains, whole-grain products, wheat germ and yeast extracts, ready-to-eat cereals, ham and other pork products, organ meats of most animals, and some green vegetables, including peas, asparagus, and okra (Figure 3). Overall, whole grains are some of the best sources

Ready-to-eat cereals are a good source of thiamin and other B-vitamins.

Nayashkova Olga/Shutterstock

beriberi A disease of muscle wasting and nerve damage caused by thiamin deficiency.

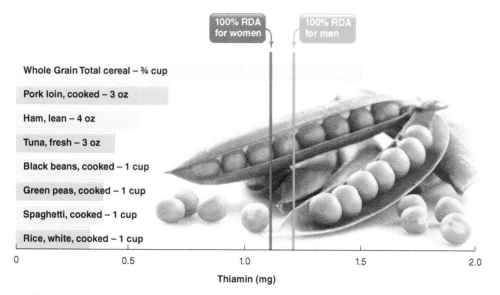

Whole Grain Total cereal – ¾ cup

Pork loin, cooked – 3 oz

Ham, lean – 4 oz

Tuna, fresh – 3 oz

Black beans, cooked – 1 cup

Green peas, cooked – 1 cup

Spaghetti, cooked – 1 cup

Rice, white, cooked – 1 cup

100% RDA for women

100% RDA for men

0   0.5   1.0   1.5   2.0

Thiamin (mg)

Figure 3 Common food sources of thiamin. The RDA for thiamin is 1.2 mg/day for men and 1.1 mg/day for women 19 years and older.

Data from U.S. Department of Agriculture, Agricultural Research Service. 2009. USDA Nutrient Database for Standard Reference, Release 22. Nutrient Data Laboratory Home Page. www.ars.usda.gov/ba/bhnrc/ndl.

of thiamin, while more processed foods, such as refined sugars and fats, are the lowest sources. Unless milled grains are fortified (that is, the thiamin is added back), they are poor sources.

Because thiamin is involved in energy-generating processes, the symptoms of beriberi include a combination of fatigue, apathy, muscle weakness, and detriments in cognitive function. The body's inability to metabolize energy or synthesize neurotransmitters also leads to muscle wasting, nerve damage, and the characteristic paralysis; in later stages, patients may be unable to move at all. The heart muscle may also be affected, and the patient may die of heart failure.

Beriberi is seen in countries in which unenriched, processed grains are a primary food source; for instance, beriberi was widespread in China when rice was processed and refined, and it still occurs in refugee camps and other settlements dependent on poor-quality food supplies. Beriberi is also seen in industrialized countries in people with heavy alcohol consumption and limited food intake. Chronic alcohol abuse is associated with a host of neurologic symptoms, collectively called Wernicke-Korsakoff syndrome, in which thiamin intake is decreased and absorption and utilization impaired.[2] Although thiamin supplementation has been the treatment of choice for beriberi for nearly 100 years, there is still uncertainty about the appropriate dose and duration of supplementation.[4] There are no known adverse effects from consuming excess amounts of thiamin.

Riboflavin (Vitamin B_2)

The theory that there might be more than one vitamin in rice bran was first proposed in the early 1900s after researchers noticed that rats fed diets of polished rice had poor growth.[3] Finally, in 1917 researchers found that there were at least two vitamins in the extracts of rice polishing, one that cured beriberi and another that stimulated growth. The latter substance was first called vitamin B_2 and then named riboflavin for its ribose-like side chain and the yellow color it produced in water (*flavus* means "yellow" in Latin).[5]

Riboflavin is an important component of coenzymes that are involved in chemical reactions occurring within the energy-producing metabolic pathways. These coenzymes, flavin mononucleotide (FMN) and flavin adenine dinucleotide (FAD), are involved in the metabolism of carbohydrates and fat. Riboflavin is also a part of the antioxidant enzyme glutathione peroxidase, thus assisting in the fight against oxidative damage.

Milk is a good source of riboflavin; however, riboflavin is destroyed when it is exposed to light. Thus, milk is generally stored in opaque containers to prevent the destruction of riboflavin. In the United States, meat and meat products, including poultry, fish, and milk and other dairy products, are the most significant sources of dietary riboflavin.[6] However, green vegetables, such as broccoli, asparagus, and spinach, are also good sources. Finally, although whole grains are relatively low in riboflavin, fortification and enrichment of grains have increased the intake of riboflavin from these sources, especially ready-to-eat cereals and energy bars, which can provide 25–100% of the Daily Value (DV) for riboflavin in 1 serving (Figure 4).

There are no known adverse effects from consuming excess amounts of riboflavin. Because coenzymes derived from riboflavin are so widely distributed in metabolism, riboflavin deficiency, referred to as **ariboflavinosis,** lacks the specificity seen with other vitamins. However, riboflavin deficiency can have profound effects on energy production, which result in "nondescript" symptoms such as fatigue and muscle weakness. More advanced riboflavin deficiency can result in lips that are dry and scaly, inflammation and ulcers of the mucous membranes of the mouth and throat, irritated patches on the skin, changes in the cornea, anemia, and in some cases personality changes.[6] It is now known that cataract formation can be decreased by higher riboflavin intakes.[7] In addition, riboflavin is important in the metabolism of four other vitamins: folic acid, vitamin B_6, vitamin K, and niacin.[6] Thus, a deficiency in riboflavin can affect a number of body systems.

Barry Gregg/Corbis

Milk is a good source of riboflavin and is stored in opaque containers to prevent the destruction of riboflavin by light.

ariboflavinosis A condition caused by riboflavin deficiency.

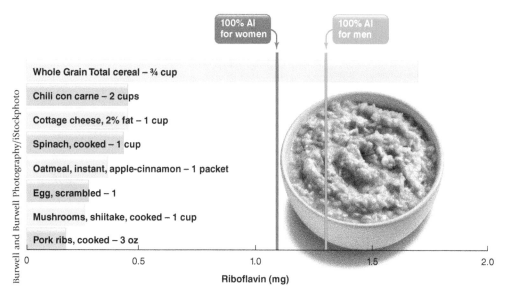

Figure 4 Common food sources of riboflavin. The RDA for riboflavin is 1.3 mg/day for men and 1.1 mg/day for women 19 years and older.

Data from U.S. Department of Agriculture, Agricultural Research Service, 2009, USDA Nutrient Database for Standard Reference, Release 22. Nutrient Data Laboratory Home Page, www.ars.usda.gov/ba/bhnrc/ndl.

Niacin

Pellagra, the deficiency of niacin, was first described in the 1700s in northern Spain but was also seen widely across the United States, Western and Eastern Europe, and the Middle East, where corn or maize was the dietary staple.[3] The term *pellagra* literally means "raw skin."[8] The four characteristic symptoms—dermatitis, diarrhea, dementia, and death—are referred to as the *four Ds*. Individuals who develop the disease first complain of inflammation and soreness in the mouth, followed by red, raw skin (dermatitis) on areas exposed to sunlight. The disease then progresses to the digestive and nervous systems. The symptoms of this stage of the disease are diarrhea, vomiting, and dementia. At the present time, pellagra is rarely seen in industrialized countries, except in cases of chronic alcoholism. Pellagra is still found in impoverished areas of some developing nations.

Corn-based diets are low in niacin and the amino acid tryptophan, which can be converted to niacin in the body. The term *niacin* actually refers to two compounds, nicotinamide and nicotinic acid, which are converted to active coenzymes that assist in the metabolism of carbohydrates and fatty acids for energy. Niacin also plays an important role in DNA replication and repair and in the process of cell differentiation. Thus, it is not surprising that a deficiency of niacin can disrupt so many systems in the body.

Niacin is widely distributed in foods, with good sources being yeast, meats (including fish and poultry), cereals, legumes, and seeds **(Figure 5)**. Other foods such as milk, leafy vegetables, coffee, and tea can also add appreciable amounts of niacin to the diet.[8] As with riboflavin, enriched or fortified breads, ready-to-eat cereals, and energy bars frequently provide 25–100% of the Daily Value for niacin.

Niacin can cause toxicity symptoms when taken in supplement form. These symptoms include *flushing,* which is defined as burning, tingling, and itching sensations accompanied by a reddened flush primarily on the face, arms, and chest. Liver damage, glucose intolerance, blurred vision, and edema of the eyes can be seen with very large doses of niacin taken over long periods of time.

Halibut is a good source of niacin.

pellagra A disease that results from severe niacin deficiency.

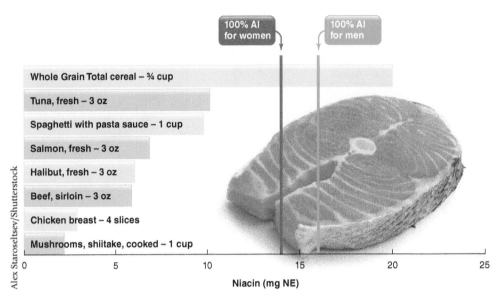

100% AI for women

100% AI for men

Whole Grain Total cereal – ¾ cup

Tuna, fresh – 3 oz

Spaghetti with pasta sauce – 1 cup

Salmon, fresh – 3 oz

Halibut, fresh – 3 oz

Beef, sirloin – 3 oz

Chicken breast – 4 slices

Mushrooms, shiitake, cooked – 1 cup

Niacin (mg NE)

Alex Staroseltsev/Shutterstock

Figure 5 Common food sources of niacin. The RDA for niacin is 16 mg niacin equivalents (NE)/day for men and 14 mg NE/day for women 19 years and older.

Data from U.S. Department of Agriculture, Agricultural Research Service, 2009, USDA Nutrient Database for Standard Reference, Release 22. Nutrient Data Laboratory Home Page, www.ars.usda.gov/ba/bhnrc/ndl.

RECAP The B-vitamins include thiamin, riboflavin, niacin, vitamin B_6 (pyridoxine), folate, vitamin B_{12} (cobalamin), pantothenic acid, and biotin. Thiamin plays critical roles in the metabolism of glucose and the branched-chain amino acids. Whole grains are good sources. Thiamin-deficiency disease is called beriberi. Riboflavin is an important coenzyme involved in the metabolism of carbohydrates and fat. Milk, meats, and green vegetables are good sources. Riboflavin-deficiency disease is called ariboflavinosis. Niacin assists in the metabolism of carbohydrates and fatty acids. It also plays an important role in DNA replication and repair and in cell differentiation. Corn-based diets can be low in niacin and can result in the deficiency disease pellagra.

Vitamin B_6 (Pyridoxine)

Researchers discovered vitamin B_6 by ruling out a deficiency of other B-vitamins as the cause of a scaly dermatitis in rats.[3] They then discovered that B_6 deficiency was associated with convulsions in birds and later that infants fed formulas lacking B_6 also had convulsions and dermatitis.[9]

Functions of Vitamin B_6

The term *vitamin B_6* can actually refer to any of six related compounds: pyridoxine (PN), pyridoxal (PL), pyridoxamine (PM), and the phosphate forms of these three compounds. A coenzyme for more than 100 enzymes, vitamin B_6 is involved in many metabolic processes within the body, including the following:

- Amino acid metabolism. Vitamin B_6 is important for the metabolism of amino acids because it plays a critical role in transamination, which is a key process in making nonessential amino acids. Without adequate vitamin B_6, all amino acids become essential, as our body cannot make them in sufficient quantities.
- Neurotransmitter synthesis. Vitamin B_6 is a cofactor for enzymes involved in the synthesis of several neurotransmitters, which is also a transamination process. Because of this, vitamin B_6 is important in cognitive function and normal brain

activity. Abnormal brain waves have been observed in both infants and adults in vitamin B_6–deficient states.[10]

- Carbohydrate metabolism. Vitamin B_6 is a coenzyme for an enzyme that breaks down stored glycogen to glucose. Thus, vitamin B_6 plays an important role in maintaining blood glucose during exercise. It is also important for the conversion of amino acids to glucose.
- Heme synthesis. The synthesis of heme, required for the production of hemoglobin and thus the transport of oxygen, requires vitamin B_6. Chronic vitamin B_6 deficiency can lead to small red blood cells with inadequate amounts of hemoglobin.[10]
- Immune function. Vitamin B_6 plays a role in maintaining the health and activity of lymphocytes and in producing adequate levels of antibodies in response to an immune challenge. The depression of immune function seen in vitamin B_6 deficiency may also be due to a reduction in the vitamin B_6–dependent enzymes involved in DNA synthesis.
- Metabolism of other nutrients. Vitamin B_6 also plays a role in the metabolism of other nutrients, including niacin, folate, and carnitine.[10]
- Reduction of cardiovascular disease (CVD) risk. As discussed later in this chapter, high blood levels of homocysteine are considered an independent risk factor for CVD.[11] **Homocysteine** is a metabolic by-product of the metabolism of methionine, an essential amino acid. The enzymes involved in homocysteine metabolism require three key vitamins: folate, vitamin B_6, and vitamin B_{12}.[12] If they are not available to completely metabolize methoinine, blood levels of homocysteine increase. Adequate intakes of folate, vitamin B_6, and vitamin B_{12} can help keep blood levels of homocysteine low.

Tuna is a good source of vitamin B_6.

Shutterstock

How Much Vitamin B_6 Should We Consume?

The recommended intakes for vitamin B_6 are listed in Table 1. Rich sources of vitamin B_6 are meats, fish, poultry, eggs, dairy products, and peanut butter (Figure 6). Many vegetables, such as asparagus, potatoes, and carrots; fruits, especially bananas; and whole-grain cereals are also good sources of vitamin B_6. As with the other B-vitamins

homocysteine An amino acid that requires adequate levels of folate, vitamin B_6, and vitamin B_{12} for its metabolism. High levels of homocysteine in the blood are associated with an increased risk for vascular diseases, such as cardiovascular disease.

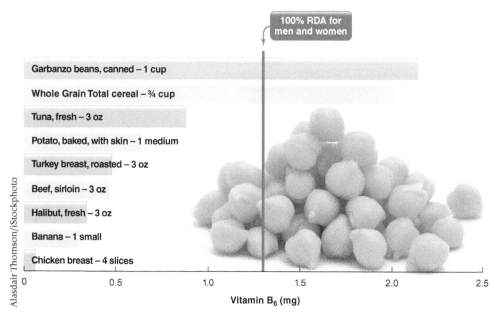

Figure 6   Common food sources of vitamin B_6. The RDA for vitamin B_6 is 1.3 mg/day for men and women 19–50 years.

Data from U.S. Department of Agriculture, Agricultural Research Service, 2009, USDA Nutrient Database for Standard Reference, Release 22. Nutrient Data Laboratory Home Page, www.ars.usda.gov/ba/bhnrc/ndl.

discussed in this chapter, fortified or enriched grains, cereals, and energy bars can provide 25–100% of the Daily Value in 1 serving. Little vitamin B_6 is lost in the storage or handling of foods, except the milling of grains; however, vitamin B_6 is sensitive to both heat and light, so it can easily be lost in cooking.

Vitamin B_6 supplements have been used to treat conditions such as premenstrual syndrome (PMS) and carpal tunnel syndrome. You need to use caution, however, when using such supplements. Whereas consuming excess vitamin B_6 from food sources does not cause toxicity, excess B_6 from supplementing can result in nerve damage and lesions of the skin. A condition called *sensory neuropathy* (damage to the sensory nerves) has been documented in individuals taking high-dose B_6 supplements. The symptoms of sensory neuropathy include numbness and tingling involving the face, neck, hands, and feet, with difficulty manipulating objects and walking.

The symptoms of vitamin B_6 deficiency include anemia, convulsions, depression, confusion, and inflamed, irritated patches on the skin. Deficiency of vitamin B_6 has also been associated with a decreased ability to metabolize the amino acid methionine and a resultant increased risk for cardiovascular, cerebrovascular, and peripheral vascular disease. This condition also occurs with a deficiency of folate and vitamin B_{12}, and is discussed in more detail in the next section.

🔊 Headaches, anxiety, irritability, tension, and depression are common symptoms of PMS.

Creatas Images/Jupiter Unlimited

Folate

Reports of the symptoms we now recognize as folate deficiency go back two centuries.[13] By the late 1800s, a disorder associated with large red blood cells had been characterized, but it wasn't until the 1930s that researchers understood that the condition is related to diet. It took another 40 years before researchers more fully understood the relationship between this blood abnormality and a deficiency of folate, a substance found in many foods, especially leafy green vegetables. The name *folate* originated from the fact the vitamin is abundant in "foliage."[13]

Functions of Folate

Folate-requiring reactions in the body are collectively called *1-C metabolism*. This means folate is involved in adding "one-carbon units" to other organic compounds during the synthesis of new compounds or the modification of existing ones. Thus, the most basic cellular functions, such as the synthesis of DNA, require folate. The following are some of these functions:

- Nucleotide synthesis. Folate is required for the synthesis of nitrogen-containing

B_6 for PMS? Think Twice!

Perform an Internet search for treatments for premenstrual syndrome (PMS) and you are likely to find many recommendations for supplementing with high doses of vitamin B_6. In addition, almost any PMS supplement sold in a pharmacy or health food store will contain 50 to 200 mg of vitamin B_6 per capsule or tablet, with the recommendation that the consumer take at least two capsules per day. The UL of vitamin B_6 is 100 mg/day, and high doses of vitamin B_6 over an extended period of time can cause neurologic disorders, including numbness, tingling, and a loss of motor function, such as inability to walk. Considering these serious adverse effects, is there any research to support recommending high levels of vitamin B_6 for PMS? Do the benefits of supplementing outweigh the risks for toxicity?

To date, nine randomized clinical trials have tested whether vitamin B_6 supplementation improves PMS symptoms. A review of these nine trials, which included 940 subjects, concluded that "there was insufficient evidence of high enough quality to give a confident recommendation for using vitamin B_6 in the treatment of PMS."[14] Many of the studies showed improvement in only some of the symptoms of PMS, such as anxiety and food cravings, but not headaches and depression. Also, the level of treatment in the studies varied from 50 to 600 mg/day of vitamin B_6. Thus, although some studies suggest a benefit, the evidence is not convincing, so before you start taking a supplement that could cause serious side effects, check with your doctor. [14–17]

compounds needed for DNA synthesis. For this reason folate is important for cell division. Adequate intake is especially critical during the first few weeks of pregnancy, when the combined sperm–egg cell multiplies rapidly to form the primitive tissues and structures of the human body. Folate continues to be important for tissue maintenance and repair throughout life. For example, low folate may predispose normal tissues to increased risk of transformation into cancer cells, while folate supplementation appears to suppress the development of tumors.[18]

- Amino acid metabolism. Folate is involved in the metabolism of many of the amino acids, including serine, glycine, histidine, and methionine. And as mentioned earlier, folate, vitamin B_{12}, and vitamin B_6 are required for the metabolism of methionine.
- Red blood cell synthesis. Without adequate folate, the synthesis of normal red blood cells is impaired.

How Much Folate Should We Consume?

The recommended intakes for folate are listed in Table 1. The critical role of folate during the first few weeks of pregnancy and the fact that many women of childbearing age do not consume adequate amounts led to the mandatory fortification of enriched breads, flours, corn meals, rice, pasta, and other grain products with folic acid in 1998. Because of fortification, getting adequate folate in your diet is not difficult. The primary sources of folate in the American diet are ready-to-eat cereals, breads, and other grain products. Other good food sources include milk and eggs; oatmeal; meats, especially liver; fruits, such as bananas, grapefruit, oranges, pears, pineapple, and strawberries; juices of these fruits; and vegetables, including asparagus, green beans, peas, beets, broccoli, cauliflower, corn, tomatoes, lentils, spinach, and romaine lettuce (Figure 7).

Because folate is sensitive to heat, it can be lost when foods are cooked. It can also leach out into cooking water, which may then be discarded.

What Happens If We Consume Too Much Folate?

Toxicity can occur when taking supplemental folate. One especially frustrating problem with folate toxicity is that it can mask a simultaneous vitamin B_{12} deficiency. This often results in failure to detect the B_{12} deficiency, and as you saw in the chapter-opening

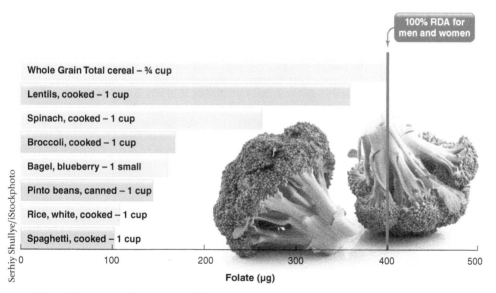

▲ **Figure 7** Common food sources of folate and folic acid. The RDA for folate is 400 μg/day for men and women.

Data from U.S. Department of Agriculture, Agricultural Research Service, 2009, USDA Nutrient Database for Standard Reference, Release 22. Nutrient Data Laboratory Home Page, www.ars.usda.gov/ba/bhnrc/ndl.

case, a delay in diagnosis of B_{12} deficiency can contribute to severe damage to the nervous system. There do not appear to be any clear symptoms of folate toxicity independent from its interaction with vitamin B_{12} deficiency.

What Happens If We Don't Consume Enough Folate?

Folate deficiency can cause many adverse health effects, the three most significant of which are discussed here.

Neural Tube Defects   A woman's requirement for folate substantially increases during pregnancy. This is because of the high rates of cell development needed for enlargement of the uterus, development of the placenta, expansion of the mother's red blood cells, and growth of the embryo and fetus. Inadequate folate intake during pregnancy is associated with major birth defects.

Neural tube defects are the most common malformations of the central nervous system that occur during embryonic and fetal development. The neural tube is formed by the fourth week of pregnancy, and it eventually develops into the brain and the spinal cord of the fetus. In a folate-deficient environment, the tube will fail to fold and close properly. The resultant defect in the newborn depends on the degree of failure and can range from protrusion of the spinal cord outside of the spinal column to a partial absence of brain tissue. Some forms of neural tube defects are minor and can be surgically repaired, while other forms are fatal.

The challenging aspect of neural tube defects is that they occur very early in a woman's pregnancy, almost always before she knows she is pregnant. Thus, adequate folate intake is extremely important for all sexually active women of childbearing age, whether or not they intend to become pregnant. To prevent neural tube defects, it is recommended that all women capable of becoming pregnant consume 400 µg of folate daily from supplements, fortified foods, or both in addition to the folate they consume in their standard diet.[19]

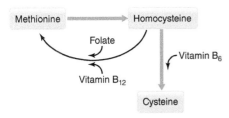

Figure 8 The metabolism of methionine, an essential amino acid, to homocysteine. Homocysteine can then be converted back to methionine through a vitamin B_{12}– and folate-dependent reaction or to cysteine through a vitamin B_6–dependent reaction. Cysteine is a nonessential amino acid important for making other biological compounds. Without these B-vitamins, blood levels of homocysteine can increase. High levels of homocysteine are a risk factor for cardiovascular disease.

Vascular Disease and Homocysteine   As mentioned earlier, folate, vitamin B_6, and vitamin B_{12} are necessary for the complete metabolism of the essential amino acid methionine (**Figure 8**). When intakes of these nutrients are insufficient, the level of homocysteine, a by-product of methionine metabolism, increases in the blood. A thorough review of recent studies on this topic showed that elevated levels of homocysteine are associated with a 1.5 to 2 times greater risk for cardiovascular, cerebrovascular, and peripheral vascular diseases.[20] These diseases substantially increase a person's risk for a heart attack or stroke.

The exact mechanism by which elevated homocysteine levels increase the risk for vascular diseases is currently unknown. It has been speculated that homocysteine may damage the lining of blood vessels and stimulate the accumulation of plaque, which can lead to hardening of the arteries.[21] Homocysteine also increases blood clotting, which could lead to an increased risk for blocked arteries. Thus, by consuming adequate amounts of vitamin B_6, folate, and vitamin B_{12}, we may decrease our risk for a heart attack or stroke.

Macrocytic Anemia   The term *anemia* literally means "without blood"; it is used to refer to any condition in which hemoglobin levels are low. Some anemias are caused by genetic problems. For instance, *sickle cell anemia* is a genetic disorder in which the red blood cells have a sickle shape. Another inherited anemia is *thalassemia,* a condition characterized by red blood cells that are small and short-lived. Other anemias are due to micronutrient deficiencies. These can be classified according to the general way they alter the size and shape of the red blood cells. Low iron, copper, and vitamin B_6 cause *microcytic anemia* (small red blood cells), while inadequate intakes of folate or vitamin B_{12} cause *macrocytic anemia* (large red blood cells). We discuss macrocytic anemia in more detail here.

neural tube defects The most common malformations of the central nervous system that occur during fetal development. A folate deficiency can cause neural tube defects.

Deficiency of either folate or vitamin B_{12} can impair DNA synthesis, which decreases the ability of blood cells to divide. If they cannot divide, differentiate, and mature, the cells remain large and immature precursors to red blood cells, known as *megaloblasts* (from *megalo*, meaning "large," and *blast*, meaning "a precursor cell"). These immature cells contain inadequate hemoglobin; thus, their ability to transport oxygen is diminished. The resulting condition is sometimes referred to as *megaloblastic anemia*, but is more commonly called **macrocytic anemia** (from *macro*, meaning "large," and *cyte*, meaning "cell"). Symptoms of macrocytic anemia are similar to those of other types of anemia, including weakness, fatigue, difficulty concentrating, irritability, headache, shortness of breath, and reduced exercise tolerance.

RECAP Vitamin B_6 is a coenzyme for more than 100 enzymes involved in processes such as the metabolism of amino acids and carbohydrates and the synthesis of neurotransmitters. It is widely found in meats, poultry, fish, dairy products, and certain fruits and vegetables. The most basic cellular functions, such as the synthesis of DNA as well as cell differentiation, require folate. Folate is widely found in green leafy vegetables and is added to breads, cereals, and other grain-based foods. Folate deficiency causes macrocytic anemia and can lead to neural tube defects in the developing fetus.

Vitamin B_{12} (Cobalamin)

In 1855, a clinician named Thomas Addison described a strange form of anemia in patients that left them feeling weak and exhausted.[22,23] To our knowledge, this is the first report describing the often fatal course of vitamin B_{12} deficiency, later called **pernicious anemia** (the word *pernicious* means "causing great harm"). Several decades passed before an "animal protein factor" was associated with the cobalt-containing vitamin B_{12}. The first clinical experiments in humans were done by Drs. Minot and Murphy in the 1920s. They fed patients with pernicious anemia large doses of liver and documented the improvement in their red blood cells.[23] For this work they were awarded the Nobel Prize in 1934. This work was extended by others who identified that some special "extrinsic factor" in the liver or meat was combined with an "intrinsic factor" in the stomach. When both of these factors were present, patients with pernicious anemia recovered. The final step in the identification of vitamin B_{12} as the extrinsic factor and in determining its structure was done by Dr. Dorothy Crowfoot Hodgkin, who was awarded the Nobel Prize for Chemistry in 1964.[23]

Functions of Vitamin B_{12}

Vitamin B_{12} is a coenzyme for two enzymes in the body that are part of two very important metabolic pathways.[22] First, vitamin B_{12} is important for the metabolism of methionine, an essential amino acid, and assists in the synthesis of biological compounds such as creatine, phospholipids, neurotransmitters, DNA, and RNA. As with folate deficiency, a deficiency in vitamin B_{12} is most pronounced in rapidly dividing cells, such as the red blood cells, and results in a form of macrocytic anemia.

As noted earlier, adequate levels of folate, vitamin B_6, and vitamin B_{12} are necessary to prevent the buildup of homocysteine. A high level of homocysteine in the blood is related to an increased risk for heart disease.

The metabolic pathway involved in the metabolism of methionine also converts folate to its active form, which is a vitamin B_{12}–dependent process. Without vitamin B_{12}, folate becomes "trapped" in an inactive form and folate deficiency symptoms develop, even though adequate amounts of folate may be present in the diet.

Vitamin B_{12} is also important for the metabolism of certain abnormal fatty acids. When vitamin B_{12} is deficient in the diet, these abnormal fatty acids accumulate in the blood and are incorporated into cell membranes, including those in the nervous system, where they cause neurologic problems. Also, as you saw in the chapter-opening scenario, B_{12} is essential for healthy functioning of the nervous system

macrocytic anemia A form of anemia manifested as the production of larger than normal red blood cells containing insufficient hemoglobin, which inhibits adequate transport of oxygen; also called megaloblastic anemia. Macrocytic anemia can be caused by a severe folate deficiency.

pernicious anemia A form of anemia that is the primary cause of a vitamin B_{12} deficiency; occurs at the end stage of a disorder that causes the loss of certain cells in the stomach.

◀ Turkey contains vitamin B$_{12}$.

because it helps maintain the myelin sheath that coats nerve fibers. When this sheath is damaged or absent, the conduction of nervous signals is slowed, causing numerous neurologic problems.

How Much Vitamin B$_{12}$ Should We Consume?

The recommended intakes for vitamin B$_{12}$ are listed in Table 1. Vitamin B$_{12}$ is found primarily in animal products, such as meats, fish, poultry, dairy products, and eggs, and in fortified cereal products, such as ready-to-eat cereals (Figure 9). Individuals consuming a vegan diet need to eat vegetable-based foods that are fortified with vitamin B$_{12}$ or take vitamin B$_{12}$ supplements or injections to ensure that they maintain adequate blood levels of this nutrient.

As we age, our sources of vitamin B$_{12}$ may need to change. Individuals younger than 51 years are generally able to meet the RDA for vitamin B$_{12}$ by consuming it in foods. However, it is estimated that about 10–30% of adults older than 50 years have a condition referred to as **atrophic gastritis,** which results in low stomach acid secretion.[19] Since stomach acid separates food-bound vitamin B$_{12}$ from dietary proteins, if the acid content of the stomach is inadequate, then we cannot free up enough vitamin B$_{12}$ from food sources alone. Because atrophic gastritis can affect almost one-third of the older adult population, it is recommended that people older than 50 years of age consume foods fortified with vitamin B$_{12}$, take a vitamin B$_{12}$–containing supplement, or have periodic B$_{12}$ injections.

What Happens If We Consume Too Much Vitamin B$_{12}$?

There are no known adverse effects from consuming excess amounts of vitamin B$_{12}$ as either food or supplements.[19]

atrophic gastritis A condition that results in low stomach acid secretion; is estimated to occur in about 10–30% of adults older than 50 years.

What Happens If We Don't Consume Enough Vitamin B$_{12}$?

The two primary causes of vitamin B$_{12}$ deficiency are insufficient intake and the inability to absorb the vitamin B$_{12}$ consumed. Either of these problems can result in the

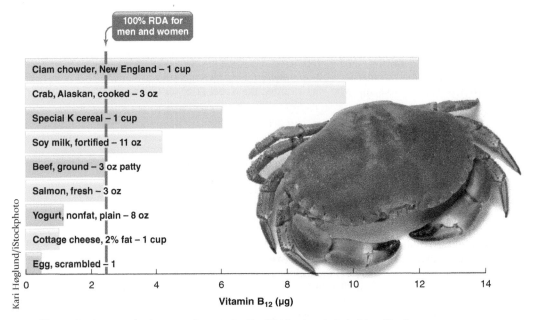

◀ **Figure 9**   Common food sources of vitamin B$_{12}$. The RDA for vitamin B$_{12}$ is 2.4 µg/day for men and women.
Data from U.S. Department of Agriculture, Agricultural Research Service, 2009, USDA Nutrient Database for Standard Reference, Release 22. Nutrient Data Laboratory Home Page, www.ars.usda.gov/ba/bhnrc/ndl.

development of pernicious anemia. The most common cause of the vitamin B_{12} deficiency seen with pernicious anemia is lack of a protein called **intrinsic factor,** which is normally secreted by certain cells in the stomach. Intrinsic factor binds to vitamin B_{12} and aids its absorption in the small intestine. Without intrinsic factor, vitamin B_{12} cannot cross the intestinal lining. Like atrophic gastritis, inadequate production of intrinsic factor occurs more commonly in older people, making them at higher risk for vitamin B_{12} deficiency and pernicious anemia. Individuals who lack intrinsic factor may receive periodic vitamin B_{12} injections, thus bypassing the need for B_{12} absorption in the intestines. Pernicious anemia is also commonly seen in people with more generalized malabsorption disorders, such as celiac disease, as well as in people with tapeworm infestation of the gut, as the worms take up the vitamin B_{12} before it can be absorbed by the intestines. Pernicious anemia can also occur in people who consume little or no vitamin B_{12} in their diets, such as Mr. Katz in our chapter opener, who followed a strict vegan diet.

Symptoms of pernicious anemia include pale skin, reduced energy and exercise tolerance, fatigue, and shortness of breath. In addition, because nerve cells are destroyed, patients with pernicious anemia lose the ability to perform coordinated movements and maintain their body's positioning. Central nervous system involvement can lead to irritability, confusion, depression, and even paranoia. As we saw in the case of Mr. Katz, after onset, such symptoms can only be partially reversed, even with prompt administration of vitamin B_{12} injections.

David Murray/Dorling Kindersley

Shiitake mushrooms contain pantothenic acid.

Pantothenic Acid

The path leading to the discovery of pantothenic acid was similar to that for the other water-soluble vitamins. First, researchers established that pantothenic acid was important for the growth of certain bacteria and yeasts. Then they identified it as important for growth and the prevention of dermatitis in chickens. Finally, it was identified as essential for other animals and humans. The vitamin was named after the Greek word meaning "from everywhere," since the vitamin is widespread in the food supply.[24]

Pantothenic acid is a component of an important coenzyme that is required for all the energy-producing metabolic pathways. It is especially important for the breakdown and synthesis of fatty acids within the body. Thus, pantothenic acid assures that the foods we eat can be used for energy and that the excess energy we consume can be stored as fat.

The recommended intakes for pantothenic acid are listed in Table 1. Food sources include chicken, beef, egg yolks, potatoes, oat cereals, tomato products, whole grains, organ meats, and yeast (Figure 10). There are no known adverse effects from consuming excess amounts of pantothenic acid. Deficiencies of pantothenic acid are very rare.

Biotin

Early in the 1900s, it was observed that rats could maintain normal growth while being fed a diet containing cooked egg whites as the sole source of protein. About the same time, other researchers observed that, if the egg whites were raw, rats developed diarrhea and skin problems.[3] The detrimental effects of feeding raw egg whites aroused great interest in the nutrition community. Could there be a toxic substance in raw egg whites that wasn't found in cooked egg whites? Experiments led to the discovery of biotin, which prevented the diarrhea and skin problems that occurred when raw egg whites were fed to rats. Raw egg whites contain a protein called avidin, which binds biotin in the gastrointestinal tract and prevents its absorption.

Biotin is a coenzyme for five enzymes that are critical in the metabolism of carbohydrate, fat, and protein. It also plays an important role in gluconeogenesis.

intrinsic factor A protein secreted by cells of the stomach that binds to vitamin B_{12} and aids its absorption in the small intestine.

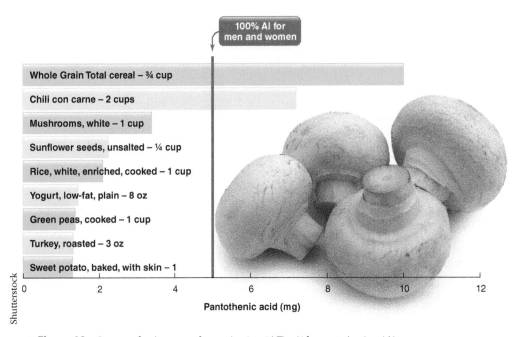

100% AI for men and women

Whole Grain Total cereal – ¾ cup

Chili con carne – 2 cups

Mushrooms, white – 1 cup

Sunflower seeds, unsalted – ¼ cup

Rice, white, enriched, cooked – 1 cup

Yogurt, low-fat, plain – 8 oz

Green peas, cooked – 1 cup

Turkey, roasted – 3 oz

Sweet potato, baked, with skin – 1

Pantothenic acid (mg)

Shutterstock

Figure 10 Common food sources of pantothenic acid. The AI for pantothenic acid is 5 mg/day for men and women.
Data from U.S. Department of Agriculture, Agricultural Research Service. 2009. USDA Nutrient Database for Standard Reference, Release 22. Nutrient Data Laboratory Home Page, www.ars.usda.gov/ba/bhnrc/ndl.

The recommended intakes for biotin are listed in Table 1. The biotin content has been determined for very few foods, and these values are not reported in food composition tables or dietary analysis programs. Biotin appears to be widespread in foods but is especially high in liver, egg yolks, and cooked cereals. Biotin is also produced by the intestinal flora in the gut, but its availability for absorption appears low.

There are no known adverse effects from consuming excess amounts of biotin. Biotin deficiencies are typically seen only in people who consume a large number of raw egg whites over long periods of time. Biotin deficiencies are also seen in people fed total parenteral nutrition (nutrients that are administered intravenously and bypass the gastrointestinal tract) that is not supplemented with biotin. Symptoms include thinning of hair; loss of hair color; development of a red, scaly rash around the eyes, nose, and mouth; depression; lethargy; and hallucinations.

As you've read about the B-vitamins, you've probably noticed that many of them are susceptible to destruction on exposure to heat, light, and other factors in the environment. In fact, no matter how careful you are when storing and preparing foods, some vitamins will be lost. So how do you preserve the highest level of vitamins in the foods you eat?[25] Check out the Quick Tips on the next page.

RECAP Vitamin B_{12} is essential for the metabolism of methionine and certain abnormal fatty acids. Deficiency leads to pernicious anemia, a type of macrocytic anemia, and nervous system damage. Low intakes of vitamin B_6, folate, and vitamin B_{12} are associated with elevated blood homocysteine levels, which increase the risk for cardiovascular, cerebrovascular, and peripheral vascular disease. Pantothenic acid is especially important for the breakdown and synthesis of fatty acids, whereas biotin is a coenzyme for enzymes that are critical in the metabolism of carbohydrate, fat, and protein.

QUICK TIPS

Retaining the Vitamins in Foods

✓ Watch the water. Soak and cook foods in as little water as possible to minimize the loss of water-soluble vitamins. For the best possible outcome, steam vegetables in a steamer basket over half an inch of water.

✓ Lower the heat. Avoid high temperatures for long periods of time. Heat causes some loss of nutrients, especially vitamin C, thiamin, and riboflavin. Cook vegetables only until tender.

✓ Limit the light. Riboflavin is destroyed by light. Since milk is an excellent source of riboflavin, it is typically packaged in light-obstructing containers, such as coated cardboard or opaque bottles.

✓ Avoid air. Vitamins A, C, E, K, and B are destroyed by exposure to air. Ways to minimize losses are to cut fruits and vegetables in large pieces and store them in air-tight containers or covered with plastic wrap. Peel and cut produce immediately before cooking and eat them as soon after cooking as possible. Finally, eat vegetables and fruits whole, unpeeled, and raw whenever possible.

✓ Don't disturb the pH. Adding baking soda to vegetables to help them retain their color is not smart. Baking soda makes cooking water alkaline, and thiamin, riboflavin, vitamin K, and vitamin C are destroyed.

Corbis

🔺 Choline is widespread in foods and can be found in eggs and milk.

Choline

Choline is a vitamin-like substance found in many foods. It is typically grouped with the B-vitamins because of its role in assisting homocysteine metabolism. Choline also accelerates the synthesis and release of **acetylcholine,** a neurotransmitter that is involved in many functions, including muscle movement and memory storage. Choline is also necessary for the synthesis of phospholipids and other components of cell membranes; thus, choline plays a critical role in the structural integrity of cell membranes. Finally, choline plays an important role in the transport and metabolism of fats and cholesterol.

The recommended intakes for choline are listed in Table 1. The choline content of foods is not typically reported in nutrient databases. However, we do know that choline is widespread in foods, especially milk, liver, eggs, and peanuts. Inadequate intakes of choline can lead to increased fat accumulation in the liver, which eventually leads to liver damage. Excessive intake of supplemental choline results in various toxicity symptoms, including a fishy body odor, vomiting, excess salivation, sweating, diarrhea, and low blood pressure.

Iodine

Iodine is a trace mineral needed to support energy regulation. The heaviest metal required for human nutrition, it is responsible for just one function within the body, the synthesis of thyroid hormones.[26] Our body requires thyroid hormones to regulate body temperature, maintain resting metabolic rate, and support reproduction and growth. The form of iodine found in the earth's environment is predominantly inorganic iodide, while iodine, the oxidized form of iodide, is the form of the nutrient most common in food. The iodine content of crops depends on the level of iodide in the soil. Iodide-deficient soils are common in mountainous areas and areas that have experienced frequent flooding. In general, the level naturally found in most foods and beverages is low.

While our body needs relatively little iodine, adequate amounts are necessary to maintain health. The recommended intakes are listed in Table 1. Very few foods naturally contain iodine. Saltwater fish and shrimp tend to have higher amounts

Andy Crawford/Dorling Kindersley

🔺 Saltwater fish, fresh or canned, provide iodine.

acetylcholine A neurotransmitter that is involved in many functions, including muscle movement and memory storage.

◀ Goiter, or enlargement of the thyroid gland, most commonly develops as a result of iodine deficiency.

Monique le Luhandre/Dorling Kindersley

◀ Our body contains very little chromium. Asparagus is a good dietary source of this trace mineral.

goiter Enlargement of the thyroid gland; can be caused by either iodine toxicity or deficiency.

cretinism A form of mental retardation that occurs in children whose mothers experienced iodine deficiency during pregnancy.

because marine animals concentrate iodine from seawater. Interestingly, iodine is added to dairy cattle feed and used in sanitizing solutions in the dairy industry, so milk and other dairy foods are an important source. In addition, iodized salt and white and whole-wheat breads made with iodized salt and bread conditioners are an important source of iodine. The United States began adding iodine to table salt in 1924. Today, a majority of households worldwide use iodized salt. For many people, iodized salt is their only source of iodine, and approximately one-half a teaspoon meets the entire adult RDA for iodine.

Iodine toxicity, which generally occurs only with excessive supplementation, blocks the synthesis of thyroid hormones. As the thyroid attempts to produce more hormones, it may enlarge, a condition known as **goiter.** But since adequate levels of iodine are necessary for the synthesis of thyroid hormones, iodine deficiency also results in goiter. In fact, iodine deficiency is the primary cause of goiter worldwide. (Note that the term *goiter* refers only to the enlarged thyroid gland, regardless of its cause.)

A low level of circulating thyroid hormones is known as *hypothyroidism*. In addition to goiter, symptoms of hypothyroidism include decreased body temperature, inability to tolerate cold environmental temperatures, weight gain, fatigue, and sluggishness. If a woman experiences iodine deficiency during pregnancy, her infant has a high risk of being born with a form of mental impairment referred to as **cretinism.** In addition to mental impairment, these children may also suffer from stunted growth, deafness, and muteness.

Chromium

Chromium is a trace mineral that plays an important role in carbohydrate metabolism. You may be interested to learn that the chromium in your body is the same metal used in the chrome plating for cars.

Chromium enhances the ability of insulin to transport glucose from the bloodstream into cells. Chromium also plays important roles in the metabolism of RNA and DNA, in immune function, and in growth. Chromium supplements are marketed to reduce body fat and enhance muscle mass and have become popular with bodybuilders and other athletes interested in improving their body composition. The Nutrition Myth or Fact? box investigates whether taking supplemental chromium is effective in improving body composition.

We have only very small amounts of chromium in our body. Whether the U.S. diet provides adequate chromium is controversial; our body appears to store less chromium as we age.

The recommended intakes for chromium are listed in Table 1. Foods that have been identified as good sources of chromium include mushrooms, prunes, dark chocolate, nuts, whole grains, cereals, asparagus, brewer's yeast, some beers, and red wine. Dairy products are typically poor sources of chromium.

There appears to be no toxicity related to consuming chromium naturally found in the diet or in most supplements. The chromium used for some industrial purposes can be toxic. Chromium deficiency appears to be uncommon in the United States. When induced in a research setting, chromium deficiency inhibits the uptake of glucose by the cells, causing a rise in blood glucose and insulin levels. Chromium deficiency can also result in elevated blood lipid levels and in damage to the brain and nervous system.

Manganese

A trace mineral, manganese is a cofactor involved in energy metabolism and in the formation of urea, the primary component of urine. It also assists in the synthesis of the protein matrix found in bone tissue and in building cartilage, a tissue that supports joints. Manganese is also an integral component of superoxide dismutase, an antioxidant enzyme. Thus, manganese assists in the conversion of free radicals to less damaging substances, protecting our body from oxidative damage.

NUTRITION MYTH OR FACT?
Can Chromium Supplements Enhance Body Composition?

Because athletes are always looking for a competitive edge, a multitude of supplements are marketed and sold to enhance exercise performance and body composition. Chromium supplements, predominantly in the form of chromium picolinate, are popular with bodybuilders and weight lifters. This popularity stems from the claims that chromium increases muscle mass and muscle strength and decreases body fat.

An early study of chromium supplementation was promising, in that chromium use in both untrained men and football players was found to decrease body fat and increase muscle mass.[27] These findings caused a surge in the popularity of chromium supplements and motivated many scientists across the United States to test the reproducibility of these early findings. The next study of chromium supplementation found no effects of chromium on muscle mass, body fat, or muscle strength.[28]

These contradictory reports led experts to closely examine the two studies and to design more sophisticated studies to assess the effect of chromium on body composition. There were a number of flaws in the methodology of these early studies. One major concern was that the chromium status of the research participants prior to the study was not measured or controlled. It is possible that the participants were de-

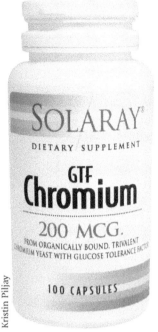

Kristin Piljay

ficient in chromium; this deficiency could have caused a more positive reaction to chromium than would be expected in people with normal chromium status.

A second major concern was that body composition was measured in these studies using the skinfold technique, in which calipers are used to measure the thickness of the skin and fat at various sites on the body. While this method gives a good general estimate of body fat in young, lean, healthy people, it is not sensitive to small changes in muscle mass. Thus, subsequent studies of chromium used more sophisticated methods of measuring body composition.

The results of research studies conducted over the past 15 years consistently show that chromium supplementation has no effect on muscle mass, body fat, or muscle strength in a variety of groups, including untrained college males and females, obese females, collegiate wrestlers, and older men and women.[29-37]

Despite the overwhelming evidence to the contrary, many supplement companies still claim that chromium supplements enhance strength and muscle mass and reduce body fat. These claims result in millions of dollars of sales of supplements to consumers each year. Armed with this information, you can avoid being fooled by such an expensive nutrition myth.

The recommended intakes for manganese are listed in Table 1. Manganese requirements are easily met, as this mineral is widespread in foods and is readily available in a varied diet. Whole-grain foods, such as oat bran, wheat flour, whole-wheat spaghetti, and brown rice, are good sources of manganese (Figure 11). Other good sources include pineapple, pine nuts, okra, spinach, and raspberries.

Manganese toxicity can occur in occupational environments in which people inhale manganese dust; it can also result from drinking water high in manganese. Toxicity results in impairment of the neuromuscular system, causing symptoms similar to those seen in Parkinson's disease, such as muscle spasms and tremors. Manganese deficiency is rare in humans. Symptoms of manganese deficiency include impaired growth and reproductive function, reduced bone density and impaired skeletal growth, impaired glucose and lipid metabolism, and skin rash.

Sulfur

Sulfur is a major mineral and a component of the B-vitamins thiamin and biotin. In addition, as part of the amino acids methionine and cysteine, sulfur helps stabilize the three-dimensional shapes of proteins. The liver requires sulfur to assist in the

Kati Molin/Shutterstock

Raspberries are one of the many foods that contain manganese.

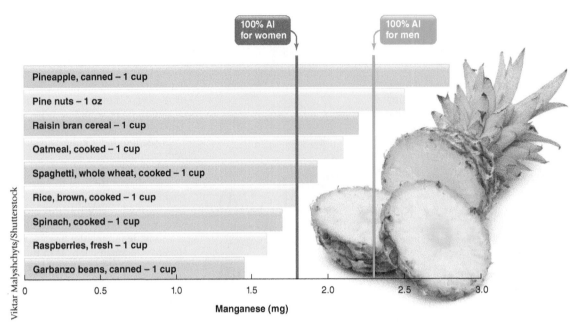

Viktar Malyshchyts/Shutterstock

Figure 11 Common food sources of manganese. The AI for manganese is 2.3 mg/day for men and 1.8 mg/day for women.
Data from U.S. Department of Agriculture, Agricultural Research Service, 2009, USDA Nutrient Database for Standard Reference, Release 22. Nutrient Data Laboratory Home Page, www.ars.usda.gov/ba/bhnrc/ndl.

detoxification of alcohol and various drugs, and sulfur helps the body maintain acid–base balance.

We are able to synthesize ample sulfur from the protein-containing foods we eat; as a result, we do not need to consume sulfur in the diet, and there is no DRI for sulfur. There are no known toxicity or deficiency symptoms associated with sulfur.

RECAP Choline is a vitamin-like substance that assists in homocysteine metabolism and the production of acetylcholine. Iodine is necessary for the synthesis of thyroid hormones, which regulate metabolic rate and body temperature. Chromium promotes glucose transport, metabolism of RNA and DNA, and immune function and growth. Manganese is involved in energy metabolism, urea formation, synthesis of bone and cartilage, and protection against free radicals. Sulfur is part of thiamin and biotin and the amino acids methionine and cysteine.

What Is the Role of Blood in Maintaining Health?

erythrocytes The red blood cells, which are the cells that transport oxygen in our blood.

leukocytes The white blood cells, which protect us from infection and illness.

platelets Cell fragments that assist in the formation of blood clots and help stop bleeding.

plasma The fluid portion of the blood; needed to maintain adequate blood volume, so that the blood can flow easily throughout our body.

Blood is critical to maintaining life, as it transports virtually everything in our body. No matter how efficiently we metabolize carbohydrates, fats, and proteins, without healthy blood to transport those nutrients to our cells, we could not survive. In addition to transporting nutrients and oxygen, blood removes the waste products generated from metabolism, so that they can be properly excreted. Our health and our ability to perform daily activities are compromised if the quantity and quality of our blood are diminished.

Blood is actually a tissue, the only fluid tissue in our body. It has four components (Figure 12). **Erythrocytes,** or red blood cells, are the cells that transport oxygen. **Leukocytes,** or white blood cells, are the key to our immune function and protect us from infection and illness. **Platelets** are cell fragments that assist in the formation of blood clots and help stop bleeding. **Plasma** is the fluid portion of the

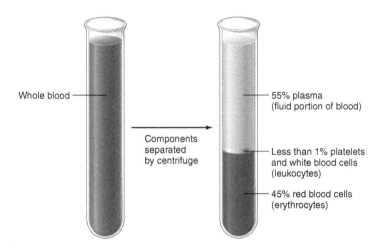

Whole blood

Components
separated
by centrifuge

55% plasma
(fluid portion of blood)

Less than 1% platelets
and white blood cells
(leukocytes)

45% red blood cells
(erythrocytes)

◆ **Figure 12** Blood has four components, which are visible when the blood is drawn into a test tube and spun in a centrifuge. The bottom layer is the erythrocytes, or red blood cells. The milky layer above the erythrocytes contains the leukocytes and platelets. The yellow fluid on top is the plasma.

blood, and it is needed to maintain adequate blood volume, so that the blood can flow easily throughout our blood vessels.

Certain micronutrients play important roles in the maintenance of blood health through their actions as cofactors, coenzymes, and regulators of oxygen transport. These nutrients are discussed in detail in the following section.

A Profile of Nutrients That Maintain Healthy Blood

The nutrients recognized as playing a critical role in maintaining blood health are vitamin K, iron, zinc, and copper. Folate and vitamin B_{12}, already discussed, are also essential for blood health. A list of recommended intakes of these nutrients is provided in **Table 2**.

Vitamin K

Vitamin K is a fat-soluble vitamin important for both bone and blood health. In addition, vitamin K acts as a coenzyme that assists in the synthesis of a number of proteins that are involved in the coagulation of blood, including *prothrombin* and the *procoagulants, factors VII, IX, and X*. Without adequate vitamin K, blood does not clot properly: clotting time can be delayed, or clotting may even fail to occur. The failure of blood to clot can lead to increased bleeding from even minor wounds, as well as internal hemorrhaging.

Our needs for vitamin K are relatively small, but intakes of this nutrient in the United States are highly variable because vitamin K is found in few foods.[38] Green, leafy vegetables are good sources, as are soybean and canola oils. The recommended intakes for vitamin K are listed in Table 2. There is no upper limit (UL) established for vitamin K at this time.[39] Healthful intestinal bacteria produce vitamin K in our large intestine, providing us with an important non-dietary source of vitamin K.

Nutrient	Recommended Intake (RDA or AI and UL)
TABLE 2 Overview of Nutrients Essential to Blood Health	
Iron	RDA: Women 19 to 50 years = 18 mg/day Men 19 to 50 years = 8 mg/day UL = 45 mg/day
Zinc	RDA: Women 19 to 50 years = 8 mg/day Men 19 to 50 years = 11 mg/day UL = 40 mg/day
Copper	RDA for all people 19 to 50 years = 90 µg/day UL = 10,000 µg/day
Vitamin K	AI: Women 19 to 50 years = 90 µg/day Men 19 to 50 years = 120 µg/day UL = none determined
Folate (folic acid)	RDA for all people 19 to 50 years = 400 µg/day UL = 1,000 µg/day
Vitamin B_{12} (cyanocobalamin)	RDA for all people 19 to 50 years = 2.4 µg/day UL = not determined (ND)

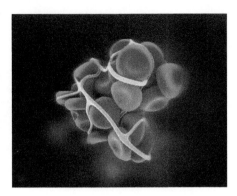

⬥ Without enough vitamin K, our blood will not clot properly.
Sebastian Kaulitzki/Shutterstock

Dorling Kindersley

⬥ Green, leafy vegetables are a good source of vitamin K.

hemoglobin The oxygen-carrying protein found in our red blood cells; almost two-thirds of all the iron in our body is found in hemoglobin.

heme The iron-containing molecule found in hemoglobin.

myoglobin An iron-containing protein similar to hemoglobin except that it is found in muscle cells.

There are no known side effects associated with consuming large amounts of vitamin K from supplements or from food.[39] In the past, a synthetic form of vitamin K was used for therapeutic purposes and was shown to cause liver damage; this form is no longer used.

Vitamin K deficiency inhibits our ability to form blood clots, resulting in excessive bleeding and even severe hemorrhaging in some cases. Although vitamin K deficiency is rare in humans, people with diseases that cause malabsorption of fat, such as celiac disease, Crohn's disease, and cystic fibrosis, can suffer secondarily from a deficiency of vitamin K. Newborns are typically given an injection of vitamin K at birth, as they lack the intestinal bacteria necessary to produce this nutrient.

The impact of vitamin K deficiency on bone health is controversial. Although a recent study found that low intakes of vitamin K were associated with a higher risk for bone fractures in women, there is not enough scientific evidence to strongly illustrate that vitamin K deficiency causes osteoporosis.[39,40]

RECAP Blood is a fluid tissue composed of erythrocytes, leukocytes, plasma, and platelets. It transports nutrients and oxygen to our cells to support life and removes the waste products generated from metabolism. Vitamin K is a fat-soluble vitamin and coenzyme that is important for blood clotting and bone metabolism. Bacteria manufacture vitamin K in our large intestine.

Iron

With few exceptions, iron is important for every known living organism. It is essential to cells but can be toxic in high doses. Thus, the body needs to regulate iron levels carefully to be sure adequate iron is supplied to cover the essential functioning of biological processes but prevent excess accumulation. Thus, iron is a trace mineral that is needed in very small amounts in our diets. Despite our relatively small need for iron, iron deficiency is the most common nutrient deficiency in the world.

Functions of Iron

Iron is a component of four primary iron-containing protein groups that carry out a number of important functions within the body. Two of these groups are oxygen-carrying proteins: hemoglobin and myoglobin. Almost two-thirds of all the iron in our body is found in **hemoglobin,** the oxygen-carrying protein in our red blood cells. As shown in **Figure 13**, the hemoglobin molecule consists of four polypeptide chains studded with four iron-containing **heme** groups. You know that we cannot survive for more than a few minutes without oxygen. Thus, hemoglobin's ability to transport oxygen throughout the body is absolutely critical to life. To carry oxygen, hemoglobin depends on the iron in its heme groups. Iron is able to bind with and release atoms such as oxygen, nitrogen, and sulfur very easily. It does this by transferring electrons to and from the other atoms as it moves between various oxidation states. In the bloodstream, iron acts as a shuttle, picking up oxygen from the environment, binding it during its transport in the bloodstream, and then dropping it off again in our tissues. Iron is also a component of **myoglobin,** a protein similar to hemoglobin but found in muscle cells. As a part of myoglobin, iron assists in the transport of oxygen into muscle cells.

Iron is also found in a number of enzymes involved in energy production. Iron-requiring enzymes called *cytochromes* are electron carriers within the metabolic pathways that result in the production of energy from carbohydrates, fats, and proteins. In the mitochondria alone, there are more than twelve of these iron-requiring enzymes that help produce energy.[41] Iron is also critical to the function of certain enzymes important to some immune cells and their communication pathways; thus, iron is required for humans to mount an effective immune response to pathogens.[41] Iron is a part of the antioxidant enzyme system that assists in fighting free radicals. Interestingly, excess iron can also act as a prooxidant and promote the production of free radicals.

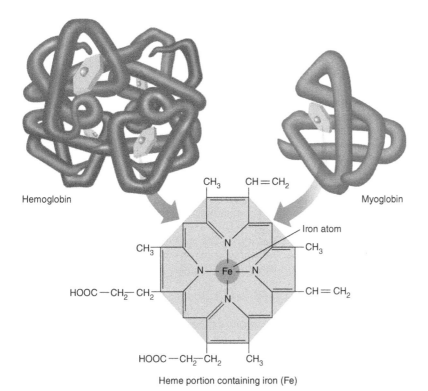

Hemoglobin

Myoglobin

Iron atom

Heme portion containing iron (Fe)

↟ Figure 13 Iron is contained in the heme portion of hemoglobin and myoglobin.

Research over the last 30 years has also documented the importance of iron in neuromuscular functions. Like vitamin B_{12}, iron is required for maintenance of the myelin sheath covering nerve fibers; as noted earlier, without adequate myelin, conduction of nerve impulses is slowed. Iron is also needed for the production of neurotransmitters, including serotonin, norepinephrine, and dopamine. Moreover, iron is important for muscle function. Individuals who have poor iron status complain of lethargy, apathy, and listlessness, which may be independent of iron's role in oxygen delivery. Some of these complaints might be due to the impact of iron deficiency on the brain or on fuel metabolism.

How Is Iron Absorbed?

Our body contains relatively little iron; men have less than 4 g of iron in their body, while women have just over 2 g. Our body is capable of storing excess iron in two storage forms, **ferritin** and **hemosiderin.** The most common areas of iron storage in our body are the liver, bone marrow, intestinal mucosa, and spleen. Because iron is so important for life, our body recycles the iron lost when aging cells are broken down, especially cells high in iron, such as red blood cells. The liver and spleen are responsible for breaking down old red blood cells and recycling the components, including the iron. This iron-recycling program reduces the body's reliance on dietary iron. Each day, about 85% of the iron released from hemoglobin breakdown is reused by the body.

Our ability to absorb iron from the diet is influenced by a number of factors, including iron status, stomach acid content, the amount and type of iron in the foods we eat, and the presence of dietary factors that can either enhance or inhibit the absorption of iron. Absorption of iron is highest when our iron stores are low. Thus, people who have poor iron status, such as those with iron deficiency, pregnant women, and people who have recently experienced blood loss (including menstruation), have the highest iron absorption rates. In addition, adequate amounts of

↟ Cooking foods in cast-iron pans significantly increases their iron content.

ferritin A storage form of iron in our body, found primarily in the intestinal mucosa, spleen, bone marrow, and liver.

hemosiderin A storage form of iron in our body, found primarily in the intestinal mucosa, spleen, bone marrow, and liver.

stomach acid are necessary for iron absorption. People with low levels of stomach acid, including many older adults, have a decreased ability to absorb iron.

The total amount of iron in your diet influences your absorption rate. People who consume low levels of dietary iron absorb more iron from their foods than those with higher dietary iron intakes. Our body can also detect when iron stores are high; when this occurs, less iron is absorbed from food.

The type of iron in the foods you eat is a major factor influencing your iron absorption. Two types of iron are found in foods: heme iron and non-heme iron. **Heme iron** is a part of hemoglobin and myoglobin and is found only in animal-based foods, such as meat, fish, and poultry. **Non-heme iron** is the form of iron that is not a part of hemoglobin or myoglobin. It is found in both plant-based and animal-based foods. Heme iron is much more absorbable than non-heme iron. Since the iron in animal-based foods is about 40% heme iron and 60% non-heme iron, animal-based foods are good sources of absorbable iron. Meat, fish, and poultry also contain a special **meat factor,** which enhances the absorption of non-heme iron. In contrast, all of the iron found in plant-based foods is non-heme iron, and no absorption-enhancing factor is present. However, any vitamin C (ascorbic acid) in the food itself or in an accompanying food or beverage will enhance the absorption of non-heme iron.

Dietary factors that impair iron absorption include phytates, polyphenols, vegetable proteins, and calcium. Phytates are found in legumes, rice, and whole grains. Polyphenols include tannins found in tea and coffee, and they are present in oregano and red wine. Soybean protein and calcium inhibit iron absorption. Because of the variability of iron absorption as a result of these dietary factors, it is estimated that the bioavailability of iron from a vegan diet is approximately 10%, while it averages 18% for a mixed Western diet.[39]

How Much Iron Should We Consume?

The variability of iron availability from food sources was taken into consideration when estimating dietary recommendations for iron, which are listed in Table 2. Notice that the higher iron requirement for younger women is due to the excess iron and blood lost during menstruation.

A number of special circumstances can significantly affect iron requirements. These are identified in **Table 3.**

Finding Iron-Rich Foods

Good food sources of heme iron are meats, poultry, and fish **(Figure 14)**. Clams, oysters, and beef liver are particularly good sources. Many breakfast cereals and breads are enriched with iron; although this iron is the non-heme type and less absorbable, it is still significant because these foods are a major part of the U.S. diet. Some vegetables and legumes are also good sources of iron, and the absorption of their non-heme iron can be enhanced by eating them with even a small amount of meat, fish, or poultry, or with vitamin C–rich foods, such as citrus foods, red and green peppers, and broccoli.

Another way to increase your iron intake is to make smart menu choices throughout the day. The Eating Right All Day feature shows menu choices high in iron. Some of these choices provide heme iron, whereas others are combination foods. For instance, the orange juice helps improve the absorption of the non-heme iron in the enriched bread. And see the Quick Tips for other iron food sources.

What Happens If We Consume Too Much Iron?

Accidental iron overdose is the most common cause of poisoning deaths in children younger than 6 years of age in the United States.[42] It is important for parents to take the same precautions with dietary supplements as they would with other drugs, keeping them in a locked cabinet or well out of reach of children. Symptoms of iron toxicity include nausea, vomiting, diarrhea, dizziness, confusion, and rapid heartbeat. If iron toxicity is not treated quickly, significant damage to the heart, central nervous system, liver, and kidneys can result in death.

Adults who take iron supplements even at prescribed doses commonly experience constipation. Taking vitamin C with the iron supplement not only enhances absorp-

heme iron Iron that is a part of hemoglobin and myoglobin; found only in animal-based foods, such as meat, fish, and poultry.

non-heme iron The form of iron that is not a part of hemoglobin or myoglobin; found in animal- and plant-based foods.

meat factor A special factor found in meat, fish, and poultry that enhances the absorption of non-heme iron.

TABLE 3   Special Circumstances Affecting Iron Status

Circumstances That Improve Iron Status	Circumstances That Diminish Iron Status
• Use of oral contraceptives: use of oral contraceptives reduces menstrual blood loss in women. • Breastfeeding: breastfeeding delays resumption of menstruation in new mothers, so it reduces menstrual blood loss. It is therefore an important health measure, especially in developing nations. • Consumption of iron-containing foods and supplements.	• Use of hormone replacement therapy: use of hormone replacement therapy in postmenopausal women can cause uterine bleeding, increasing iron requirements. • Eating a vegetarian diet: vegetarian diets, particularly vegan diets, contain no sources of heme iron or meat factor. Due to the low absorbability of non-heme iron, vegetarians have iron requirements that are 1.8 times higher than those of nonvegetarians. • Intestinal parasitic infection: approximately 1 billion people suffer from intestinal parasitic infection. Many of these parasites cause intestinal bleeding and occur in countries in which iron intakes are inadequate. Iron-deficiency anemia is common in people with intestinal parasitic infection. • Blood donation: blood donors have lower iron stores than nondonors; people who donate frequently, particularly premenopausal women, may require iron supplementation to counter the iron losses that occur with blood donation. • Intense endurance exercise training: people engaging in intense endurance exercise appear to be at risk for poor iron status due to many factors, including suboptimal iron intake and increased iron loss in sweat and increased fecal losses.

Data from "Dietary Reference Intakes for Vitamin A, Vitamin K, Arsenic, Boron, Chromium, Copper, Iodine, Manganese, Molybdenum, Nickel, Silicon, Vanadium, and Zinc," © 2002 by the National Academy of Sciences. Reprinted by permission.

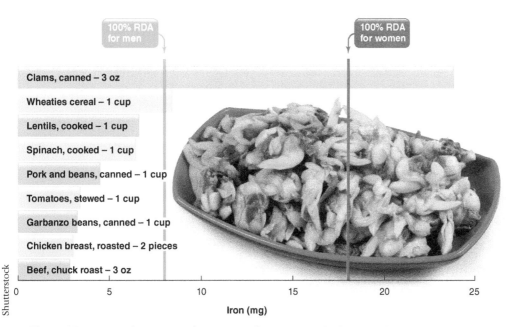

◄ **Figure 14**   Common food sources of iron. The RDA for iron is 8 mg/day for men and 18 mg/day for women aged 19 to 50 years.
Data from U.S. Department of Agriculture, Agricultural Research Service, 2009, USDA Nutrient Database for Standard Reference, Release 22. Nutrient Data Laboratory Home Page, www.ars.usda.gov/ba/bhnrc/ndl.

QUICK TIPS

Increasing Your Iron Intake

✓ Shop for iron-fortified breads and breakfast cereals. Check the Nutrition Facts Panel!

✓ Consume a food or beverage that is high in vitamin C along with plant or animal sources of iron. For instance, drink a glass of orange juice with your morning toast to increase the absorption of the non-heme iron in the bread. Or add chopped tomatoes to beans or lentils. Or sprinkle lemon juice on fish.

✓ Add small amounts of meat, poultry, or fish to baked beans, vegetable soups, stir-fried vegetables, or salads to enhance the absorption of the non-heme iron in the plant-based foods.

✓ Cook foods in cast-iron pans to significantly increase the iron content of foods: the iron in the pan will be absorbed into the food during the cooking process.

✓ Avoid drinking red wine, coffee, or tea when eating iron-rich foods, as the polyphenols in these beverages will reduce iron absorption.

✓ Avoid drinking cow's milk or soy milk with iron-rich foods, as both calcium and soybean protein inhibit iron absorption.

✓ Avoid taking calcium supplements or zinc supplements with iron-rich foods, as these minerals decrease iron absorption.

---

tion but also can help reduce constipation. Other gastrointestinal symptoms include nausea, vomiting, and diarrhea. Some individuals suffer from a hereditary disorder called hemochromatosis. This disorder affects between 1 in 200 and 1 in 400 individuals of northern European descent.[43] Hemochromatosis is characterized by excessive absorption of dietary iron and altered iron storage. The accumulation of iron in these individuals over many years causes cirrhosis of the liver, liver cancer, heart attack and heart failure, diabetes, and arthritis. Men are more at risk for this disease than women due to the higher losses of iron in women through menstruation. Treatment includes reducing dietary intake of iron, avoiding high intakes of vitamin C, and withdrawing blood occasionally.

What Happens If We Don't Consume Enough Iron?

Iron deficiency is the most common nutrient deficiency in the world. People at particularly high risk for iron deficiency include infants and young children, adolescent girls, premenopausal women, and pregnant women.

Iron deficiency progresses through three stages (Figure 15). The first stage of iron deficiency causes a decrease in iron *stores*, resulting in reduced levels of ferritin.

Stage I, iron depletion
- Decreased iron stores
- Reduced ferritin level
- No physical symptoms

Stage II, iron-deficiency erythropoiesis
- Decreased iron transport
- Reduced transferrin
- Reduced production of heme
- Physical symptoms include reduced work capacity

Stage III, iron-deficiency anemia
- Decreased production of normal red blood cells
- Reduced production of heme
- Inadequate hemoglobin to transport oxygen
- Symptoms include pale skin, fatigue, reduced work performance, impaired immune and cognitive functions

transferrin The transport protein for iron.

iron-deficiency anemia A form of anemia that results from severe iron deficiency.

◆ **Figure 15** Iron deficiency passes through three stages. The first stage is identified by decreased iron stores, or reduced ferritin levels. The second stage is identified by decreased iron transport, or a reduction in transferrin. The final stage of iron deficiency is iron-deficiency anemia, which is identified by decreased production of normal, healthy red blood cells and inadequate hemoglobin levels.

During this first stage, there are generally no physical symptoms because hemoglobin levels are not yet affected. The second stage of iron deficiency causes a decrease in the *transport* of iron. This manifests as a reduction in the transport protein for iron, called **transferrin.** The production of heme also starts to decline during this stage, leading to symptoms of reduced work capacity. During the third and final stage of iron deficiency, **iron-deficiency anemia** results.

In iron-deficiency anemia, the production of normal, healthy red blood cells decreases. Red blood cells that are produced are smaller than normal and do not contain enough hemoglobin to transport adequate oxygen or to allow the proper transfer of electrons to produce energy. This type of anemia is often referred to as *microcytic anemia* (*micro,* meaning "small," and *cyte,* meaning "cell"). As normal cellular death occurs over time, more and more healthy red blood cells are replaced by these deficient cells, and the classic symptoms of oxygen and energy deprivation develop. These symptoms include impaired work performance, general fatigue, pale skin, depressed immune

Eating Right All Day

Breakfast
Whole-grain iron-fortified toast with orange juice instead of white toast with coffee!

Joshua Morris/iStockphoto

Lunch
Pasta with clams and tomatoes instead of mac & cheese!

Shutterstock

Dinner
Beef stew with vegetables instead of a burger with fries!

Robyn Mackenzie/iStockphoto

Snack
Low-cal nutrition bar instead of a chocolate bar!

Andy Dean Photography/Shutterstock

NUTRI-CASE LIZ

"It was really hard spending last summer with my parents, because we kept arguing over food! Even though I'd told them that I'm a vegetarian, they kept serving meals with meat! Then they'd get mad when I'd fix myself a hummus sandwich! When it was my turn to cook, I made lentils with brown rice, whole-wheat pasta primavera, vegetarian curries, and lots of other yummy meals, but my dad kept insisting, "You have to eat meat or you won't get enough iron!" I told him that plant foods have lots of iron, but he wouldn't listen. Was I ever glad to get back onto campus this fall!"

Recall that Liz is a ballet dancer who trains daily. If she eats a vegetarian diet including meals such as the ones she describes here, will she be at risk for iron deficiency? Why or why not? Are there any other micronutrients that might be low in Liz's diet because she avoids meat? If so, what are they? Overall, will Liz get enough energy to support her high level of physical activity on a vegetarian diet? How would she know if she were low energy?

Rubberball/Getty Images

function, impaired cognitive and nerve function, and impaired memory. Pregnant women with severe anemia are at higher risk for low-birth-weight infants, premature delivery, and increased infant mortality.

RECAP Iron is a trace mineral that, as part of the hemoglobin protein, plays a major role in the transportation of oxygen in our blood. Iron is also a coenzyme in many metabolic pathways involved in energy production. Meat, fish, and poultry are good sources of heme iron, which is more absorbable than non-heme iron. Toxicity symptoms for iron range from nausea and vomiting to organ damage and potentially death. If left untreated, iron deficiency eventually leads to iron-deficiency anemia.

Zinc

Zinc is a trace mineral that acts as a cofactor for approximately a hundred different enzymes. It thereby plays an important role in many physiologic processes in nearly every body system.

Functions of Zinc

As a cofactor, zinc assists in the production of hemoglobin, indirectly supporting the adequate transport of oxygen to our cells. Zinc is also part of the superoxide dismutase antioxidant enzyme system and thus helps fight the oxidative damage caused by free radicals. It assists enzymes in generating energy from carbohydrates, fats, and protein and in activating vitamin A in the retina of the eye.

Zinc also plays a role in facilitating the folding of proteins into biologically active molecules used in gene regulation. Thus, it is critical for cell replication and normal growth. In fact, zinc deficiency was discovered in the early 1960s, when researchers were trying to determine the cause of severe growth retardation, anemia, and poorly developed testicles in a group of Middle Eastern men. These symptoms of zinc deficiency illustrate its critical role in normal growth and sexual maturation.

Zinc is vital for the proper development and functioning of the immune system. In fact, zinc has received so much attention for its contribution to immune system health that zinc lozenges have been formulated to fight the common cold. The Nutrition Debate at the end of this chapter explores the question of whether or not these lozenges are effective.

How Much Zinc Should We Consume?

As with iron, our need for zinc is relatively small, but our intakes are variable and absorption is influenced by a number of factors. Overall, zinc absorption is similar to that of iron, ranging from 10% to 35% of dietary zinc. People with poor zinc status absorb more zinc than individuals with optimal zinc status, and zinc absorption increases during times of growth, sexual development, and pregnancy.

Several dietary factors influence zinc absorption. High non-heme iron intakes can inhibit zinc absorption, which is a primary concern with iron supplements (which are non-heme), particularly during pregnancy and lactation. High intakes of heme iron appear to have no effect on zinc absorption. The phytates and fiber found in whole grains and beans strongly inhibit zinc absorption. In contrast, dietary protein, especially animal-based protein, enhances zinc absorption. It's not surprising, then, that the primary cause of the zinc deficiency in the Middle Eastern men just mentioned was their low consumption of meat and high consumption of beans and unleavened breads (also called *flat breads*). In leavening bread, the baker adds yeast to the dough. This not only makes the bread rise but also helps reduce the phytate content of the bread.

The recommended intakes for zinc are listed in Table 2. Good food sources of zinc include red meats, some seafood, whole grains, and enriched grains and cereals. The dark meat of poultry has a higher content of zinc than white meat. As zinc is significantly more absorbable from animal-based foods, zinc deficiency is a concern for

Isabelle Rozenbaum & Frederic Cirou/Getty Images

Zinc can be found in pork and beans.

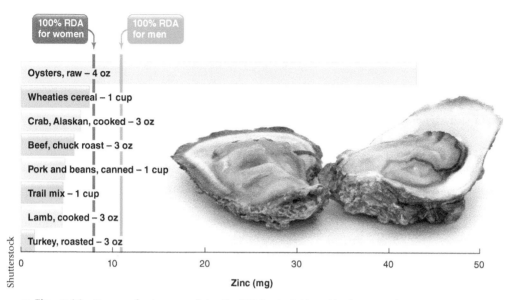

Figure 16 Common food sources of zinc. The RDA for zinc is 11 mg/day for men and 8 mg/day for women.

Data from U.S. Department of Agriculture, Agricultural Research Service, 2009, USDA Nutrient Database for Standard Reference, Release 22. Nutrient Data Laboratory Home Page, www.ars.usda.gov/ba/bhnrc/ndl.

people eating a vegan diet. **Figure 16** shows various foods that are relatively high in zinc.

What Happens If We Consume Too Much Zinc?

Eating high amounts of dietary zinc does not appear to lead to toxicity. Zinc toxicity can occur from consuming zinc in supplement form and in fortified foods. Toxicity symptoms include intestinal pain and cramps, nausea, vomiting, loss of appetite, diarrhea, and headaches. Excessive zinc supplementation has also been shown to depress immune function and decrease high-density lipoprotein concentrations. High intakes of zinc can also reduce copper status, as zinc absorption interferes with the absorption of copper.

What Happens If We Don't Consume Enough Zinc?

Zinc deficiency is uncommon in the United States but occurs more often in countries in which people consume predominantly grain-based foods. Symptoms of zinc deficiency include growth retardation, diarrhea, delayed sexual maturation and impotence, eye and skin lesions, hair loss, and impaired appetite. As zinc is critical to a healthy immune system, zinc deficiency also results in increased incidence of infections and illnesses.

Copper

Copper is a trace mineral that functions as a cofactor in many physiologic reactions. It functions as a cofactor in the metabolic pathways that produce energy, in the production of the connective tissues collagen and elastin, and as part of the superoxide dismutase enzyme system that fights the damage caused by free radicals. Copper is a component of *ceruloplasmin*, a protein that is critical for the proper transport of iron. If ceruloplasmin levels are inadequate, iron accumulation results, causing symptoms similar to those described with the genetic disorder hemochromatosis. Copper is also necessary for the regulation of certain neurotransmitters important to brain function.

Figure 17 Common food sources of copper. The RDA for copper is 900 μg/day for men and women.
Data from U.S. Department of Agriculture, Agricultural Research Service, 2009, USDA Nutrient Database for Standard Reference, Release 22. Nutrient Data Laboratory Home Page, www.ars.usda.gov/ba/bhnrc/ndl.

Lobster is a food that contains copper.

As you can see in Table 2, our need for copper is small. Copper is widely distributed in foods, and people who eat a varied diet can easily meet their requirements. Good food sources of copper include organ meats, seafood, nuts, and seeds. Whole-grain foods are also relatively good sources. **Figure 17** identifies some foods relatively high in copper.

As we saw with iron and zinc, people with low dietary copper intakes absorb more copper than people with high dietary intakes. Also recall that high zinc intakes can reduce copper absorption and, subsequently, copper status. In fact, zinc supplementation is used to treat a rare disorder called Wilson's disease, in which copper toxicity occurs. High iron intakes can also interfere with copper absorption in infants.

The long-term effects of copper toxicity are not well studied in humans. Toxicity symptoms include abdominal pain and cramps, nausea, diarrhea, and vomiting. Liver damage occurs in the extreme cases of copper toxicity that occur with Wilson's disease and other health conditions associated with excessive copper levels.

Copper deficiency is rare but can occur in premature infants fed milk-based formulas and in adults fed prolonged formulated diets that are deficient in copper. Deficiency symptoms include anemia, reduced levels of white blood cells, and osteoporosis in infants and growing children.

RECAP Zinc is a trace mineral that is a part of almost a hundred enzymes that impact virtually every body system. It plays a critical role in hemoglobin synthesis, physical growth and sexual maturation, and immune function and assists in fighting oxidative damage. Copper is a trace mineral that functions as a cofactor in the metabolic pathways that produce energy, in the production of connective tissues, and as part of an antioxidant enzyme system. It is also a component of ceruloplasmin, a protein that is critical for the transport of iron.

Nutrition DEBATE

Do Zinc Lozenges Help Fight the Common Cold?

Approximately 1 billion colds occur in the United States each year. [44] Children suffer from six to ten colds each year, and adults average two to four. Although colds are typically benign, they result in significant absenteeism from work and cause discomfort and stress. It is estimated that more than two hundred different viruses can cause a cold. Because of this variety, developing vaccines or other preventive measures for colds is extremely challenging. Thus, finding a cure for the common cold has been at the forefront of modern medicine for many years.

The role of zinc in the health of our immune system is well known, but zinc has also been shown to inhibit the replication of some of the viruses that cause the common cold. These findings have led to speculation that taking zinc supplements may reduce the length and severity of colds. [45,46] Zinc lozenges were formulated as a means of providing potential relief from cold symptoms. These lozenges are readily found in a variety of formulations and dosages in most drugstores.

Does taking zinc in lozenge form actually reduce the length and severity of a cold? During the past 20 years, numerous research studies have been conducted to try to answer this question. Unfortunately, the results of these studies are inconclusive: about half have found that zinc lozenges do reduce the length and severity of a cold, whereas about half have found that zinc lozenges have no effect on cold symptoms or duration. [47] Some reasons that researchers have proposed to explain these different findings include the following:

- Researchers are unable to truly "blind" participants to the treatment. Because zinc lozenges have a unique taste, it may be difficult to keep the research participants uninformed about whether they are getting zinc lozenges or a placebo. Knowing what they are taking could lead participants to report biased results.
- Self-reported symptoms are subject to inaccuracy. Many studies had the research participants self-report changes in symptoms. Such self-reports may be inaccurate and influenced by emotional factors.
- A wide variety of viruses can cause a cold. We noted that more than two hundred different viruses can cause a cold, and it is highly unlikely that zinc can combat all of these. It is possible that people who do not respond favorably to zinc lozenges are suffering from a cold virus that cannot be treated with zinc.
- Zinc dosages and formulations differ. The dosages of zinc consumed, the timing of consumption, and the formulation of the lozenge used differed across studies. For example, it is estimated that, for zinc to be effective, at least 80 mg of zinc should be consumed each day and that people should begin using zinc lozenges within 48 hours of the onset of cold symptoms, yet the studies followed a variety of dosing and timing protocols. Also, different sweeteners and flavorings found in different zinc-lozenge formulations may bind the zinc and inhibit its ability to be absorbed into the body, limiting its effectiveness.
- Supplements may provide excessive zinc and actually impair immune function! The level of zinc noted earlier as the effective dose—80 mg/day—is nearly ten times the RDA and can decrease the absorption of copper and iron if continued for long periods of time. In addition, one experimental study showed that

Kristin Piljay

Zinc lozenges come in different formulations and dosages.

300 mg/day of supplemental zinc *reduced* immune cell response and *decreased* destruction of bacteria. [48] This amount is about six tablets of a zinc gluconate pill that has 50 mg of elemental zinc.

- Measuring the compliance of test participants can be difficult. Typically, participants need to take one zinc lozenge every 2 to 3 hours while they are awake for the duration of the study, which can last 6 to 10 days. Unless the participants are monitored by research staff, researchers have to rely on the participants to self-report their compliance to the study protocol. Of course, different compliance rates can alter the outcomes of different studies.

In short, there is no conclusive evidence supporting or refuting the effectiveness of zinc lozenges in treating the common cold.

One word of caution: if you decide to use zinc lozenges, more is not better. Excessive or prolonged zinc supplementation can reduce immune function and cause other mineral imbalances. Check the label of the product you are using, and do not exceed its recommended dosage or duration of use.

Chapter Review

1. False. B-vitamins do not directly provide energy for our body. However, they play critical roles in ensuring that our body is able to generate energy from carbohydrates, fats, and proteins.

2. True. People who consume a vegan diet need to pay particularly close attention to consuming enough vitamin B_{12},

iron, and zinc. In some cases, these individuals may need to take supplements to consume adequate amounts of these nutrients.

3. True. This deficiency is particularly common in infants, children, and women of childbearing age.

Find the Quack

Like many college students, Dionna maintains a full course load and works part-time. She also participates in aerobics and yoga classes four afternoons a week, is a member of her college math and chess clubs, and spends Saturday mornings volunteering at a local food bank. With so much going on in her life, she's had to stay up way past midnight almost every night for the past few weeks to finish homework assignments and study for exams. Coming out of aerobics class yesterday, she collapsed onto the bench in the locker room, feeling utterly exhausted. Her friend Addie asked what was wrong and, when Dionna explained, gave her a hug and opened her gym bag. "Here," she said, handing Dionna a bottle of supplements. The label said *Fatigue-Fighting Formula for Women*, and the ingredients list indicated that the supplement provided 100% of the Daily Value for all eight B-vitamins, as well as iron, selenium, chromium, and manganese. "Start taking one of these every day, like I do, and you'll have all the energy you need!"

Dionna took a swig from her water bottle and swallowed a tablet. Then she read the back of the supplement label. It said:

- "If you experience fatigue, muscle weakness, difficulty concentrating, or depression, you may have a deficiency of the vitamins and minerals important in maintaining an adequate level of energy."
- "One tablet a day of *Fatigue-Fighting Formula for Women* may help restore your natural vitality."

- Our average customer rating for this product is five stars! A typical satisfied customer: "I used to feel so exhausted that I could barely drag myself through the days. *Fatigue-Fighting Formula for Women* has given me energy to spare!" —Tasha from Santa Monica.

Dionna asked her friend how much a bottle of the supplement—which included 60 tablets, or a 2-month supply—cost. Addie said that she ordered them online for $23.99 and would be placing another order soon. "Want me to get a bottle for you?"

1. Read carefully the first two bulleted statements from the back of the supplement label. Do these assertions strike you as reasonable, exaggerated, misleading, or entirely false? Explain your answer.

2. What, if any, health concerns might the level of vitamins and minerals in this supplement raise?

3. Tasha from Santa Monica states that the supplement "has given me energy to spare." Comment on the implication of her statement that the micronutrients it provides give us energy.

4. Should Dionna have Addie order a bottle of the supplements for her? Why or why not?

Answers can be found on the companion website, at www.pearsonhighered.com/thompsonmanore.

 **NutriTools** Check out the companion website at www.pearsonhighered.com/thompsonmanore, or use MyNutritionLab.com, to access interactive animations including:

- Nutrient Functionality
- Metabolism: General Terms

Review Questions

1. The B-vitamins include
   a. niacin, folate, and iodine.
   b. cobalamin, iodine, and chromium.
   c. manganese, riboflavin, and pyridoxine.
   d. thiamin, pantothenic acid, and biotin.

2. The micronutrient most closely associated with blood clotting is
   a. iron.
   b. vitamin K.
   c. zinc.
   d. vitamin B_{12}.

3. Which of the following statements about iron is true?
   a. Iron is stored primarily in the liver, the blood vessel walls, and the heart muscle.
   b. Iron is a component of hemoglobin, myoglobin, and certain enzymes.
   c. Iron is a component of red blood cells, platelets, and plasma.
   d. Excess iron is stored primarily in the form of ferritin, cytochromes, and intrinsic factor.

4. Homocysteine is
   a. a by-product of glycolysis.
   b. a trace mineral.
   c. an amino acid.
   d. a B-vitamin.

5. Which of the following statements about choline is true?
   a. Choline is found exclusively in foods of animal origin.
   b. Choline is a B-vitamin that assists in homocysteine metabolism.
   c. Choline is a neurotransmitter that is involved in muscle movement and memory storage.
   d. Choline is necessary for the synthesis of phospholipids and other components of cell membranes.

6. True or false? Blood has four components: erythrocytes, leukocytes, platelets, and plasma.

7. True or false? There is no DRI for sulfur.

8. True or false? Iron is found only in foods of animal origin.

9. True or false? The best way for a pregnant woman to protect her fetus against neural tube defects is to begin taking a folate supplement as soon as she learns she is pregnant.

10. True or false? Wilson's disease occurs when copper deficiency allows accumulation of iron in the body.

Answers to Review Questions can be found at the back of this text, and additional essay questions and answers are located on the companion website at www.pearsonhighered.com/thompsonmanore.

Web Resources

www.ars.usda.gov
Nutrient Data Laboratory Home Page

Click on Search to find reports listing food sources for selected nutrients.

www.anemia.com
Anemia Lifeline

Visit this site to learn about anemia and its various treatments.

www.unicef.org/nutrition
UNICEF-Nutrition

This site provides information about micronutrient deficiencies in developing countries and the efforts to combat them.

www.thearc.org
The Arc

Search this site for "neural tube defects" and find a wealth of information on the development and prevention of these conditions.

References

1. Bernstein, L. 2000. Dementia without a cause: Lack of vitamin B12 can cause dementia. *Discover Magazine,* February 2000.

2. Bates, C. J. 2006. Thiamin. In: Bowman, B. A., and R. M. Russel, eds. Present Knowledge in Nutrition, 9th edn., pp. 242–249. Washington, DC: ILSI Press.

3. McCollum, E. V. 1957. A History of Nutrition. Boston: Houghton Mifflin Co.

4. Day, E., P. Bentham, R. Callaghan, T. Kuruvilla, and S. George. 2004. Thiamine for Wernicke-Korsakoff Syndrome in people at risk from alcohol abuse (review). *Cochrane Database Syst. Rev.* 1:CD0040033.

5. McCormick, D. B. 2005. Riboflavin. In: Shils, M. E., M. Shike, A. C. Ross, B. Caballero, and R. Cousins, eds. Modern Nutrition in Health and Disease, 10th edn., pp. 434–441. Philadelphia: Lippincott Williams & Wilkins.

6. Rivlin, R. S. 2006. Riboflavin. In: Bowman, B. A., and R. M. Russel, eds. Present Knowledge in Nutrition, 9th edn., pp. 250–259. Washington, DC: ILSI Press.

7. Jacques, P. F., A. Taylor, S. Moeller, et al. 2005. Long-term nutrient intake and 5-year change in nuclear lens opacities. *Arch. Ophthalmol.* 123:571–526.

8. Jacob, R. A. 2006. Niacin. In: Bowman, B. A., and R. M. Russel, eds. Present Knowledge in Nutrition, 9th edn., pp. 260–268. Washington, DC: ILSI Press.

9. Jukes, T. H. 1990. Nutrition science from vitamins to molecular biology. *Annual Reviews of Nutrition,* 10:1–10.

10. Mackey, A. D., S. R. Davis, and J. F. Gregory III. 2006. Vitamin B6. In: Shils, M. E., M. Shike, A. C. Ross, B. Caballero, and R. Cousins, eds. *Modern Nutrition in Health and Disease,* 10th edn., pp. 452–261. Philadelphia: Lippincott Williams & Wilkins.

11. Boushey, C. J., S. A. Beresford, G. S. Omenn, and A. G. Motulsky. 1995. A quantitative assessment of plasma homocysteine as a risk factor for vascular disease. Probable benefits of increasing folic acid intakes. *JAMA* 274:1049–1057.

12. Joubert, L. M., and M. M. Manore. 2006. Exercise, nutrition and homocysteine. Int. *J. Sport Nutr. Exer. Metab.* 16:341–361.

13. Carmel, R. 2006. Folic acid. In: Shils, M. E., M. Shike, A. C. Ross, B. Caballero, and R. Cousins, eds. Modern Nutrition in Health and Disease, 10th edn., pp. 470–481. Philadelphia: Lippincott Williams & Wilkins.

14. Wyatt, K. M., P. W. Dimmock, P. W. Jones, and P. M. Shaughn O'Brien. 1999. Efficacy of vitamin B-6 in the treatment of premenstrual syndrome: Systemic review. *Br. J. Med.* 318:1375–1381.

15. Rapkin, A. 2003. The review of treatment of premenstrual syndrome & premenstrual dysphoric disorder. *Psychoneuroendocrinology* 28:39–53.

16. Schaumburg, H., J. Kaplan, A. Winderbank, N. Vick, S. Rasmus, D. Pleasure, and M. J. Brown. 1983. Sensory neuropathy from pyridoxine abuse: A new megavitamin syndrome. *N. Engl. J. Med.* 309:445–448.

17. Connolly, M., 2001. Premenstrual syndrome: An update on definitions, diagnosis and management. *Advances in Psychiatric Treatment* 7:469–477.

18. Kim, Y. 2006. Does a high folate intake increase the risk of breast cancer? *Nutr. Rev.* 64(10):468–475.

19. Institute of Medicine, Food and Nutrition Board. 1998. Dietary Reference Intakes for Thiamin, Riboflavin, Niacin, Vitamin B6, Folate, Vitamin B12, Pantothenic Acid, Biotin, and Choline. Washington, DC: National Academies Press.

20. Beresford, S. A., and C. J. Boushey. 1997. Homocysteine, folic acid, and cardiovascular disease risk. In: Bendich, A., and R. J. Deckelbaum, eds. Preventive Nutrition: The Comprehensive Guide for Health Professionals. Totowa, NJ: Humana Press.

21. Mayer, E. L., D. W. Jacobsen, and K. Robinson. 1996. Homocysteine and coronary atherosclerosis. *J. Am. Coll. Cardiol.* 27:517–527.

22. Sabler, S. P. 2006. Vitamin B12. In: Bowman, B. A., and R. M. Russel, eds. Present Knowledge in Nutrition, 9th edn., pp. 302–313. Washington, DC: ILSI Press.

23. Carmel, R. 2006. Cobalamin (vitamin B12). In: Shils, M. E., M. Shike, A. C. Ross, B. Caballero, and R. Cousins, eds. *Modern Nutrition in Health and Disease,* 10th edn., pp. 482–497. Philadelphia, PA: Lippincott Williams & Wilkins.

24. Miller, W. J., L. M. Rogers, and R. B. Rubker, 2006. Pantothenic acid. In: Bowman, B. A., and R. M. Russel, eds. *Present Knowledge in Nutrition,* 9th edn., pp. 327–339.Washington, DC: ILSI Press.

25. Combs G. F. The vitamins. 2008. Fundamental Aspects in Nutrition and Health. 3rd ed. Elsevier: San Francisco, p. 62.

26. Freake, H. C. 2006. Iodine. In: Stipanuk, M. H., ed. Biochemical and Physiological Aspects of Human Nutrition, 2nd Ed pp. 1068–1090. Philadelphia, PA: W. B. Saunders Co.

27. Evans, G. W. 1989. The effect of chromium picolinate on insulin controlled parameters in humans. Int. *J. Biosoc. Med. Res.* 11:163–180.

28. Hasten, D. L., E. P. Rome, D. B. Franks, and M. Hegsted. 1992. Effects of chromium picolinate on beginning weight training students. *Int. J. Sports Nutr.* 2:343–350.

29. Lukaski, H. C., W. W. Bolonchuk, W. A. Siders, and D. B. Milne. 1996. Chromium supplementation and resistance training: effects on body composition, strength, and trace element status of men. *Am. J. Clin. Nutr.* 63:954–965.

30. Hallmark, M. A., T. H. Reynolds, C. A. DeSouza, C. O. Dotson, R. A. Anderson, and M. A. Rogers. 1996. Effects of chromium and resistive training on muscle strength and body composition. *Med. Sci. Sports Exerc.* 28:139–144.

31. Pasman, W. J., M. S. Westerterp-Plantenga, and W. H. Saris. 1997. The effectiveness of long-term supplementation of carbohydrate, chromium, fibre and caffeine on weight maintenance. *Int. J. Obes. Relat. Metab. Disord.* 21:1143–1151.

32. Walker, L. S., M. G. Bemben, D. A. Bemben, and A. W. Knehans. 1998. Chromium picolinate effects on body composition and muscular performance in wrestlers. *Med. Sci. Sports Exerc.* 30:1730–1737.

33. Campbell, W. W., L. J. Joseph, S. L. Davey, D. Cyr-Campbell, R. A. Anderson, and W. J. Evans. 1999. Effects of resistance training and chromium picolinate on body composition and skeletal muscle in older men. *J. Appl. Physiol.* 86:29–39.

34. Volpe, S. L., H. W. Huang, K. Larpadisorn, and I. I. Lesser. 2001. Effect of chromium supplementation and exercise on body composition, resting metabolic rate and selected biochemical parameters in moderately obese women following an exercise program. *J. Am. Coll. Nutr.* 20:293–306.

35. Campbell, W. W., L. J. O. Joseph, R. A. Anderson, S. L. Davey, J. Hinton, and W. J. Evans. 2002. Effects of resistive training and chromium picolinate on body composition and skeletal muscle size in older women. *Int. J. Sports Nutr. Exerc. Metab.* 12:125–135.

36. Lukaski H. C., Siders W. A., Penland J. G. 2007. Chromium picolinate supplementation in women: effects on body weight, composition and iron status. *Nutr* 23:187–185.

37. Diaz M. L., B. A. Watkins, Y. Li, R. A. Anderson, and W. W. Campbell. 2008. Chromium picolinate and conjugated linoleic acid do not synergistically influence diet- and exercise-inuded changes in body composition and health indexes in overweight women. *J. Nutr Biochem* 19:61–68.

38. Booth, S. L., and J. W. Suttie. 1998. Dietary intake and adequacy of vitamin K. *J. Nutr.* 128:785–788.

39. Institute of Medicine, Food and Nutrition Board. 2001. Dietary Reference Intakes for Vitamin A, Vitamin K, Arsenic, Boron, Chromium, Copper, Iodine, Iron, Manganese, Molybdenum, Nickel, Silicon, Vanadium, and Zinc. Washington, DC: National Academies Press.
40. Feskanich, D., S. A. Korrick, S. L. Greenspan, H. N. Rosen, and G. A. Colditz. 1999. Moderate alcohol consumption and bone density among post-menopausal women. *J. Women's Health* 8:65–73.
41. Beard, J. 2006. Iron. In: Bowman, B. A., and R. M. Russel, eds. Present Knowledge in Nutrition, 9th edn., pp. 430–444. Washington, DC: ILSI Press.
42. U.S. Food and Drug Administration. 1997. Preventing Iron Poisoning in Children. FDA Backgrounder. www.cfsan.fda.gov/~dms/bgiron.html. (Accessed April 2007.)
43. Bacon, B. R., J. K. Olynyk, E. M. Brunt, R. S. Britton, and R. K. Wolff. 1999. HFE genotype in patients with hemochromatosis and other liver diseases. *Ann. Intern. Med.* 130:953–962.
44. National Institute of Allergy and Infectious Diseases, National Institutes of Health. 2007. The Common Cold. www3.niaid.nih.gov/topics/commonCold.
45. Prasad, A. 1996. Zinc: the biology and therapeutics of an ion. *Ann. Intern. Med.* 125:142–143.
46. Jackson, J. L., E. Lesho, and C. Peterson. 2000. Zinc and the common cold: A meta-analysis revisited. *J. Nutr.* 130:1512S–1515S.
47. Caruso, T. J., C. G. Prober, and J. M Gwaltney. 2007. Treatment of naturally acquired common colds with zinc: a structured review. *Clin. Infect Dis.* 45(5):569–574.
48. Chandra, R. K. 1984. Excessive intake of zinc impairs immune responses. *JAMA.* 252:1443–1446.

Answers to Review Questions

Answers to Review Questions 11-15 (essay questions) for this chapter are located on the Companion Website at **www.pearsonhighered.com/thompsonmanore**

1. **d.** thiamin, pantothenic acid, and biotin.
2. **b.** vitamin K.
3. **b.** Iron is a component of hemoglobin, myoglobin, and certain enzymes.
4. **c.** an amino acid.
5. **d.** Choline is necessary for the synthesis of phospholipids and other components of cell membranes.
6. True.
7. True.
8. False. Non-heme iron is found in both plant-based and animal-based foods.
9. False. Neural tube defects occur during the first four weeks of pregnancy; this is often before a woman even knows she is pregnant. Thus, the best way for a woman to protect her fetus against neural tube defects is to make sure she is consuming adequate folate before she is pregnant.
10. False. Wilson's disease is a rare disorder that causes copper toxicity.

Nutrition and Physical Activity: Keys to Good Health

From Chapter 12 of *Nutrition: An Applied Approach*, Third Edition. Janice Thompson, Melinda Manore. Copyright © 2012 by Pearson Education, Inc. Published by Pearson Benjamin Cummings. All rights reserved.

Redlink/Corbis

Nutrition and Physical Activity: Keys to Good Health

CHAPTER OBJECTIVES

After reading this chapter you will be able to:

1. Explain the differences between physical activity and exercise.

2. Define the four components of fitness.

3. List at least four health benefits of being physically active on a regular basis.

4. Describe the FIT principle and calculate your maximal and training heart rate range.

5. List and describe at least three processes we use to break down fuels to support physical activity.

6. Discuss at least three changes in nutrient needs that can occur in response to an increase in physical activity or vigorous exercise training.

7. Define the term *ergogenic aids* and discuss the potential benefits and risks of at least four ergogenic aids that are currently on the market.

Test Yourself

1. **T** **F** Despite the multitude of health benefits of participating in regular physical activity, more than half of all Americans are insufficiently active.

2. **T** **F** Eating extra protein helps us build muscle.

3. **T** **F** Most ergogenic aids are not effective, and many can be dangerous or cause serious health consequences.

Test Yourself answers can be found at the end of the chapter.

I n the summer of 2009, Millie Bolton of Ohio and Glenn Dody of Arizona each took the gold medal for the 400-meter dash in track and field at the National Senior Games. Bolton clocked 2 minutes, 31 seconds, and Dody's time was 1 minute, 42 seconds. If these performance times don't amaze you, perhaps they will when you consider these athletes' ages: both were competing in the class for 85- to 89-year-olds!

There's no doubt about it: regular physical activity dramatically improves strength, stamina, health, and quality of life—throughout the life span. But what qualifies as "regular physical activity"? In other words, how much do we need to do to reap the benefits? And if we do become more active, does our diet have to change, too?

Healthy eating practices and regular physical activity are like two sides of the same coin, interacting in a variety of ways to improve our strength and stamina and increase our resistance to many chronic diseases and acute illnesses. In fact, the nutrition and physical activity recommendations for reducing your risk for heart disease also reduce your risk for high blood pressure, type 2 diabetes, obesity, and some forms of cancer! In this chapter, we'll define physical activity, identify its many benefits, and discuss the nutrients needed to maintain an active life.

Why Engage in Physical Activity?

With the help of a nutritious diet, many people are able to remain physically active—and even competitive—throughout adult life.

A lot of people are looking for a "magic pill" that will help them maintain weight loss, reduce their risk for diseases, make them feel better, and improve their quality of sleep. Although many people are not aware of it, regular physical activity is this magic pill. **Physical activity** is any movement produced by muscles that increases energy expenditure. Different categories of physical activity include occupational, household, leisure-time, and transportation.[1] **Leisure-time physical activity** is any activity not related to a person's occupation and includes competitive sports, planned exercise training, and recreational activities such as hiking, walking, and bicycling. **Exercise** is therefore considered a subcategory of leisure-time physical activity and refers to activity that is purposeful, planned, and structured.[2]

The current recommendations for physical activity include accumulating at least 30 minutes of moderate physical activity on most, preferably all, days of the week. One of the most important benefits of regular physical activity is that it increases our physical fitness. **Physical fitness** is a state of being that arises largely from the interaction between nutrition and physical activity. It is defined as the ability to carry out daily tasks with vigor and alertness, without undue fatigue, and with ample energy to enjoy leisure-time pursuits and meet unforeseen emergencies.[1] Physical fitness has several components[3] (**Table 1**), including:

- *Cardiorespiratory fitness* is the ability of the heart, lungs, and circulatory system to efficiently supply oxygen and nutrients to working muscles.
- *Musculoskeletal fitness* involves fitness of both the muscles and bones. It includes *muscular strength*, the maximal force or tension level that can be produced by a muscle group, and *muscular endurance*, the ability of a muscle to maintain submaximal force levels for extended periods of time.
- *Flexibility* is the ability to move a joint fluidly through the complete range of motion, and *body composition* is the amount of bone, muscle, and fat tissue in the body.

Although many people are interested in improving their physical fitness, some are more interested in maintaining general fitness, while others are interested in achieving higher levels of fitness to optimize their athletic performance. Other benefits of regular physical activity include the following:

- *It reduces our risks for, and complications of, heart disease, stroke, and high blood pressure.* Regular physical activity increases high-density lipoprotein cholesterol (HDL, the "good" cholesterol) and lowers triglycerides in the blood, improves the strength of the heart, helps maintain healthy blood pressure, and limits the progression of atherosclerosis (hardening of the arteries).
- *It reduces our risk for obesity.* Regular physical activity maintains lean body mass and promotes more healthful levels of body fat, may help in appetite control, and increases energy expenditure and the use of fat as an energy source.
- *It reduces our risk for type 2 diabetes.* Regular physical activity enhances the action of insulin, which improves the cells' uptake of glucose from the blood, and it can improve blood glucose control in people with diabetes, which in turn reduces the risk for, or delays the onset of, diabetes-related complications.

physical activity Any movement produced by muscles that increases energy expenditure; includes occupational, household, leisure-time, and transportation activities.

leisure-time physical activity Any activity not related to a person's occupation; includes competitive sports, recreational activities, and planned exercise training.

exercise A subcategory of leisure-time physical activity; any activity that is purposeful, planned, and structured.

physical fitness The ability to carry out daily tasks with vigor and alertness, without undue fatigue, and with ample energy to enjoy leisure-time pursuits and meet unforeseen emergencies.

TABLE 1	The Components of Fitness
Fitness Component	**Examples of Activities One Can Do to Achieve Fitness in Each Component**
Cardiorespiratory	Aerobic-type activities, such as walking, running, swimming, cross-country skiing
Musculoskeletal fitness:	Resistance training, weight lifting, calisthenics, sit-ups, push-ups
Muscular strength	Weight lifting or related activities using heavier weights with few repetitions
Muscular endurance	Weight lifting or related activities using lighter weights with more repetitions
Flexibility	Stretching exercises, yoga
Body composition	Aerobic exercise, resistance training

Robert W. Ginn/AGE Fotostock

- *It reduces our risk for osteoporosis.* Regular physical activity strengthens bones and enhances muscular strength and flexibility, thereby reducing the likelihood of falls and the incidence of fractures and other injuries when falls occur.
- *It potentially reduces our risk for colon cancer.* Although the exact role that physical activity may play in reducing colon cancer risk is still unknown, we do know that regular physical activity enhances gastric motility, which reduces the transit time of potential cancer-causing agents through the gut.

Regular physical activity is also known to improve our sleep patterns, reduce our risk for upper respiratory infections by improving immune function, improve self-esteem, and reduce anxiety and mental stress. It also can be effective in treating mild and moderate depression. During pregnancy, regular physical activity helps maintain the mother's fitness and muscle tone and helps control weight gain. It is also associated with a reduced risk for pregnancy-related complications.[4]

Hiking is a leisure-time physical activity that can contribute to your physical fitness.

Despite the plethora of benefits derived from regular physical activity, most people find that this magic pill is not easy to swallow. In fact, most people in the United States are physically inactive. The Centers for Disease Control and Prevention reports that over half of all U.S. adults do not do enough physical activity to meet national health recommendations, and almost 25% of adults in the United States admit to doing no leisure-time physical activity at all.[5,6] These statistics mirror the reported increases in obesity, heart disease, and type 2 diabetes in industrialized countries.

This trend toward inadequate physical activity levels is also occurring in young people. Only 37% of young people are meeting the recommended 60 minutes per day on 5 or more days per week.[7] Although physical education (PE) is part of the mandated curriculum in most states, only 28.4% of high school students attend PE classes daily, and only 6.4% of middle schools offer daily PE for the entire school year.[8] Since our habits related to eating and physical activity are formed early in life, it is imperative that we provide opportunities for children and adolescents to engage in regular, enjoyable physical activity. An active lifestyle during childhood increases the likelihood of a healthier life as an adult.

RECAP Physical activity is any movement produced by muscles that increases energy expenditure. Physical fitness is the ability to carry out daily tasks with vigor and alertness, without undue fatigue, and with ample energy to enjoy leisure-time pursuits and meet unforeseen emergencies. Physical activity provides a multitude of health benefits, including reducing our risks for obesity and many chronic diseases and relieving anxiety and stress. Despite the many health benefits of physical activity, most people in the United States, including many children, are inactive.

What Is a Sound Fitness Program?

There are several widely recognized qualities of a sound fitness program, as well as guidelines to help you design one that is right for you. These are explored here. Keep in mind that people with heart disease, high blood pressure, diabetes, obesity, osteoporosis, asthma, or arthritis should get approval to exercise from their healthcare practitioner prior to starting a fitness program. In addition, a medical evaluation should be conducted before starting an exercise program for an apparently healthy but currently inactive man 40 years or older or woman 50 years or older.

A Sound Fitness Program Meets Your Personal Goals

A fitness program that may be ideal for you is not necessarily right for everyone. Before designing or evaluating any program, it is important to define your personal

Photodisc/Getty Images

Moderate physical activity, such as gardening, helps maintain overall health.

fitness goals. Do you want to prevent osteoporosis, diabetes, or another chronic disease that runs in your family? Do you simply want to increase your energy and stamina? Or do you intend to compete in athletic events? Each of these scenarios requires a unique fitness program.

For example, if you want to train for athletic competition, a traditional approach that includes planned, purposive exercise sessions under the guidance of a trainer or coach would probably be most beneficial. Or if you want to achieve cardiorespiratory fitness, participating in an aerobics class at least three times per week may be recommended.

In contrast, if your goal is to maintain your overall health, you might do better to follow the 1996 report of the Surgeon General on achieving health through regular physical activity.[1] This report emphasizes that significant health benefits, including reducing your risk for chronic diseases (such as heart disease, osteoporosis, and type 2 diabetes), can be achieved by participating in a moderate amount of physical activity (such as 45 minutes of gardening, 20 minutes of brisk walking, or 30 minutes of basketball) on most, if not all, days of the week. These health benefits occur even when the time spent performing the physical activities is cumulative (for example, brisk walking for 10 minutes three times per day). While these guidelines are appropriate for achieving health benefits, they are not necessarily of sufficient intensity and duration to improve physical fitness.

Recently, the Institute of Medicine published guidelines stating that the minimum amount of physical activity that should be done each day to maintain health and fitness is 60 minutes—not 30 minutes, as published in the Surgeon General's report.[1,9] This discrepancy in fitness guidelines has caused some confusion among consumers. Refer to the Nutrition Debate at the end of this chapter to learn more about this controversy.

A Sound Fitness Program Is Varied, Consistent, . . . and Fun!

Watching television or reading can provide variety while running on a treadmill.

Physical Activity Pyramid
A pyramid-shaped graphic that suggests types and amounts of activity that should be done weekly to increase physical activity levels.

One of the most important goals for everyone is fun; unless you enjoy being active, you will find it very difficult to maintain your physical fitness. If you enjoy the outdoors, hiking, camping, fishing, and rock climbing are potential activities for you. If you would rather exercise with friends on your lunch break, walking, climbing stairs, and bicycle riding may be more appropriate. Or you may prefer to use the programs and equipment at your local fitness club or purchase your own treadmill and free weights.

Variety is critical to maintaining your fitness. While some people enjoy doing similar activities day after day, most of us get bored with the same fitness routine. Incorporating a variety of activities into your fitness program will help maintain your interest and increase your enjoyment while you are active. Variety can be achieved by engaging in different indoor and outdoor activities on different days of the week, taking a different route when you walk each day, or watching different TV programs or listening to music while you ride a stationary bicycle or work out on a rowing machine. This smorgasbord of activities can increase your activity level without leading to monotony and boredom.

A useful tool has been developed to help you increase the variety of your physical activity choices (Figure 1). The **Physical Activity Pyramid** makes recommendations for the type and amount of activity you should do weekly to increase your physical activity level. The bottom of the pyramid describes activities that should be done every day, including walking more, taking the stairs instead of the elevator, and working in your garden. Aerobic types of exercises (such as bicycling and brisk walking) and recreational activities (such as soccer, tennis, and basketball) should be done three to five times each week, for at least 20 or 30 minutes. Flexibility, strength, and leisure activities should be done two or three times each week. The

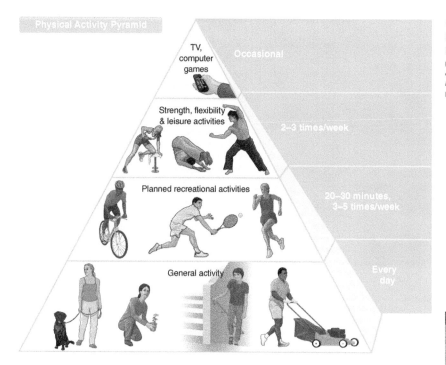

◀ **Figure 1** You can use this Physical Activity Pyramid as a guide to increase your level of physical activity. Data from Corbin, C. B., and R. D. Pangrazi. 1998. Physical Activity Pyramid rebuffs peak experience. *ACSM's Health Fitness J.* 2(1). Copyright © 1998. Used with permission.

top of the pyramid emphasizes things we should do less of, including watching TV, playing computer games, and sitting for more than 30 minutes at one time.

It is important to understand that you cannot do just one activity to achieve overall fitness because every activity is specific to a certain fitness component. Refer back to Table 1, and notice the various activities listed as examples for the various components. For instance, participating in aerobic-type activities will improve cardiorespiratory fitness but will do little to improve muscular strength. To achieve that goal, we must participate in some form of **resistance training,** or exercises in which our muscles work against resistance. Flexibility is achieved by participating in stretching activities. By following the recommendations put forth in the Physical Activity Pyramid, you can achieve physical fitness in all components.

A Sound Fitness Program Appropriately Overloads the Body

In order to improve your fitness, you must place an extra physical demand on your body. This is referred to as the **overload principle.** A word of caution is in order here: *the overload principle does not advocate subjecting your body to inappropriately high stress* because this can lead to exhaustion and injuries. In contrast, an appropriate overload on various body systems will result in healthy improvements in fitness.

To achieve an appropriate overload, you should consider three factors, collectively known as the **FIT principle:** *f*requency, *i*ntensity, and *t*ime of activity. You can use the FIT principle to design either a general physical fitness program or a performance-based exercise program. **Figure 2** shows how the FIT principle applies to a cardiorespiratory, musculoskeletal, and flexibility fitness program. Let's consider each of the FIT principle's three factors in more detail.

Frequency

Frequency refers to the number of activity sessions per week. Depending on your goals for fitness, the frequency of your activities will vary. To achieve cardiorespiratory fitness, you should train more than 2 days per week. On the other hand, training

Will & Deni McIntyre/Photo Researchers

▲ Testing in a fitness lab is the most accurate way to determine maximal heart rate.

resistance training Exercises in which our muscles act against resistance.

overload principle Placing an extra physical demand on your body in order to improve your fitness level.

FIT principle The principle used to achieve an appropriate overload for physical training; FIT stands for frequency, intensity, and time of activity.

frequency The number of activity sessions per week you perform.

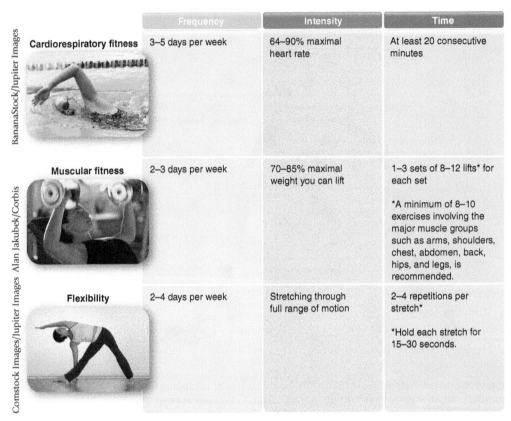

	Frequency	Intensity	Time
Cardiorespiratory fitness	3–5 days per week	64–90% maximal heart rate	At least 20 consecutive minutes
Muscular fitness	2–3 days per week	70–85% maximal weight you can lift	1–3 sets of 8–12 lifts* for each set *A minimum of 8–10 exercises involving the major muscle groups such as arms, shoulders, chest, abdomen, back, hips, and legs, is recommended.
Flexibility	2–4 days per week	Stretching through full range of motion	2–4 repetitions per stretch* *Hold each stretch for 15–30 seconds.

Image credits (left margin, top to bottom): BananaStock/Jupiter Images; Alan Jakubek/Corbis; Comstock Images/Jupiter Images

◆ Figure 2 Using the FIT principle to achieve cardiorespiratory and musculoskeletal fitness and flexibility.

more than 5 days per week does not cause significant gains in fitness but can substantially increase your risk for injury. Training 3 to 5 days per week appears optimal to achieve and maintain cardiorespiratory fitness. In contrast, only 2 to 3 days are needed to achieve musculoskeletal fitness.

Intensity

intensity The amount of effort expended during the activity, or how difficult the activity is to perform.

low-intensity activities Activities that cause very mild increases in breathing, sweating, and heart rate.

moderate-intensity activities Activities that cause moderate increases in breathing, sweating, and heart rate.

vigorous-intensity activities Activities that produce significant increases in breathing, sweating, and heart rate; talking is difficult when exercising at a vigorous intensity.

maximal heart rate The rate at which your heart beats during maximal-intensity exercise.

Intensity refers to the amount of effort expended or to how difficult the activity is to perform. In general, **low-intensity activities** are those that cause very mild increases in breathing, sweating, and heart rate, while **moderate-intensity activities** cause moderate increases in these responses. **Vigorous-intensity activities** produce significant increases in breathing, sweating, and heart rate, so that talking is difficult when exercising.

Traditionally, heart rate has been used to indicate level of intensity during aerobic activities. You can calculate the range of exercise intensity that is appropriate for you by estimating your **maximal heart rate,** which is the rate at which your heart beats during maximal intensity exercise (see the You Do the Math box on the next page). Maximal heart rate is estimated by subtracting your age from 220. The Centers for Disease Control and Prevention recommends that to achieve moderate-intensity physical activity, your target heart rate should be 50–70% of your estimated maximal heart rate; to achieve vigorous-intensity physical activity, your target heart rate should be 70–85% of your estimated maximal heart rate.[10] People who are older or who have been inactive for a long time may want to exercise at the lower end of the moderate-intensity range. Those who are more physically fit or are striving for a more rapid improvement in fitness may want to exercise at the higher end of the

YOU DO THE MATH
Calculating Your Maximal and Training Heart Rate Range

Judy was recently diagnosed with type 2 diabetes, and her healthcare provider has recommended she begin an exercise program. She is considered obese according to her body mass index, and she has not been regularly active since she was a teenager. Judy's goals are to improve her cardiorespiratory fitness and achieve and maintain a more healthful weight. Fortunately, Valley Hospital, where she works as a nurse's aide, recently opened a small fitness center for the use of its employees. Judy plans to begin by either walking on the treadmill or riding the stationary bicycle at the fitness center during her lunch break.

Judy needs to exercise at an intensity that will help her improve her cardiorespiratory fitness and lose weight. She is 38 years of age, is obese, has type 2 diabetes, and has been approved to do moderate-intensity activity by her healthcare provider. She does a lot of walking and lifting in her work as a nurse's aide, and her doctor has recommended that she start her program by setting her training heart rate range at 50%; once her fitness improves, she can work toward exercising at 75% of her maximal heart rate.

Let's calculate Judy's maximal heart rate values:

- Maximal heart rate: 220 – age = 220 – 38 = 182 beats per minute (bpm)
- Lower end of intensity range: 50% of 182 bpm = $0.50 \times$ 182 bpm = 91 bpm
- Higher end of intensity range: 75% of 182 bpm = $0.75 \times$ 182 bpm = 137 bpm

Because Judy is a trained nurse's aide, she is skilled at measuring a heart rate, or pulse. To measure your own pulse,

- Place your second (index) and third (middle) fingers on the inside of your wrist, just below the wrist crease and near the thumb. Press lightly to feel your pulse. Don't press too hard, or you will occlude the artery and be unable to feel its pulsation.
- If you can't feel your pulse at your wrist, try the carotid artery at your neck. This is located below your ear, on the side of your neck directly below your jaw. Press lightly against your neck under the jaw bone to find your pulse.
- Begin counting your pulse with the count of "zero;" then count each beat for 15 seconds.
- Multiply that value by 4 to estimate heart rate over 1 minute.
- Do not take your pulse with your thumb, as it has its own pulse, which would prevent you from getting an accurate estimate of your heart rate.

As you can see from these calculations, when Judy walks on the treadmill or rides the bicycle, her heart rate should be between 91 and 137 bpm; this will put her in her aerobic training zone and allow her to achieve cardiorespiratory fitness. It will also help her lose weight.

vigorous-intensity range. Competitive athletes generally train at a higher intensity, around 80–95% of their maximal heart rate.

Although the calculation *220 – age* has been used extensively for years to predict maximal heart rate, it was never intended to represent everyone's true maximal heart rate or to be used as the standard of aerobic training intensity. The most accurate way to determine your own maximal heart rate is to complete a maximal exercise test in a fitness laboratory; however, this test is not commonly conducted with the general public and can be very expensive. Although not completely accurate, the estimated maximal heart rate method can still be used to give you a general idea of your aerobic training range.

Time of Activity

Time of activity refers to how long each session lasts. To achieve general health, you can do multiple short bouts of activity that add up to 30 minutes each day. However, to achieve higher levels of fitness, it is important that the activities be done for at least 20 to 30 consecutive minutes.

For example, let's say you want to compete in triathlons. To be successful during the running segment of the triathlon, you will need to be able to run for at least 5 miles. Thus, it is appropriate for you to train so that you can complete 5 miles during one session and still have enough energy to swim and bicycle during the race. You will need to consistently train at a distance of 5 miles; you will also benefit from running longer distances.

time of activity The period of time that an exercise session lasts.

A Sound Fitness Plan Includes a Warm-Up and a Cool-Down Period

To properly prepare for and recover from an exercise session, warm-up and cool-down activities should be performed. **Warm-up,** which properly prepares muscles for exertion by increasing blood flow and temperature, includes general activities (such as stretching and calisthenics) and specific activities that prepare you for the actual activity (such as jogging or swinging a golf club). The warm-up should be brief (5 to 10 minutes), gradual, and sufficient to increase muscle and body temperature, but it should not cause fatigue or deplete energy stores.

Cool-down activities are done after the exercise session. The cool-down should be gradual, allowing your body to recover slowly, with ample stretching as well as a lower-intensity version of some of the same activities you performed during the exercise session. Cool-down after exercise assists in the prevention of injury and may help reduce muscle soreness.

Simple Changes Can Boost Your Physical Activity

There are 1,440 minutes in every day. Spend just 30 of those minutes in physical activity, and you'll be taking an important step toward improving your health. Here are some tips adapted from the Centers for Disease Control and Prevention and the United States Department of Health and Human Services for working daily activity into your life:[11,12]

Stretching should be included in the warm-up before and the cool-down after exercise.
Moodboard/Alamy

QUICK TIPS

Increasing Your Physical Activity

✓ Walk as often and as far as possible: park your car farther away from your dorm, lecture hall, or shops; walk to school or work; go for a brisk walk between classes; get on or off the bus one stop away from your destination.

✓ Take the stairs instead of the elevator.

✓ Exercise while watching television—for example, by doing sit-ups, stretching, or using a treadmill or stationary bike.

✓ Put on a CD and dance!

✓ Get an exercise partner: join a friend for walks, hikes, cycling, skating, tennis, or a fitness class.

✓ Take up a group sport.

✓ Register for a class from the physical education department in an activity you've never tried before, maybe yoga or fencing.

✓ Register for a dance class, such as jazz, tap, or ballroom.

✓ Join a health club, gym, or YMCA/YWCA and use the swimming pool, weights, rock-climbing wall, and other facilities.

✓ Join an activity-based club, such as a skating or hiking club.

If you have been inactive for a while, use a sensible approach by starting out slowly. Gradually build up the time you spend doing the activity by adding a few minutes every few days until you reach 30 minutes a day. As this 30-minute minimum becomes easier, gradually increase either the length of time you spend in activity, the intensity of the activities you choose, or both.

RECAP A sound fitness program must meet your personal fitness goals. It should be fun and include variety and consistency to help you maintain interest and achieve fitness in all components. It must also place an extra physical demand, or an overload, on your body. To achieve appropriate overload, follow the FIT principle: *frequency* refers to the number of activity sessions per week; *intensity* refers to how difficult the activity is to perform, and *time* refers to how long each activity session lasts. Warm-up and cool-down activities help the body prepare for and recover from exertion.

warm-up Activities that prepare you for an exercise bout, including stretching, calisthenics, and movements specific to the exercise bout; also called preliminary exercise.

cool-down Activities done after an exercise session is completed; should be gradual and allow your body to slowly recover from exercise.

What Fuels Our Activities?

In order to perform exercise, or muscular work, we must be able to generate energy. The common currency of energy for virtually all cells in the body is **adenosine triphosphate,** or ATP. As you might guess from its name, a molecule of ATP includes an organic compound called adenosine and three phosphate groups (Figure 3). When one of the phosphates is cleaved, or broken away, from ATP, energy is released. The products remaining after this reaction are adenosine diphosphate (ADP) and an independent inorganic phosphate group (P_i). In a mirror image of this reaction, the body regenerates ATP by adding a phosphate group back to ADP. In this way, we continually provide energy to our cells.

The amount of ATP stored in a muscle cell is very limited; it can keep the muscle active for only about 1 to 3 seconds. Thus, we need to generate ATP from other sources to fuel activities for longer periods of time. Fortunately, we are able to generate ATP from the breakdown of carbohydrate, fat, and protein, providing our cells with a variety of sources from which to receive energy. The primary energy systems that provide energy for physical activities are the adenosine triphosphate–creatine phosphate (ATP-CP) energy system and the anaerobic and aerobic breakdown of carbohydrates. Our body also generates energy from the breakdown of fats. As you will see, the type, intensity, and duration of the activities performed determine the amount of ATP needed and therefore the energy system that is used.

The amount of daily physical activity you should participate in is determined by your personal fitness goals.

Image Source/Jupiter Images

The ATP-CP Energy System Uses Creatine Phosphate to Regenerate ATP

As previously mentioned, muscle cells store only enough ATP to maintain activity for 1 to 3 seconds. When more energy is needed, a high-energy compound called **creatine phosphate (CP)** (also called *phosphocreatine,* or *PCr*) can be broken down to support the regeneration of ATP (Figure 4). Because this reaction can occur in the absence of oxygen, it is referred to as an **anaerobic** (meaning "without oxygen") reaction.

Muscle tissue contains about four to six times as much CP as ATP, but there is still not enough CP available to fuel long-term activity. CP is used the most during very

adenosine triphosphate (ATP) The common currency of energy for virtually all cells of the body.

creatine phosphate (CP) A high-energy compound that can be broken down for energy and used to regenerate ATP.

anaerobic Means "without oxygen;" the term used to refer to metabolic reactions that occur in the absence of oxygen.

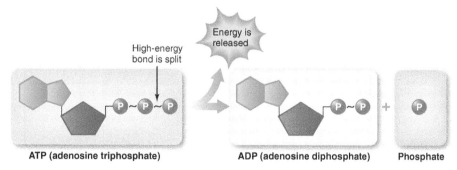

ATP (adenosine triphosphate)   **ADP (adenosine diphosphate)**   **Phosphate**

High-energy bond is split

Energy is released

Figure 3 Structure of adenosine triphosphate (ATP). Energy is produced when ATP is split into adenosine diphosphate (ADP) and inorganic phosphate (P_i).

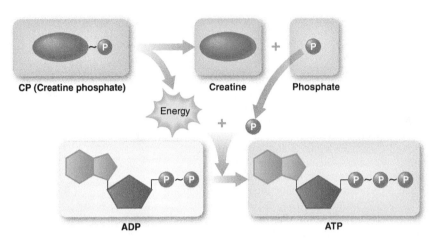

⬆ **Figure 4** When the compound creatine phosphate (CP) is broken down into a molecule of creatine and an independent phosphate molecule, energy is released. This energy, along with the independent phosphate molecule, can then be used to regenerate ATP.

intense, short bouts of activity, such as lifting, jumping, and sprinting (**Figure 5**). Together, our stores of ATP and CP can support a *maximal* physical effort for only about 3 to 15 seconds. We must rely on other energy sources, such as carbohydrate and fat, to support activities of longer duration.

The Breakdown of Carbohydrates Provides Energy for Both Brief and Long-Term Exercise

During activities lasting about 30 seconds to 3 minutes, our body needs an energy source that can be used quickly to produce ATP. The breakdown of carbohydrates, specifically glucose, provides this quick energy in a process called **glycolysis.** The most common source of glucose during exercise comes from glycogen stored in the muscles and glucose found in the blood. As shown in **Figure 6**, for every glucose molecule that goes through glycolysis, two ATP molecules are produced. The primary end product of glycolysis is **pyruvic acid.**

When oxygen availability is limited in the cell, pyruvic acid is converted to **lactic acid.** For years it was assumed that lactic acid was a useless, even potentially toxic, by-product of high-intensity exercise. We now know that lactic acid is an important intermediate of glucose breakdown and that it plays a critical role in supplying fuel for working muscles, the heart, and resting tissues (see the Nutrition Myth or Fact box two pages ahead).

The major advantage of glycolysis is that it is the fastest way that we can regenerate ATP for exercise, other than the ATP-CP system. However, this high rate of ATP production can be sustained only briefly, generally less than 3 minutes. To perform exercise that lasts longer than 3 minutes, we must rely on the aerobic energy system to provide adequate ATP.

To generate even more ATP molecules, pyruvic acid can go through additional metabolic pathways in the presence of oxygen (see Figure 6). Although this process is slower than glycolysis occurring under anaerobic conditions, the breakdown of 1 glucose molecule going through aerobic metabolism yields 36 to 38 ATP molecules for energy, while the anaerobic process yields only 2 ATP molecules. Thus, this aerobic process supplies eighteen times more energy! Another advantage of the aerobic process is that it does not result in the significant production of acids and other compounds that contribute to muscle fatigue, which means that a low-intensity activity can be performed for hours. Aerobic metabolism of glucose is the primary source of fuel for our muscles during activities lasting from 3 minutes to 4 hours (see Figure 5).

We can store only a limited amount of glycogen in our body. An average, well-nourished man who weighs about 154 pounds (70 kg) can

glycolysis The breakdown of glucose; yields two ATP molecules and two pyruvic acid molecules for each molecule of glucose.

pyruvic acid The primary end product of glycolysis.

lactic acid A compound that results when pyruvic acid is metabolized in the presence of insufficient oxygen.

store about 200 to 500 g of muscle glycogen, which is equal to 800 to 2,000 kcal of energy. Although trained athletes can store more muscle glycogen than the average person, even their bodies do not have enough stored glycogen to provide an unlimited energy supply for long-term activities. Thus, we also need a fuel source that is very abundant and can be broken down under aerobic conditions, so that it can support activities of lower intensity and longer duration. This fuel source is fat.

Aerobic Breakdown of Fats Supports Exercise of Low Intensity and Long Duration

When we refer to fat as a fuel source, we mean stored triglycerides, which is the primary storage form of fat in our cells. A triglyceride molecule is composed of a glycerol backbone attached to three fatty acid molecules. It is these fatty acid molecules that provide much of the energy we need to support long-term activity. Fatty acids are classified by their length—that is, by the number of carbons they contain. The longer the fatty acid, the more ATP that can be generated from its breakdown. For instance, palmitic acid is a fatty acid with 16 carbons. If palmitic acid is broken down completely, it yields 129 ATP molecules! Obviously, far more energy is produced from this one fatty acid molecule than from the aerobic breakdown of a glucose molecule.

There are two major advantages of using fat as a fuel. First, fat is an abundant energy source, even in lean people. For example, a man who weighs 154 pounds (70 kg) who has a body fat level of 10% has approximately 15 pounds of body fat, which is equivalent to more than 50,000 kcal of energy! This is significantly more energy than can be provided by his stored muscle glycogen (800 to 2,000 kcal). Second, fat provides 9 kcal of energy per gram, more than twice as much energy per gram as carbohydrate. The primary disadvantage of using fat as a fuel is that the breakdown process is relatively slow; thus, fat is used predominantly as a fuel source during activities of lower intensity and longer duration. Fat is also our primary energy source during rest, sitting, and standing in place.

What specific activities are primarily fueled by fat? Walking long distances uses fat stores, as does hiking, long-distance cycling, and other low- to moderate-intensity forms of exercise. Fat is also an important fuel source during endurance events, such as marathons (26.2 miles) and ultra-marathon races (49.9 miles). Endurance exercise training improves our ability to use fat for energy, which may be one reason that people who exercise regularly tend to have lower body fat levels than people who do not exercise.

It is important to remember that we are almost always using some combination of carbohydrate and fat for energy. At rest, we use very little carbohydrate, relying mostly on fat. However this does not mean that we can reduce our body fat by resting and doing very little activity! To lose weight and reduce body fat, a person needs to exercise regularly and reduce energy intake, so that negative energy balance results. During

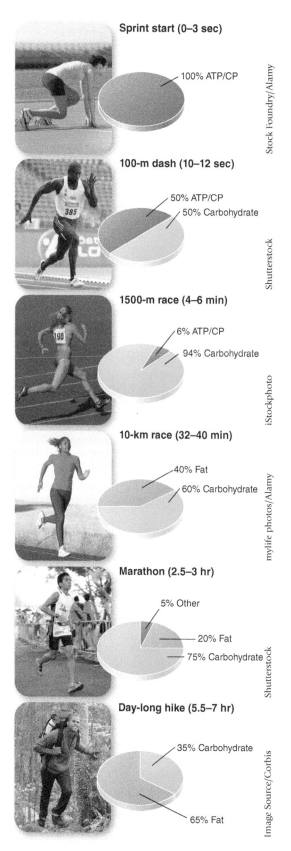

Sprint start (0–3 sec)
100% ATP/CP

100-m dash (10–12 sec)
50% ATP/CP
50% Carbohydrate

1500-m race (4–6 min)
6% ATP/CP
94% Carbohydrate

10-km race (32–40 min)
40% Fat
60% Carbohydrate

Marathon (2.5–3 hr)
5% Other
20% Fat
75% Carbohydrate

Day-long hike (5.5–7 hr)
35% Carbohydrate
65% Fat

Stock Foundry/Alamy · Shutterstock · iStockphoto · mylife photos/Alamy · Shutterstock · Image Source/Corbis

▶ **Figure 5** The relative contributions of ATP–CP, carbohydrate, and fat to activities of various durations and intensities.

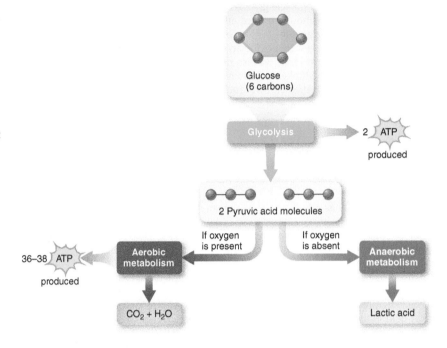

▶ Figure 6 The breakdown of one molecule of glucose, or the process of glycolysis, yields two molecules of pyruvic acid and two ATP molecules. The further metabolism of pyruvic acid in the presence of insufficient oxygen (anaerobic process) results in the production of lactic acid. The metabolism of pyruvic acid in the presence of adequate oxygen (aerobic process) yields 36 to 38 molecules of ATP.

NUTRITION MYTH OR FACT?
Does Lactic Acid Cause Muscle Fatigue and Soreness?

Theo and his teammates won their basketball game last night, but just barely. With two of the players sick, Theo got more court time than usual, and when he got back to the dorm, he could hardly get his legs to carry him up the stairs. This morning, Theo's muscles ache all over, and he wonders if a buildup of lactic acid is to blame.

Lactic acid is a by-product of glycolysis. For many years, both scientists and athletes believed that lactic acid caused muscle fatigue and soreness. Does recent scientific evidence support this belief?

The exact causes of muscle fatigue are not known, and there appear to be many contributing factors. Recent evidence suggests that fatigue may be due not only to the accumulation of many acids and other metabolic by-products, such as inorganic phosphate,[13] but also to the depletion of creatine phosphate and changes in calcium in the cells that affect muscle contraction. Depletion of muscle glycogen, liver glycogen, and blood glucose, as well as psychological factors, can all contribute to fatigue.[14] Thus, it appears that lactic acid only contributes to fatigue but does not cause fatigue independently.

So what causes muscle soreness? As with fatigue, there are probably many factors. It is hypothesized that soreness usually results from microscopic tears in the muscle fibers as a result of strenuous exercise. This damage triggers an inflammatory reaction, which causes an influx of fluid and various chemicals to the damaged area. These substances work to remove damaged tissue and initiate tissue repair, but they may also stimulate pain. However, it appears highly unlikely that lactic acid is an independent cause of muscle soreness.

Recent studies indicate that lactic acid is produced even under aerobic conditions! This means it is produced at rest as well as during exercise at any intensity. The reasons for this constant production of lactic acid are still being studied. What we do know is that lactic acid is an important fuel for resting tissues, for working cardiac and skeletal muscles, and even for the brain both at rest and during exercise.[15,16] That's right—skeletal muscles not only *produce* lactic acid but also *use* it for energy, both directly and after it is converted into glucose and glycogen in the liver. We also know that endurance training improves the muscles' ability to use lactic acid for energy. Thus, contrary to being a waste product of glucose metabolism, lactic acid is actually an important energy source for muscle cells during rest and exercise.

Corbis Super RF/Alamy

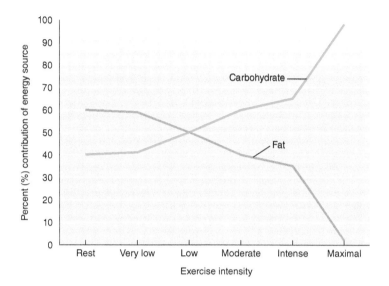

Figure 7 For most daily activities, including exercise, we use a mixture of carbohydrate and fat for energy. At lower exercise intensities, we rely more on fat as a fuel source. As exercise intensity increases, we rely more on carbohydrate for energy.

Data from Brooks, G. A., and J. Mercier. 1994. Balance of carbohydrate and lipid utilization during exercise: the "crossover" concept. *J. Appl. Physiol.* 76(6):2253–2261.

maximal exercise (at 90–100% effort), we are using virtually all carbohydrate. However, most activities we do each day involve some use of both fuels (**Figure 7**).

When it comes to eating properly to support regular physical activity or exercise training, the nutrient to focus on is carbohydrate. This is because most people store more than enough fat to support exercise, whereas our storage of carbohydrate is limited. It is especially important that we maintain adequate stores of glycogen for moderate to intense exercise. Dietary recommendations for fat, carbohydrate, and protein are reviewed later in this chapter.

Amino Acids Are Not Major Sources of Fuel during Exercise

Proteins, or more specifically amino acids, are not major energy sources during exercise. Amino acids can be used directly for energy if necessary, but they are more often used to make glucose to maintain our blood glucose levels during exercise. Amino acids also help build and repair tissues after exercise. Depending on the intensity and duration of the activity, amino acids may contribute about 1–6% of the energy needed.[17]

Given this, why is it that so many people are concerned about their protein intakes? Our muscles are not stimulated to grow when we eat extra dietary protein. Only appropriate physical training can stimulate our muscles to grow and strengthen. Thus, while we need enough dietary protein to support activity and recovery, consuming very high amounts does not provide an added benefit. The protein needs of athletes are only slightly higher than the needs of non-athletes, and most of us eat more than enough protein to support even the highest requirements for competitive athletes! Thus, there is generally no need for recreationally active people or even competitive athletes to consume protein or amino acid supplements.

RECAP The amount of ATP stored in a muscle cell is limited and can keep a muscle active for only about 1 to 3 seconds. For intense activities lasting about 3 to 15 seconds, creatine phosphate can be broken down to provide energy and support the regeneration of ATP. To support activities that last from 30 seconds to 2 minutes, energy is produced from glycolysis. Fatty acids can be broken down aerobically to support activities of low intensity and longer duration. The two major advantages of using fat as a fuel are that it is an abundant energy source and it provides more than twice the energy per gram as compared with carbohydrate. Amino acids may contribute from 3% to 6% of the energy needed during exercise, depending on the intensity and duration of the activity. Amino acids help build and repair tissues after exercise.

What Kind of Diet Supports Physical Activity?

Lots of people wonder, "Do my nutrient needs change if I become more physically active?" The answer to this question depends on the type, intensity, and duration of the activity in which you participate. It is not necessarily true that our requirement for every nutrient is greater if we are physically active.

People who are performing moderate-intensity daily activities for health can follow the dietary guidelines put forth in the USDA Food Guide. For smaller or less active people, the lower end of the range of recommendations for each food group may be appropriate. For larger or more active people, the higher end of the range is suggested. Modifications may be necessary for people who exercise vigorously every day, particularly for athletes training for competition. **Table 2** provides an overview of the nutrients that can be affected by regular, vigorous exercise training. Each of these nutrients is described in more detail in the following section.[18]

Small snacks can be helpful to meet daily energy demands.

Stephen Oliver/Dorling Kindersley

TABLE 2	Suggested Intakes of Nutrients to Support Vigorous Exercise	
Nutrient	**Functions**	**Suggested Intake**
Energy	Supports exercise, activities of daily living, and basic body functions	Depends on body size and the type, intensity, and duration of activity. For many female athletes: 1,800 to 3,500 kcal/day For many male athletes: 2,500 to 7,500 kcal/day
Carbohydrate	Provides energy, maintains adequate muscle glycogen and blood glucose; high complex carbohydrate foods provide vitamins and minerals	45–65% of total energy intake Depending on sport and gender, should consume 6–10 g of carbohydrate per kg body weight per day
Fat	Provides energy, fat-soluble vitamins, and essential fatty acids; supports production of hormones and transport of nutrients	20–35% of total energy intake
Protein	Helps build and maintain muscle; provides building material for glucose; energy source during endurance exercise; aids recovery from exercise	10–35% of total energy intake Endurance athletes: 1.2–1.4 g per kg body weight Strength athletes: 1.2–1.7 g per kg body weight
Water	Maintains temperature regulation (adequate cooling); maintains blood volume and blood pressure; supports all cell functions	Consume fluid before, during, and after exercise Consume enough to maintain body weight Consume at least 8 cups (64 fl. oz) of water daily to maintain regular health and activity Athletes may need up to 10 liters (170 fl. oz) every day; more is required if exercising in a hot environment
B-vitamins	Critical for energy production from carbohydrate, fat, and protein	May need slightly more (one to two times the RDA) for thiamin, riboflavin, and vitamin B_6
Calcium	Builds and maintains bone mass; assists with nervous system function, muscle contraction, hormone function, and transport of nutrients across cell membrane	Meet the current AI: 14–18 years: 1,300 mg/day 19–50 years: 1,000 mg/day 51 and older: 1,200 mg/day
Iron	Primarily responsible for the transport of oxygen in blood to cells; assists with energy production	Consume at least the RDA: Males: 14–18 years: 11 mg/day 19 and older: 8 mg/day Females: 14–18 years: 15 mg/day 19–50 years: 18 mg/day 51 and older: 8 mg/day

Vigorous Exercise Increases Energy Needs

Athletes generally have higher energy needs than moderately physically active or sedentary people. The amount of extra energy needed to support regular training is determined by the type, intensity, and duration of the activity. In addition, the energy needs of male athletes are higher than those of female athletes because male athletes weigh more, have more muscle mass, and expend more energy during activity. This is relative, of course: a large woman who trains 3 to 5 hours each day will probably need more energy than a small man who trains 1 hour each day. The energy needs of athletes can range from only 1,500 to 1,800 kcal/day for a small female gymnast to more than 7,500 kcal/day for a male cyclist competing in the Tour de France cross-country cycling race!

Figure 8 shows a sample of meals that total 1,800 kcal per day and 4,000 kcal per day, with the carbohydrate content of these meals meeting more than 60% of total energy intake. As you can see, athletes who require more than 4,000 kcal per day need to consume very large quantities of food. However, the heavy demands of daily physical training, work, school, and family responsibilities often leave these athletes with little time to eat adequately. Thus, many athletes meet their energy demands by planning regular meals and snacks and **grazing** (eating small meals throughout the day) consistently. They may also take advantage of the energy-dense snack foods and meal replacements specifically designed for athletes participating in vigorous training. These steps help athletes maintain their blood glucose and energy stores.

grazing Consistently eating small meals throughout the day; done by many athletes to meet their high energy demands.

1,800 kcal/day	4,000 kcal/day
Breakfast: 1½ cups Cheerios 4 oz skim milk 1 medium banana 8 fl. oz orange juice	**Breakfast:** 3 cups Cheerios 8 fl. oz skim milk 1 medium banana 2 slices whole-wheat toast 1 tbsp. butter 16 fl. oz orange juice

Lunch:
Turkey sandwich with:
  2 slices whole-wheat bread
  3 oz turkey lunch meat
  1 oz Swiss cheese slice
  1 leaf iceberg lettuce
  2 slices tomato
1 cup tomato soup
  (made with water)
	Lunch:
	Two turkey sandwiches with:
	  2 slices whole-wheat bread
	  3 oz turkey lunch meat
	  1 oz Swiss cheese slice
	  1 leaf iceberg lettuce
	  2 slices tomato
	2 cups tomato soup
	  (made with water)
	Two 8-oz containers of
	  low-fat fruit yogurt
	24 fl. oz Gatorade

Dinner:
4 oz grilled skinless
  chicken breast
1½ cups mixed salad greens
1 tbsp. French salad dressing
1 cup steamed broccoli
1 cup cooked brown rice
8 fl. oz skim milk
	Dinner:
	6 oz grilled skinless
	  chicken breast
	3 cups mixed salad greens
	3 tbsp. French salad dressing
	2 cups cooked
	  spaghetti noodles
	1 cup spaghetti sauce
	  with meat
	16 fl. oz skim milk

Laura Murray

Figure 8 High-carbohydrate (approximately 60% of total energy) meals that contain approximately 1,800 kcal/day (on left) and 4,000 kcal/day (on right). Athletes, particularly those with very high energy needs, must plan their meals carefully to meet energy demands.

Some athletes diet to meet a predefined weight category.

If an athlete is losing body weight, then his or her energy intake is inadequate. Conversely, weight gain may indicate that energy intake is too high. Weight maintenance is generally recommended to maximize performance. If weight loss is warranted, food intake should be lowered no more than 200 to 500 kcal/day, and athletes should try to lose weight prior to the competitive season, if at all possible. Weight gain may be necessary for some athletes and can usually be accomplished by consuming 500 to 700 kcal/day more than needed for weight maintenance. The extra energy should come from a healthy balance of carbohydrate (45–60% of total energy intake), fat (20–35% of total energy intake), and protein (10–35% of total energy intake).

Many athletes are concerned about their weight. Jockeys, boxers, wrestlers, judo athletes, and others are required to "make weight"—to meet a predefined weight category. Others, such as distance runners, gymnasts, figure skaters, and dancers, are required to maintain a very lean figure for performance and aesthetic reasons. These athletes tend to eat less energy than they need to support vigorous training, which puts them at risk for inadequate intakes of all nutrients. These athletes are also at a higher risk of suffering from health consequences resulting from poor energy and nutrient intake, including eating disorders, osteoporosis, menstrual disturbances, dehydration, heat and physical injuries, and even death.

Carbohydrate Needs Increase for Many Active People

As you know, carbohydrate (in the form of glucose) is one of the primary sources of energy needed to support exercise. Both endurance athletes and strength athletes require adequate carbohydrate to maintain their glycogen stores and provide quick energy.

How Much of an Athlete's Diet Should Be Carbohydrate?

The AMDR for carbohydrates is 45–65% of total energy intake. Athletes should consume carbohydrate within this recommended range. Although high-carbohydrate diets (greater than 60% of total energy intake) have been recommended in the past, this percentage value may not be appropriate for all athletes.

To illustrate the importance of carbohydrate intake for athletes, let's see what happens to Theo when he participates in a study designed to determine how carbohydrate intake affects glycogen stores during a period of heavy training. Theo was asked to go to the exercise laboratory at the university and ride a stationary bicycle for 2 hours a day for 3 consecutive days at 75% of his maximal heart rate. Before and after each ride, samples of muscle tissue were taken from his thighs to determine the amount of glycogen stored in the working muscles. Theo performed these rides under two different experimental conditions—once when he had eaten a high-carbohydrate diet (80% of total energy intake) and again when he had eaten a moderate-carbohydrate diet (40% of total energy intake). As you can see in Figure 9, Theo's muscle glycogen levels decreased dramatically after each training session. More important, his muscle glycogen levels did not recover to baseline levels over the 3 days when Theo ate the lower-carbohydrate diet. He was able to maintain his muscle glycogen levels only when he was eating the higher-carbohydrate diet. Theo also told the researchers that completing the 2-hour rides was much more difficult when he had eaten the moderate-carbohydrate diet as compared to when he ate the diet that was higher in carbohydrate.

When Should Carbohydrates Be Consumed?

It is important for athletes not only to consume enough carbohydrate to maintain glycogen stores but also to time their intake optimally. Our body stores glycogen very rapidly during the first 24 hours of recovery from exercise, with the highest storage rates occurring during the first few hours.[19] Higher carbohydrate intakes during the first 24 hours of recovery from exercise are associated with higher amounts of glucose being stored as muscle glycogen. A daily carbohydrate intake of approximately 6 to

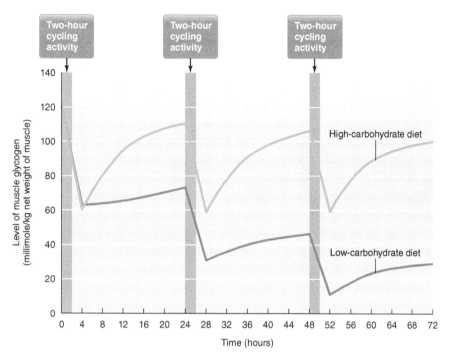

Figure 9 The effects of a low-carbohydrate diet on muscle glycogen stores. When a low-carbohydrate diet is consumed, glycogen stores cannot be restored during a period of regular vigorous training.

Data from Costill, D. L., and J. M. Miller. 1980. Nutrition for endurance sport: CHO and fluid balance. *Int. J. Sports Med.* 1:2–14. Copyright © 1980 Georg Thieme Verlag. Used with permission.

10 g of carbohydrate per kg body weight will optimize muscle glycogen stores in many athletes. However, this need might be much greater in athletes who are training heavily daily, as they have less time to recover and require more carbohydrate to support both training and storage needs.

If an athlete has to perform or participate in training bouts that are scheduled less than 8 hours apart, then he or she should try to consume enough carbohydrate in the few hours following training to allow for ample glycogen storage. However, with a longer recovery time (generally 12 hours or more), the athlete can eat when he or she chooses, and glycogen levels should be restored as long as the total carbohydrate eaten is sufficient.

Interestingly, studies have shown that muscle glycogen can be restored to adequate levels in the muscle whether the food is eaten in small, multiple snacks or in larger meals,[19] although some studies show enhanced muscle glycogen storage during the first 4 to 6 hours of recovery when athletes are fed large amounts of carbohydrate every 15 to 30 minutes.[20,21] There is also evidence that consuming high glycemic index foods during the immediate postrecovery period results in higher glycogen storage than is achieved as a result of eating low glycemic index foods. This may be due to a greater malabsorption of the carbohydrate in low glycemic index foods, as these foods contain more indigestible forms of carbohydrate.[19]

What Food Sources of Carbohydrates Are Good for Athletes?

What are good carbohydrate sources to support vigorous training? In general, complex, less processed carbohydrate foods, such as whole grains and cereals, fruits, vegetables, and juices, are excellent sources that also supply fiber, vitamins, and minerals. Guidelines recommend that intake of simple sugars be less than 10% of total energy intake, but some athletes who require very large energy intakes to support training may need to consume more. In addition, as previously mentioned, glycogen storage can be enhanced by consuming foods with a high glycemic index immediately postrecovery. Thus, there are advantages to consuming a wide variety of carbohydrate sources.

Photodisc/Getty Images

Fruit and vegetable juices can be a good source of carbohydrates.

As a result of time constraints, many athletes have difficulties consuming enough food to meet carbohydrate demands. Thus, many sports drinks and energy bars have been designed to help athletes increase their carbohydrate intake. Table 3, below, identifies some energy bars and other simple, inexpensive snacks and meals that contain 50 to 100 g of carbohydrate.

When Does Carbohydrate Loading Make Sense?

As you know, carbohydrate is a critical energy source to support exercise, particularly endurance-type activities. Because of the importance of carbohydrates as an exercise fuel and our limited capacity to store them, discovering ways to maximize our storage of carbohydrates has been at the forefront of sports nutrition research for many years. The practice of **carbohydrate loading,** also called *glycogen loading,* involves altering both exercise duration and carbohydrate intake such that it maximizes the amount of muscle glycogen. Table 4 reviews a schedule for carbohydrate loading for an endurance athlete.

Athletes who may benefit from maximizing muscle glycogen stores include those competing in marathons, ultra-marathons, long-distance swimming, cross-country skiing, and triathlons. Athletes who compete in baseball, American football, 10-kilometer runs, walking, hiking, weight lifting, and most swimming events will not gain any performance benefits from this practice, nor will people who regularly participate in moderately intense physical activities to maintain fitness.

It is important to realize that carbohydrate loading does not always improve performance. There are many adverse side effects of this practice, including extreme gastrointestinal distress, particularly diarrhea. We store water along with the extra glycogen in our muscles, which leaves many athletes feeling heavy and sluggish. Athletes who want to try carbohydrate loading should experiment prior to competition to determine whether it is an acceptable and beneficial approach for them.

carbohydrate loading Also known as glycogen loading. A process that involves altering training and carbohydrate intake, so that muscle glycogen storage is maximized.

TABLE 3	Carbohydrate and Total Energy in Various Foods				
Food	Amount	Carbohydrate (g)	Energy from Carbohydrate (%)	Total Energy (kcal)
Sweetened applesauce	1 cup	50	97	207
Large apple with	1 each	50	82	248
Saltine crackers	8 each			
Whole-wheat bread	1-oz slice	50	71	282
with jelly	4 tsp.			
and skim milk	12 fl. oz			
Spaghetti (cooked)	1 cup	50	75	268
with tomato sauce	1/4 cup			
Brown rice (cooked)	1 cup	100	88	450
with mixed vegetables	1/2 cup			
and apple juice	12 fl. oz			
Grape-Nuts cereal	1/2 cup	100	84	473
with raisins	3/8 cup			
and skim milk	8 fl. oz			
Clif Bar (chocolate chip)	2.4 oz	45	72	250
Meta-Rx (fudge brownie)	3.53 oz	48	60	320
Power Bar (chocolate)	2.25 oz	42	75	225
PR Bar Ironman	2 oz	24	42	230

Data from Manore, M. M., N. L. Meyer, and J. Thompson. 2009. *Sport Nutrition for Health and Performance,* 2nd ed. Champaign, IL: Human Kinetics.

TABLE 4	Recommended Carbohydrate Loading Guidelines for Endurance Athletes	
Days Prior to Event	Exercise Duration (minutes) at 70% Maximal Effort	Carbohydrate Content of Diet (g/kg of body weight)
6	90	5
5	40	5
4	40	5
3	20	10
2	20	10
1	Rest	10
Day of race	Competition	Precompetition food and fluid

Data from Coleman, E. 2006. Carbohydrate and exercise. In: Dunford, M., ed. *Sports Nutrition*, 4th ed. Chicago, IL: The American Dietetic Association. Used with permission.

Moderate Fat Consumption Is Enough to Support Most Activities

As you have learned, fat is an important energy source for both moderate physical activity and vigorous endurance training. When athletes reach a physically trained state, they are able to use more fat for energy; in other words, they become better "fat burners." This can also occur in people who are not athletes but who regularly participate in aerobic-type fitness activities. This training effect occurs for a number of reasons, including an increase in the number and activity of various enzymes involved in fat metabolism, improved ability of the muscle to store fat, and improved ability to extract fat from the blood for use during exercise. By using fat as a fuel, athletes can spare carbohydrate, so that they can use it during prolonged, intense training or competition.

Many athletes concerned with body weight and physical appearance believe they should eat less than 15% of their total energy intake as fat, but this is inadequate for vigorous activity. Instead, a fat intake of 20–35% of total energy intake is generally recommended for most athletes, with less than 10% of total energy intake as saturated fat.

These recommendations are also put forth for non-athletes. Fat provides not only energy but also fat-soluble vitamins and essential fatty acids that are critical to maintaining general health. If fat consumption is too low, inadequate levels of these nutrients can eventually prove detrimental to training and performance. Athletes who have chronic disease risk factors, such as high blood lipids, high blood pressure, or unhealthful blood glucose levels, should work with their physician to adjust their intake of fat and carbohydrate according to their health risks.

Scott T. Smith/Corbis

Carbohydrate loading may benefit endurance athletes, such as cross-country skiers.

Many Athletes Have Increased Protein Needs

The protein intakes suggested for competitive athletes and moderately active people are given in Table 5. Let's consider the terminology used in the table:

- Competitive male and female endurance athletes train 5 to 7 days per week for more than an hour each day; many of these individuals may train for 3 to 6 hours per day. These athletes need significantly more protein than the current RDA of 0.8 g of protein per kg body weight.
- Resistance athletes focus on building and maintaining muscle mass and strength. Those who are already trained need less protein than those who are initiating training. Studies do not support the claim that consuming more than 2 g of protein per kg body weight improves protein synthesis, muscle strength, or performance.[17]
- Moderate-intensity endurance athletes are people exercising four or five times per week for 45 to 60 minutes each time; these individuals may compete in community races and other activities. Their protein needs are only modestly increased above the RDA.

TABLE 5 Estimated Protein Requirements for Athletes

Group	Protein Requirements (g/kg of body weight)
Competitive male and female athletes	1.4–1.6
Moderate-intensity endurance athletes	1.2
Recreational endurance athletes	0.8–1.0
Football, power sports players	1.4–1.7
Resistance athletes, weight lifters (early training)	1.5–1.7
Resistance athletes, weight lifters (steady-state training)	1.0–1.2

Data from Tarnopolsky, M. 2006. Protein and amino acid needs for training and bulking up. In: Burke, L., and Deakin, V., eds. *Clinical Sports Nutrition*, 3rd ed. New York: McGraw-Hill.

- Recreational endurance athletes are people who exercise four or five times per week for 30 minutes at less than 60% of their maximal effort. These individuals have a protein need that is equal to or only slightly higher than the RDA.

As noted previously, most inactive people and many athletes in the United States consume more than enough protein to support their needs.[22] However, some athletes do not consume enough protein; these typically include individuals with very low energy intakes, vegetarians or vegans who do not consume high-protein food sources, and young athletes who are growing and are not aware of their higher protein needs.

In 1995, Dr. Barry Sears published *The Zone: A Dietary Road Map*, a book that claims numerous benefits of a high-protein, low-carbohydrate diet for athletes.[23] Since that time, Sears has published several additional books espousing the same principles, which are still being recommended to both athletes and non-athletes. Low-carbohydrate, high-protein diets are quite popular, especially among people who want to lose weight. Unlike many of the current high-protein diets, the Zone Diet was developed and marketed specifically for competitive athletes. It recommends that athletes eat a 40–30–30 diet, or one composed of 40% carbohydrate, 30% fat, and 30% protein. Dr. Sears claims that high-carbohydrate diets impair athletic performance because of unhealthy effects of insulin. These claims have never been supported by research—in fact, many of Dr. Sears's claims are not consistent with human physiology. The primary problem with the Zone Diet for athletes is that it is too low in both energy and carbohydrate to support training and performance.

High-quality protein sources include lean meats, poultry, fish, eggs and egg whites, low-fat dairy products, legumes, and soy products. By following the USDA Food Guide and meeting energy needs, people of all fitness levels can consume more than enough protein without the use of supplements or specially formulated foods.

RECAP The type, intensity, and duration of activities a person participates in determine his or her nutrient needs. Carbohydrate needs may increase for some active people. In general, athletes should consume 45–65% of their total energy as carbohydrate. Carbohydrate loading involves altering physical training and the diet such that the storage of muscle glycogen is maximized. Active people use more fat than carbohydrates for energy because they experience an increase in the number and activity of the enzymes involved in fat metabolism, and they have an improved ability to store fat and extract it from the blood for use during exercise. A dietary fat intake of 20–35% is recommended for athletes, with less than 10% of total energy intake as saturated fat. Although protein needs can be higher for athletes, most people in the United States already consume more than twice their daily needs for protein.

Regular Exercise Increases Our Need for Fluids

In this chapter, we will focus on the role of water during exercise.

Dave King/Dorling Kindersley

Water is essential for maintaining fluid balance and preventing dehydration.

Cooling Mechanisms

Heat production can increase fifteen to twenty times during heavy exercise! The primary way in which we dissipate this heat is through sweating, which is also called **evaporative cooling.** When body temperature rises, more blood (which contains water) flows to the surface of the skin. Heat is carried in this way from the core of our body to the surface of our skin. By sweating, the water (and body heat) leaves our body, and the air around us picks up the evaporating water from our skin, cooling our body.

Dehydration and Heat-Related Illnesses

Heat illnesses occur because when we exercise in the heat, our muscles and skin constantly compete for blood flow. When there is no longer enough blood flow to provide adequate blood to both our muscles and our skin, muscle blood flow takes priority and evaporative cooling is inhibited. Exercising in heat plus humidity is especially dangerous because whereas the heat dramatically raises body temperature, the high humidity inhibits evaporative cooling; that is, the environmental air is already so saturated with water that it is unable to absorb the water in sweat. Body temperature becomes dangerously high, and heat illness is likely.

It is important to remember that dehydration significantly increases our risk for heat illnesses. In **Figure 10**, specific signs of dehydration during heavy exercise are listed.

Guidelines for Proper Fluid Replacement

How can we prevent dehydration and heat illnesses? Obviously, adequate fluid intake is critical before, during, and after exercise. Unfortunately, our thirst mechanism cannot be relied upon to signal when we need to drink. If we rely only on our feelings of thirst, we will not consume enough fluid to support exercise.

General fluid replacement recommendations are based on maintaining body weight. Athletes who are training and competing in hot environments should weigh themselves before and after the training session or event and should regain the weight lost over the subsequent 24-hour period. They should avoid losing more than 2–3% of body weight during exercise, as performance can be impaired with fluid losses as small as 1% of body weight.

Table 6 reviews the guidelines for proper fluid replacement. For activities lasting less than 1 hour, plain water is generally adequate to replace fluid losses. However, for training and competition lasting longer than 1 hour in any weather, sports

Drinking sports beverages during training and competition lasting more than 1 hour replaces fluid, carbohydrates, and electrolytes.
David Young-Wolff/Getty Images

evaporative cooling Another term for sweating, which is the primary way in which we dissipate heat.

Symptoms of Dehydration During Heavy Exercise:
- Decreased exercise performance
- Increased level in perceived exertion
- Dark yellow or brown urine color
- Increased heart rate at a given exercise intensity
- Decreased appetite
- Decreased ability to concentrate
- Decreased urine output
- Fatigue and weakness
- Headache and dizziness

Lily Valde/Pixland/Jupiter Images

Dominic Burke/Alamy

Figure 10 Symptoms of dehydration during heavy exercise.

TABLE 6   Guidelines for Fluid Replacement

Activity Level	Environment	Fluid Requirements (liters per day)
Sedentary	Cool	2–3
Active	Cool	3–6
Sedentary	Warm	3–5
Active	Warm	5–10

Before Exercise or Competition:

- Drink adequate fluids during the 24 hours before event; should be able to maintain body weight.
- Slowly drink about 0.17 to 0.24 fl. oz per kg body weight of water or a sports drink at least 4 hours prior to exercise or event to allow time for excretion of excess fluid prior to event.
- Slowly drink another 0.10 to 0.17 fl. oz per kg body weight about 2 hours before event.
- Consuming beverages with sodium and/or small amounts of salted snacks at a meal will help stimulate thirst and retain fluids consumed.

During Exercise or Competition:

- Drink early and regularly throughout event to sufficiently replace all water lost through sweating.
- Amount and rate of fluid replacement depend on individual sweating rate, exercise duration, weather conditions, and opportunities to drink.
- Fluids should be cooler than the environmental temperature and flavored to enhance taste and promote fluid replacement.

During Exercise or Competition That Lasts More Than 1 Hour:

- Fluid replacement beverage should contain 5–10% carbohydrate to maintain blood glucose levels; sodium and other electrolytes should be included in the beverage in amounts of 0.5–0.7 g of sodium per liter of water to replace the sodium lost by sweating.

Following Exercise or Competition:

- Consume about 3 cups of fluid for each pound of body weight lost.
- Fluids after exercise should contain water to restore hydration status, carbohydrates to replenish glycogen stores, and electrolytes (for example, sodium and potassium) to speed rehydration.
- Consume enough fluid to permit regular urination and to ensure the urine color is very light or light yellow in color; drinking about 125–150% of fluid loss is usually sufficient to ensure complete rehydration.

In General:

- Products that contain fructose should be limited, as these may cause gastrointestinal distress.
- Caffeine and alcohol should be avoided, as these products increase urine output and reduce fluid retention.
- Carbonated beverages should be avoided, as they reduce the desire for fluid intake due to stomach fullness.

Data from Murray, R. 1997. Drink more! Advice from a world class expert. *ACSM's Health and Fitness Journal* 1:19–23; American College of Sports Medicine Position Stand. 2007. Exercise and fluid replacement. *Med. Sci. Sports Exerc.* 39(2):377–390; and Casa, D. J., L. E. Armstrong, S. K. Hillman, S. J. Montain, R. V. Reiff, B. S. E. Rich, W. O. Roberts, and J. A. Stone. 2000. National Athletic Trainers' Association position statement: fluid replacement for athletes. *J. Athlet. Train.* 35:212–224.

beverages containing carbohydrates and electrolytes are recommended. These beverages are also recommended for people who will not drink enough water because they don't like the taste. If drinking these beverages will guarantee adequate hydration, they are appropriate to use.

Inadequate Intakes of Some Vitamins and Minerals Can Diminish Health and Performance

When individuals train vigorously for athletic events, their requirements for certain vitamins and minerals may be altered. Many highly active people do not eat enough food or a variety of foods that allows them to consume enough of these nutrients, yet it is imperative that active people do their very best to eat an adequate, varied, and balanced diet to try to meet the increased needs associated with vigorous training.

B-Vitamins

The B-vitamins are directly involved in energy metabolism. There is reliable evidence that the requirements of active people for thiamin, riboflavin, and vitamin B_6 may be slightly higher than the current RDA due to increased production of energy in active people and inadequate dietary intake in some individuals.[22] However, these increased needs are easily met by consuming adequate energy and a lot of complex carbohydrates, fruits, and vegetables. Athletes and physically active people at risk for poor B-vitamin status are those who consume inadequate energy or who consume mostly refined carbohydrate foods, such as soda pop and sugary snacks. Vegan athletes and active individuals may be at risk for inadequate intake of vitamin B_{12}. Food sources enriched with this nutrient include soy and cereal products.

Calcium and the Female Athlete Triad

Calcium supports proper muscle contraction and ensures bone health. Calcium intakes are inadequate for most women in the United States, including both sedentary and active women. This is most likely due to a failure to consume foods that are high in calcium, particularly dairy products. While vigorous training does not appear to increase our need for calcium, we need to consume enough calcium to support bone health. If we do not, stress fractures and severe loss of bone can result.

Some female athletes suffer from a syndrome known as the *female athlete triad*. This condition is discussed in the **In Depth** following this chapter. In the female athlete triad, nutritional inadequacies cause irregularities in the menstrual cycle and hormonal disturbances that lead to a significant loss of bone mass. Thus, for female athletes, consuming the recommended amounts of calcium is critical. For female athletes who are physically small and have lower energy intakes, calcium supplementation may be needed to meet current recommendations.

Iron

Iron is a part of the hemoglobin molecule and is critical for the transport of oxygen in our blood to our cells and working muscles. Iron also is involved in energy production. Research has shown that active individuals lose more iron in the sweat, feces, and urine than do inactive individuals and that endurance runners lose iron when their red blood cells break down in their feet due to the high impact of running.[24] Female athletes and non-athletes lose more iron than male athletes because of menstrual blood losses, and females in general tend to eat less iron in their diet. Vegetarian athletes and active people may also consume less iron. Thus, many athletes and active people are at higher risk for iron deficiency. Depending on its severity, poor iron status can impair athletic performance and our ability to maintain regular physical activity.

Not all athletes suffer from iron deficiency. A phenomenon known as *sports anemia* was identified in the 1960s. Sports anemia is not true anemia, but a transient decrease in iron stores that occurs at the start of an exercise program for some people, and it is seen in athletes who increase their training intensity. Exercise training increases the amount of water in our blood (called *plasma volume*); however, the amount of hemoglobin does not increase until later in the training period. Thus, the iron content in the blood appears to be low but instead is falsely depressed due to increases in plasma volume. Sports anemia, since it is not true anemia, does not affect performance.

In general, it appears that physically active females are at relatively high risk of suffering from the first stage of iron depletion, in which iron stores are low.[25,26] Because of this, it is suggested that blood tests of iron stores and monitoring of dietary iron intake be done routinely for active females.[22] In some cases, iron needs cannot be met through the diet, and supplementation is necessary. Iron supplementation should be done with a physician's approval and proper medical supervision.

"Ever since I did that cycling test in the fitness lab, I've been watching my carbohydrates. Lately, I've been topping 500 grams of carbs a day. But now I'm beginning to wonder, am I getting enough protein? I'm starting to feel really wiped out, especially after games. We've won four out of the last five games, and I'm giving it everything I've got, but today I was really dragging myself through practice. I'm eating about 150 grams of protein a day, but I think I'm going to try one of those protein powders they sell at my gym. I guess I just feel like, when I'm competing, I need some added insurance."

Theo's weight averages about 190 pounds during basketball season. Given what you've learned about the role of the energy nutrients in vigorous physical activity, what do you think might be causing Theo to feel "wiped out"? Would you recommend that Theo try the protein supplement? What other strategies might be helpful for him to consider?

Stockbyte/Getty Images

RECAP Regular exercise increases fluid needs. Fluid is critical to cool our internal body temperature and prevent heat illnesses. Dehydration is a serious threat during exercise in extreme heat and high humidity. Active people may need more thiamin, riboflavin, and vitamin B_6 than inactive people. Exercise itself does not increase our calcium needs, but most women, including active women, do not consume enough calcium. Some female athletes suffer from the female athlete triad, a condition that involves the interaction of low energy availability, osteoporosis, and amenorrhea. Many active individuals require more iron, particularly female athletes and vegetarian athletes.

Are Ergogenic Aids Necessary for Active People?

Many competitive athletes and even some recreationally active people search continually for that something extra that will enhance their performance. **Ergogenic aids** are substances used to improve exercise and athletic performance. For example, nutrition supplements can be classified as ergogenic aids, as can anabolic steroids and other pharmaceuticals. Interestingly, people report using ergogenic aids not only to enhance athletic performance but also to improve their physical appearance, prevent or treat injuries, treat diseases, and help them cope with stress. Some people even report using them because of peer pressure!

As you have learned in this chapter, adequate nutrition is critical to athletic performance and to regular physical activity, and products such as sports bars and beverages can help athletes maintain their competitive edge. However, as we will explore shortly, many of these products are not effective, some are dangerous, and most are very expensive. For the average consumer, it is virtually impossible to track the latest research findings for these products. In addition, many have not been adequately studied, and unsubstantiated false claims surrounding them are rampant. How can you become a more educated consumer about ergogenic aids?

New ergogenic aids are available virtually every month, and keeping track of these substances is a daunting task. It is therefore not possible to discuss every avail-

ergogenic aids Substances used to improve exercise and athletic performance.

Ergogenic Aids: Let the Buyer Beware?

The sale of ergogenic aids is a multibillion-dollar industry, and some companies resort to misleading claims to boost their share of the market. Beware of the following deceptive tactics used to market ergogenic aids:

1. Taking published research out of context, applying the findings in an unproven manner, or having inappropriate control over study results. Some companies claim that research has been done or is currently being done, but fail to provide specific information.

2. Paying celebrities to endorse products—remember that testimonials can be faked, bought, and exaggerated.

3. Stating that the product is patented and that this proves its effectiveness. Patents are granted to indicate differences among products.

4. Advertizing through infomercials and mass-media marketing videos. Although the Federal Trade Commission (FTC) regulates false claims in advertising, products are generally investigated only if they pose significant public danger.

5. Offering mail-order fitness evaluations or anabolic measurements. Most of these evaluations are inappropriate and inaccurate.

able product in this chapter. However, a brief review of a number of currently popular ergogenic aids is provided.

Anabolic Products Are Touted as Muscle and Strength Enhancers

Many ergogenic aids are said to be **anabolic,** meaning that they build muscle and increase strength. Most anabolic substances promise to increase testosterone, which is the hormone that is associated with male sex characteristics and that increases muscle size and strength. Although some anabolic substances are effective, they are generally associated with harmful side effects.

Anabolic Steroids

Anabolic steroids are testosterone-based drugs that have been used extensively by strength and power athletes. Anabolic steroids are known to be effective in increasing muscle size, strength, power, and speed. However, these products are illegal in the United States, and their use is banned by all major collegiate and professional sports organizations, in addition to both the U.S. and the International Olympic Committees. The following are proven long-term and irreversible effects of steroid use:

- infertility
- early closure of the plates of the long bones, resulting in permanent shortened stature
- shriveled testicles, enlarged breast tissue (that can be removed only surgically), and other signs of "feminization" in men
- enlarged clitoris, facial hair growth, and other signs of "masculinization" in women
- increased risk for certain forms of cancer
- liver damage
- unhealthful changes in blood lipids
- hypertension
- severe acne
- hair thinning or baldness
- disorders such as depression, delusions, sleep disturbances, and extreme anger (so-called roid rage)

Anabolic substances are often marketed to people wishing to increase muscle size, but carry risks for harmful side effects.
Altrendo/Getty Images

Androstenedione and Dehydroepiandrosterone

Androstenedione ("andro") and dehydroepiandrosterone (DHEA) are precursors of testosterone. Manufacturers of these products claim that taking them will increase testosterone levels and muscle strength. Androstenedione became very popular after baseball player Mark McGwire claimed he used it during the time he was breaking home run records. A national survey found that, in 2002, about one of every forty high-school seniors had used it in the past year.[27] Contrary to popular claims, recent

anabolic The term applied to a substance that builds muscle and increases strength.

studies have found that neither androstenedione nor DHEA increases testosterone levels, and androstenedione has been shown to increase the risk for heart disease in men aged 35 to 65.[28] There are no studies that support claims that these products improve strength or increase muscle mass.

Gamma-Hydroxybutyric Acid

Gamma-hydroxybutyric acid, or GHB, has been promoted as an alternative to anabolic steroids for building muscle. The production and sale of GHB have never been approved in the United States; however, it was illegally produced and sold on the black market. For many users, GHB caused only dizziness, tremors, or vomiting, but others experienced severe side effects, including seizures. Many people were hospitalized and some died.

After GHB was banned, a similar product (gamma-butyrolactone, or GBL) was marketed in its place. This product was also found to be dangerous and was removed from the market. Recently, another replacement product called BD, or 1,4-butanediol, was banned because it has caused at least seventy-one deaths, with forty more under investigation. BD is an industrial solvent and is listed on ingredient labels as tetramethylene glycol, butylene glycol, or sucol-B. Side effects include wild, aggressive behavior; nausea; incontinence; and sudden loss of consciousness.

Creatine

Creatine is a supplement that has become wildly popular with strength and power athletes. Creatine, or creatine phosphate, is found in meat and fish and stored in our muscles. As described earlier in this chapter, we use creatine phosphate (CP) to regenerate ATP. It is hypothesized that, by taking creatine supplements, individuals have more CP available to replenish ATP, which will prolong their ability to train and perform in short-term, explosive activities, such as weight lifting and sprinting. Between 1994 and 2010, more than 1,700 research articles related to creatine and exercise in humans were published. These studies indicate that creatine does not enhance performance in aerobic-type events, but it does enhance sprint performance in swimming, running, and cycling.[28-32] Other studies have shown that creatine increases the work performed and the amount of strength gained during resistance exercise.[31,33,34] Currently, creatine is not banned by any sports governing bodies, and many collegiate sports programs readily provide creatine supplements for their athletes.

In January 2001, the *New York Times* reported that the French government had claimed that creatine use could lead to cancer.[35] The news spread quickly across national and international news organizations and over the Internet. These claims were subsequently found to be false, as there are no studies in humans that suggest an increased risk for cancer with creatine use. In fact, numerous studies show an anticancer effect for creatine.[36,37] Although side effects such as dehydration, muscle cramps, and gastrointestinal disturbances have been reported with creatine use, there is very little information on how the long-term use of creatine impacts health. Further research is needed to determine the effectiveness and safety of creatine use over prolonged periods of time.

Some Products Are Said to Optimize Fuel Use during Exercise

Certain ergogenic aids are touted as increasing energy levels and improving athletic performance by optimizing our use of fat, carbohydrate, and protein. The products reviewed here are caffeine, ephedrine, carnitine, chromium, and ribose.

Caffeine

Caffeine is a stimulant that makes us feel more alert and energetic, decreasing feelings of fatigue during exercise. Caffeine has been shown to increase the use of fat as a fuel during endurance exercise, which spares muscle glycogen and improves performance.[38,39] Energy drinks that contain high amounts of caffeine, such as Red Bull, have become popular with athletes and many college students. These drinks should be avoided during exercise, as severe dehydration can result due to the combination of fluid loss from exercise and caffeine consumption. It should be recognized that caffeine is a controlled or restricted drug in the athletic world, and athletes can be banned from Olympic competition if urine caffeine levels are too high. However, the amount of caffeine that is banned is quite high, and athletes would need to consume caffeine in pill form to reach this level. Side effects of caffeine use include increased blood pressure, increased heart rate, dizziness, insomnia, headache, and gastrointestinal distress.

Ephedrine is made from the herb *Ephedra sinica* (Chinese ephedra).

Ephedrine

Ephedrine, also known as ephedra, Chinese ephedra, or *ma huang,* is a strong stimulant marketed as a weight-loss supplement and energy enhancer. In reality, many products sold as Chinese ephedra (or herbal ephedra) contain ephedrine from the laboratory and other stimulants, such as caffeine. The use of ephedra supplements does not appear to enhance performance, but supplements containing both caffeine and ephedra have been shown to prolong the amount of exercise that can be done until exhaustion is reached.[40] Ephedra is known to reduce body weight and body fat in sedentary women, but its impact on weight loss and body fat levels in athletes is unknown. Side effects of ephedra use include headaches, nausea, nervousness, anxiety, irregular heart rate, and high blood pressure, and at least seventeen deaths have been attributed to its use.[41] It is currently illegal to sell ephedra-containing supplements in the United States.

Carnitine

Carnitine is a compound made from amino acids that is found in the mitochondrial membrane of our cells. Carnitine helps shuttle fatty acids into the mitochondria, so that they can be used for energy. In theory, it has been proposed that exercise training depletes our cells of carnitine and that supplementation should increase the amount of carnitine in our cell membranes. By increasing cellular levels of carnitine, we should be able to improve our use of fat as a fuel source. Thus, carnitine is marketed not only as a performance-enhancing substance but also as a "fat burner." Research studies of carnitine supplementation do not support these claims, as neither the transport of fatty acids nor their oxidation appears to be enhanced with supplementation.[42,43] Use of carnitine supplements has not been associated with significant side effects.

Chromium

Chromium is a trace mineral that enhances insulin's action of increasing the transport of amino acids into the cell. It is found in whole-grain foods, cheese, nuts, mushrooms, and asparagus. It is theorized that many people are chromium deficient and that supplementation will enhance the uptake of amino acids into muscle cells, which will increase muscle growth and strength. Like carnitine, chromium is marketed as a fat burner, as it is speculated that its effect on insulin stimulates the brain to decrease food intake.[41] Chromium supplements are available as chromium picolinate and chromium nicotinate. Early studies of chromium supplementation showed promise, but more recent, better-designed studies do not support any benefit of chromium supplementation to muscle mass, muscle strength, body fat, or exercise performance.[44]

Ribose

Ribose is a five-carbon sugar that is critical to the production of ATP. Ribose supplementation is claimed to improve athletic performance by increasing work output and promoting a faster recovery time from vigorous training. While ribose has been shown to improve exercise tolerance in patients with heart disease,[45] several studies have reported that ribose supplementation has no impact on athletic performance.[46–48]

From this review of ergogenic aids, you can see that most of these products are not effective in enhancing athletic performance or optimizing muscle strength or body composition. It is important to be a savvy consumer when examining these products to make sure you are not wasting your money or putting your health at risk by using them.

RECAP Ergogenic aids are substances used to improve exercise and athletic performance. Anabolic steroids are effective in increasing muscle size, power, and strength, but they are illegal and can cause serious health problems. Androstenedione and dehydroepiandrosterone are precursors of testosterone; neither of these products has been shown to effectively increase testosterone levels or to increase strength or muscle mass. Creatine supplements are popular and can enhance sprint performance in swimming, running, and cycling. Caffeine is a stimulant that increases the use of fat during exercise; its use in the athletic world is controlled. Ephedrine is a stimulant that has potentially fatal side effects. Carnitine, chromium, and ribose are marketed as ergogenic aids but studies do not support their effectiveness.

Nutrition DEBATE

How Much Physical Activity Is Enough?

Your aerobics instructor tells you to work out at your target heart rate for 20 minutes a day, whereas your doctor tells you to walk for half an hour three or four times a week. A magazine article exhorts you to work out to the point of exhaustion, while a new weight-loss book claims that you can be perfectly healthy without ever breaking a sweat. As if these mixed messages about what constitutes "regular physical activity" weren't enough, a report from the Institute of Medicine (IOM), which contributed to the 2005 Dietary Guidelines for Americans, inadvertently added to the confusion. This report recommended that Americans be active 60 minutes per day to optimize health.[9] This message appears contradictory to the Surgeon General's report published in 1996, which recommended that Americans accumulate 30 minutes of physical activity on most, if not all, days of the week to optimize health.[1]

So how much activity is really enough? To try to answer this question, let's take a closer look at how the two reports differ. The Surgeon General's report considers a combination of what we have learned from two types of studies not used by the IOM: exercise training studies and population-based epi-demiological studies. *Exercise training studies* involve putting individuals through a clearly defined training program and assessing fitness and health outcomes. These studies consis-tently show that less fit and older individuals can significantly improve their cardiorespiratory fitness and reduce their risk for chronic diseases by participating in moderate levels of physical activity.[49,50] In contrast, *population-based epidemiological studies* compare self-reports of physical activity and/or fitness to rates of illness and mortality.[51,52] In other words, these studies do not assess the direct effect of exercise training; instead, they assess only the relationship between level of physical activity/fitness and rates of disease and premature death. These studies show that unfit, sedentary people suffer from the highest rates of disease and premature mortality and that increased physical activity significantly correlates to decreased risks for chronic diseases and premature mortality.

One challenge highlighted in the Surgeon General's report was how to determine the exact dose of exercise needed to improve physical fitness and health. Although the authors of this report acknowledged that using epidemiological studies to determine this dose was problematic, they pointed to studies indicating that expending an average of 150 kcal/day, which is equivalent to about 30 minutes of moderate physical activity per day, is associated with significant reductions in disease risk and premature mortality.[53–56] They therefore used this infor-mation to shape the recommendations put forth in the Surgeon General's report. It is important to emphasize that these recommendations were intended for individuals who are currently inactive. They were not intended to apply to individuals who are already doing more than 30 minutes of activity a day. In fact, the Surgeon General's report emphasizes that additional health and fitness benefits will result by doing more moderate-intensity physical activity or by substituting vigorous physical activities for those that are moderate in intensity.

In contrast, the IOM based its physical activity recommendations on metabolic studies determining the energy expenditure associated with maintaining a healthful body weight (defined as a BMI of 18.5 to 25 kg/m²). After reviewing a large number of studies that assessed energy expenditure and BMI, the Institute of Medicine concluded that participating in about 60 minutes of moderately intense physical activity per day will move people from a very sedentary to an active lifestyle and will allow them to maintain a healthful body weight.

Although this recommendation appears to be very different from that of the Surgeon General's report, and may seem unrealistic, the IOM emphasizes that it includes all activities a person does above resting levels, including gardening, dog walking, housekeeping, and shopping.

So are these two recommendations really that different? Probably not. Nutrition experts, exercise physiologists, and other healthcare professionals all recognize that weight loss and healthful weight maintenance are easier to achieve by people who do more, not less, physical activity each day.

Stockbyte/Getty Images

Chapter Review

Test Yourself ANSWERS

1. True. About 54% of Americans are insufficiently active, and almost 16% report doing no leisure activity at all.

2. False. Our muscles are not stimulated to grow when we eat extra protein, whether as food or supplements. Weight-bearing exercise appropriately stresses the body and produces increased muscle mass and strength.

3. True. Most ergogenic aids do not produce the results that are advertised. Many ergogenic aids, such as anabolic steroids and ephedrine, can actually cause serious health consequences, even death.

Find the Quack

When Brian joined the track team his first year in high school, he found his passion. Now in his third year of college, he's built a reputation as a winning distance runner, and he has several medals to prove it. One day his friend Jim, who is the track team's top sprinter, tells him about creatine supplements. Jim says that since he started using them several weeks ago, his performance times have improved. With an intercollegiate marathon event approaching, Brian is looking to improve his performance, so he goes online to check out the creatine supplements website Jim recommends. Here's what he learns:

- "Creatine is an amino acid synthesized by the body that plays a vital role in anaerobic energy production by regenerating ATP in skeletal muscle."

- "Creatine supplementation has been shown in several controlled studies to increase muscle stores of creatine and to improve performance in athletes whose sports rely heavily on the creatine phosphate anaerobic energy pathway." (The article cites six recent studies published in academic journals.)

- "Creatine supplementation is most effective for the performance of intense bursts of activity."

- "The manufacturer has on file more than 1,000 testimonials from satisfied customers whose athletic performance improved after taking creatine supplements."

- "The recommended dosage for an athlete's 'loading phase' varies according to gender, weight, and other factors, but a general recommendation is to consume four or five doses of 5 g each per day, for 5 to 7 days. This will fill the muscles' creatine phosphate stores to capacity. After this, a reduced maintenance dose of approximately 2–5 g/day is recommended. Taken as recommended, the supplements cost as little as $1 a day!"

1. Explain what the website article means by "the creatine phosphate anaerobic energy pathway."

2. Brian is a distance runner. Would you recommend he purchase creatine supplements? Why or why not?

3. Brian's track teammate Jim is a sprinter. Do you think it's possible that he has experienced physiologic benefits from creatine supplementation, or do you think his increased performance times are due to the placebo effect? Explain.

4. Recall the Hot Topic on deceptive practices used to market ergogenic aids. How many of these were employed by the creatine supplements website? Is this website an example of quackery? Why or why not?

Answers can be found on the companion website, at www.pearsonhighered.com/thompsonmanore.

Review Questions

1. For moderate-intensity exercise, the intensity range typically recommended is
   a. 25–50% of your estimated maximal heart rate.
   b. 35–75% of your estimated maximal heart rate.
   c. 50–70% of your estimated maximal heart rate.
   d. 75–95% of your estimated maximal heart rate.

2. The amount of ATP stored in a muscle cell can keep a muscle active for about
   a. 1 to 3 seconds.
   b. 10 to 30 seconds.
   c. 1 to 3 minutes.
   d. 1 to 3 hours.

3. To support a long afternoon of gardening, the body predominantly uses which nutrient for energy?
   a. carbohydrate
   b. fat
   c. amino acids
   d. lactic acid

4. Creatine
   a. seems to enhance performance in aerobic-type events.
   b. appears to increase an individual's risk for bladder cancer.
   c. seems to increase strength gained in resistance exercise.
   d. is stored in the liver.

5. Athletes participating in an intense athletic competition lasting more than 1 hour should

   a. drink caffeinated beverages to improve their performance while maintaining their hydration.
   b. drink plain warm water copiously both before and during the event in response to fluid losses from sweating and desire to drink.
   c. drink plain ice water both before and during the event in response to thirst.
   d. drink a beverage containing carbohydrate and electrolytes both before and during the event in amounts that balance hydration with energy, carbohydrate, and electrolyte needs.

6. True or false? A sound fitness program overloads the body.

7. True or false? A dietary fat intake of 20–35% is generally recommended for athletes.

8. True or false? Carbohydrate loading involves altering the duration and intensity of exercise and intake of carbohydrate such that the storage of fat is minimized.

9. True or false? Sports anemia is a chronic decrease in iron stores that occurs in some athletes who have been training intensely for several months to years.

10. True or false? FIT stands for frequency, intensity, and time.

Answers to Review Questions can be found at the back of this text, and additional essay questions and answers are located on the companion website at www.pearsonhighered.com/ thompsonmanore.

Web Resources

www.americanheart.org
American Heart Association

The Healthy Lifestyle section of this site has sections on health tools, exercise and fitness, healthy diet, lifestyle management, and more.

www.acsm.org
American College of Sports Medicine

Click on "General Public" for guidelines on healthful aerobic activity and calculating your exercise heart rate range. You can also click on the "Fit Society Page" section to access ACSM's Fit Society Page newsletter.

www.cdc.gov/physicalactivity/everyone/guidelines
Centers for Disease Control and Prevention Physical Activity for Everyone

Visit on this site to learn more about how much physical activity is enough for children, adults, and older adults and how to set physical activity and fitness goals.

www.mypyramid.gov/pyramid/physical_activity
USDA MyPyramid Inside the Pyramid

Visit this site to learn more about physical activity and how to find ways to incorporate more physical activity into your daily life.

www.win.niddk.nih.gov/publications/physical
Weight Control Information Network

Find out more about healthy fitness programs from this website produced by the National Institute of Diabetes and Digestive and Kidney Diseases.

www.dietary-supplements.info.nih.gov
NIH Office of Dietary Supplements

Look on this National Institutes of Health site to learn more about the health effects of specific nutritional supplements.

www.nal.usda.gov/fnic
Food and Nutrition Information Center

Visit this site for links to detailed information about ergogenic aids and sports nutrition.

www.nutrition.arizona.edu/new
Nutrition Exercise Wellness

Check this University of Arizona site for information for athletes on nutrition, fluid intake, and ergogenic aids.

References

1. U.S. Department of Health and Human Services. 1996. Physical Activity and Health: A Report of the Surgeon General. Atlanta, GA: U.S. Department of Health and Human Services, Centers for Disease Control and Prevention, National Centers for Chronic Disease Prevention and Health Promotion.

2. Caspersen, C. J., K. E. Powell, and G. M. Christensen. 1985. Physical activity, exercise, and physical fitness: definitions and distinctions for health-related research. *Publ. Health Rep.* 100:126–131.

3. Heyward, V. H. 2006. Advanced Fitness Assessment and Exercise Prescription, 5th ed. Champaign, IL: Human Kinetics.

4. Davidson, M. R., M. L. London, and P. W. Ladewig. 2008. Olds' Maternal-Newborn Nursing and Women's Health Across the Lifespan, 8th edn. Upper Saddle River, NJ: Prentice Hall Health.

5. Centers for Disease Control and Prevention (CDC). 2005. Adult participation in recommended levels of physical activity—United States, 2001 and 2003. *Morbid. Mortal. Wkly. Rep.* 54(47):1208–1212.

6. Department of Health and Human Services. Centers for Disease Control and Prevention (CDC). 2010. Physical Activity Statistics. 1988-2008 No Leisure Time Physical Activity Trend Chart. http://www.cdc.gov/nccdphp/dnpa/physical/stats/leisure_time.htm.

7. Department of Health and Human Services. Centers for Disease Control and Prevention (CDC). 2007. YRBSS. 2007 National Youth Risk Behavior Survey Overview. http://www.cdc.gov/HealthyYouth/yrbs/pdf/yrbs07_us_overview.pdf.

8. Pate, R. R., M. G. Davis, T. N. Robinson, E. J. Stone, T. L. McKenzie, and J. C. Young. 2006. Promoting physical activity in children and youth. A leadership role for schools: A scientific statement from the American Heart Association Council on Nutrition, Physical Activity and Metabolism (Physical Activity Committee) in collaboration with the Councils on Cardiovascular Disease in the Young and Cardiovascular Nursing. *Circulation* 114:1214–1224.

9. Institute of Medicine, Food and Nutrition Board. 2002. Dietary Reference Intakes for Energy, Carbohydrates, Fiber, Fat, Protein and Amino Acids (Macronutrients). Washington, DC: National Academies Press.

10. Centers for Disease Control and Prevention. 2010. Physical Activity for Everyone. Target Heart Rate and Estimated Maximum Heart Rate. http://www.cdc.gov/physicalactivity/everyone/measuring/heartrate.html.

11. Centers for Disease Control and Prevention. 2005. Physical activity for everyone: Making physical activity part of your life: Tips for being more active. Available at http://www.cdc.gov/nccdphp/dnpa/physical/life/tips.htm.

12. United States Department of Health and Human Services. 2005. Get active: Goals. Available at http://www.smallstep.gov/step_3/step_3_goals.html.

13. Westerblad, H., D. G. Allen, and J. Lännergren. 2002. Muscle fatigue: lactic acid or inorganic phosphate the major cause? *News Physiol. Sci.* 17(1):17–21.

14. Brooks, G. A. 2000. Intra- and extra-cellular lactate shuttles. *Med. Sci. Sports Exerc.* 32:790–799.

15. Brooks, G. A. 2009. Cell-cell and intracellular lactate shuttles. *J. Physiol.* 587(23):5591–5600.

16. van Hall G., M. Stromstad, P. Rasmussen, O. Jans, M. Zaar, C. Gam, B. Quistorff, N.H. Secher, and H.B. Nielsen. 2009. Blood lactate is an important energy source for the human brain. *J. Cerebral Blood Flow & Metab.* 29(6):1121–1129.

17. Tarnopolsky, M. 2010. Protein and amino acid needs for training and bulking up. In: Burke, L., and Deakin, V., eds. Clinical Sports Nutrition, 3rd edn. Sydney, Australia: McGraw-Hill, pp. 61–95.

18. American College of Sports Medicine, American Dietetic Association, and Dietitians of Canada. 2009. Nutrition and athletic performance. Joint position statement. *Med. Sci. Sports Exerc.* 41:709–731.

19. Burke, L. 2010. Nutrition for recovery after training and competition. In: Burke, L., and Deakin, V., eds. Clinical Sports Nutrition, 4th ed. Sydney, Australia: McGraw-Hill, pp. 358–392.

20. van Loon, L. J. C., W. H. M. Saris, M. Kruijshoop, and A. J. M. Wagenmakers. 2000. Maximizing postexercise muscle glycogen synthesis: carbohydrate supplementation and the application of amino acid or protein hydrolysate mixtures. *Am. J. Clin. Nutr.* 72:106–111.

21. Jentjens, R. L., L. J. C. van Loon, C. H. Mann, A. J. M. Wagenmakers, and A. E. Jeukendrup. 2001. Addition of protein and amino acids to carbohydrates does not enhance postexercise muscle glycogen synthesis. *J. Appl. Physiol.* 91:839–846.

22. Manore, M., N. L. Meyer, and J. Thompson. 2009. Sports Nutrition for Health and Performance. 2nd Edition. Champaign, IL: Human Kinetics (117).

23. Sears, B. 1995. The Zone: A Dietary Road Map. New York: HarperCollins Publishers.

24. Weaver, C. M., and S. Rajaram. 1992. Exercise and iron status. *J. Nutr.* 122:782–787.

25. Haymes, E. M. 1998. Trace minerals and exercise. In: Wolinsky, I., ed. Nutrition and Exercise and Sport. Boca Raton, FL: CRC Press, pp. 1997–2218.

26. Haymes, E. M., and P. M. Clarkson. 1998. Minerals and trace minerals. In: Berning, J. R., and Steen, S. N., eds. Nutrition and Sport and Exercise. Gaithersburg, MD: Aspen Publishers, pp. 77–107.

27. Food and Drug Administration (FDA). 2004. HHS Launches Crackdown on Products Containing Andro. http://www.fda.gov/NewsEvents/Newsroom/PressAnnouncements/2004/ucm108262.htm.

28. Broeder, C. E., J. Quindry, K. Brittingham, L. Panton, J. Thomson, S. Appakondu, K. Breuel, R. Byrd, J. Douglas, C. Earnest, C. Mitchell, M. Olson, T. Roy, and C. Yarlagadda. 2000. The Andro Project: physiological and hormonal influences of androstenedione supplementation in men 35 to 65 years old participating in a high-intensity resistance training program. *Arch. Intern. Med.* 160:3093–3104.

29. Balsom, P. D., K. Söderlund, B. Sjödin, and B. Ekblom. 1995. Skeletal muscle metabolism during short duration high-intensity exercise: influence of creatine supplementation. *Acta Physiol. Scand.* 1154:303–310.

30. Grindstaff, P. D., R. Kreider, R. Bishop, M. Wilson, L. Wood, C. Alexander, and A. Almada. 1997. Effects of creatine supplementation on repetitive sprint performance and body composition in competitive swimmers. *Int. J. Sport Nutr.* 7:330–346.

31. Kreider, R. B., M. Ferreira, M. Wilson, P. Grindstaff, S. Plisk, J. Reinardy, E. Cantler, and A. L. Almada. 1998. Effects of creatine supplementation on body composition, strength, and sprint performance. *Med. Sci. Sports Exerc.* 30:73–82.

32. Tarnopolsky, M. A., and D. P. MacLennan. 2000. Creatine monohydrate supplementation enhances high-intensity exercise performance in males and females. *Int. J. Sport Nutr. Exerc. Metab.* 10:452–463.

33. Kreider, R., M. Ferreira, M. Wilson, and A. L. Almada. 1999. Effects of calcium beta-hydroxy-beta-methylbutyrate (HMB) supplementation during resistance-training on markers of catabolism, body composition and strength. *Int. J. Sports Med.* 20(8):503–509.

34. Volek, J. S., N. D. Duncan, S. A. Mazzetti, R. S. Staron, M. Putukian, A. L. Gomez, D. R. Pearson, W. J. Fink, and W. J. Kraemer. 1999. Performance and muscle fiber adaptations to

creatine supplementation and heavy resistance training. *Med. Sci. Sports Exerc.* 31:1147–1156.

35. Reuters. 2001. Creatine use could lead to cancer, French government reports. *New York Times*, January 25.

36. Jeong, K. S., S. J. Park, C. S. Lee, T. W. Kim, S. H. Kim, S. Y. Ryu, B. H. Williams, R. L. Veech, and Y. S. Lee. 2000. Effects of cyclocreatine in rat hepatocarcinogenesis model. *Anticancer Res.* 20(3A):1627–1633.

37. Ara, G., L. M. Gravelin, R. Kaddurah-Daouk, and B. A. Teicher. 1998. Antitumor activity of creatine analogs produced by alterations in pancreatic hormones and glucose metabolism. *In Vivo* 12:223–231.

38. Anderson, M. E., C. R. Bruce, S. F. Fraser, N. K. Stepto, R. Klein, W. G. Hopkins, and J. A. Hawley. 2000. Improved 2000-meter rowing performance in competitive oarswomen after caffeine ingestion. *Int. J. Sport Nutr. Exerc. Metab.* 10:464–475.

39. Spriet, L. L., and R. A. Howlett. 2000. Caffeine. In: Maughan, R. J., ed. Nutrition in Sport. Oxford: Blackwell Science.

40. Bucci, L. 2000. Selected herbals and human exercise performance. *Am. J. Clin. Nutr.* 72:624S–636S.

41. Williams, M. H. 1998. The Ergogenics Edge. Champaign, IL: Human Kinetics.

42. Hawley, J. A. 2002. Effect of increased fat availability on metabolism and exercise capacity. *Med. Sci. Sports Exerc.* 34(9):1485–1491.

43. Heinonen, O. J. 1996. Carnitine and physical exercise. *Sports Med.* 22:109–132.

44. Vincent, J. B. 2003. The potential value and toxicity of chromium picolinate as a nutritional supplement, weight loss agent and muscle development agent. *Sports Med.* 33(3):213–230.

45. Pliml, W., T. von Arnim, A. Stablein, H. Hofmann, H. G. Zimmer, and E. Erdmann. 1992. Effects of ribose on exercise-induced ischaemia in stable coronary artery disease. *Lancet* 340(8818):507–510.

46. Earnest, C. P., G. M. Morss, F. Wyatt, A. N. Jordan, S. Colson, T. S. Church, Y. Fitzgerald, L. Autrey, R. Jurca, and A. Lucia. 2004. Effects of a commercial herbal-based formula on exercise performance in cyclists. *Med. Sci. Sports Exerc.* 36(3):504–509.

47. Hellsten, Y., L. Skadhauge, and J. Bangsbo. 2004. Effect of ribose supplementation on resynthesis of adenine nucleotides after intense intermittent training in humans. *Am. J. Physiol. Regul. Integr. Comp. Physiol.* 286:R182–R188.

48. Kreider, R. B., C. Melton, M. Greenwood, C. Rasmussen, J. Lundberg, C. Earnest, and A. Almada. 2003. Effects of oral D-ribose supplementation on anaerobic capacity and selected metabolic markers in healthy males. *Int. J. Sport Nutr. Exerc. Metab.* 13(1):76–86.

49. King, A. C., W. L. Haskell, C. B. Taylor, H. C. Kraemer, and R. F. DeBusk. 1991. Group- vs. home-based exercise training in healthy older men and women: a community-based clinical trial. *JAMA* 266:1535–1542.

50. Kohrt, W. M., M. T. Malley, A. R. Coggan, R. J. Spina, T. Ogawa, A. A. Ehsani, R. E. Bourey, W. H. Martin, 3rd, and J. O. Holloszy. 1991. Effects of gender, age, and fitness level on response of Vo2max to training in 60–71 yr olds. *J. Appl. Physiol.* 71:2004–2011.

51. LaCroix, A. Z., S. G. Leveille, J. A. Hecht, L. C. Grothaus, and E. H. Wagner. 1996. Does walking decrease the risk of cardiovascular disease hospitalizations and death in older adults? *J. Am. Geriatr. Soc.* 44:113–120.

52. Blair, S. N., H. W. Kohl III, C. E. Barlow, R. S. Paffenbarger Jr., L. W. Gibbons, and C. A. Macera. 1995. Changes in physical fitness and all-cause mortality: a prospective study of healthy and unhealthy men. *JAMA* 273:1093–1098.

53. Paffenbarger, R. S., Jr., R. T. Hyde, A. L. Wing, and C.-C. Hsieh. 1986. Physical activity, all-cause mortality, and longevity of college alumni. *N. Engl. J. Med.* 314:605–613.

54. Leon, A. S., J. Connett, D. R. Jacobs Jr., and R. Rauramaa. 1987. Leisure-time physical activity levels and risk of coronary heart disease and death: the Multiple Risk Factor Intervention Trial. *JAMA* 258:2388–2395.

55. Slattery, M. L., D. R. Jacobs Jr., and M. Z. Nichaman. 1989. Leisure-time physical activity and coronary heart disease death: the U.S. Railroad Study. *Circulation* 79:304–311.

56. Helmrich, S. P., D. R. Ragland, R. W. Leung, and R. S. Paffenbarger Jr. 1991. Physical activity and reduced occurrence of non-insulin-dependent diabetes mellitus. *N. Engl. J. Med.* 325:147–152.

Answers to Review Questions

Answers to Review Questions 11-15 (essay questions) for this chapter are located on the Companion Website at **www.pearsonhighered.com/thompsonmanore**

1. **c.** 50 to 70% of your estimated maximal heart rate.
2. **a.** 1 to 3 seconds.
3. **b.** fat
4. **c.** seems to increase strength gained in resistance exercise.
5. **d.** drink a beverage containing carbohydrate and electrolytes both before and during the event in amounts that balance hydration with energy, carbohydrate, and electrolyte needs.
6. True.
7. False. A dietary fat intake of 15 to 25% of total energy intake is generally recommended for athletes.
8. False. Carbohydrate loading involves altering duration and intensity of exercise and intake of carbohydrate such that the storage of carbohydrate is maximized.
9. False. Sports anemia is not true anemia, but a transient decrease in iron stores that occurs at the start of an exercise program. This is a result of an initial increase in plasma volume (or water in our blood) that is not matched by an increase in hemoglobin.
10. True.

Cardiovascular Disease

WANT TO FIND OUT...

- **if high blood pressure and heart disease are the same thing?**

- **what makes "good cholesterol" good and "bad cholesterol" bad?**

- **whether you're at risk for cardiovascular disease?**

READ ON.

Only couch potatoes develop heart disease . . . or so we like to think. That's why the world was stunned in the summer of 2002 when Darryl Kile, a 33-year-old Major League Baseball pitcher for the St. Louis Cardinals, died of a heart attack in his Chicago hotel room the night before a scheduled game. An autopsy revealed a 90% blockage in two of Kile's coronary arteries—the vessels that supply blood to the heart. Although cardiovascular disease in an athlete is rare, Kile's family history revealed one very important risk factor: his father died of a heart attack at age 44.

Science Photo Library/Getty Images

What causes a heart attack? Are genetics always to blame? If you have a family history of cardiovascular disease, is there anything you can do to reduce your risk? We explore these questions *In Depth* here.

What Is Cardiovascular Disease?

Cardiovascular disease is a general term used to refer to any abnormal condition involving dysfunction of the heart (*cardio-* means "heart") and blood vessels (*vasculature*). There are many forms of this disease, but the three most common are the following:

- *Coronary heart disease* occurs when blood vessels supplying the heart (the *coronary arteries*) become blocked or constricted; such blockage reduces the flow of blood—and the oxygen and nutrients it carries—to the heart. This can result in chest pain, called *angina pectoris*, and lead to a heart attack.
- *Stroke* is caused by a blockage of one of the blood vessels supplying the brain (the *cerebral arteries*). When this occurs, the region of the brain that depends on that artery for oxygen and nutrients cannot function. As a result, the movement, speech, or other body functions controlled by that part of the brain suddenly stop.
- *Hypertension*, also called *high blood pressure*, is a condition that may not cause any symptoms, but

it increases your risk for a heart attack or stroke. If your blood pressure is high, it means that the force of the blood flowing through your arteries is above normal.

To understand cardiovascular disease, we need to look at a condition called *atherosclerosis*, which is responsible for the blockage of arteries that leads to heart attacks and strokes. What's more, hypertension is often a sign of underlying atherosclerosis. So let's take a closer look.

Atherosclerosis Is Narrowing of Arteries

Atherosclerosis is a disease in which arterial walls accumulate deposits of lipids and scar tissue that build up to such a degree that they impair blood flow. It's a complex process that begins with injury to the cells that line the insides of all arteries. Factors that commonly promote such injury are the forceful pounding of blood under

high pressure and blood-vessel damage from irritants, such as the nicotine in tobacco or the excessive blood glucose in people with poorly controlled diabetes. Whatever the cause, the injury leads to vessel inflammation, which is increasingly being recognized as an important marker of cardiovascular disease.[1] Inflamed vessels become weakened, allowing lipids, mainly cholesterol, to seep through the layers of the vessel wall and eventually become trapped in thick, grainy deposits called *plaque*. The term *atherosclerosis* reflects the presence of these deposits: *athere* is a Greek word meaning "a thick porridge."

As plaques form, they narrow the interior of the blood vessel **(Figure 1)**. This slowly diminishes the blood supply to any tissues "downstream." As a result, these tissues—including heart muscle—wither, and gradually lose their ability to function. Alternatively, the blockage may occur suddenly, because a plaque ruptures and *platelets*,

---

cardiovascular disease A general term that refers to abnormal conditions involving dysfunction of the heart and blood vessels; cardiovascular disease can result in heart attack or stroke.

atherosclerosis A condition characterized by accumulation of deposits of lipids and scar tissue on artery walls. These deposits build up to such a degree that they impair blood flow.

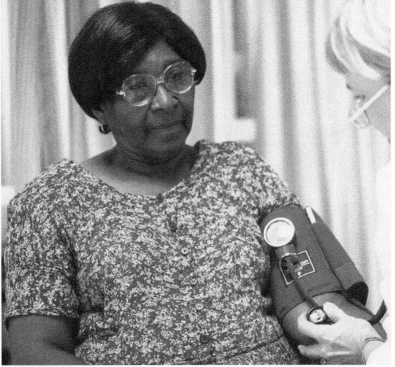

▲ Hypertension is a major chronic disease in the United States, affecting more than 50% of adults over 65 years old.

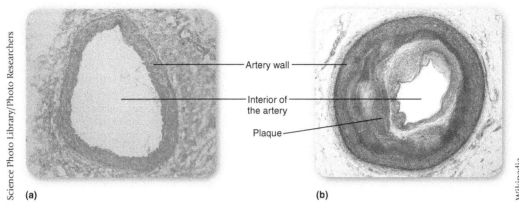

Artery wall

Interior of the artery

Plaque

(a)   (b)

Figure 1 These light micrographs show a cross section of **(a)** a normal artery containing little plaque and allowing adequate blood flow through the heart and **(b)** an artery that is partially blocked with cholesterol-rich plaque, which can lead to a heart attack.

substances in blood that promote clotting, stick to the damaged area. This quickly obstructs the artery, causing the death of the tissue it supplies. As a result, the person experiences a heart attack or stroke.

Arteries damaged by atherosclerosis become stiff; that is, they lose their ability to stretch and spring back with each heartbeat. This characteristic, often referred to as "hardening of the arteries," forces the heart to increase the pressure of each burst of blood it ejects into the stiffened vessels. Physicians refer to this increased pressure as *systolic hypertension*, as we explain next.

Hypertension Signals an Increased Risk for Heart Attack and Stroke

Hypertension is one of the major chronic diseases in the United States. It affects over 29% of all adults in the United States and more than 67% of people over the age of 60.[2] Although hypertension itself is often without symptoms, it is a warning sign that a person's risk for heart disease and stroke is increased. Hypertension can also damage the kidneys, reduce brain

function, impair physical mobility, and cause death.

When we define hypertension as blood pressure above the normal range, what exactly do we mean? Well, we measure blood pressure in two phases, systolic and diastolic. *Systolic blood pressure* represents the pressure exerted in our arteries at the

---

hypertension A chronic condition characterized by above-average blood pressure readings—specifically, systolic blood pressure over 140 mm Hg or diastolic blood pressure over 90 mm Hg.

NUTRI-CASE GUSTAVO

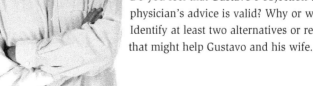

"Sometimes I wonder where doctors get their funny ideas. Yesterday I had my annual check-up and my doctor says, 'You're doing great! Your weight is fine, your blood sugar's good. The only thing that concerns me is that your blood pressure is a little high, so I want you to watch your diet. Choose fish more often. When you eat red meat, trim off the fat. Use one of the new heart-healthy margarines instead of butter, and use olive oil instead

of lard. And when you have eggs, don't eat the yolks.' I know he means well, but my wife's just now able to move around again after breaking her hip. How am I supposed to tell her she has to learn a whole new way to cook?"

Do you feel that Gustavo's objection to his physician's advice is valid? Why or why not? Identify at least two alternatives or resources that might help Gustavo and his wife.

Ned Frisk Photography/Corbis

369

moment that the heart contracts, sending blood into our blood vessels. *Diastolic blood pressure* represents the pressure in our arteries between contractions, when our heart is relaxed.

Blood pressure measurements are recorded in millimeters of mercury (mm Hg). Optimal systolic blood pressure is *less than* 120 mm Hg, while optimal diastolic blood pressure is *less than* 80 mm Hg. *Prehypertension* is defined as a systolic blood pressure between 120 and 139 mm Hg, or a diastolic blood pressure between 80 and 89 mm Hg. About 28% of adults in the United States are prehypertensive.[2] You would be diagnosed with true hypertension if your systolic blood pressure were greater than or equal to 140 mm Hg or your diastolic blood pressure were greater than or equal to 90 mm Hg.

What causes hypertension? For about 45–55% of people, hypertension is hereditary. This type is referred to as *primary* or *essential hypertension*. For the other 45% of people with hypertension, causes may include kidney disease, sleep apnea (a sleep disorder that affects breathing), certain medications, psychosocial stressors, tobacco use, obesity, low physical activity, excessive alcohol intake, and dietary factors, including sensitivity to salt and low potassium intake.[3]

Who Is at Risk for Cardiovascular Disease?

According to the Centers for Disease Control and Prevention, coronary heart disease is the leading cause of death in the United States, and stroke is the third leading cause of death. Hypertension contributes to both of these types of cardiovascular disease, which together account for more than 35% of all deaths annually, or one death every 38 seconds.[3, 4] Overall, about 80 million Americans of all ages suffer from cardiovascular disease. So—who's at risk?

Many Risk Factors Are within Your Control

Over the last two decades, researchers have identified a number of factors that contribute to an increased risk for cardiovascular disease. Some of these risk factors are nonmodifiable, meaning they are beyond your control. These include age—the older you are, the higher your risk—male gender, and family history. Like pitcher Darryl Kile, you have an increased risk for cardiovascular disease if a parent suffered a heart attack, especially at a young age.

Other risk factors are modifiable—meaning they are at least partly within your control. Following is a brief description of each of these modifiable risk factors. Notice that many of them have a dietary component.[5, 6, 7]

- *Overweight.* Being overweight is associated with cardiovascular disease and higher rates of death from cardiovascular disease. The risk is due primarily to a greater occurrence of high blood pressure, inflammation, abnormal blood lipids (discussed in more detail shortly), and higher rates of type 2 diabetes in people who are overweight. In general, an overweight condition develops from an energy

imbalance from eating too much and exercising too little.
- *Physical inactivity.* Numerous research studies have shown that physical activity can reduce your risk for cardiovascular disease by improving several risk factors associated with the disease, including improved blood lipid levels, lower resting blood pressure, lower body fat and weight, and improved blood glucose levels both at rest and after eating. Physical activity can also significantly reduce the risk for type 2 diabetes, a major cardiovascular disease risk factor.[7] According to the 2008 U.S. Physical Activity Guidelines,[8] physical activity can reduce your risk for heart disease by 20–30%, stroke by 25–30%, and type 2 diabetes by 25–35%.
- *Smoking.* There is strong evidence that smoking increases your risk for blood-vessel injury and cardiovascular disease. Research indicates that smokers have a two- to threefold greater chance of developing cardiovascular disease than nonsmokers.[5] If you smoke, quitting is one of the best ways to reduce your risk for cardiovascular disease. People who stop smoking live longer than those who continue to smoke, and a 15-year ces-

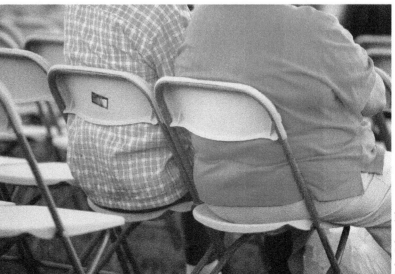

Gabe Palmer/Alamy

Being overweight is associated with higher rates of death from cardiovascular disease.

Because foods fried in hydrogenated vegetable oils, such as french fries, are high in *trans* fatty acids, these types of foods should be limited in our diet.

AP Photos

sation period will reduce your risk factors for cardiovascular disease to those of a nonsmoker.[9]

- *Type 2 diabetes mellitus.* In many individuals with type 2 diabetes, the condition is directly related to being overweight or obese, which is also associated with abnormal blood lipids and high blood pressure. The risk for cardiovascular disease is three times higher in women with diabetes and two times higher in men with diabetes compared to individuals without diabetes.
- *Inflammation.* We noted earlier that inflammation is considered a major contributor to cardiovascular disease.[1] When injury occurs to the arteries, the resulting inflammatory response eventually leads to the deposition of plaque in the arterial walls. Plaque buildup increases the risk for a heart attack or stroke. C-reactive protein (CRP) is a non-specific marker of inflammation

that is associated with cardiovascular disease. Risk for cardiovascular disease appears to be higher in individuals who have high CRP levels in addition to other risk factors, such as high blood lipids.[10] Thus, reducing the factors that promote inflammation, such as obesity and a diet low in omega-3 fatty acids and high in saturated fats, can lower your risk for cardiovascular disease.

- *Abnormal blood lipids.* As we explain next, high LDL-cholesterol and triglycerides and low HDL-cholesterol are associated with an increased risk for cardiovascular disease. Making lifestyle changes, such as lowering your intake of saturated and *trans* fat, increasing your physical activity and soluble fiber intake, and achieving a healthful body weight, can help improve your blood lipid profile.

The Role of Dietary Fats in Cardiovascular Disease

Recall that lipids are transported in the blood by lipoproteins made up of a lipid center and a protein outer coat. The names of lipoproteins reflect their proportion of lipid, which is less dense, to protein, which is very dense. For example, very-low-density lipoproteins (VLDLs) have a high ratio of lipid to protein. Because lipoproteins are soluble in blood, they are commonly called *blood lipids.*

Our intake of certain types of dietary fats influences our risk for heart disease by increasing or decreasing certain blood lipids. Research indicates that high intakes of saturated and *trans* fatty acids increase the blood's level of those lipids associated

with heart disease—namely, total blood cholesterol and the cholesterol found in very-low-density lipoproteins (VLDLs) and low-density lipoproteins (LDLs). Conversely, omega-3 fatty acids decrease our risk for heart disease in a number of ways, such as by reducing inflammation and blood triglycerides[11] and increasing high-density lipoproteins (HDLs).[12] Let's look at each of these blood lipids in more detail to determine how they are linked to your risk for heart disease (Figure 2).

Chylomicrons

Only after a meal does the blood contain chylomicrons, which we learned earlier are produced in the small intestine to transport dietary fat into the lymphatic vessels and from there into the bloodstream. At 85% triglyceride, chylomicrons have the lowest density.

Very-Low-Density Lipoproteins

More than half of the substance of **very-low-density lipoproteins (VLDLs)** is triglyceride. The liver is the primary source of VLDLs, but they are also produced in the intestines. VLDLs are primarily transport vehicles ferrying triglycerides from their source to the body's cells, including to adipose tissues for storage. The enzyme lipoprotein lipase frees most of the triglyceride from the VLDL molecules, resulting in its uptake by the body's cells.

Diets high in fat, simple sugars, and extra calories can increase the production of endogenous VLDLs, whereas diets high in omega-3 fatty acids can help reduce their production. In addition, exercise can reduce VLDLs because the fat produced in the body is quickly used for energy instead of remaining to circulate in the blood.

Low-Density Lipoproteins

The molecules resulting when VLDLs release their triglyceride load are

very-low-density lipoprotein (VLDL) A lipoprotein made in the liver and intestine that functions to transport endogenous lipids, especially triglycerides, to the tissues of the body.

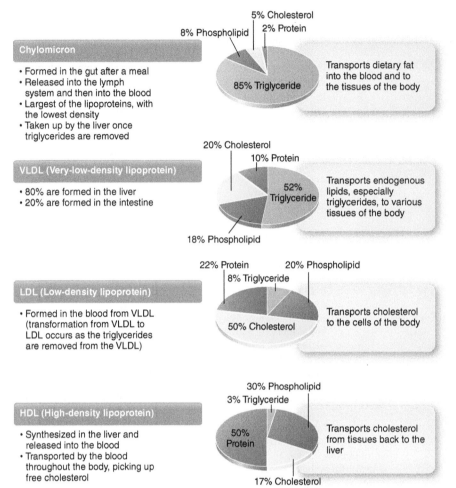

Chylomicron
- Formed in the gut after a meal
- Released into the lymph system and then into the blood
- Largest of the lipoproteins, with the lowest density
- Taken up by the liver once triglycerides are removed

5% Cholesterol
2% Protein
8% Phospholipid
85% Triglyceride
Transports dietary fat into the blood and to the tissues of the body

VLDL (Very-low-density lipoprotein)
- 80% are formed in the liver
- 20% are formed in the intestine

20% Cholesterol
10% Protein
52% Triglyceride
18% Phospholipid
Transports endogenous lipids, especially triglycerides, to various tissues of the body

LDL (Low-density lipoprotein)
- Formed in the blood from VLDL (transformation from VLDL to LDL occurs as the triglycerides are removed from the VLDL)

22% Protein
20% Phospholipid
8% Triglyceride
50% Cholesterol
Transports cholesterol to the cells of the body

HDL (High-density lipoprotein)
- Synthesized in the liver and released into the blood
- Transported by the blood throughout the body, picking up free cholesterol

30% Phospholipid
3% Triglyceride
50% Protein
17% Cholesterol
Transports cholesterol from tissues back to the liver

Figure 2 The chemical components of various lipoproteins. Notice that chylomicrons contain the highest proportion of triglycerides, making them the least dense, whereas high-density lipoproteins (HDLs) have the highest proportion of protein, making them the most dense.

much higher in cholesterol, phospholipids, and protein and therefore somewhat more dense. These **low-density lipoproteins (LDLs)** circulate in the blood, delivering their cholesterol to cells. Diets high in saturated fat *decrease* the removal of LDLs by body cells.

low-density lipoprotein (LDL) A lipoprotein formed in the blood from VLDLs that transports cholesterol to the cells of the body. Often called the "bad cholesterol."

high-density lipoprotein (HDL) A lipoprotein made in the liver and released into the blood. HDLs function to transport cholesterol from the tissues back to the liver. Often called the "good cholesterol."

What happens to LDLs not taken up by body cells? As LDLs degrade over time, they release their cholesterol; thus, failure to remove LDLs from the bloodstream results in an increased load of cholesterol in the blood. The more cholesterol circulating in the blood, the greater the risk that some of it will adhere to the walls of the blood vessels, contributing to the development of atherosclerosis. Because high blood levels of LDL-cholesterol increase the risk for heart disease, it is often labeled the "bad cholesterol."

High-Density Lipoproteins

As their name indicates, **high-density lipoproteins (HDLs)** are small, dense lipoproteins with a very low cholesterol content and a high protein content. They are released from the liver and intestines to circulate in the blood, picking up cholesterol from dying cells and arterial plaques and transferring it to other lipoproteins, which return it to the liver. The liver takes up the cholesterol and uses it to synthesize bile, thereby removing it from the circulatory system. High blood levels of HDL-cholesterol are therefore associated with a low risk for coronary artery disease. That's why HDL-cholesterol is often referred to as the "good cholesterol." There is some evidence that diets high in omega-3 fatty acids and participation in regular physical exercise can modestly increase HDL-cholesterol levels.[13]

Total Serum Cholesterol

Normally, as the dietary level of cholesterol increases, the body decreases the amount of cholesterol it makes, which keeps the body's level of cholesterol constant. Unfortunately, this feedback mechanism does not work well in everyone. For some individuals, eating dietary cholesterol doesn't decrease the amount of cholesterol produced in the body, and their body cholesterol level rises. This also increases the level of cholesterol in the blood. These individuals benefit from reducing their intake of dietary cholesterol.

Although this appears somewhat complicated, both dietary cholesterol and saturated fats are found in animal foods; thus, by limiting intake of animal products or selecting low-fat animal products, people reduce their intake of both saturated fat and cholesterol. Based on data collected in 1994–1996, U.S. adults get the majority of their dietary cholesterol from eggs (30%), beef and poultry (28%), and milk and cheese (11%).[14] Selecting low-fat meat, poultry, and dairy

What About You?

Blood Lipid Levels: How Do Yours Measure Up?

One of the most important steps you can take to reduce your risk for heart disease is to know your "numbers"—that is, your blood lipid values. The next time you go to a physician, ask to have your blood lipid levels measured. Record these numbers and have them checked every 1 to 2 years, or each time you visit your physician for a checkup. Many college and university health clinics, as well as community health fairs, offer a screening for total cholesterol as well. Based on your total cholesterol values, you can go to your physician to have a more complete testing of all your blood lipids. In this way, you can know your own blood lipid levels and keep track of your risk for heart disease.

Let's look at the different blood lipid parameters and the target values. These are the normal values you want to show up on your lab results! Notice that each of the blood lipids discussed in this chapter is listed here. We've included space for you to write in your own blood lipid values. How do yours compare with the target values? Draw a ☺ in each row of the final column if your values are within the target range. If not, draw a ☹. Make sure to discuss with your doctor any values that are outside of the target range.

Blood Lipid Profile: Compare Your Values

Blood Lipid Parameter	Target Values*	Your Values	How Are You Doing? ☺ / ☹
Total blood cholesterol	<200 mg/dl	_____ mg/dl	
HDL-cholesterol	>40 mg/dl	_____ mg/dl	
LDL-cholesterol	<100 mg/dl	_____ mg/dl	
Triglycerides	<150 mg/dl	_____ mg/dl	

*Data from the National Institutes of Health, *Third Report of the National Cholesterol Education Program: Detection, Evaluation and Treatment of High Blood Cholesterol in Adults (ATP: III)*. Bethesda, MD. National Cholesterol Education Program, National Heart, Lung, and Blood Institute, NIH, May 2001. http://www.nhlbi.nih.gov/guidelines/cholesterol/atp3xsum.pdf.

products and consuming egg whites without yolks can dramatically reduce the amount of cholesterol in the diet.

Calculating Your Risk for Cardiovascular Disease

Now that you know more about blood lipids, you're probably wondering what your levels look like. If so, check out the What About You? above. It explains the simple lab test that can show you how your own blood lipids measure up.

To estimate your overall risk of developing cardiovascular disease, you also need to know your blood pressure. If you have a family history of heart disease, it's especially important to have your blood pressure checked regularly.

After you've found out your blood pressure and blood lipid levels, the next step in assessing your risk for cardiovascular disease is to calculate the number of points for each risk factor in Figure 3, and then compare your total points to the points in the 10-year risk column. There is also an online version of this risk calculator. See the Web Resources located at the end of this chapter.

Lifestyle Choices Can Help Prevent or Control Cardiovascular Disease

Many diet and exercise interventions aimed at reducing the risk for cardiovascular disease center on reducing high levels of triglycerides and LDL-cholesterol while raising HDL-cholesterol. Approaches aimed specifically at reducing blood pressure include most of the same recommendations, along with strict monitoring of sodium intake.

Recommendations to Improve Blood Lipid Levels

The Centers for Disease Control and Prevention (CDC) and the Expert Panel on Detection, Evaluation, and Treatment of High Blood Cholesterol in Adults (APT: III) have made the following recommendations to improve blood lipid levels and reduce the risk for cardiovascular disease.[1, 5, 11, 15, 16, 17]

- Maintain total fat intake to within 20–35% of energy.[18] Polyunsaturated fats (for example, soy and canola oil) can comprise up to 10% of total energy intake, while monounsaturated fats (for example, olive oil) can comprise up to 20% of total energy intake. For some people, a lower fat intake

WHAT IS YOUR AGE?

Female:

Age	Points
20–34	−7
35–39	−3
40–44	0
45–49	3
50–54	6
55–59	8
60–64	10
65–69	12
70–74	14
75–79	16

Male:

Age	Points
20–34	−9
35–39	−4
40–44	0
45–49	3
50–54	6
55–59	8
60–64	10
65–69	11
70–74	12
75–79	13

Enter your points [ ]

WHAT IS YOUR TOTAL CHOLESTEROL NUMBER?

Female:

Age	Total Cholesterol				
	<160	160–199	200–239	240–279	≥280
20–39	0	4	8	11	13
40–49	0	3	6	8	10
50–59	0	2	4	5	7
60–69	0	1	2	3	4
70–79	0	1	1	2	2

Points

Male:

Age	Total Cholesterol				
	<160	160–199	200–239	240–279	≥280
20–39	0	4	7	9	11
40–49	0	3	5	6	8
50–59	0	2	3	4	5
60–69	0	1	1	2	3
70–79	0	0	0	1	1

Points

Enter your points [ ]

DO YOU SMOKE?

Nonsmoker, Female:

Age	Points
20–39	0
40–49	0
50–59	0
60–69	0
70–79	0

Nonsmoker, Male:

Age	Points
20–39	0
40–49	0
50–59	0
60–69	0
70–79	0

Smoker, Female:

Age	Points
20–39	9
40–49	7
50–59	4
60–69	2
70–79	1

Smoker, Male:

Age	Points
20–39	8
40–49	5
50–59	3
60–69	1
70–79	1

Enter your points [ ]

WHAT IS YOUR HIGH-DENSITY LIPOPROTEIN NUMBER (HDL)?

Female:

HDL (mg/dL)	Points
≥60	−1
50–59	0
40–49	1
<40	2

Male:

HDL (mg/dL)	Points
≥60	−1
50–59	0
40–49	1
<40	2

Enter your points [ ]

WHAT IS YOUR SYSTOLIC BLOOD PRESSURE (the top number)?

Female:

Systolic BP (mm Hg)	If untreated	If treated
<120	0	0
120–129	1	3
130–139	2	4
140–159	3	5
≥160	4	6

Male:

Systolic BP (mm Hg)	If untreated	If treated
<120	0	0
120–129	0	1
130–139	1	2
140–159	1	2
≥160	2	3

Enter your points [ ]

WHAT IS YOUR TOTAL NUMBER OF POINTS (what is your 10-year risk)?

Female:

Point total	10-Year risk %
<9	<1
9	1
10	1
11	1
12	1
13	2
14	2
15	3
16	4
17	5
18	6
19	8
20	11
21	14
22	17
23	22
24	27
≥25	≥30

Male:

Point total	10-Year risk %
<0	<1
0	1
1	1
2	1
3	1
4	1
5	2
6	2
7	3
8	4
9	5
10	6
11	8
12	10
13	12
14	16
15	20
16	25
≥17	≥30

Enter your 10-year risk percentage [ ]

Figure 3 Calculation matrix to estimate the 10-year risk for cardiovascular disease for men and women.

Data from National Institutes of Health, *Third Report of the National Cholesterol Education Program: Detection, Evaluation and Treatment of High Blood Cholesterol in Adults (ATP: III)*. **Bethesda, MD:** National Cholesterol Education Program, National Heart, Lung, and Blood Institute, NIH, May 2001. www.nhlbi.nih.gov/guideline/cholesterol/atp3xsum.pdf.

Consuming whole fruits and vegetables can reduce your risk for cardiovascular disease.

Consuming fish, especially oily fish, at least twice a week will increase omega-3 fatty acid intake.

- Consume 400 µg/day of folate from dietary or supplemental sources to help maintain low blood levels of the amino acid homocysteine. High homocysteine levels in the blood are associated with increased risk for cardiovascular disease.
- Increase dietary intakes of whole grains, fruits, and vegetables, so that total dietary fiber is 20 to 30 g per day, with 10 to 25 g per day coming from fiber sources such as oat bran, beans, and fruits. Foods high in fiber decrease blood LDL-cholesterol levels.
- Maintain blood glucose and insulin concentrations within normal ranges. High

blood glucose levels are associated with high blood triglycerides. Dietary changes can help here as well: consume foods whole (such as whole-wheat breads and cereals, whole fruits and vegetables, and beans and legumes), and select low-saturated-fat meats and dairy products, while limiting your intake of foods high in sugar and fat (for example, cookies, high-sugar drinks and snacks, candy, fried foods, and convenience and fast foods).

- Eat throughout the day (for example, smaller meals and snacks) instead of eating most of your Calories in the evening before bed.
- Consume no more than two alcoholic drinks per day for men and one drink per day for women. Because heavy alcohol consumption can worsen high blood pressure, it is suggested that people with diagnosed hypertension abstain from drinking alcohol entirely.
- If you smoke, stop. As noted earlier, smoking significantly increases the risk for cardiovascular disease.
- Maintain an active lifestyle. Exercise most days of the week for 30 to 60 minutes if possible. Exercise will increase HDL-cholesterol while lowering blood triglyceride levels. Exercise also helps you maintain a healthful body weight

may help them maintain a healthful body weight.

- Decrease dietary saturated fat to less than 7% of total energy intake. Decrease cholesterol intake to less than 300 mg per day, and keep *trans* fatty acid intake as low as possible (<1% of energy). Lowering the intakes of these fats will lower your LDL-cholesterol level. Replace saturated fat (for example, butter, margarine, vegetable shortening, or lard) with more healthful cooking oils, such as olive or canola oil. Select lean meats and meat alternatives and use fat-free (skim), 1% fat, or low-fat dairy products.
- Increase intake of dietary omega-3 fatty acids from dark green, leafy vegetables, fatty fish, soybeans or soybean oil, walnuts or walnut oil, flaxseed meal or oil, or canola oil.

The DASH diet emphasizes fruits and vegetables, whole grains, low-fat or nonfat dairy, and lean protein sources.

Shutterstock

Clive Streeter/Dorling Kindersley

375

and a lower blood pressure and reduces your risk for type 2 diabetes.

- Maintain a healthful body weight by balancing energy intake with physical activity. Blood lipids and glucose levels typically improve when overweight or obese individuals lose weight and engage in regular physical activity. Obesity promotes inflammation; thus, keeping body weight within a healthful range helps keep inflammation low.[10] In addition, blood pressure values have been shown to decrease six to seven points in people who have lost less than 20 pounds of body weight.[19]

Recommendations to Reduce Blood Pressure

Again, because hypertension is itself a form of cardiovascular disease and a risk factor in the development of atherosclerosis, the lifestyle changes just identified are recommended for anyone diagnosed with hypertension or prehypertension. In addition, the recommendations for reducing blood pressure include limiting dietary sodium intake and following the DASH diet.

Limit Dietary Sodium

To help keep blood pressure normal, it is recommended that we reduce our intake of sodium. However, this recommendation is not without controversy.

For years it was believed that the high sodium intakes of the typical American diet led to hypertension.

DASH diet The diet developed in response to research into hypertension funded by the National Institutes of Health: DASH stands for "Dietary Approaches to Stop Hypertension."

This is because people who live in countries where sodium intake is high have greater rates of hypertension than people from countries where sodium intake is low. We have recently learned, however, that not everyone with hypertension is sensitive to sodium. Unfortunately, it is impossible to know who is sensitive and who is not, as there is no ready test for sodium sensitivity. Moreover, lowering sodium intake does not reduce blood pressure in all people with hypertension. Thus, there is significant debate over whether everyone can benefit from eating a lower-sodium diet.

Despite this debate, the leading health organizations, including the American Heart Association, the National High Blood Pressure Education Program, and the National Heart, Lung, and Blood Institute of the National Institutes of Health (NIH), continue to support a reduction in dietary sodium to 2,400 mg/day, as recommended in the Dietary Guidelines for Americans.[8] Currently, the average sodium intake in the United States is about 3,300 mg/day.

Follow the DASH Diet

The impact of diet on reducing the risk for cardiovascular disease—including hypertension—was clearly demonstrated in a study from the NIH called Dietary Approaches to Stop Hypertension (DASH). The **DASH diet** is an eating plan that is high in several minerals that have been shown to help reduce hypertension, including calcium, magnesium, and potassium. At the same time, it is moderately low in sodium, low in saturated fat, and high in fiber, and it includes 10 servings of fruits and vegetables each day. **Table 1** shows the DASH eating plan for a 2,000-kcal diet.

The results of the NIH study showed that eating the DASH diet can dramatically improve blood lipids and

lower blood pressure.[20, 21] For the study participants overall, systolic blood pressure decreased by an average of 5.5 mm Hg, and diastolic blood pressure decreased by an average of 3.0 mm Hg. For the study participants who had high blood pressure, systolic blood pressure dropped an average of 11.4 mm Hg, and diastolic blood pressure dropped by an average of 5.5 mm Hg. These decreases occurred within the first 2 weeks of eating the DASH diet and were maintained throughout the duration of the study. Researchers estimated that if all Americans followed the DASH diet plan and experienced reductions in blood pressure similar to this study, then heart disease would be reduced by 15% and the number of strokes would be 27% lower.

Further study of the DASH diet has found that blood pressure decreases even more as sodium intake is reduced below 3,000 mg per day. In the subsequent study, participants ate a DASH diet that provided 3,300 mg (average U.S. intake), 2,400 mg (upper recommended intake), or 1,500 mg of sodium each day.[21] After 1 month on this diet, all people eating the DASH diet saw a significant decrease in their blood pressure; however, those who ate the lowest-sodium version of the DASH diet experienced the largest decrease. These results indicate that eating a diet low in sodium and high in fruits and vegetables reduces blood pressure and decreases your risk for heart attack and stroke.

Prescription Medications Can Improve Blood Lipids and Blood Pressure

For some individuals, lifestyle changes are not completely effective in normalizing blood lipids and blood

TABLE 1   The DASH Eating Plan

Food Group	Daily Servings	Serving Size
Grains and grain products	7–8	1 slice bread
		1 cup ready-to-eat cereal*
		1/2 cup cooked rice, pasta, or cereal
Vegetables	4–5	1 cup raw leafy vegetables
		1/2 cup cooked vegetable
		6 fl. oz vegetable juice
Fruits	4–5	1 medium fruit
		1/4 cup dried fruit
		1/2 cup fresh, frozen, or canned fruit
		6 fl. oz fruit juice
Low-fat or fat-free dairy foods	2–3	8 fl. oz milk
		1 cup yogurt
		1 1/2 oz cheese
Lean meats, poultry, and fish	2 or less	3 oz cooked lean meats, skinless poultry, or fish
Nuts, seeds, and dry beans	4–5 per week	1/3 cup or 1 1/2 oz nuts
		1 tbsp. or 1/2 oz seeds
		1/2 cup cooked dry beans
Fats and oils[†]	2–3	1 tsp. soft margarine
		1 tbsp. low-fat mayonnaise
		2 tbsp. light salad dressing
		1 tsp. vegetable oil
Sweets	5 per week	1 tbsp. sugar
		1 tbsp. jelly or jam
		1/2 oz jelly beans
		8 fl. oz lemonade

Note: The plan is based on 2,000-kcal/day. The number of servings in a food group may differ from the number listed, depending on your own energy needs.

*Serving sizes vary between 1/2 cup and 1 1/4 cups. Check the product's nutrition label.

[†]Fat content changes serving counts for fats and oils: for example, 1 tbsp. of regular salad dressing equals 1 serving; 1 tbsp. of a low-fat dressing equals 1/2 serving; 1 tablespoon of a fat-free dressing equals 0 servings.
Data from National Institutes of Health. Healthier Eating with DASH. www.nhlbi.nih.gov/health/public/heart/hbp/dash/new_dash.pdf.

pressure. When this is the case, a variety of medications can be prescribed. Some inhibit the body's production of cholesterol. Others prevent bile acids from being reabsorbed in the GI tract. Since bile is made from cholesterol, blocking its reabsorption means the liver must draw on cholesterol stores to make more. Diuretics may be prescribed to flush excess water and sodium from the body, reducing blood pressure. Other hypertension medications work to relax the blood vessel walls, giving more room for blood flow. Individuals taking such medications should also continue to practice the lifestyle changes listed earlier in this section, as these changes will continue to benefit their long-term health.

Web Resources

www.americanheart.org
American Heart Association

Learn the best way to help lower your blood cholesterol level. Access the AHA's online cookbook for healthy-heart recipes and cooking methods.

www.nhlbi.nih.gov
National Heart, Lung, and Blood Institute

Use this online risk assessment tool to estimate your 10-year risk of having a heart attack.

www.nlm.nih.gov/medlineplus
MEDLINE Plus Health Information

Find the latest news on dietary lipids and cardiovascular disease.

References

1. Wilson, P. W. F. 2004. CDC/AHA workshop on markers of inflammation and cardiovascular disease. Application to clinical and public health practice. Ability of inflammatory markers to predict disease in asymptomatic patients. A background paper. Circulation 110:e568–e571.

2. Ostchega Y., S. S. Yoon, J. Hughes, and T. Louise. 2008. Hypertension awareness, treatment and control—continued disparities in adults: United States, 2005–2006. National Center for Health Statistics (NCHS) data brief no. Hyattsville, MD: NCHS.

3. Lloyd-Jones D., R. J. Adams, T. M. Brown, M. Carnethon, S. Dai, G. DeSimone, et al. 2010. Heart Disease and Stroke Statistics 2010 Update. A Report from the American Heart Association. *Circulation* 121:e1–e170.

4. National Center for Chronic Disease Prevention and Health Promotion (NCCDPHP). 2008. Division for Heart Disease and Stroke Prevention addressing the nation's leading killers. At a glance 2008. Available online at http://www.cdc.gov/print .do?url=http://www.cdc.gov/nccdphp/publications/AAG/ dhdsp.htm.

5. Hahn, R. A., and G. W. Heath. 1998. Cardiovascular disease risk factors and preventive practices among adults—United States, 1994: a behavioral risk factor atlas. *Morbid. Mortal. Wkly. Rep.* 47(SS-5):35–69.

6. Rippe, J. M., T. J. Angelopoulos, and L. Zukley. 2007. The rationale for intervention to reduce the risk of coronary heart disease. *Am. J. Lifestyle Med.* 1(1):10–19.

7. Marwick T. H., M. D. Hordern, T. Miller, D. A. Chyun, A. G. Bertoni, R. S. Blumenthal, G. Philippides, and A. Rocchini. 2009. Exercise training for type 2 diabetes Mellitus: Impact on cardiovascular risk: A Scientific Statement from the American Heart Association. *Circulation.* 119:3244–3262.

8. Department of Health and Human Services (DHHS). 2008. Physical Activity Guidelines Advisory Committee, Phyiscal Activity Guidelines Advisory Committee Report, 2008. Washington DC.

9. Dept of Health and Human Services (DHHS), Centers for Disease Control and Prevention (CDC), Smoking and Tobacco Use, Frequently Asked questions. Accessed, Feb. 2010. http:// apps.nccd.cdc.gov/osh_faq/topic.aspx?TopicID=8#11.

10. Libby P., P. M. Ridker, and A. Maseri. 2002. Inflammation and atherosclerosis. *Circulation* 105:1135–1143.

11. Kris-Etherton, P. M., W. S. Harris, L. J. Appel, and the Nutrition Committee of the American Heart Association. 2002. Fish consumption, fish oil, omega-3 fatty acids and cardiovascular disease. *Circulation* 106:2747–2757.

12. Harris, W. S. 1997. n-3 Fatty acids and serum lipoproteins: human studies. *Am. J. Clin. Nutr.* 65(suppl.):1645S–1654S.

13. Zoeller, R. F. 2007. Physical activity and fitness in the prevention of coronary heart disease and associated risk factors. *Am. J. Lifestyle Med.* 1(1):29–33.

14. Cotton P. A., A. F. Subar, J. E. Friday, and A. Cook. 2004. Dietary sources of nutrients among US adults, 1994–1996. *J. Am. Diet. Assoc.* 104:921–931.

15. Expert Panel on Detection, Evaluation, and Treatment of High Blood Cholesterol in Adults, National Institutes of Health. 2001. Executive summary of the Third Report of the National Cholesterol Education Program (NCEP) Expert Panel on Detection, Evaluation, and Treatment of High Blood Cholesterol in Adults (Adult Treatment Panel III). *JAMA* 285(19):2486–2509.

16. Lichtenstein A. H., L. J. Appel, M. Brands, M. Carnethon, S. Daniels, H. A. Franch, B. Franklin, P. Kris-Ethergon, W. S. Harris, B. Howard, N. Karanja, M. Lefevre, L. Rudel, F. Sancks, L. Van Horn, M. Winston, and J. Wylie-Rosett. 2006. Diet and lifestyle recommendations revision 2006: A scientific statement from the American Heart Association Nutrition Committee. *Circulation* 114:82–96.

17. Gidding S. S., A. H. Lichtenstein, M. S. Faith, A. Karpyn, J. A. Mennella, B. Popkin, J. Rowe, L. Van Horn, and L. Whitsel. 2009. Implementing American Heart Association Pediatric and Adult Nutrition Guidelines. *Circulation.* 119:1161–1175.

18. Institute of Medicine, Food and Nutrition Board. 2002. Dietary Reference Intakes for Energy, Carbohydrate, Fiber, Fat, Fatty Acids, Cholesterol, Protein, and Amino Acids (Macronutrients). Washington, DC: National Academies Press.

19. Blumenthal, J. A., A. Sherwood, E. C. D. Gullette, M. Babyak, R. Waugh, A. Georgiades, L. W. Craighead, D. Tweedy, M. Feinglos, M. Applebaum, J. Hayano, and A. Hinderliter. 2000. Exercise and weight loss reduce blood pressure in men and women with mild hypertension. *Arch. Intern Med.* 160:1947–1958.

20. Appel, L. J., T. J. Moare, E. Obarzanek, W. M. Vollmer, L. P. Svetkey, F. M. Sacks, G. A. Bray, T. M. Vogt, J. A. Cutler, M. M. Windhauser, P. H. Lin, and N. Karanja. 1997. A clinical trial of the effecs of dietary patterns on blood pressure. *New Engl. J. Medicine.* 336:1117–1124.

21. Sacks, F. M., L. P. Svetkey, W. M. Vollmer, L. J. Appel, G. A. Bray, D. Harsha, E. Obarzanek, P. R. Conlin, E. R. Miller III, D. G. Simons-Morton, N. Karanja, and P. H. Lin. 2001. Effects of blood pressure on reduced dietary sodium and the Dietary Approaches to Stop Hypertension (DASH) diet. *New Engl. J. Medicine.* 244:3–10.

\# 104511   Cust: PE Benjamin Cummings   Au: Thompson   Pg. No. 184   C/M/ /K
Title: Nutrition: An Applied Approach   Server: Jobs4   Short / Normal

In Depth: Disordered Eating

Disordered Eating

WANT TO FIND OUT. . .

- **what is the leading cause of death in females age 15 through 24?**

- **whether men experience disordered eating?**

- **what's keeping some overweight people up all night?**

READ ON.

On August 2, 2006, Uruguayan fashion model Luisel Ramos collapsed during a fashion show. Just 22 years old, she was pronounced dead of heart failure brought on by *anorexia nervosa,* a condition of self-imposed starvation. Family members said that, in the months prior to her death, she had adopted a diet of lettuce leaves and Diet Coke, and at 5'9" tall, her weight had dropped to just 98 pounds. The following month, Madrid's "Fashion Week" responded to Ramos's death by banning from its runway fashion models who could not meet a minimum weight–height standard. A similar rul-

Image Source/Corbis

ing was quickly adopted by the Milan fashion show, and several modeling agencies began to require prospective models to present medical records certifying that they are healthy. Although promising, such measures alone are clearly inadequate, and at least three more fashion models had died from self-starvation by the summer of 2008.

Do only models develop eating disorders, or can they occur in people like you? When does normal dieting cross the line into disordered eating? What early warning signs might tip you off that a friend was crossing that line? If you noticed the signs in a friend or family member, would you confront him or her? If so, what would you say? In the following pages, we explore *In Depth* some answers to these important questions.

Eugenio Savio/AP Photo

A string of models have died because of eating disorders.

Suppose that for several years you've skipped breakfast in favor of a mid-morning snack, but now you find yourself avoiding the cafeteria until early afternoon. Is this normal? To answer that question, you'd need to consider your feelings about food and your **body image**—the way you perceive your body.

Take a moment to take the self-test in the accompanying What About You? box. It will help you clarify how you feel about your body and about food and whether you're at risk for disordered eating.

Many Factors Contribute to Disordered Eating Behaviors

The factors that result in the development of disordered eating are very complex, but research indicates that a number of psychological, interpersonal, social, and biological factors may contribute in any particular individual.

---

disordered eating A variety of abnormal or atypical eating behaviors that are used to keep or maintain a lower body weight.

eating disorder A clinically diagnosed psychiatric disorder characterized by severe disturbances in body image and eating behaviors.

anorexia nervosa A serious, potentially life-threatening eating disorder characterized by self-starvation, which eventually leads to a deficiency in energy and the essential nutrients the body requires to function normally.

bulimia nervosa A serious eating disorder characterized by recurrent episodes of binge eating and recurrent inappropriate compensatory behaviors in order to prevent weight gain, such as self-induced vomiting, fasting, excessive exercise, or misuse of laxatives, diuretics, enemas, or other medications.

body image A person's perception of his or her body's appearance and functioning.

Eating Behaviors Occur on a Continuum

Disordered eating is a general term used to describe a variety of atypical eating behaviors that people use to achieve or maintain a lower body weight. These behaviors may be as simple as going on and off diets or as extreme as refusing to eat any fat. Such behaviors don't usually continue for long enough to make the person seriously ill, nor do they significantly disrupt the person's normal routine.

In contrast, some people restrict their eating so much or for so long that they become dangerously underweight. These people have an **eating disorder,** a psychiatric condition that involves extreme body dissatisfaction and long-term eating patterns that negatively affect body functioning. The two more commonly diagnosed

eating disorders are anorexia nervosa and bulimia nervosa. **Anorexia nervosa** is a potentially life-threatening eating disorder characterized by self-starvation, which eventually leads to a severe nutrient deficiency. In contrast, **bulimia nervosa** is characterized by recurrent episodes of extreme overeating and compensatory behaviors to prevent weight gain, such as self-induced vomiting, misuse of laxatives, fasting, excessive exercise, or several of these in combination. Both disorders will be discussed in more detail shortly.

When does normal dieting cross the line into disordered eating? Eating behaviors occur on a *continuum*, a spectrum that can't be divided neatly into parts. One example of a continuum is a rainbow—where exactly does the red end and the orange begin? Thinking about eating behaviors as a continuum makes it easier to understand how a person can progress from relatively normal eating behaviors to a pattern that is disordered.

What About You?

Are You at Risk for Disordered Eating?

Take a look at the Eating Issues and Body Image Continuum figure **(Figure 1)** near this box. Which of the five columns best describes your feelings about food and your body? If you find yourself identifying with the statements on the left side of the continuum, you probably have few issues with food or body image. Most likely, you accept your body size and view food as a normal part of maintaining your health and fueling your daily physical activity.

As you progress to the right side of the continuum, food and body image become bigger issues, with food restriction becoming the norm. If you identify with the statements on the far right, you may be afraid of eating and dislike your body. If so, you should consult a healthcare professional as soon as possible. The earlier you seek treatment, the more likely it is you'll succeed in taking ownership of your body and developing a more healthful approach to food.

Influence of Genetic Factors

Overall, the diagnosis of anorexia nervosa and bulimia nervosa is several times more common in females, and in siblings and other blood relatives who also have the diagnosis, than in the general population.[1] This observation might imply the existence of an "eating disorder gene"; however, it is difficult to separate the contribution of genetic from other biological and social factors.[2]

Influence of Family

Research suggests that family conditioning, structure, and patterns of interaction can influence the development of an eating disorder. Based on observational studies, compared to families without a member with an eating disorder, families with an anorexic member show more rigidity in their family structure and less clear interpersonal boundaries, and they tend to avoid open discussions on topics of disagreement. Conversely, families with a member diagnosed with bulimia nervosa tend to have a less stable family organization and to

be less nurturing, more angry, and more disruptive.[3] In addition, childhood physical or sexual abuse can increase the risk for an eating disorder.[4]

Influence of Media

As media saturation has increased over the last century, so has the incidence of eating disorders among white women.[5] Every day, we are confronted with advertisements in which computer-enhanced images of lean, beautiful women promote everything from beer to cars **(Figure 2)**. Most adult men and women understand that these images are unrealistic, but adolescents, who are still developing a sense of their identity and body image, lack the same ability to distance themselves from what they see.[6] Because body image influences eating behaviors, it is not unlikely that the barrage of media models may be contributing to the increase in eating disorders. However, scientific evidence demonstrating that the media are *causing* increased eating disorders is difficult to obtain.

Influence of Social and Cultural Values

Eating disorders are significantly more common in white females in developed Western societies than in other women worldwide.[2] This may be due in part to the white Western culture's association of slenderness with health, wealth, and high fashion **(Figure 3)**. In contrast, until recently,

Digital Vision/Getty Images

◄ Family environment often influences when, what, and how much we eat.

• I am not concerned about what others think regarding what and how much I eat. • When I am upset or depressed I eat whatever I am hungry for without any guilt or shame. • I feel no guilt or shame no matter how much I eat or what I eat. • Food is an important part of my life but only occupies a small part of my time. • I trust my body to tell me what and how much to eat.	• I pay attention to what I eat in order to maintain a healthy body. • I may weigh more than what I like, but I enjoy eating and balance my pleasure with eating with my concern for a healthy body. • I am moderate and flexible in goals for eating well. • I try to follow Dietary Guidelines for healthy eating.	• I think about food a lot. • I feel I don't eat well most of the time. • It's hard for me to enjoy eating with others. • I feel ashamed when I eat more than others or more than what I feel I should be eating. • I am afraid of getting fat. • I wish I could change how much I want to eat and what I am hungry for.	• I have tried diet pills, laxatives, vomiting, or extra time exercising in order to lose or maintain my weight. • I have fasted or avoided eating for long periods of time in order to lose or maintain my weight. • I feel strong when I can restrict how much I eat. • Eating more than I wanted to makes me feel out of control.	• I regularly stuff myself and then exercise, vomit, or use diet pills or laxatives to get rid of the food or calories. • My friends/family tell me I am too thin. • I am terrified of eating fat. • When I let myself eat, I have a hard time controlling the amount of food I eat. • I am afraid to eat in front of others.
FOOD IS NOT AN ISSUE	**CONCERNED/WELL**	**FOOD PREOCCUPIED/ OBSESSED**	**DISRUPTIVE EATING PATTERNS**	**EATING DISORDERED**
BODY OWNERSHIP	**BODY ACCEPTANCE**	**BODY PREOCCUPIED/ OBSESSED**	**DISTORTED BODY IMAGE**	**BODY HATE/ DISASSOCIATION**
• Body image is not an issue for me. • My body is beautiful to me. • My feelings about my body are not influenced by society's concept of an ideal body shape. • I know that the significant others in my life will always find me attractive. • I trust my body to find the weight it needs to be at so I can move and feel confident about my physical body.	• I base my body image equally on social norms and my own self-concept. • I pay attention to my body and my appearance because it is important to me, but it only occupies a small part of my day. • I nourish my body so it has the strength and energy to achieve my physical goals. • I am able to assert myself and maintain a healthy body without losing my self-esteem.	• I spend a significant amount time viewing my body in the mirror. • I spend a significant amount time comparing my body to others. • I have days when I feel fat. • I am preoccupied with my body. • I accept society's ideal body shape and size as the best body shape and size. • I believe that I'd be more attractive if I were thinner, more muscular, etc.	• I spend a significant amount of time exercising and dieting to change my body. • My body shape and size keep me from dating or finding someone who will treat me the way I want to be treated. • I have considered changing or have changed my body shape and size through surgical means so I can accept myself. • I wish I could change the way I look in the mirror.	• I often feel separated and distant from my body—as if it belongs to someone else. • I hate my body and I often isolate myself from others. • I don't see anything positive or even neutral about my body shape and size. • I don't believe others when they tell me I look OK. • I hate the way I look in the mirror.

Figure 1 The Eating Issues and Body Image Continuum. The progression from normal eating (far left) to eating disorders (far right) occurs on a continuum.

Data from Smiley, L., L. King, and H. Avery. University of Arizona Campus Health Service. Original Continuum, C. Shlaalak. Preventive Medicine and Public Health. Copyright ©1997 Arizona Board of Regents. Used with permission.

the prevailing view in developing societies has been that excess body fat is desirable as a sign of health and material abundance.

The members of society with whom we most often interact—our family members, friends, classmates, and co-workers—also influence the way we see ourselves. Their comments related to our body weight or shape can be particularly hurtful—enough so to cause some people to start down the path of disordered eating. For example, individuals with bulimia nervosa report that they

perceived greater pressure from their peers to be thin than controls, while research shows that peer teasing about weight increases body dissatisfaction and eating disturbances.[7] Thus, our comments to others regarding their weight do count.

Influence of Personality

A number of studies suggest that people with anorexia nervosa exhibit increased rates of obsessive-compulsive

behaviors and perfectionism. They also tend to be socially inhibited, compliant, and emotionally restrained.[8] Unfortunately, many studies observe these behaviors only in individuals who are very ill and in a state of starvation, which may affect personality. Thus, it is difficult to determine if personality is a contributing factor or an effect of the disorder.

In contrast to people with anorexia nervosa, people with bulimia nervosa tend to be more impulsive, have low self-esteem, and demonstrate an extroverted, erratic personality style that

Laura Murray

Figure 2 Photos of celebrities and models are often airbrushed or otherwise altered to "enhance" physical appearance. Unfortunately, many people regard these as accurate portrayals and strive to reach an unrealistic level of physical beauty.

Karl Prouse/Catwalking/Getty Images

Figure 3 The preferred look among runway models can require extreme emaciation, often achieved by self-starvation and/or drug abuse.

amenorrhea The absence of menstruation. In females who had previously been menstruating, it is defined as the absence of menstrual periods for 3 or more months.

seeks attention and admiration. In these people, negative moods are more likely to cause overeating than food restriction.[8]

Anorexia Nervosa Is a Potentially Deadly Eating Disorder

According to the American Psychiatric Association, 90–95% of individuals with anorexia nervosa are young girls or women.[1] Approximately 0.5–1% of American women develop anorexia, and between 5% and 20% will die from complications of the disorder within 10 years of the initial diagnosis.[4] These statistics make anorexia nervosa the most common and deadly psychiatric disorder diagnosed in women and the leading cause of death in females between the ages of 15 and 24 years.[4] As the statistics indicate, anorexia nervosa also occurs in males, but the prevalence is much lower than in females.[2,9]

Signs and Symptoms of Anorexia Nervosa

The classic sign of anorexia nervosa is an extremely restrictive eating pattern

that leads to self-starvation (Figure 4). These individuals may fast completely, restrict energy intake to only a few kilocalories per day, or eliminate all but one or two food groups from their diet. They also have an intense fear of weight gain, and even small amounts (such as 1–2 lb) trigger high stress and anxiety.

In females, **amenorrhea** (no menstrual periods for at least 3 months) is a common feature of anorexia nervosa. It occurs when a young woman consumes insufficient energy to maintain normal body functions.

The American Psychiatric Association identifies the following conditions of anorexia nervosa:[10]

- Refusal to maintain body weight at or above a minimally normal weight for age and height
- Intense fear of gaining weight or becoming fat, even though considered underweight by all medical criteria

Kendall Samantha Alon/SIPA

Figure 4 People with *anorexia nervosa* experience an extreme drive for thinness, resulting in potentially fatal weight loss.

Muscle Dysmorphia: The Male Eating Disorder?

Is there an eating disorder unique to men? Recently, experts have defined a disorder called muscle dysmorphia. Men with muscle dysmorphia perceive themselves as small and frail, even though they may actually be large and muscular. They spend long hours lifting weights, but no matter how "chiseled" they become, their biology cannot match their idealized body size and shape.[12]

A common behavior of men with muscle dysmorphia is abuse of performance-enhancing drugs. Additionally, men with muscle dysmorphia tend to consume excessive amounts of high-protein foods and dietary supplements, such as protein powders.

Men with muscle dysmorphia share some characteristics with men and women with other eating disorders. For instance, they report "feeling fat" and express significant discomfort with the idea of exposing their bodies to others. They also have increased rates of mental illness.[13]

Outward indications that someone is struggling with muscle dysmorphia include:

- Rigid and excessive weight training
- Strict adherence to a high-protein, muscle-enhancing diet
- Use of muscle-enhancing drugs or supplements
- Avoiding social engagements that might interfere with following a strict diet or training schedule
- Frequent and critical body self-evaluation

Muscle dysmorphia can cause distress and despair. Therapy can help.

Men are more likely than women to exercise excessively in an effort to control their weight.

Blake Little/Getty Images

- Disturbance in the way in which one's body weight or shape is experienced, undue influence of body weight or shape on self-evaluation, or denial of the seriousness of the current low body weight
- Amenorrhea in females who are past puberty; a woman is considered to have amenorrhea if her periods occur only when given hormones, such as estrogen or oral contraceptives

The signs of an eating disorder, such as anorexia nervosa, may be somewhat different in males. Females with eating disorders say they *feel* fat even though they typically are normal weight or even underweight before they develop the disorder. In contrast, males who develop eating disorders are more likely to have actually *been* overweight or even obese.[9,11] Thus, the male's fear of "getting fat again" is based on reality. In addition, males with disordered eating are less concerned with actual body weight (scale weight) than females but are more concerned with body composition (percentage of muscle mass compared to fat mass).

The methods that men and women use to achieve weight loss also appear to differ. Males are more likely to use excessive exercise as a means of weight control, whereas females tend to use severe energy restriction, vomiting, and laxative abuse. These weight-control differences may stem from sociocultural biases; that is, dieting is considered to be more acceptable for women, whereas the overwhelming sociocultural belief is that "real men don't diet."[11]

Health Risks of Anorexia Nervosa

Left untreated, anorexia nervosa eventually leads to a deficiency in energy and other nutrients that are required by the body to function normally. The body will then use stored fat and lean tissue (such as organ and muscle tissue) as an energy source to maintain brain tissue and vital body functions. The body will also shut down or reduce nonvital body functions to conserve energy. Electrolyte imbalances can lead to heart failure and death. **Figure 5** highlights many of the health problems that occur in people with anorexia nervosa. The best chance of recovery is when an individual receives intensive treatment early.

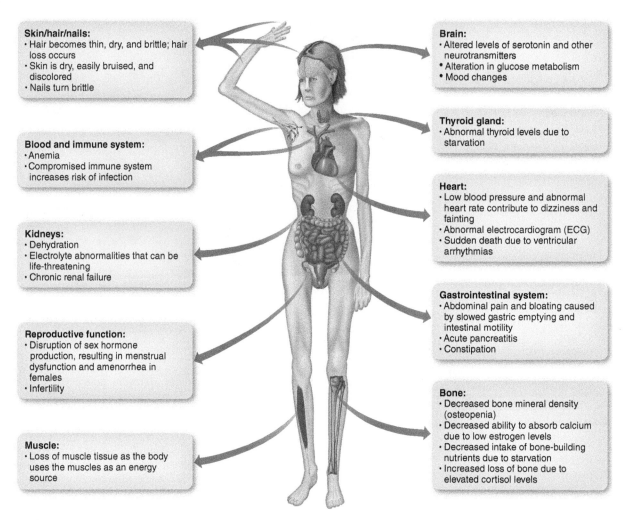

Skin/hair/nails:
- Hair becomes thin, dry, and brittle; hair loss occurs
- Skin is dry, easily bruised, and discolored
- Nails turn brittle

Blood and immune system:
- Anemia
- Compromised immune system increases risk of infection

Kidneys:
- Dehydration
- Electrolyte abnormalities that can be life-threatening
- Chronic renal failure

Reproductive function:
- Disruption of sex hormone production, resulting in menstrual dysfunction and amenorrhea in females
- Infertility

Muscle:
- Loss of muscle tissue as the body uses the muscles as an energy source

Brain:
- Altered levels of serotonin and other neurotransmitters
- Alteration in glucose metabolism
- Mood changes

Thyroid gland:
- Abnormal thyroid levels due to starvation

Heart:
- Low blood pressure and abnormal heart rate contribute to dizziness and fainting
- Abnormal electrocardiogram (ECG)
- Sudden death due to ventricular arrhythmias

Gastrointestinal system:
- Abdominal pain and bloating caused by slowed gastric emptying and intestinal motility
- Acute pancreatitis
- Constipation

Bone:
- Decreased bone mineral density (osteopenia)
- Decreased ability to absorb calcium due to low estrogen levels
- Decreased intake of bone-building nutrients due to starvation
- Increased loss of bone due to elevated cortisol levels

▲ **Figure 5** The impact of *anorexia nervosa* on the body.

Bulimia Nervosa Is Characterized by Bingeing and Purging

Bulimia nervosa is an eating disorder characterized by repeated episodes of

binge eating followed by some form of **purging.** While binge eating, the person feels a loss of self-control, including an inability to end the binge once it has started.[14] At the same time, the person feels a sense of euphoria not unlike a drug-induced high. A "binge" is usually defined as a quantity of food that is large for the person and for the amount of time in which it is eaten **(Figure 6)**. For example, a person may eat a dozen brownies with 2 quarts of ice cream in 30 minutes.

The prevalence of bulimia nervosa is higher than that of anorexia nervosa and is estimated to affect 1–4% of women. Like anorexia nervosa, bulimia nervosa is found predominately in women: six to ten females are diagnosed for every one male. The mortal-

ity rate is lower than for anorexia nervosa, with 1% of patients dying within 10 years of diagnosis.[4]

Although the prevalence of bulimia nervosa is much higher in women, rates for men are significant in some predominantly "thin-build" sports in which participants are encouraged to maintain a low body weight (for instance, horse racing, wrestling, crew, and gymnastics). Individuals in these sports typically do not have all the characteristics of bulimia nervosa, however, and the purging behaviors they practice usually stop once the sport is discontinued.

An individual with bulimia nervosa typically purges after most episodes, but not necessarily on every occasion, and weight gain as a

---

binge eating Consumption of a large amount of food in a short period of time, usually accompanied by a feeling of loss of self-control.

purging An attempt to rid the body of unwanted food by vomiting or other compensatory means, such as excessive exercise, fasting, or laxative abuse.

Roel Loopers/Photolibrary

Men who participate in "thin-build" sports, such as jockeys, have a higher risk for *bulimia nervosa* than men who do not.

Baumgartner Olivia/Corbis

Figure 6 People with *bulimia nervosa* can consume relatively large amounts of food in brief periods of time.

result of binge eating can be significant. Methods of purging include vomiting, laxative or diuretic abuse, enemas, fasting, or excessive exercise. For example, after a binge, a runner may increase her daily mileage to equal the "calculated" energy content of the binge.

Symptoms of Bulimia Nervosa

As with anorexia nervosa, the American Psychiatric Association has identified conditions of bulimia nervosa:[10]

- Recurrent episodes of binge eating, such as eating a large amount of food within a short period of time (about 2 hours).
- Recurrent inappropriate compensatory behavior in order to prevent weight gain, such as self-induced vomiting; misuse of laxatives, diuretics, enemas, or

other medications; fasting; or excessive exercise.
- Binge eating occuring on average at least twice a week for 3 months.
- Body shape and weight unduly influencing self-evaluation.
- The disturbance not necessarily occuring exclusively during episodes of anorexia nervosa. Some individuals will have periods of binge eating and then periods of starvation, which makes classification of their disorder difficult.

How can you tell if someone has bulimia nervosa? In addition to the recurrent and frequent binge eating and purging episodes, the National Institutes of Health have identified the following symptoms of bulimia nervosa:

- chronically inflamed and sore throat
- swollen glands in the neck and below the jaw
- worn tooth enamel and increasingly sensitive and decaying teeth as a result of exposure to stomach acids
- gastroesophageal reflux disorder
- intestinal distress and irritation from laxative abuse
- kidney problems from diuretic abuse
- severe dehydration from purging of fluids

Health Risks of Bulimia Nervosa

The destructive behaviors of bulimia nervosa can lead to illness and even death. The most common health consequences associated with bulimia nervosa are the following:

- Electrolyte imbalance typically caused by dehydration and the loss of potassium and sodium from the body from frequent vomiting. This can lead to irregular heartbeat and even heart failure and death.
- Gastrointestinal problems: inflammation, ulceration, and possible rupture of the esophagus and stomach from frequent bingeing and vomiting. Chronic irregular bowel movements and

constipation may result in people with bulimia who chronically abuse laxatives.

- Dental problems: tooth decay and staining from stomach acids released during frequent vomiting

As with anorexia nervosa, the chance of recovery from bulimia nervosa increases, and the negative effects on health decrease, if the disorder is detected and treated at an early stage. Familiarity with the warning signs of bulimia nervosa can help you identify friends and family members who might be at risk.

Binge-Eating Disorder Can Cause Significant Weight Gain

When was the last time a friend or relative confessed to you about "going on an eating binge"? Most likely, the person explained that the behavior followed some sort of stressful event, such as a problem at work, the break-up of a relationship, or a poor grade on an exam. Many people have one or two binge episodes every year or so, in response to stress. But in people with **binge-eating disorder,** the behavior occurs an average of twice a week or more and is not usually followed by purging. This lack of compensation for the binge distinguishes binge-eating disorder from bulimia nervosa and explains why the person tends to gain a lot of weight.

The prevalence of binge-eating disorder is estimated to be 2–3% of the adult population and 8% of the

binge-eating disorder A disorder characterized by binge eating an average of twice a week or more, typically without compensatory purging.

night-eating syndrome A disorder characterized by intake of the majority of the day's energy between 8:00 PM and 6:00 AM. Individuals with this disorder also experience mood and sleep disorders.

obese population.[15] In contrast to anorexia and bulimia, binge-eating disorder is also common in men. Our current food environment, which offers an abundance of good-tasting, cheap food any time of the day, makes it difficult for people with binge-eating disorder to avoid food triggers.

As you would expect, the increased energy intake associated with binge eating significantly increases a person's risk of being overweight or obese. In addition, the types of foods individuals typically consume during a binge episode are high in fat and sugar, which can increase blood lipids. Finally, the stress associated with binge eating can have psychological consequences, such as low self-esteem, avoidance of social contact, depression, and negative thoughts related to body size.

Night-Eating Syndrome Can Lead to Obesity

Night-eating syndrome was first described in a group of patients who were not hungry in the morning but spent the evening and night eating and reported insomnia. Like binge-eating disorder, it is associated with obesity because, although night eaters don't binge, they do consume significant energy in their frequent snacks, and they don't compensate for the excess energy intake.

D. Hurst/Alamy

People with night-eating syndrome consume most of their daily energy between 8 PM and 6 AM.

Symptoms of Night-Eating Syndrome

The distinguishing characteristic of night-eating syndrome is the time during which most of the day's energy intake occurs. Night eaters eat relatively little during the day, consuming the majority of their energy between 8:00 PM and 6:00 AM. They even get up in the night to eat. Night eating is also characterized by a depressed mood and insomnia. In short, night eaters appear to have a unique combination of three disorders: an eating disorder, a sleep disorder, and a mood disorder.[16]

Health Risks of Night-Eating Syndrome

Night-eating syndrome is important clinically because of its association with obesity, which increases the risk for several chronic diseases, including heart disease, high blood pressure, stroke, type 2 diabetes, and arthritis. Obesity also increases the risk for sleep apnea, which can further disrupt the night eater's already abnormal sleeping pattern.

The Female Athlete Triad Consists of Three Disorders

The **female athlete triad** is a serious syndrome that consists of three clinical conditions in some physically active females: (1) low energy availability (such as inadequate energy intake to maintain menstrual function or to cover energy expended in exercise) (with or without eating disorders), (2) amenorrhea (the absence of menstruation), and (3) osteoporosis[17] (Figure 7). Certain sports that strongly emphasize leanness or a thin body build may place a young girl or a woman at risk for the female athlete triad. These sports typically include figure skating, gymnastics, and diving; classical ballet dancers are also at increased risk for the disorder.

Components of the Female Athlete Triad

Active women experience the general social and cultural demands placed on women to be thin, as well as pressure from their coach, teammates, judges, and/or spectators to meet weight standards or body-size expectations for their sport. Failure to meet these standards can result in severe consequences, such as being cut from the team, losing an athletic scholarship, or decreased participation with the team.

As the pressure to be thin mounts, active women may restrict their energy intake, typically by engaging in disordered eating behaviors. Energy restriction combined with high levels of physical activity can disrupt the menstrual cycle and result in amenorrhea. Menstrual dysfunction can also occur in active women who are not dieting and don't have an eating disorder. These women are simply not eating enough to cover the energy costs of their exercise training and all the other energy demands of the body and daily living. Female athletes with menstrual dysfunction, regardless of the cause, typically have reduced levels of the reproductive hormones, such as estrogen and progesterone. When estrogen levels in the body are low, it is difficult for bone to retain calcium, and gradual loss of bone mass occurs. Thus, many female athletes develop premature bone loss (osteoporosis) and are at increased risk for fractures.

Figure 7 The female athlete triad is a syndrome composed of three coexisting disorders: low energy availability (with or without eating disorders), menstrual dysfunction (such as amenorrhea), and osteoporosis. Energy availability is defined as dietary energy intake minus exercise energy expenditure.

female athlete triad A serious syndrome that consists of three clinical conditions in some physically active females: low energy availability (with or without eating disorders), amenorrhea, and osteoporosis.

AP Photos

⬥ Sports that emphasize leanness, or that require athletes to wear body-contouring clothing, increase the risk for female athlete triad.

Treatment for Disordered Eating Requires a Multidisciplinary Approach

As with any health problem, prevention is the best treatment for disordered eating. People having trouble with eating and body image issues need help to deal with these issues before they develop into something more serious.

Treating anyone with disordered eating requires a multidisciplinary approach, which typically includes the physician and psychologist, a nutritionist, and family members. The severity of the eating disorder will dictate the treatment. Patients who are severely underweight, display signs of malnutrition, are medically unstable, or are suicidal may require immediate hospitalization. Conversely, patients who are underweight but are still medically stable may enter an outpatient program designed to meet their specific needs.

Do you have a friend you suspect has an eating disorder? Discussing a friend's eating behaviors can be difficult. It is important to choose an appropriate time and place to raise your concerns and to listen closely and with great sensitivity to your friend's feelings. It is also important to locate a health professional specializing in eating disorders whom you can recommend. If you are at a university or college, check with the student health center to see what resources it has. Finally, the National Eating Disorders Association provides a list of steps to consider before talking to your friend about his or her eating disorder.[18] You can find it under Information and Resources at its website listed in Web Resources.

Recognizing and Treating the Female Athlete Triad

Recognition of an athlete with one or more of the components of the female athlete triad can be difficult, especially if the athlete is reluctant to be honest when questioned about the symptoms. For this reason, familiarity with the early warning signs is criti-cal. These include excessive dieting and/or weight loss, excessive exercise, stress fractures, and self-esteem that appears to be dictated by body weight and shape.

Treating an athlete requires a multidisciplinary approach. This means that the sports medicine team, sports dietitian, exercise physiologist, psychologist, coach, trainer, parents, friends of the athlete, and athlete all must work together.

NUTRI-CASE LIZ

"I used to dance with a really cool modern company, where everybody looked sort of healthy and 'real.' No waifs! When they folded after Christmas, I was disappointed, but this spring, I'm planning to audition for the City Ballet. My best friend dances with them, and she told me that they won't even look at anybody over 100 pounds. So I've just put myself on a strict diet. Most days, I come in under 1,200 calories, though some days I cheat and then I feel so out of control. Last week, my dance teacher stopped me after class and asked me whether or not I was menstruating. I thought that was a pretty weird question, so I just said sure, but when I thought about it, I realized that I've been so focused and stressed out lately that I really don't know! The audition is only a week away, so I'm going on a juice fast this weekend. I've just got to make it into the City Ballet!"

What factors increase Liz's risk for the female athlete triad? What, if anything, do you think Liz's dance teacher should do? Is intervention even necessary, since the audition is only a week away?

Rubberball/Getty Images

Web Resources

www.harriscentermgh.org
Harris Center, Massachusetts General Hospital

This site provides information about current eating disorder research, as well as sections on understanding eating disorders and resources for those with eating disorders.

www.nimh.nih.gov
National Institute of Mental Health (NIMH) Office of Communications and Public Liaison

Search this site for "disordered eating" or "eating disorders" to find numerous articles on the subject.

www.anad.org
National Association of Anorexia Nervosa and Associated Disorders

Visit this site for information and resources about eating disorders.

www.nationaleatingdisorders.org
National Eating Disorders Association

This site is dedicated to expanding public understanding of eating disorders and promoting access to treatment for those affected and support for their families.

References

1. American Psychiatric Association. 1994. Diagnostic and Statistical Manual of Mental Disorders (DSM-IV). 4th ed. Washington, DC: American Psychiatric Association.
2. Treasure J., Claudino A. M., Zucker N. Eating Disorders. 2010. *Lancet* 375:583–593.
3. Vandereycken, W. 2002. Families of patients with eating disorders. In: Fairburn, D. G., and K. D. Brownell, eds. Eating Disorders and Obesity: A Comprehensive Handbook. 2nd ed. New York Guilford Press, pp. 215–220.
4. Patrick, L. 2002. Eating disorders: A review of the literature with emphasis on medical complication and clinical nutrition. *Altern. Med. Rev.* 7(3):184–202.
5. Striegel-Moore, R. H., and L. Smolak. 2002. Gender, ethnicity, and eating disorders. In: Fairburn, D. G., and K. D. Brownell, eds. Eating Disorders and Obesity: A Comprehensive Handbook. 2nd ed. New York: Guilford Press, pp. 251–255.
6. Steinberg, L. 2002. Adolescence. 6th ed. New York: McGraw-Hill.
7. Stice E. 2002. Sociocultural influences on body image and eating disturbances. In: Fairburn, D. G., and K. D. Brownell, eds. Eating Disorders and Obesity: A Comprehensive Handbook. 2nd ed. New York: Guilford Press, pp. 103–107.
8. Wonderlich, S. A. 2002. Personality and eating disorders. In: Fairburn, D. G., and K. D. Brownell, eds. Eating Disorders and Obesity: A Comprehensive Handbook. 2nd ed. New York: Guilford Press, pp. 204–209.
9. Robb, A. S., and M. J. Dadson. 2002. Eating disorders in males. Child Adolesc. *Psychiatric. Clin. N. Am.* 11:399–418.
10. American Psychiatric Association, 2000. Diagnostic and Statistical Manual of Mental Disorders, Text Revision.
11. Beals, K. A. 2004. Disordered Eating in Athletes: A Comprehensive Guide for Health Professionals. Champaign, IL: Human Kinetics Publishers.
12. Andersen, A. E. 2001. Eating disorders in males: Gender divergence management. Currents 2(2). University of Iowa Health Care. Available at http://www.uihealthcare.com/news/currents/vol2issue2/eatingdisordersinmen.html.
13. Pope H. G., K. A. Phillips, and R. Olivardia. 2000. The Adonis Complex: The Secret Crisis of Male Body Obsession. New York: The Free Press.
14. Garfinkel, P. E. 2002. Classification and diagnosis of eating disorders. In: Fairburn D. G., and K. D. Brownell, eds. Eating

Disorders and Obesity: A Comprehensive Handbook. 2nd ed. New York: Guilford Press, pp. 155–161.

15. Grilo, C. M. 2002. Binge eating disorder. In: D. G. Fairburn and K. D. Brownell, eds. Eating Disorders and Obesity: A Comprehensive Handbook. 2nd ed. New York: Guilford Press, pp. 178–182.

16. Stunkard, A. J. 2002. Night eating syndrome. In: DG Fairburn and KD Brownell, eds. Eating Disorders and Obesity: A Comprehensive Handbook. 2nd ed. New York: Guilford Press, pp. 183–187.

17. Nattiv A., A. B. Loucks, M. M. Manore, C. F. Sanborn, J. Sundgot-Borgen, and M. P. Warren. 2007. The female athlete triad. *Medicine and Science in Sport and Exercise.* 39(10):1867–1882.

18. National Eating Disorders Association. 2005. What should I say? Tips for talking to a friend who may be struggling with an eating disorder. Available at http://www.nationaleatingdisorders.org/p.asp?WebPage_ID5322&Profile_ID541174.

Food Safety and Technology: Impact on Consumers

From Chapter 13 of *Nutrition: An Applied Approach*, Third Edition. Janice Thompson, Melinda Manore. Copyright © 2012 by Pearson Education, Inc. Published by Pearson Benjamin Cummings. All rights reserved.

Food Safety and Technology: Impact on Consumers

CHAPTER OBJECTIVES

After reading this chapter you will be able to:

1. Identify the types of contaminants involved in food-borne illness.

2. Describe strategies for preventing food-borne illness at home, while eating out, and when traveling to other countries.

3. Discuss the advantages of newer food-preservation methods, such as innovative packaging techniques and irradiation, over traditional methods used to preserve foods.

4. Debate the safety of food additives, including the role of the GRAS list.

5. Describe the process of genetic modification and discuss its potential risks and benefits.

6. Describe the process by which persistent organic pollutants accumulate in foods.

7. Discuss the benefits and safety concerns related to pesticides.

8. Explain the current system of labeling for organic foods.

I n late 2008, the United States Centers for Disease Control and Prevention (CDC) began conducting an epidemiological assessment of a growing cluster of cases of food-borne illness due to infection with a microscopic organism called *Salmonella*. By early 2009, the total number of people infected had grown to 691 in 46 states, plus a handful of individuals in Canada and other countries. Of these, more than 150 had to be hospitalized, and the infection was thought to have contributed to 9 deaths. Detailed interviews conducted by the CDC revealed a likely association with consumption of peanut butter or peanut paste, granules, or meal produced by Peanut Corporation of America (PCA). Testing of samples of PCA's peanut butter revealed *Salmonella* contamination, and the United States Food and Drug Administration (FDA) issued an immediate advisory calling upon consumers to destroy any of over 400 recalled food products, including cookies, crackers, ice cream, snack bars, and even pet foods, that contained peanut products from PCA facilities.[1]

By spring of 2009, this had become one of the largest food recalls ever undertaken in the United States, yet within a few weeks, new recalls of *Salmonella*-contaminated foods had begun, involving pistachio nuts, then alfalfa sprouts, jalapeno peppers, and in early 2010 salami, hydrolyzed vegetable protein, and crushed red pepper.[2] Unfortunately, these incidents are not unusual. Every year in the United States, *Salmonella* infection, called salmonellosis, causes more than 40,000 reported illnesses, perhaps 30 times more unreported illnesses, and 400 deaths.[3] What's worse, *Salmonella* is just one of several culprits responsible for millions of cases of food-borne illness in the United States annually.

We'll begin this chapter by considering the key reasons that food-borne illness has become a priority public health issue. We'll then identify the major culprits in food-borne illness and describe some simple ways to protect yourself from getting sick. We'll also examine information about food preservation, take a quick look at the issues surrounding genetically modified foods, then conclude by discussing chemical residues that can affect food safety, from pollutants to pesticides. Whether your food comes from South America or your own backyard, you'll learn about the safeguards that must be in place to ensure food safety.

Why Is Food-Borne Illness a Critical Concern?

Food-borne illness is a term generally used to encompass any symptom or illness that arises from ingesting food or water that contains an infectious agent or a toxic substance. Food-borne illness is commonly called *food poisoning*.

Food-Borne Illness Affects Millions of Americans Annually

According to the CDC, approximately 76 million Americans report experiencing food-borne illness each year at an annual cost of $152 billion.[4] It is estimated that over half the population of the United States have had symptoms of food-borne illness without ever knowing or reporting it. The people most at risk for serious consequences of food-borne illness include:

- Developing fetuses, infants, and young children, whose immune systems are still immature
- The very old and the frail elderly, whose immune systems may be compromised
- People with chronic illnesses, such as diabetes
- People with acquired immunodeficiency syndrome (AIDS)
- People who are receiving immune system–suppressing drugs, such as transplant recipients and cancer patients

Of those afflicted by food-borne illness, 300,000 are hospitalized and 5,000 die each year.[5] Although these statistics may seem frightening, most experts consider our food supply safe. That's partly because not all cases of food contamination make all people sick; in fact, even virulent strains cause illness in only a small percentage of people. In the PCA *Salmonella* case, although more than 500 people became ill, thousands are assumed to have eaten the tainted products. Moreover, modern science and technology have given us a wide array of techniques to preserve foods. We'll discuss these later in this chapter. Finally, food safety in the United States is monitored by several government agencies. In addition to the CDC and the FDA, mentioned earlier, the United States Department of Agriculture (USDA) and the Environmental Protection Agency (EPA) monitor and regulate food production and preservation. Together, these agencies help set standards to ensure the safety of our food supply. Information about these agencies and how to access them is in **Table 1**.

Food Production Is Increasingly Complex and Oversight Has Decreased

Despite the safeguards, food-borne illness is emerging as a major public health issue for two key reasons. First, more foods are mass-produced than ever before, with a combination of ingredients from a much greater number of sources, including fields, feedlots, and a variety of processing facilities all over the world. These various sources can remain hidden not only to consumers but even to food companies

▲ A nationwide food recall in early 2009 as a result of *Salmonella* contamination included hundreds of products made from peanuts.

matka_Wariatka/Shutterstock

food-borne illness An illness transmitted through food or water, either by an infectious agent, a poisonous substance, or a protein that causes an immune reaction.

TABLE 1 Government Agencies That Regulate Food Safety

Name of Agency	Year Established	Role in Food Regulations	Website
U.S. Department of Agriculture (USDA)	1785	Oversees safety of meat, poultry, and eggs sold across state lines. Also regulates which drugs can be used to treat sick cattle and poultry.	www.usda.gov
U.S. Food and Drug Administration (FDA)	1862	Regulates food standards of food products (except meat, poultry, and eggs) and bottled water. Regulates food labeling and enforces pesticide use as established by the EPA.	www.fda.gov
Centers for Disease Control and Prevention (CDC)	1946	Works with public health officials to promote and educate the public about health and safety. Able to track information needed in identifying food-borne illness outbreaks.	www.cdc.gov
Environmental Protection Agency (EPA)	1970	Regulates use of pesticides and designates which crops they can be applied to. Establishes standards for water quality.	www.epa.gov

using the ingredients. Contamination can occur at any point from farm to table (Figure 1), and when it does, it can be difficult to trace. For example, in the PCA outbreak, many of the manufacturers of the recalled cookies and other products could not identify the source of their peanut ingredients.

Second, federal oversight has decreased: 35 years ago, the FDA inspected about half of the nation's food-processing facilities annually. By 2008, the inspection rate had dropped below 5%. Not surprisingly, in the same year, the CDC reported that there had been little progress in reducing the incidence of food-borne illness during the previous 4 years.[6] And in 2009, the CDC warned that, after decades of steady progress, the safety of the nation's food supply was no longer improving and, in the case of *Salmonella*, the number of infections may be creeping upward.[7] The same year, President Barack Obama called the government's failure to inspect 95% of food-processing plants "a hazard to public health" and announced the creation of a Food Safety Working Group to foster coordination across federal agencies, sponsor changes in food-safety laws, improve the enforcement of these laws, and increase inspections.[8] The U.S. Congress responded by crafting a new food-safety bill, expected to be passed into law in 2010 or 2011.[9]

RECAP Food-borne illness affects 76 million Americans a year at an annual cost of $152 billion. Contamination can occur at any point from farm to table. The Centers for Disease Control and Prevention, the Food and Drug Administration, the United States Department of Agriculture, and the Environmental Protection Agency monitor and regulate food production and preservation. As the complexity of food manufacturing has increased steadily for decades, oversight by federal agencies has decreased.

What Causes Most Food-Borne Illness?

Microorganisms—that is, microscopic living organisms—and their toxins are responsible for most cases of food-borne illness. The consumption of food containing pathogenic microorganisms—those capable of causing disease—results in *food infections*. *Food intoxications* result from consuming food in which microorganisms have secreted harmful substances called *toxins*. Naturally occurring plant and marine toxins also contaminate food. Finally, chemical residues in foods, such as pesticides and pollutants in soil or water, can cause illness. Residues are discussed later in this chapter.

Several Types of Microorganisms Contaminate Foods

The microorganisms that most commonly cause food infections are bacteria and viruses;[10] however, other tiny organisms and non-living particles can also contaminate foods.

Bacteria are microorganisms that lack a true nucleus and have a chemical called peptidoglycan in their cell walls (Table 2). They make their way into food and

bacteria Microorganisms that lack a true nucleus and have a chemical called peptidoglycan in their cell walls.

397

▶ **Figure 1** Food is at risk for contamination at any of the five stages from farm to table, but following food-safety guidelines can reduce the risks.

Farms

Animals raised for meat can harbor harmful microorganisms, and crops can be contaminated with pollutants from irrigation, runoff from streams, microorganisms or toxins in soil, or pesticides. Contamination can also occur during animal slaughter or from harvesting, sorting, washing, packing, and/or storage of crops.

Exactostock/SuperStock

Processing

Some foods, such as produce, may go from the farm directly to the market, but most foods are processed. Processed foods may go through several steps at different facilities. At each site, people, equipment, or environments may contaminate foods. Federal safeguards, such as cleaning protocols, testing, and training, can help prevent contamination.

Fotolia

Transportation

Foods must be transported in clean, refrigerated vehicles and containers to prevent multiplication of microorganisms and microbial toxins.

David Wei/Alamy

Retail

Employees of food markets and restaurants may contaminate food during storage, preparation, or service. Conditions such as inadequate refrigeration or heating may promote multiplication of microorganisms or microbial toxins. Establishments must follow FDA guidelines for food safety and pass local health inspections.

Frank Rumpenhorst/Newscom

Table

Consumers may contaminate foods with unclean hands, utensils, or surfaces. They can allow the multiplication of microorganisms and microbial toxins by failing to follow the food-safety guidelines for storing, preparing, cooking, and serving foods discussed in this chapter.

Huntstock, Inc/Alamy

TABLE 2 Common Bacterial Causes of Food-Borne Illness

Bacteria	Incubation Period	Duration	Symptoms	Foods Most Commonly Affected	Usual Sources of Contamination	Steps for Prevention
Campylobacter jejuni	1–7 days	7–10 days	Fever Headache and muscle pain followed by diarrhea (sometimes bloody) Nausea Abdominal cramps	Raw and undercooked meat, poultry, or shellfish Raw eggs Cake icing Untreated water Unpasteurized milk	Intestinal tracts of animals and birds Raw milk Untreated water and sewage sludge	Drink only pasteurized milk Cook foods properly Avoid cross-contamination
Salmonella (more than 2,300 types)	12–24 hours	4–7 days	Diarrhea Abdominal pain Chills Fever Vomiting Dehydration	Raw or undercooked eggs, poultry, and meat Raw milk and dairy products Seafood Fruits and vegetables	Intestinal tract and feces of poultry *Salmonella enteritidis* in raw shell eggs	Cook foods thoroughly Avoid cross-contamination Use sanitary practices
Escherichia coli (O157:H7 and other strains that can cause human illness)	2–4 days	5–10 days	Diarrhea (may be bloody) Abdominal cramps Nausea Can lead to kidney and blood complications	Contaminated water Raw milk Raw or rare ground beef, sausages Unpasteurized apple juice or cider Uncooked fruits and vegetables	Intestinal tracts of cattle Raw milk Unchlorinated water	Cook meats thoroughly Avoid cross-contamination
Clostridium botulinum	12–36 hours	1–8 days	Nausea Vomiting Diarrhea Fatigue Headache Muscle paralysis; difficulty speaking, swallowing, and breathing	Improperly canned or vacuum-packed food Meats Sausage Fish Garlic in oil Honey	Widely distributed in nature In soil, in water, on plants, and in intestinal tracts of animals and fish Grows only in little or no oxygen	Properly can foods, following recommended procedures Cook foods properly Children under 16 months should not consume raw honey
Staphylococcus	1–6 hours	2–3 days	Severe nausea and vomiting Abdominal cramps Diarrhea	Custard- or cream-filled baked goods Ham Poultry Dressings, sauces, and gravies Eggs Mayonnaise-based salads	Human skin Infected cuts Pimples Noses and throats	Refrigerate foods Use sanitary practices
Listeria monocytogenes	2 days–3 weeks	None reported	Fever Muscle aches Nausea Diarrhea Headache, stiff neck, confusion, loss of balance, or convulsions if infection spreads to nervous system. Infections during pregnancy can lead to miscarriage or stillbirth	Uncooked meats and vegetables Soft cheeses Lunch meats and hot dogs Unpasteurized milk	Intestinal tract and feces of animals Soil and manure used as fertilizer Raw milk	Cook meats thoroughly Wash produce before eating Avoid cross-contamination Avoid unpasteurized milk and foods made with unpasteurized milk People at high risk should: • not eat hot dogs or lunch meats unless they are reheated until steaming hot • avoid getting fluid from hot dog packages on foods, utensils, and surfaces • wash hands after handling hot dogs or lunch meats • avoid eating refrigerated smoked seafood unless it is cooked

Data from Iowa State University Extension, Food Safety and Quality Project. 2000. Safe Food: It's Your Job Too! www.extension.iastate.edu/foodsafety/Lesson/?CFID=2587460&CFTOKEN=69223455. U.S. Food and Drug Administration (FDA). How Can I Prevent Foodborne Illness? www.cfsan.fda.gov/~dms/qa-topfd.html; and Centers for Disease Control and Prevention (CDC), Division of Bacterial and Mycotic Diseases. Disease Information, Foodborne Illness. www.cdc.gov/ncidod/dbmd/diseaseinfo/foodborneinfections_g.htm.

Dr. Tony Brain/Photo Researchers

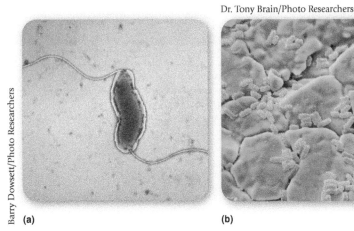
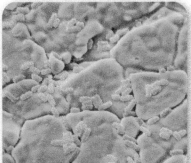
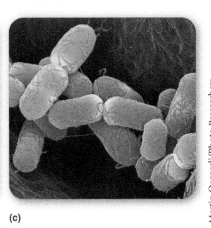

(a)   **(b)**   **(c)**

Figure 2 The three bacteria responsible for the majority of food-borne infections. **(a)** Infection with *Campylobacter jejuni* causes fever, cramping, abdominal pain, and diarrhea (which may be bloody). **(b)** Salmonellosis, the disease caused by eating food contaminated by *Salmonella*, causes fever, diarrhea, and abdominal cramps, and cells of some strains of *Salmonella* can perforate the intestines and invade the blood. Shown is *S. enteritidis*, one of more than 2000 strains. **(c)** The bacterial species called *Escherichia coli* (*E. coli*) includes strains that are harmless, but the strain shown here, *E. coli* O157:H7, can cause severe and bloody diarrhea and can lead to kidney failure and death.

water in a variety of ways, but many thrive naturally in the intestines of birds and mammals, including poultry, pigs, and cattle. Often, food-borne infection results from consuming undercooked or raw meats, foods contaminated with juices from raw meats, or milk or water contaminated with infected animal feces. Of the several species involved, *Campylobacter jejuni*, *Salmonella*, and *E. coli* are thought to be the most common culprits, causing millions of cases each year in the United States (**Figure 2**).[11]

Although bacteria are the primary cause of food-borne infections, some food-borne **viruses** also cause disease. Viruses are infectious agents that are much smaller than bacteria, lack independent metabolism, and are incapable of growth or reproduction apart from living cells. Noroviruses are the most common cause of outbreaks of acute gastroenteritis worldwide.[12] Gastroenteritis is inflammation of the lining of the stomach and intestines; it results in stomach cramps, vomiting, and diarrhea. Infected food-service workers can contaminate foods during preparation or serving if they have the virus on their hands. This was the suspected mode of transmission of a norovirus outbreak in 2009 at the University of Michigan that sickened eight people who had eaten at the same university cafeteria.[13] Hepatitis A and hepatitis E viruses also commonly contaminate foods during harvesting, processing, and preparation. They can cause acute liver damage and even death.

Parasites are microorganisms that simultaneously derive benefit from and harm their host. They include multicellular worms called helminths and single-celled organisms called protozoa. **Helminths,** which include tapeworms, flukes, and roundworms (**Figure 3**), reproduce by releasing their eggs into the environment, such as in vegetation or water. Animals, including fish, then consume the contaminated matter. The eggs hatch inside their host, and larvae develop in the host's tissue. The larvae can survive in the flesh long after the host is killed for food. Thoroughly cooking beef, pork, and fish destroys the larvae. In contrast, people who eat contaminated meat or fish either raw or undercooked consume living larvae, which then mature into adult worms in their small intestine. Some worms cause mild symptoms, such as nausea and diarrhea, but others can grow large enough to cause intestinal obstruction and some can even cause death.

Unlike helminths, **protozoa** most commonly cause water-borne illness. One of the most common culprits worldwide is *Giardia duodenalis* (formerly called *Giardia lamblia*), which causes a diarrheal illness called *giardiasis*.[14] *Giardia* lives in the intestines of infected animals and humans, and it is passed into the environment from

viruses A group of infectious agents that are much smaller than bacteria, lack independent metabolism, and are incapable of growth or reproduction apart from living cells.

parasite A microorganism that simultaneously derives benefit from and harms its host.

helminth A multicellular microscopic worm.

protozoa Single-celled, mobile microorganisms.

their stools. People typically consume *Giardia* by swallowing contaminated water (this includes water in lakes, streams, rivers, swimming pools, hot tubs, and fountains) or by eating uncooked food contaminated with *Giardia.* It can also be transmitted by putting something in your mouth that has come in contact with the stool of an infected person or animal. Symptoms include diarrhea, loose or watery stools, stomach cramps, and upset stomach, but some people show no symptoms. The symptoms usually begin within 1 to 2 weeks of being infected and generally last 2 to 6 weeks.

Fungi are plantlike, spore-forming organisms that can grow either as single cells or multicellular colonies. Two types of fungi are yeasts, which are globular, and molds, which are long and thin. The growth of fungi on foods rarely causes food infection. This is due in part to the fact that very few species of fungi cause serious disease in people with healthy immune systems, and those that do cause disease in humans are not typically food-borne.[15] In addition, unlike bacterial growth, which is invisible and often tasteless, fungal growth typically makes food look and taste so unappealing that we immediately discard it (**Figure 4**).

A food-borne illness in beef cattle that has had front-page exposure in recent years is mad cow disease, or *bovine spongiform encephalopathy* (*BSE*). This neurologic disorder is caused by a **prion,** a proteinaceous infectious particle that is self-replicating. Prions are normal proteins of animal tissues that can misfold and become infectious. When they do, they can transform other normal proteins into abnormally shaped prions until they eventually cause illness. The human form of BSE can develop in people who consume contaminated meat or tissue. If you eat beef, are you at risk? Check out the Nutrition Myth or Fact? box on the next page.

▲ **Figure 3** Tapeworms have long, wormlike bodies and hooks and suckers, which help them attach to human tissues.

Some Microorganisms Release Toxins

The microbes just discussed cause illness by directly infecting and destroying body cells. In contrast, other bacteria and fungi secrete chemicals, called **toxins,** that are responsible for serious and even life-threatening illnesses. These toxins bind to body cells and can cause a variety of symptoms, such as diarrhea, vomiting, organ damage, convulsions, and paralysis. Toxins can be categorized depending on the type of cell they bind to; the two primary types of toxins associated with food-borne illness are neurotoxins, which damage the nervous system and can cause paralysis, and enterotoxins, which target the gastrointestinal system and generally cause severe diarrhea and vomiting.

One of the most common and deadly toxins is produced by the bacterium *Clostridium botulinum* (see Table 2). The botulism toxin blocks nerve transmission to muscle cells and causes paralysis, including of the muscles required for breathing. Common sources of contamination are split or pierced, bulging cans; foods improperly canned at home; and raw honey.

▲ **Figure 4** Molds rarely cause human illness, in part because they look so unappealing that we throw the food away.

Some fungi produce poisonous chemicals called *mycotoxins.* (The prefix *myco-* means "fungus.") These toxins are typically found in grains stored in moist environments. In some instances, moist conditions in the field encourage fungi to reproduce and release their toxins on the surface of growing crops. Long-term consumption of mycotoxins can cause organ damage or cancer, and they can be fatal if consumed in large doses. A mycotoxin called *aflatoxin* is produced by the mold *Aspergillus flavus.* Aflatoxin has been associated with peanuts and other crops and, if ingested, can cause illness in livestock and humans.

Some Toxins Occur Independently of Microorganisms

Some toxins develop in foods independently of microorganisms. For example, a highly visible fungus that causes food intoxication is the poisonous mushroom. Most

fungi Plantlike, spore-forming organisms that can grow either as single cells or multicellular colonies.

prion An infectious, self-replicating protein.

toxin A harmful substance; specifically, a chemical produced by a microorganism that harms tissues or causes adverse immune responses.

NUTRITION MYTH OR FACT?

Mad Cow Disease: Is It Safe to Eat Beef?

Mad cow disease is a fatal brain disorder in cattle caused by a *prion*, which is an abnormally folded, infectious protein. Prions influence other proteins to mimic their abnormal shape, and these abnormal proteins then cause brain damage. Mad cow disease is also called *bovine spongiform encephalopathy (BSE)*. The disease eats away at a cow's brain, leaving it full of spongelike holes, and eventually the brain can no longer control vital life functions. Unfortunately, people who eat meat from infected cattle will also be infected. Symptoms may take years to appear, but eventually an infected person will develop the human form of mad cow disease, called *variant Creutzfeldt-Jakob disease (vCJD)*. This disease has killed at least 168 people in Great Britain, as well as people in France and other nations.[16] So if you eat beef, are you at risk?

Scientists are not certain how the prions are introduced to cattle. They think that cattle become infected by eating feed containing tissue from the brains and spinal cords of other infected cattle. Decades ago in Great Britain and Europe, it was common practice to feed livestock with meal made from other animals. This practice there has since ceased.

The effect of mad cow disease on the European beef market has been staggering, with beef consumption dropping 25–70% in some countries, and ranchers have been forced to slaughter almost 5 million cattle.

For years, experts in North American believed that BSE was a

StockFood/Getty Images

problem limited to Europe. But from 2003 to 2006, eight cases of BSE were found in cows in Canada. In December 2003, the first case of mad cow disease was reported in the United States, shocking those who believed the U.S. food supply was safe from this disease. These discoveries prompted many countries to swiftly ban importation of Canadian and American beef. In the United States, the federal government and beef industry took quick action to restore confidence in the beef supply. Steps included the destruction of potentially infected beef, as well as changes in feeding practices, including greater enforcement of a ban on livestock meal made with animal by-products. In addition, cattle in the United States have for many years been slaughtered at an early age. Because BSE takes years to develop, this practice reduces the likelihood of advanced infection.

So is it safe to eat beef? The U.S. Department of Agriculture, the FDA, the National Institutes of Health, and the Centers for Disease Control and Prevention are working together to eliminate the use of animal-based feed and to enhance technology that can track signs of BSE and act quickly if it reappears. The U.S. beef industry is highly motivated to comply with safety regulations, since reduced beef consumption translates into millions of dollars in lost income. Although it may not be possible to guarantee the safety of U.S. beef, adherence to strict standards should minimize the risk and keep beef safe for human consumption.

mushrooms are not toxic, but a few, such as the deathcap mushroom (*Amanita phalloides*), can be fatal. Some poisonous mushrooms are quite colorful **(Figure 5)**, a fact that helps to explain why the victims of mushroom poisoning are often children.[17]

In February 2010, scientists predicted that a severe "red tide" could threaten the New England shellfish industry and cause paralysis in anyone consuming mussels or clams.[18] Red tides are caused by an excessive production of certain species of toxic algae, whose bloom turns ocean waters red. Humans don't consume these marine toxins directly, but they can accumulate in mussels, clams, and other seafoods. When humans consume the seafood, which typically looks, smells, and tastes normal, illness results.[19]

Ciguatoxins are among the most common marine toxins. They are produced by microscopic sea plants called *dinoflagellates*, which are consumed by small fish. The toxins become progressively more concentrated as larger fish eat these small fish, and high concentrations can be present in grouper, sea bass, snapper, and a number of other large fish from tropical regions. Symptoms of ciguatoxin poisoning include nausea, vomiting, diarrhea, headache, itching, a "pins-and-needles" feeling, and even nightmares or hallucinations, but the illness is rarely fatal and typically resolves within a few weeks.[20]

Potatoes that have turned green contain the toxin solanine, which forms during the greening process. The green color is actually due to chlorophyll, a harmless pigment that forms when the potatoes are exposed to light. Although the production of solanine occurs simultaneously with the production of chlorophyll, the two processes are separate and unrelated.[21] Although there is a potential for toxicity from consuming potatoes with a very high solanine content, because solanine formation occurs near the potato's skin, the green areas can be cut away to remove any toxins. A good guide is to taste a small piece of the potato after the green areas have been removed. If the potato tastes bitter, then throw it away. If you're in doubt, or if you're serving the potato to someone with allergies or compromised immunity, you should discard the potato. You can avoid the greening of potatoes by storing them for only short periods in a dark cupboard or brown paper bag in a cool area. Wash the potato to expose its color, and cut away and discard any green areas. Cooked potatoes cannot turn green or produce solanine, but cooking green potatoes does not remove the chlorophyll or solanine that is formed prior to cooking.

Neil Fletcher/Dorling Kindersley Media Library

Figure 5 Some mushrooms, such as this fly agaric, contain toxins that can cause illness or even death.

The Body Responds to Contaminated Foods with Acute Illness

Many food-borne microbes are killed in the mouth by antimicrobial enzymes in saliva or in the stomach by hydrochloric acid. Any microbe that survives these chemical assaults will usually trigger vomiting and/or diarrhea as the gastrointestinal tract attempts to expel the offender. Simultaneously, the white blood cells of the immune system will be activated, and a generalized inflammatory response will cause the person to experience nausea, fatigue, fever, and muscle cramps. Depending on the state of one's health, the precise microbe involved, and the number of microbes ingested, the symptoms can range from mild to severe, including double vision, loss of muscle control, and excessive or bloody diarrhea. As noted earlier, some cases, if left untreated, can result in death.

To diagnose a food-borne illness, a specimen must be obtained and cultured. This means the specimen is analyzed in a laboratory setting in which the offending microorganisms are grown in a specific chemical medium. Stool (fecal) cultures are usually analyzed, especially if diarrhea is a symptom. Blood is cultured if the patient has a high fever. Treatment usually involves keeping the person hydrated and comfortable, as most food-borne illness tends to be self-limiting; the person's vomiting and/or diarrhea, although unpleasant, rid the body of the offending agent. In treating botulism, the patient's intestinal tract is flushed repeatedly to remove the microorganisms, and antibodies are injected to neutralize its deadly toxin.

In the United States, all confirmed cases of food-borne illness must be reported to the state health department, which in turn reports these illnesses to the CDC in Atlanta, Georgia. The CDC monitors its reports for indications of epidemics of food-borne illness and assists local and state agencies in controlling such outbreaks.

Jean-Louis Vosgien/Shutterstock

Sea bass may look appealing, but like several other large, predatory tropical fish, can be contaminated with a high concentration of marine toxins.

Certain Conditions Help Microorganisms Multiply in Foods

Given the correct environmental conditions, microorganisms can thrive in many types of food. Four factors affect the survival and reproduction of food microorganisms:

- *Temperature.* Many microorganisms capable of causing human illness thrive at warm temperatures, from about 40°F to 140°F (4°C to 60°C). You can think of this range of temperatures as the **danger zone.** These microorganisms can be destroyed by thoroughly heating or cooking foods, and their reproduction can be slowed by refrigeration and freezing. We'll identify safe cooking and food-storage temperatures later in this chapter.

danger zone The range of temperature at which many microorganisms capable of causing human illness thrive; about 40°F to 140°F (4°C to 60°C).

Peels protect foods against contamination; however, you should still wash fruit before peeling.
Vanessa Davies/Dorling Kindersley

- *Humidity.* Many microorganisms require a high level of moisture; thus, foods such as boxed dried pasta do not make suitable microbial homes, although cooked pasta left at room temperature would prove hospitable.
- *Acidity.* Most microorganisms have a preferred range of acidity, or pH, in which they thrive. For instance, *Clostridium botulinum* thrives in alkaline environments. It cannot grow or produce its toxin in acidic environments, so the risk for botulism is decreased in citrus fruits, pickles, and tomato-based foods. In contrast, alkaline foods, such as fish and low-acid vegetables, are a magnet for *C. botulinum.*
- *Oxygen content.* Many microorganisms require oxygen to function; thus, food-preservation techniques that remove oxygen, such as industrial canning and bottling, keep foods safe for consumption. Because *C. botulinum* thrives in an oxygen-free environment, the canning process heats foods to an extremely high temperature to destroy this organism.

In addition, microorganisms need an entryway into a food. Just as our skin protects our body from microbial invasion, the peels, rinds, and shells of many foods seal off access to the nutrients within. Eggshells are a good example of a natural food barrier. Once such a barrier is removed, however, the food loses its primary defense against contamination.

RECAP Food infections result from the consumption of food containing living microorganisms, such as bacteria, whereas food intoxications result from consuming food in which microbes have secreted toxins. Some foods develop toxins independently of microbes. The body has several defense mechanisms, such as saliva, stomach acid, vomiting, diarrhea, and the inflammatory response, which help rid us of offending microorganisms or their toxins. In order to reproduce in foods, microbes require a precise range of temperature, humidity, acidity, and oxygen content.

How Can Food-Borne Illness Be Prevented?

Foods of animal origin are most commonly associated with food-borne illness. These include not only raw meat, poultry, and fish but also eggs, shellfish, and unpasteurized milk. Fruits and vegetables can also cause problems when they are consumed unwashed and raw. For example, in 2006, more than 200 people became ill and 3 died after eating raw spinach contaminated with *E. coli*, and this was quickly followed by an outbreak of salmonellosis traced to fresh tomatoes.[22] So how can you

Justin Sullivan/Getty Images

*Spinach was pulled from supermarket shelves during an *E. coli* outbreak in 2006.*

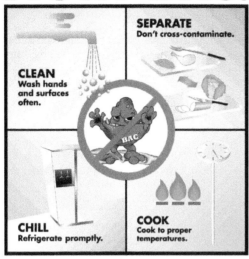

Figure 6 The FightBAC! logo is the food-safety logo of the U.S. Department of Agriculture.

protect yourself when eating foods of animal origin and fresh fruits and vegetables? Here, we discuss food-safety tips for when you're preparing foods at home, eating out, or traveling to other countries.

When preparing foods at home, you can prevent food-borne illness by following four basic rules: clean, separate, chill, and cook (**Figure 6**):

1. Clean. Wash your hands and kitchen surfaces often.
2. Separate. Keep foods separated to prevent **cross-contamination**—that is, the spread of bacteria or other microbes from one food to another. This commonly occurs when raw, unwashed foods are cut on the same cutting board or served together on the same plate.
3. Chill. Refrigerate or freeze foods to prevent microbes from growing.
4. Cook. Cook foods to their proper temperatures.

Each of these rules is discussed in detail in the following sections.

Wash Your Hands and Kitchen Surfaces Often

One of the easiest and most effective ways to prevent food-borne illness is to wash your hands both before and after preparing food. Although you should wash dishes in hot water, it's too harsh for normal hand washing: it causes the surface layer of the skin to break down, increasing the risk that microbes will be able to penetrate your skin. Instead, use gentle soap under warm, running water. Scrub for at least 20 seconds (sing "Happy Birthday" or say the ABCs to time yourself). Pay special attention to the areas underneath your fingernails and between your fingers. Also, it's a good idea to remove rings and bracelets while cooking, as they can harbor bacteria. To prevent cross-contamination, always wash your hands after working with each raw food and before progressing to the next one.

A clean area and tools are also essential in reducing cross-contamination. Wash utensils, containers, and cutting boards in the dishwasher or with hot, soapy water before and after contact with food. If a cutting board, plate, countertop, or other surface has held raw meat, poultry, or seafood, sanitize it with a solution of 1 teaspoon of chlorine bleach to 1 quart of water, or use a commercial kitchen cleaning agent.[23] It's

Digital Vision/Getty Images

Washing dishes, utensils, and cutting boards reduces the chances for food contamination.

cross-contamination Contamination of one food by another via the unintended transfer of microbes through physical contact.

also important to wash utensils, faucets, cabinet knobs, countertops, and other areas you have touched. Rinse; then air-dry or dry with fresh paper towels. For cutting foods, use a nonporous, smooth plastic or stone cutting board, because porous wood and scratched plastic can hold juices and harbor bacteria.

Dishtowels, cloths, and aprons should be washed in hot water often. It's a good idea to wash sponges in the dishwasher each time you run it and to replace them regularly. If you don't have a dishwasher, put sponges in boiling water for 3 minutes to sterilize them.

Separate Foods to Prevent Cross-Contamination

Raw meat, poultry, and seafood harbor an array of microbes and can easily contaminate other foods through direct contact, as well as by the juices they leave behind on surfaces (including hands). Avoid contact between foods that have already been cooked or that won't be cooked (such as salad ingredients) and raw foods or their juices. Also avoid placing cooked or ready-to-eat foods on a plate or other surface that previously held raw meat, seafood, or poultry. When preparing meals with a marinade, reserve some of the fresh marinade in a clean container; then add the raw ingredients to the remainder. In this way, some noncontaminated marinade will be available if needed later in the cooking process. Raw food should always be marinated in the refrigerator.

Store Foods in the Refrigerator or Freezer

Different microbes thrive in different environmental temperatures. The majority of the bacteria that cause food-borne illness grow best in temperatures at or above 40°F.[24] Because of this, refrigeration (keep your refrigerator at or below 40°F) and freezing (keep your freezer at 0°F) are two of the most reliable methods of diminishing the ability of bacteria to cause illness.[25] Not all bacteria in cool environments are killed, but the rate at which they reproduce is drastically reduced. Also, naturally occurring enzymes that cause food decomposition are stopped at freezing temperatures.

Shopping for Perishable Foods

When shopping for food, pick up refrigerated and frozen foods last. Many grocery stores are designed so that these foods are in the last aisles. Put packaged meat, poultry, or fish into a plastic bag before placing it in your shopping cart.[26] This prevents food drippings from coming into contact with the other foods in your cart.

When buying perishable foods, look for the "sell by" or "use by" date on their packaging. The "sell by" date indicates the last day a product can be sold and still maintain its quality during normal home storage and consumption. It is generally best to purchase foods prior to this date. The "use by" date indicates how long a product will maintain optimum quality.[27] It is best to avoid consuming foods after the "use by" date, even though they are generally still safe to eat. For nonperishable foods, such as cereal and baking mixes, the "best if used by (or before)" dates indicate the shelf-life of the product or the date at which the product is no longer at peak flavor, texture, and appearance. These foods can be safely eaten past the listed date if they have been stored properly, but they may not taste as good or be as nutritious as they were before this date. Properly store nonperishable items in a dry, clean, cool (less than 85°F) cabinet or pantry.

Do not purchase foods with punctured or otherwise damaged packaging. Dented or bulging cans are especially dangerous, as they could harbor potentially deadly bacteria. Report any damaged packaging to the store manager.

Watch for unsanitary practices and conditions inside the store. For example, the unsafe displaying of food products, such as cooked shrimp on the same bed of ice as raw seafood, is illegal, as is trimming raw meat with the same knife used to slice cold cuts. Report such unsanitary practices or conditions to your local health authorities.

Kristin Piljay

▲ The "sell by" date tells the store how long to display the product for sale.

After purchasing perishable foods, get them home and into the refrigerator or freezer within 1 hour. If your trip home will take longer than an hour, take along a cooler to transport them.

Refrigerating Foods

Once you get home, put meat, poultry, and seafood in the coldest part of the refrigerator. Keep them wrapped in plastic, so that their juices do not drip onto any other foods. If you are not going to use ground beef, poultry, or fish within 48 hours, store them in the freezer.[28] Remember that eggs are also perishable and should be kept refrigerated. Avoid overstocking your refrigerator or freezer, as air needs to circulate around food to cool it quickly and discourage microbial growth. Purchase a refrigerator thermometer and check it regularly to ensure that your refrigerator is at or below 40°F.

After a meal, promptly refrigerate leftovers—even if still hot—to discourage microbial growth. The standard rule for storing leftovers is *2 hours/2 inches/4 days.* Food should be refrigerated *within 2 hours* of serving. If the environmental temperature is 90°F or higher, such as at a picnic, then foods should be refrigerated within 1 hour.[29] Because a larger quantity of food takes longer to cool and will allow more microbes to thrive, food should be stored at a depth of no greater than *2 inches.* The interior of deeper containers of foods can remain warm long enough to allow bacteria to multiply rapidly even when the surface of the food has cooled. Leftovers should only be refrigerated for *up to 4 days.* If you don't plan on using the food within 4 days, freeze it. A guide for storing foods in your refrigerator is provided in Figure 7.

Freezing and Thawing Foods

The temperature in your freezer should be set at 0°F.[30] Use a thermometer to check periodically that a freezing temperature is being maintained. If your electricity goes out, avoid opening the freezer until the power is restored. When the power does come back on, check to make sure the temperature on the top shelf of the freezer compartment is no warmer than 40°F (5°C). If it is warmer, you should inspect your freezer's contents and discard any items that are not firmly frozen.

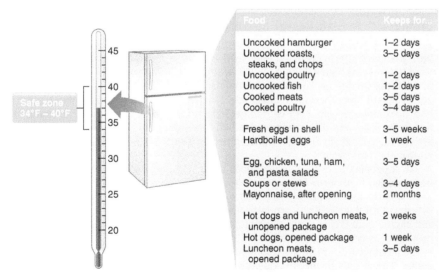

Food	Keeps for...
Uncooked hamburger	1–2 days
Uncooked roasts, steaks, and chops	3–5 days
Uncooked poultry	1–2 days
Uncooked fish	1–2 days
Cooked meats	3–5 days
Cooked poultry	3–4 days
Fresh eggs in shell	3–5 weeks
Hardboiled eggs	1 week
Egg, chicken, tuna, ham, and pasta salads	3–5 days
Soups or stews	3–4 days
Mayonnaise, after opening	2 months
Hot dogs and luncheon meats, unopened package	2 weeks
Hot dogs, opened package	1 week
Luncheon meats, opened package	3–5 days

Figure 7 While it's important to keep a well-stocked refrigerator, it's also important to know how long foods will keep.
Data from U.S. Department of Agriculture, Food Safety and Inspection Service. 2009. Fact Sheets. Safe Food Handling. Refrigeration and Food Safety. www.fsis.usda.gov/Fact_Sheets/Refrigeration_&_Food_Safety/index.asp.

TABLE 3 A Guide to Thawing Poultry

Method Needed	Size of Poultry	Approximate Length of Time
Refrigerator	1–3 lb, small chickens, pieces	1 day
	3–6 lb, large chickens, ducks, small turkeys	2 days
	4–12 lb, large turkeys	1–3 days
	12–16 lb, whole turkey	3–4 days
	16–20 lb, whole turkey	4–5 days
	20–24 lb, whole turkey	5–6 days
Microwave (read instructions)	1–3 lb, small chickens, pieces	8–15 minutes* (standing time 10 minutes)
	3–6 lb, large chickens, ducks, small turkeys	15–30 minutes* (standing time 20 minutes)

*Approximate; read microwave's instructions.

Note: Turkeys purchased stuffed and frozen with the USDA or state mark of inspection on the packaging are safe because they have been processed under controlled conditions. These turkeys *should not* be thawed before cooking. Follow package directions for handling.

Data from Lacey, R. W. 1994. *Hard to Swallow: A Brief History of Food.* Cambridge: Cambridge University Press, pp. 85–187. U.S. Department of Agriculture, Food Safety and Inspection Service. 2005. Poultry Preparation. www.fsis.usda.gov/Fact_Sheets/Poultry_Preparation_Fact_Sheets/index.asp#talk_turkey.

When freezing items, remember that smaller packages will freeze more quickly. So rather than attempting to freeze an entire casserole or a whole batch of home-made spaghetti sauce, divide the food into multiple portions in freezer-safe containers; then freeze.

Sufficient thawing will ensure adequate cooking throughout, which is essential to preventing food-borne illness. Raw poultry is a good example of a food item that needs to be carefully contained as it thaws, so that its juices don't contaminate other foods. The perfect place to thaw poultry is on the bottom shelf of the refrigerator in a large bowl to catch any of its juices. Table 3 shows recommended poultry thawing times based on weight. Never thaw frozen meat, poultry, or seafood on a kitchen counter or in a basin of warm water. Room temperatures allow the growth of bacteria on the surface of food, although the inside may still be frozen.[31] A microwave is also useful for thawing if the food is to be cooked immediately afterwards, but be sure to follow your microwave's instructions carefully.

Dealing with Molds in Refrigerated Foods

Have you ever taken cheese out of the refrigerator and noticed that it had a fuzzy, blue growth on it? This is mold, one of the two types of fungus. Interestingly, cool temperatures and high acidity do not slow the growth of some molds; in fact, some prefer these conditions. For instance, when acidic foods, such as applesauce, yogurt, and spaghetti sauce, are refrigerated, they readily support the growth of mold. But how does mold get into a closed, refrigerated container? Mold spores are common in the atmosphere, and they randomly land on food, either in the processing plant or in open containers at your home. If the temperature and acidity of the food are hospitable, they will grow.

Most people throw away moldy foods because they are so unappealing, but as we noted earlier, food-borne illnesses aren't commonly caused by fungi. If the surface of a small portion of a solid food, such as hard cheese, becomes moldy, it is generally safe to cut off that section down to about an inch and eat the unspoiled portion. If soft cheese, sour cream, yogurt, tomato sauce, applesauce, or another soft or fluid product becomes moldy, discard it.

Some fungi are actually used in the food industry to create popular foods and beverages. The distinct flavor of Roquefort and blue cheeses can be attributed to the molds used in their ripening process. Yeast, the globular form of fungi, gives a distinct flavor to fermented foods such as sourdough bread, miso, soy sauce, beer, wine, and distilled spirits. Even the production of chocolate requires the help of yeasts, which ferment the cacao seeds, causing them to lose their bitter taste.

Cook Foods Thoroughly

Thoroughly cooking food is a sure way to kill the intestinal worms discussed earlier and many other microbes. The proper internal temperatures for doneness of meat, poultry, seafood, and eggs vary, as shown in Figure 8.

The color of cooked meat can be deceiving. Grilled meat and poultry often brown very quickly on the outside but may not be thoroughly cooked on the inside. The only way to be sure meat is thoroughly cooked is with a food thermometer. Test the food in several places to be sure it's cooked evenly, and remember to wash the thermometer after each use.

Microwave cooking is convenient, but you need to be sure that your food is thoroughly cooked and that there are no cold spots in the food where bacteria can thrive. For best results when microwaving, remember to cover food, stir often, and rotate for even cooking. If you are microwaving meat or poultry, use a thermometer to check internal temperatures in several spots, because temperatures vary in different parts of food more in microwave cooking than in conventional ovens.[32] The USDA has published a helpful fact sheet describing how to cook safely in the microwave; see the Web Resources at the end of this chapter.

Raw and semiraw (such as marinated or partly cooked) fish delicacies, such as sushi and sashimi, may be tempting, but their safety cannot be guaranteed. Always cook fish thoroughly. When done, fish should be opaque and flake easily with a fork. It is important to recognize that sushi restaurants cannot guarantee the safety of their food. All fish to be used for sushi must be flash frozen at $-31°$ F $(-35°C)$ or below for 15 hours, or be regularly frozen to $-4°F$ $(-20°C)$ or below for 7 days.[33] Although this effectively kills any parasites that might be in the fish, it does not kill bacteria or viruses. Thus, eating raw seafood remains risky, and people with compromised immunity, children, pregnant women, and the elderly should avoid it.

You may have memories of licking the cake batter off a spoon when you were a kid, but such practices are no longer safe. That's because most cake batters contain

Figure 8 The U.S. Department of Agriculture's "Thermy" provides temperature rules for safely cooking foods at home.

QUICK TIPS

Staying Food-Safe at Your Next Barbecue

- Wash your hands, utensils, and food-preparation surfaces.
- If running water might not be available, take along a water jug, some soap, a basin, and paper towels or a box of moist disposable towelettes to wash hands and dishes as you go.
- Keep foods cold during transport. Use several small coolers with ice or frozen gel packs to keep food at or below 40°F. Meat, poultry, and seafood may be packed while still frozen, so that they stay colder longer. Be sure they are wrapped securely, so that juices don't leak inside the cooler. Keep coolers in the air-conditioned passenger compartment of your car rather than in a hot trunk.
- Grill foods thoroughly. Use a food thermometer to be sure the food has reached an adequate internal temperature before serving; for example,
  - Steaks should reach 145°F for medium rare, 160°F for medium, and 170°F for well done.
- Ground beef should reach 160°F.
- Poultry breasts should reach 170°F.
- Fish should reach 145°F or be cooked until the flesh is opaque and separates easily with a fork.
- When taking food from the grill to the table, never use the same platter or utensils that previously held raw meat or seafood!
- Keep grilled food hot until it is served by moving it to the side of the grill, just away from the coals, so that it stays at or above 140°F. If grilled food isn't going to be eaten right away, wrap it well and place it in an insulated container.
- Keep cold foods, such as chicken salad, in a bowl of ice during your barbecue. Drain off water as the ice melts and replace the ice frequently.
- Don't let any perishable food sit out longer than 2 hours. In temperatures above 90°F, don't let food sit out for more than 1 hour.

raw eggs, and an estimated one-third of chicken eggs in the United States are contaminated with *Salmonella.* For this reason, the USDA recommends that you cook eggs until the yolk and whites are firm. For example, hard-boiled eggs should be boiled for 7 minutes, and fried eggs should be cooked for 3 minutes on one side, 1 minute on the other. Scrambled eggs should not be runny. If you are using eggs in a casserole or custard, make sure that the internal temperature reaches at least 160°F.[34]

Planning a barbecue? Check out the Quick Tips at left, from the USDA's Food Safety and Inspection Service.[35]

Protect Yourself from Toxins in Foods

Killing microorganisms with heat is an important step in keeping food safe, but it won't protect people against their toxins. That's because toxins are unaffected by heat and are capable of causing severe illness even when the microbes that produce them have been destroyed.

For example, let's say you prepare a casserole for a team picnic. Too bad you forget to wash your hands before serving it to your teammates because you contaminate the casserole with the bacteria *Staphylococcus aureus*, which is commonly found on human skin (see Table 2). You and your friends go off and play soccer, leaving the food in the sun, and a few hours later you take the rest of the casserole home. At supper, you heat the leftovers thoroughly, thinking as you do so that this will kill any bacteria that might have multiplied while it was left out. That night you wake up with nausea, severe vomiting, and abdominal pain. What happened? While your food was left out, the bacteria from your hands multiplied in the casserole and produced a toxin (Figure 9). When you reheated the food, the microorganisms were killed, but their toxin was unaffected by the heat. When you then ate the food, the toxin made you sick. Fortunately, in the case of *S. aureus*, symptoms typically resolve on their own in healthy people in about 24 hours.

When Eating Out

When choosing a place to eat out, avoid restaurants that don't look clean. Grimy tabletops and dirty restrooms indicate indifference to hygiene. On the other hand, the cleanliness of areas used by the public doesn't guarantee that the kitchen is clean. That is why health inspections are important. Public health inspectors randomly visit and inspect the food-preparation areas of all businesses that serve food, whether eaten in or taken out. The results of these inspections can usually be found by look-

Alan Richardson/Foodpix/Jupiter Images

At a barbecue, it's essential to heat foods to the proper temperature.

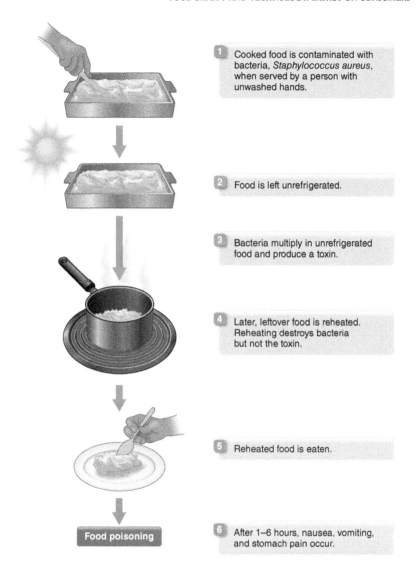

1. Cooked food is contaminated with bacteria, *Staphylococcus aureus*, when served by a person with unwashed hands.

2. Food is left unrefrigerated.

3. Bacteria multiply in unrefrigerated food and produce a toxin.

4. Later, leftover food is reheated. Reheating destroys bacteria but not the toxin.

5. Reheated food is eaten.

Food poisoning

6. After 1–6 hours, nausea, vomiting, and stomach pain occur.

Figure 9 Food intoxication can occur long after the microbe itself has been destroyed.

ing in the local newspaper, by contacting your local health department, or by checking the inspection results posted in the restaurant.

Another way to protect yourself when dining out is by ordering foods to be cooked thoroughly. If you order a hamburger that arrives pink in the middle, send it back and ask for it to be cooked longer. If you order scrambled eggs that arrive runny, send them back to be cooked thoroughly or order something else.

When Traveling to Other Countries

When planning a trip to another country, tell your physician your travel plans and ask about vaccinations needed or any medications that should be taken along in case you get sick. Also pack a waterless antibacterial hand cleanser, and use it frequently during the trip. When dining, select foods and beverages carefully. All raw food has the potential for contamination, especially in areas where hygiene and sanitation are inadequate. If fish is a local delicacy, be aware that some tropical species can contain marine toxins, even when well cooked.

NUTRI-CASE THEO

"I got really sick yesterday after eating lunch in the cafeteria. I had a turkey sandwich, potato salad, and a cola. I remember thinking that the potato salad looked a little off, as if it had been sitting around too long, but I was late for lunch and the cafeteria was about to close, so I had to make my choices fast. Anyway, around five o'clock, in the middle of basketball practice, I started to shake and sweat. I got really nauseated and barely made it to the bathroom before vomiting. Then I went back to my dorm room and crawled into bed. This morning I still feel a little nauseated and sort of weak. I asked some of my friends who ate in the cafeteria yesterday if they got sick, and none of them did, but I still think it was the food. I'm going off-campus for lunch from now on!"

Do you think that Theo's illness was food-borne? If so, what food and/or ingredient(s) do you most suspect, and why? What microbe? (Hint: see Table 2.) What do you think of his plan to go off-campus for lunch? Are there any other actions he might take?

Stockbyte/Getty Images

Tap water is seldom a safe option, even if chlorinated, as chlorine doesn't kill all the organisms that can cause disease. If you think the local water may be contaminated, don't even brush your teeth with it: use bottled water or boil the water for 1 minute; then allow it to return to room temperature before brushing. You can find more information about food and water safety when traveling by visiting the CDC's website (see Web Resources at the end of this chapter) or by contacting your local health department.

RECAP Food-borne illness can be prevented at home by following four tips. Clean: wash your hands and kitchen surfaces often. Separate: isolate foods to prevent cross-contamination. Chill: store foods in the refrigerator or freezer. Cook: heat foods long enough and at proper temperatures to ensure proper cooking. When eating out, avoid restaurants that don't look clean, and ask that all food be cooked thoroughly. When traveling, avoid all raw foods unless they are thoroughly washed in bottled or boiled water, and choose beverages that are boiled, bottled, or canned, without ice.

How Is Food Spoilage Prevented?

Any food that has been harvested and that people aren't ready to eat must be preserved in some way, or before long it will degrade enzymatically and become home to a variety of microorganisms. Even **processed foods**—foods that are manipulated mechanically or chemically—have the potential to spoil.

Spoilage makes food unsafe to eat: because decomposition of foods is accomplished in part by microorganisms, if you eat a food that has spoiled, you risk developing a food-borne illness. Fortunately, spoilage usually degrades the appearance, texture, and smell of food so much that we throw it away uneaten. Would you eat fish with a strong odor or a tomato that has turned to "mush"?

Modern science and technology have given us a wide array of techniques to produce, preserve, and transport food. But these advances have not eliminated the threat of food spoilage, which can occur at any point on the journey from farm to table. Any food that has been harvested and that people aren't ready to eat must be preserved. Here, we look at some techniques that people have used for centuries to preserve food, as well as more modern techniques used in the food industry.

processed foods Foods that are manipulated mechanically or chemically during their production or packaging. Processed foods may or may not resemble the original ingredients in their final form.

Natural Methods Are Effective in Preserving Foods

Some methods of preserving foods have been used for thousands of years and employ naturally derived substances, such as salt, sugars, and smoke, or techniques such as drying and cooling.

- *Salting.* Salt preserves food by drawing the water out of the plant or animal cells by osmosis. This dehydrates the food, making it inhospitable to microbes. It also slows the action of enzymes that would otherwise degrade the food. Some meats are preserved with salt: a good example is Parma ham from Italy.
- *Sugaring.* Sugar has an osmotic effect similar to that of salt. However, foods preserved with sugar retain much of their shape, color, and texture because some of the sugar is absorbed into the cells, replacing the water drawn out. The downside to using sugar is that fungi tend to flourish in sweet, acidic environments, such as jams.
- *Drying.* Drying is an ancient method of preserving food that, like salting and sugaring, works by drawing water out of the food. Fish, poultry, beans, peas, and fruits are commonly preserved by drying. One drawback to drying is that it can change a food's color, texture, and flavor and can decrease its vitamin content. A modern version, called *freeze-drying*, preserves color, texture, and flavor: the food is first flash-frozen, so any water within it converts to fine ice crystals. These are evaporated in a vacuum and the product is immediately packaged. Freeze-dried foods have a shelf life of several years.
- *Smoking.* Smoking has been used for centuries to preserve meats, poultry, and fish. Historically, if food did not dry well, it was hung near a campfire or chimney, so that the smoke of the fire permeated the food, further drying it. A commercial version of smoking is still used but, unfortunately, smoking does not guarantee that a food is safe to eat. For example, *Listeria monocytogenes* is a type of bacterium that can survive in smoked fish (see Table 2).
- *Cooling.* As the temperature of a bacterium's environment is lowered, its metabolism is slowed, and it becomes less able to multiply or produce toxins. Before the advent of electric refrigerators, people stored foods in underground cellars, caves, running streams, and even "cold pantries," north-facing rooms of the house that were kept dark and unheated and often were stocked with ice. The forerunner of our refrigerator, the miniature icehouse, was developed in the early 1800s, and in cities and towns the local iceman would make rounds, delivering ice to homes.

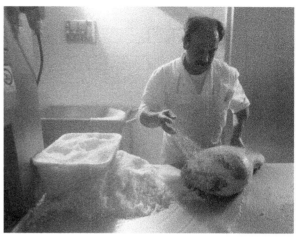

☛ A worker salting a Parma ham.
Owen Franken/Corbis

Hulton Archive Photos/Getty Images

Modern Techniques Improve Food Safety

To be successful, food producers have had to find ways to preserve the integrity of their products during the days, weeks, or months between harvesting and consumption. By the mid-20th century, technological advances in food preservation had given us canning, pasteurization, and preservative chemicals. However, in the past few decades, modern packaging techniques, and irradiation have greatly expanded our food choices.

Industrial Canning

The French inventor Nicolas-François Appert first developed the canning process in the late 1700s, and modern techniques have contributed to the retention of flavor, texture, and nutrients in canned foods. In the United States, 20 million canned foods are consumed per day.[36]

Producers of canned foods are required by law to ensure that all spores of *Clostridium botulinum* are eliminated from their goods. If the spores of this bacterium were to germinate inside a can of food, the food would soon become saturated with the deadly botulism toxin. The same process that destroys *C. botulinum* spores—one

☛ Before the modern refrigerator, an iceman delivered ice to homes and businesses.

step of which is heating the cans of food to an extremely high temperature—also kills other microorganisms that could contaminate the food.

Canned food has an average shelf life of at least 2 years from the date of purchase. In fact, the U.S. Army has found canned meats, vegetables, and jam in "excellent states of preservation" after 46 years.

Pasteurization

Pasteurization was developed in 1864 by Louis Pasteur to destroy microorganisms that spoiled wine. The technique involves the quick use of heat to eliminate pathogens, typically in fluids—for example, 162°F (72°C) for 15 seconds pasteurizes milk. This barely alters the taste or quality of the product, making pasteurization particularly useful in the dairy and juice industries.

Innovations in Packaging Techniques

Many different packaging techniques have arisen over the past several decades:

- *Aseptic packaging* is probably most easily recognized as "juice boxes." Aseptic packaging was first introduced in the United States in the 1980s. Foods and beverages are first sterilized in a flash-heating and cooling process, then placed in a sterile container, which is formulated to provide a unique barrier against light and oxygen. Nutrient quality as well as overall food quality remain high as long as the package seals are not broken. The process uses less energy than traditional canning.[37]
- *Modified atmosphere packaging* is a process in which the oxygen in a package of food is replaced with an inert gas, such as nitrogen or carbon dioxide. This slows the growth of bacteria that require oxygen, as well as the oxidation reactions that commonly spoil foods. The process can be used with a variety of foods, including meats, fish, vegetables, and fruits.
- *High-pressure processing* is a technique that subjects food to extremely high pressure. This inactivates most bacteria while retaining the food's quality and freshness.

Addition of Preservatives

Food preservatives are substances added to foods to prevent or slow spoilage. There are many natural and synthetically derived preservatives used in our food supply. One of the most commonly used natural preservatives is vitamin C. This powerful antioxidant helps protect foods from damage due to oxygen exposure. EDTA (ethylenediaminetetraacetic acid) is a commonly used synthetic preservative. It is used to trap trace amounts of metal impurities that can get into foods from containers and processing machinery.

Most processed foods contain preservatives, unless the package touts that it is "preservative free." All preservatives must be listed in the ingredients, but to recognize them, you need to know their chemical names. Table 4 identifies some common preservatives and the types of foods in which they are typically found. A few of these are discussed in more detail here.

Antioxidants   In addition to certain vitamins, two antioxidants commonly used in foods are BHT (butylated hydroxytoluene) and BHA (butylated hydroxyanisole). They keep oils and fats in packaged foods from going rancid. BHT is frequently added to breakfast cereals to decrease spoilage. BHA is stable at high temperatures and is used in soup bases, ice cream, potato flakes, gelatin desserts, dry mixes for desserts, unsmoked dry sausage, and chewing gum.

Propyl gallate, another antioxidant, works synergistically with both BHA and BHT to enhance their effectiveness. Propyl gallate is used in mayonnaise, ice cream, potato flakes, gelatin desserts, fruits, baked goods, and chewing gum.

Mold Inhibitors   The bread you bought, left on the counter, and finally got around to eating a week later would have become moldy if it hadn't been treated with mold in-

Canning food involves several steps to ensure that all microorganisms in the food are killed.
Digital Vision/Getty Images

AKG/Photo Researchers

Louis Pasteur.

pasteurization A form of sterilization using high temperatures for short periods of time.

food preservatives Chemicals that help prevent microbial spoilage and enzymatic deterioration.

Polluted Packaging?

In December 2009, *Consumer Reports* magazine published the results of a study that shocked food-safety experts nationwide. It had found a chemical called bisphenol A, or BPA, in nearly all of the canned foods it had tested, from soups to infant formula. Why the concern about BPA? Although the effects of this chemical on humans are unknown, it's a form of synthetic estrogen, a female reproductive hormone, and scientists have linked it to genital abnormalities and breast cancer in both males and females, prostate cancer, miscarriage, reduced sperm count, and even heart disease and diabetes.

In early 2010, the FDA announced that it had "raised its level of concern" about BPA and would be conducting research into its effects. In the meantime, it was supporting industry efforts to replace BPA in food can linings. But the problem involves more than cans. BPA is in beverage containers (including baby bottles), plastic dinnerware, auto parts, toys, dental sealants, and other products. So it's no wonder that scientists at the CDC have found measurable levels of BPA in the urine of nearly all the people it has tested.[38]

What to do? Though you can't control the level of BPA in canned foods you eat, you can control your use of plastics. Avoid carrying, storing, or microwave-heating foods or liquids in bottles with the recycling code 3 or 7. Although number 2, 4, 5, and 6 plastics are generally considered to be BPA-free and safe for carrying or storing food, water, and other beverages, always use glass or ceramics to microwave foods and fluids.[39]

hibitors. *Propionic acid* occurs naturally in apples, strawberries, and tea and is used to prevent mold growth in baked goods and processed cheese. *Sodium propionate* and *calcium propionate* are salts synthesized from propionic acid and are used as mold inhibitors in a variety of foods.

Sulfites Sodium bisulfite and sulfur dioxide are *sulfites*, sulfur-containing compounds used as preservatives, antioxidants, bleaching agents, and antibrowning agents. Sulfites also have antibacterial and antifungal properties. They are widely used in the beer and wine industry as well as in dehydrated foods, Maraschino cherries, and processed potatoes. Sulfites are not used in enriched grain products because of their capacity to bind with thiamin (vitamin B_1), making it unavailable for absorption.

Sulfur dioxide is used to control mold growth on fresh fruits and vegetables. For example, it has become standard commercial practice to fumigate stored grapes every 10 days with this chemical. Because of such procedures, it's important to remember to wash all fresh fruit and vegetables before eating.

The FDA has banned the use of sulfites as a preservative in salad bars because some people have had adverse asthmatic reactions. All foods that contain added sulfites must be labeled to warn those with sensitivities.

Nitrates and Nitrites The processed meat industry has long relied on *nitrates* and *nitrites* as antibacterial agents and color enhancers. They give ham, hot dogs, and bologna their familiar pink color. They also inhibit microbial growth and rancidity. However, nitrites can easily be converted to *nitrosamines* during the cooking process. Nitrosamines have been found to be carcinogenic in animals, so the FDA has required all foods with nitrites to contain additional antioxidants to decrease the formation of nitrosamines.

Irradiation

Irradiation eliminates harmful food-borne bacteria in meats and poultry, and it inhibits spoilage by fungus. In the United States, the process typically involves exposing food and its packaging to the energy of gamma rays from radioactive metals. Most of this energy simply passes through the food, leaving no residue. While the food remains relatively unchanged, bacteria and fungi are killed or left unable to reproduce.

Irradiation has been approved for use by fifty countries and endorsed by the World

Lon C. Diehl/PhotoEdit

◆ Aseptic packaging allows foods to be stored unrefrigerated for several months without spoilage.

irradiation A sterilization process using gamma rays or other forms of radiation, but which does not impart radiation to the food being treated.

Figure 10 Radura—the international symbol of irradiated food—is required by the Food and Drug Administration to be displayed on all irradiated food sold in the United States.

Health Organization (WHO), the Food and Agricultural Organization of the United Nations (FAO), and the International Atomic Energy Agency (IAEA). In the United States, many foods are preserved using irradiation, among them spices, grains, fruits, pork products, beef, and poultry.[40] Although irradiation rids foods of most pathogenic microbes, frozen foods remain frozen and raw foods stay raw through the process. Although many foods can safely be irradiated without any noticeable changes, the flavor of milk and other dairy products becomes unpalatable after irradiation, making them inappropriate for this process. Only a few nutrients, including vitamins A, E, K, and thiamin, seem to be affected by irradiation. Losses of these nutrients are comparable to what would be lost in conventional processing and preparation.

Although irradiated food has been shown to be safe to consume, the FDA requires that all irradiated foods be labeled with a "radura" symbol. The words "treated by irradiation, do not irradiate again" or "treated with radiation, do not irradiate again" must accompany the symbol (Figure 10). Irradiated food can be contaminated by improper handling and preparation, so consumers still need to store, clean, prepare, and cook them appropriately.

RECAP Natural food-preservation techniques include salting, sugaring, drying, and smoking, as well as storage in cellars and other cold areas. The canning process was developed in the late 18th century and pasteurization in the 19th century. Aseptic packaging, modified atmosphere packaging, and high-pressure processing are relatively new techniques that increase shelf life. Preservatives are often added to keep foods fresher longer. Irradiation typically involves the use of gamma rays to destroy microbes in foods.

What Are Food Additives, and Are They Safe?

Have you ever picked up a loaf of bread and started reading its ingredients? You'd expect to see flour, yeast, water, and some sugar, but what are all those other items? And why does it feel as if you have to have a degree in chemistry to understand what they are? They are collectively called **food additives,** and they are in almost every processed food. Without additives, that loaf of bread would go stale within a day or two.

Although their use is regulated by the FDA, food additives have been a source of controversy for the past 50 years. Nevertheless, their use has steadily increased, allowing food producers to offer consumers a greater variety of foods at lower costs.

Additives Can Enhance a Food's Taste, Appearance, Safety, or Nutrition

It's estimated that more than 3,000 different additives are currently used in the United States. A few of these are identified in Table 4, and this section discusses some of the most common.

Many of the additives used by the food industry come from natural sources. Beet juice (a natural food coloring), salt, and citric acid are common, naturally derived food additives. Often, supply or cost prohibits using naturally derived additives. In such cases, additives are synthesized. For instance, vanillin, the main flavoring substance in vanilla beans, is synthesized at a cost considerably lower than the cost of extracting it from the natural beans. Even if the costs were comparable, it is doubtful that natural sources of vanillin could meet consumer demands.

Flavorings

Flavoring agents can be obtained from natural or synthetic sources. Essential oils, extracts, and spices supply most of the naturally derived flavorings.

food additives Substances intentionally put into food to enhance appearance, palatability, and quality.

TABLE 4	Examples of Common Food Additives
Food Additive	**Foods Found In**
Coloring Agents	
Beet extract	Beverages, candies, ice cream
Beta-carotene	Beverages, sauces, soups, baked goods, candies, macaroni and cheese mixes
Caramel	Beverages, sauces, soups, baked goods
Tartrazine	Beverages, cakes and cookies, ice cream
Preservatives	
Alpha-tocopherol (vitamin E)	Vegetable oils
Ascorbic acid (vitamin C)	Breakfast cereals, cured meats, fruit drinks
BHA	Breakfast cereals, chewing gum, oils, potato chips
BHT	Breakfast cereals, chewing gum, oils, potato chips
Calcium propionate/sodium propionate	Bread, cakes, pies, rolls
EDTA	Beverages, canned shellfish, margarine, mayonnaise, processed fruits and vegetables, sandwich spreads
Propyl gallate	Mayonnaise, chewing gum, chicken soup base, vegetable oils, meat products, potato products, fruits, ice cream
Sodium benzoate	Carbonated beverages, fruit juice, pickles, preserves
Sodium chloride (salt)	Most processed foods
Sodium nitrate/sodium nitrite	Bacon, corned beef, luncheon meats, smoked fish
Sorbic acid/potassium sorbate	Cakes, cheese, dried fruits, jellies, syrups, wine
Sulfites (sodium bisulfite, sulfur dioxide)	Dried fruits, processed potatoes, wine
Texturizers, Emulsifiers, and Stabilizers	
Calcium chloride	Canned fruits and vegetables
Carageenan/pectin	Ice cream, chocolate milk, soy milk, frostings, jams, jellies, cheese, salad dressings, sour cream, puddings, syrups
Cellulose gum/guar gum/gum arabic/locust gum/xanthan gum	Soups and sauces, gravies, sour cream, ricotta cheese, ice cream, syrups
Gelatin	Desserts, canned meats
Lecithin	Mayonnaise, ice cream
Humectants	
Glycerin	Chewing gum, marshmallows, shredded coconut
Propylene glycol	Chewing gum, gummy candies

Flavor enhancers are also widely used. These additives have little or no flavor of their own but accentuate the natural flavor of foods. They are often added when very little of a natural ingredient is used.[41] The most common flavor enhancers are maltol and MSG (monosodium glutamate). MSG is the sodium salt of glutamic acid, one of the nonessential amino acids, which also serves as a neurotransmitter. It is found in many processed foods; however, the glutamate portion of MSG can cross the blood–brain barrier and, in susceptible people, can cause symptoms such as headaches, difficulty breathing, and heart palpitations. A review of the research conducted in this area indicates that most individuals who report sensitivity to MSG do not show adverse reactions when they are fed MSG in controlled studies, particularly when MSG is given with food.[42]

Colorings

Food colorings, derived from both natural and synthetic sources, are used extensively in processed foods. Natural colorings such as beet juice (which gives a red color), beta-carotene (which gives a yellow color), and caramel (which adds brown color)

Many foods, such as ice cream, contain colorings.

417

are commonly used and do not need to be tested for safety. The coloring tartrazine (FD&C yellow #5) causes an allergic reaction in some people, and its use must be indicated on the product packaging.

Vitamins and Other Nutrients

Vitamin E is usually added to fat-based products to keep them from going rancid, and vitamin C is commonly added to foods such as frozen fruit, dry milk, apple juice, soft drinks, candy, and meat products containing sodium nitrates. Sodium ascorbate, a form of vitamin C with sodium added to produce a salt, is used as an antioxidant in foods such as concentrated milk products, cereals, and cured meats.

Iodine, calcium, vitamin D, and folate are examples of purely nutritive additives. Iodine is added to table salt to help decrease the incidence of goiter, a condition that causes the thyroid gland to enlarge. Calcium and vitamin D are added to foods to promote bone health. Folate is added to many breads and ready-to-eat cereals to decrease the incidence of neural tube defects during fetal development.

Additives That Improve Texture or Moisture Content

Certain chemicals are added to foods to improve their texture. For instance, *texturizers,* such as calcium chloride, are added to canned tomatoes and potatoes, so that they don't fall apart. *Stabilizers* are added to products to give them "body" and help them maintain a desired texture or color. *Emulsifiers* help keep fats evenly dispersed within foods. *Humectants* maintain the correct moisture levels in foods, keeping marshmallows and chewing gum soft and stretchy. Similarly, *thickening agents* are used to absorb water, and *desiccants* keep foods dry by preventing moisture absorption from the air.

Mayonnaise contains emulsifiers to prevent the separation of fats.

Are Food Additives Considered Safe?

Federal legislation was passed in 1958 to regulate food additives. The Delaney Clause, also enacted in 1958, states that "No additive may be permitted in any amount if tests show that it produces cancer when fed to man or animals or by other appropriate tests." Before a new food additive can be marketed or used in food, the producer of the additive must submit data on its reasonable safety to the FDA. The FDA then makes a determination of the additive's safety based on these data.

Also in 1958, the U.S. Congress recognized that many substances added to foods would not require a formal safety review by the FDA prior to marketing and use, as their safety had already been established through long-term use or scientific studies by qualified experts. These substances are exempt from the more stringent testing criteria for new food additives and are referred to as substances that are **Generally Recognized as Safe (GRAS).** The GRAS list identifies substances that either have been tested in the past and determined by the FDA to be safe and approved for use in the food industry or are deemed safe as a result of consensus among experts qualified by scientific training and experience.

In 1985, the FDA established the Adverse Reaction Monitoring System (ARMS). Under this system, the FDA investigates complaints from consumers, physicians, or food companies. Many of the complaints are about sulfite preservatives causing headaches, asthmatic reactions, and in some cases anaphylactic shock. Because of these complaints and the investigations that followed, the FDA has banned the use of sulfites on raw fruit and vegetables, with the exception of potatoes, while continuing to monitor sulfite use on other foods.

Generally Recognized as Safe (GRAS) A designated list established by Congress that identifies several hundred substances that either have been tested and found to be safe and approved by the FDA for use in the food industry or are deemed safe as a result of consensus among experts qualified by scientific training and experience.

RECAP Food additives are chemicals intentionally added to foods to enhance their color, flavor, texture, nutrient density, moisture level, or shelf life. Although there is continuing controversy over food additives, they are considered safe based on testing and use in the food industry or as a result of consensus among experts qualified by scientific training and experience.

How Is Genetic Modification Used in Food Production?

In **genetic modification,** also referred to as *genetic engineering,* the genetic material, or DNA, of an organism is altered to bring about specific changes in its seeds or off-spring. Selective breeding is one example of genetic modification; for instance, Brahman cattle that have poor-quality meat but high resistance to heat and humidity are bred with English shorthorn cattle that have good meat but low resistance to heat and humidity. The outcome of this selective breeding process is Santa Gertrudis cattle, which have the desired characteristics of higher-quality meat and resistance to heat and humidity. Although selective breeding is effective and has helped increase crop yields and improve the quality and quantity of our food supply, it is a relatively slow and imprecise process, as a great deal of trial and error typically occurs before the desired characteristics are achieved.

Recently, advances in biotechnology have moved genetic modification beyond selective breeding. These advances include the manipulation of the DNA of living cells of one organism to produce the desired characteristics of a different organism. Called **recombinant DNA technology,** the process commonly begins when scientists isolate from the cell of an animal, a plant, or a microbe a particular segment of DNA that codes for a protein conferring a desirable trait, such as salt tolerance in tomato plants. Scientists extract and copy the DNA, then identify, isolate, and cultivate the precise genes that code for the desired functions. The next step is to splice the genes into strands of DNA in a "host cell," usually a microorganism. The cell is cultured to produce many copies—a *gene library*—of the beneficial gene. Now many scientists can readily obtain these genes to modify other organisms that lack the desired trait—for example, traditional tomato plants. The modified DNA causes the plant's cells to build the protein of interest, and the plant expresses the desired trait (Figure 11). Not only plants but also animals and even microorganisms (including bacteria and fungi) can be genetically engineered. The term *genetically modified organism* (*GMO*) refers to any organism in which the DNA has been altered using recombinant DNA technology.

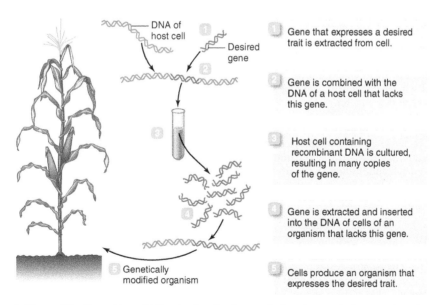

DNA of host cell

Desired gene

1 Gene that expresses a desired trait is extracted from cell.

2 Gene is combined with the DNA of a host cell that lacks this gene.

3 Host cell containing recombinant DNA is cultured, resulting in many copies of the gene.

4 Gene is extracted and inserted into the DNA of cells of an organism that lacks this gene.

5 Genetically modified organism

5 Cells produce an organism that expresses the desired trait.

genetic modification The process of changing an organism by manipulating its genetic material.

recombinant DNA technology A type of genetic modification in which scientists combine DNA from different sources to produce a transgenic organism that expresses a desired trait.

◆ **Figure 11** Recombinant DNA technology involves producing plants and other organisms that contain modified DNA that enables them to express desirable traits that are not present in the original organism.

Image100/Corbis

◆ Corn is one of the most widely cultivated genetically modified crops.

In agriculture, the initial objective for developing GMOs was to improve crop protection.[43] A common protective measure is to induce resistance to herbicides and pesticides. For example, genetically modified soybean, corn, and cotton crops can be sprayed with chemicals that kill weeds without harming the plants. Genetic modification can also increase resistance to insects or viruses that cause disease in plants. Scientists can also insert genes to protect crops from environmental conditions, such as drought or soils high in salt. Another use is to increase the nutritional value of a crop. For instance, researchers have modified soybeans and canola to increase their content of monounsaturated fatty acids.

Since 1994, hundreds of plants and animals have been genetically modified and incorporated into our current food market. In the United States, soy, corn, canola, and cotton crops make up the majority of the genetically modified crop acreage. The U.S. Department of Agriculture reports that 52% of all corn crops, 79% of all cotton crops, and 87% of all soybean crops grown in the United States are genetically engineered varieties.[44] However, the commercial success of GM foods is not guaranteed: in 1994, the FlavrSavr tomato became the first commercially sold GMO. Developing this tomato involved identifying the gene that codes for an enzyme called polygalacturonase, which causes ripening in the tomato. This gene was removed and inserted back in reverse orientation. As a result, polygalacturonase was not synthesized, and ripening slowed dramatically—making the tomato appear "fresh" longer and enabling it to maintain a longer shelf life.[45] Unfortunately, consumers felt the FlavrSavr tomato had poor flavor, and it was taken off the market in 1997.

The relative benefits and harm of genetic modification have been debated worldwide. For instance, some environmentalists have raised the concern that seeds from genetically modified crops disrupt other crops through cross-pollination, even those many miles from where the altered ones are growing. Another concern is the long-term effect of genetically modified crops on the plants, insects, and animals that consume them or use them for their habitat. For more information about the debate surrounding genetic modification, see the Nutrition Debate at the end of this chapter.

RECAP In genetic modification, the genetic material, or DNA, of an organism is altered to enhance certain qualities. In agriculture, genetic modification is often used to improve crop protection or to increase nutrients in the resulting food. Genetic modification is also used in animals and microorganisms.

Do Residues Harm Our Food Supply?

Food **residues** are chemicals that remain in foods despite cleaning and processing. Three types of residues of global concern are persistent organic pollutants, pesticides, and hormones and antibiotics used in animals. Although residues can cause nerve damage, skin rashes, and other health problems, the most common concern related to residues is an increased risk for cancer. In 2010, the President's Cancer Panel released a list of recommendations for reducing your exposure to environmental chemicals.[46] The recommendations related to food residues are included in the following discussion.

residues Chemicals that remain in foods despite cleaning and processing.

Persistent Organic Pollutants Can Cause Illness

Many different organic chemicals are released into the atmosphere as a result of industry, agriculture, automobile emissions, and improper waste disposal. These chemicals, collectively referred to as **persistent organic pollutants (POPs),** eventually enter the food supply through the soil or water. If a pollutant gets into the soil, a plant can absorb the chemical into its structure and pass it on as part of the food chain. Fish and land animals can also absorb the pollutants into their tissues or consume them when feeding on plants in the polluted water or soil. Fat-soluble pollutants are especially problematic, as they tend to accumulate in the animal's body tissues and are then absorbed by humans when the animal is used as a food source. *Bioaccumulation,* the process by which increasing concentrations of pollutants are seen in species higher up the food chain, is illustrated in Figure 12.

POP residues have been found in virtually all categories of foods, including baked goods, fruits, vegetables, meat, poultry, and dairy products. The chemicals can travel long distances in trade winds and water currents, moving from tropical and temperate regions to concentrate in the northern latitudes. It is believed that all living organisms on Earth carry a measurable level of POPs in their tissues.[47]

Mercury and Lead Are Nerve Toxins

Mercury, a naturally occurring element, is found in soil and rocks, lakes, streams, and oceans. It is also released into the environment by pulp and paper processing and the burning of garbage and fossil fuels. As mercury is released into the environment, it falls from the air, eventually finding its way to streams, lakes, and the ocean, where it accumulates. Fish absorb mercury as they feed on aquatic organisms. This mercury is passed on to humans when they consume the fish. As mercury accumulates in the body, it has a toxic effect on the nervous system.

persistent organic pollutants (POPs) Chemicals released into the environment as a result of industry, agriculture, or improper waste disposal; automobile emissions also are considered POPs.

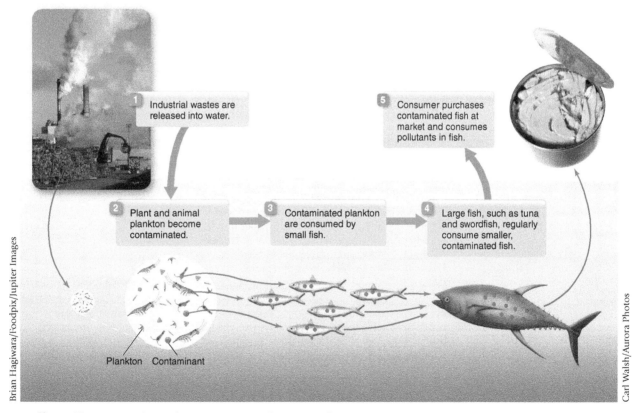

1 Industrial wastes are released into water.

2 Plant and animal plankton become contaminated.

3 Contaminated plankton are consumed by small fish.

4 Large fish, such as tuna and swordfish, regularly consume smaller, contaminated fish.

5 Consumer purchases contaminated fish at market and consumes pollutants in fish.

Plankton   Contaminant

Brian Hagiwara/Foodpix/Jupiter Images

Carl Walsh/Aurora Photos

Figure 12 Bioaccumulation of persistent organic pollutants in the food supply.

One of the ways mercury is released into the environment is by burning fossil fuels.
Corbis

Antique porcelain is often coated with lead-based glaze.

Large, predatory fish, such as swordfish, shark, king mackerel, and tilefish, tend to contain the highest levels of mercury.[48] Because mercury is especially toxic to the developing nervous system of fetuses and growing children, pregnant and breastfeeding women and young children are advised to avoid eating these types of fish. Canned tuna, salmon, cod, pollock, sole, shrimp, mussels, and scallops do not contain high levels of mercury and are safe to consume; however, the FDA advises against eating any one type of fish more often than once a week.[49] Freshwater fish caught in local lakes and rivers have variable levels of mercury; thus, local and state governments routinely monitor mercury levels and post advisories when levels are too high. To learn more about the risks of mercury in seafood, contact the USDA Center for Food Safety and Applied Nutrition (see Web Resources for contact information).

Lead, another naturally occurring element, can be found in the soil, the water, and even the air. It also occurs as industrial waste from leaded gasolines, lead-based paints, and lead-soldered cans, now outlawed but decomposing in landfills. Some ceramic mugs and other dishes are fired with lead-based glaze. Thus, residues can build up in foods. Excessive lead exposure can cause learning and behavioral impediments in children and cardiovascular and kidney disease in adults. It is impossible to avoid lead residues completely, but because of its health implications, everyone should try to limit his or her exposure. To find out how to limit lead exposure, visit the Environmental Protection Agency's website (see Web Resources at the end of this chapter).

Dioxins Have Many Adverse Health Effects

Dioxins are industrial pollutants typically formed as a result of combustion processes, such as waste incineration or the burning of wood, coal, or oil. There is concern that long-term exposure to dioxins can result in skin rashes, liver damage, an increased risk for cancer, and reproductive system disorders.[50] Dioxins enter the soil and can persist in the environment for years. Thus, even though dioxin levels have been declining for the last 30 years, largely as a result of increased regulation, some of the dioxins from emissions decades ago will still be in the environment years from now. Because dioxins easily accumulate in the fatty tissues of animals, over 95% of dioxin exposure in humans occurs through the dietary intake of animal fats.[51] The Environmental Protection Agency (EPA) is working to further reduce levels of all types of dioxins.

Pesticides Protect Against Crop Losses

Pesticides are a family of chemicals used in both the field and storage areas to help protect crops from weeds, insects, fungi, and other organisms, including birds and mammals. Rodents, for example, in addition to consuming food, also contaminate large quantities of food with their excreta. Pesticides also help reduce the number of microorganisms on crops and increase overall crop yield and crop diversity. The three most common types of pesticides used in food production are insecticides, herbicides, and fungicides. Insecticides are used to control insects that can infest crops; herbicides are used to control weeds and other unwanted plant growth; and fungicides are used to control plant-destroying fungal growth.

Pesticides Can Be Natural or Synthetic

Many pesticides used today are **biopesticides,** species-specific chemicals or microorganisms that work to suppress a pest's population, not eliminate it. Biopesticides do not leave residues on crops—most degrade rapidly and are easily washed away with water. Synthetic pheromones are a type of chemical biopesticide. In nature, insects use pheromones, chemicals that act as signals, to attract mates. Synthetic pheromones are used to disrupt insect mating by attracting males into traps. Microbial biopesticides are derived from naturally occurring or genetically altered bacteria, viruses, or fungi. Earlier we mentioned the genetically engineered microbial biopesticide *Bacillus thuringiensis,* or *Bt.* This is a common soil bacterium that is genetically altered to be toxic to several species of insects.

pesticides Chemicals used either in the field or in storage to destroy plant, fungal, and animal pests.

biopesticides Chemicals—primarily insecticides—that are derived naturally in order to reduce crop damage.

Aside from biopesticides, many natural products, such as salt, boric acid, dried blood, crushed egg shells, and diatomaceous earth (soil made up of a type of algae called *diatoms*), are used as pesticides. Ladybugs are bred and sold commercially to reduce aphids, and marigolds, mint, sage, garlic, chives, onion, and other strong-smelling plants can be placed among crops to deter slugs and insect pests.

Many synthetic pesticides are made from petroleum-based products. Examples of commonly used synthetic pesticides are thiabendazole (a fungicide used on potatoes) and fungicides commonly used to prevent apple diseases (such as dithane, manzate, and polyram).

Synthetic Pesticides Are Potential Toxins

Years of studies show that synthetic pesticides can remain on food and pose a risk to human health. The liver is responsible for detoxifying chemicals that enter the body; however, if diseases (such as cancer or AIDS) or toxins (such as alcohol) already stress the liver, it may be unable to effectively remove pesticide residues. When pesticide residues are not effectively removed, they can build up and damage body tissues. The health effects depend on the type of pesticide. Some affect the nervous system, others the endocrine system; still others are potential carcinogens.[52] These effects depend on how toxic the pesticide is and how much of it is consumed.[53]

Children may be especially sensitive to pesticides for several reasons. First, their internal organs are still developing and maturing.[54] Second, they consume more food and water per unit of body weight than adults, possibly increasing their exposure. If a child's excretory system is not fully developed, the child may have a limited ability to remove pesticide residues. Also, pesticides may harm a developing fetus or child by blocking the absorption of important food nutrients necessary for normal healthy growth. Because of the potential risks from pesticides to a developing child, pregnant and breastfeeding women should peel fruit and vegetable rinds to decrease their exposure to residues. This is also a sensible precaution when preparing fruits or vegetables for small children.

Government Regulations Control the Use of Pesticides

The EPA is the government agency responsible for regulating the labeling, sale, distribution, use, and disposal of all pesticides in the United States. The EPA also sets a tolerance level, which is the maximum residue level of a pesticide permitted in or on food or feed grown in the United States or imported into the United States from other countries. The EPA reviews every registered pesticide on a 15-year cycle.[55]

Before a pesticide can be accepted by the EPA for use, it must be determined that it performs its intended function with minimal impact to the environment. Once the EPA has certified a pesticide, states may set their own regulations for its use. Canadian regulation of pesticides closely resembles U.S. laws, with provinces and territories given free range to limit pesticide use. The EPA provides the data for these Quick Tips to reduce your exposure to pesticides.[56]

QUICK TIPS

Reducing Your Exposure to Pesticides

- Wash and scrub all fresh fruits and vegetables thoroughly under running water. Using running water instead of soaking fruits and vegetables is more effective in removing pesticides, as running water is more abrasive than soaking. It is important to understand that not all pesticide residues can be removed by washing.
- Peel fruits and vegetables whenever possible, and discard the outer leaves of leafy vegetables, such as cabbage and lettuce. Trim the excess fat from meat and remove the skin from poultry and fish because some pesticide residues collect in the fat.
- Eat a variety of foods from various sources, as this can reduce the risk of exposure to a single pesticide.
- Consume more organically grown foods. It's especially smart to choose organic when purchasing any of the "Dirty Dozen"—the twelve foods most likely to contain high levels of pesticide residue. They are identified in **Table 5**, along with the fifteen foods lowest in pesticides, called the "Clean 15."
- If you garden, avoid using fertilizers and pesticides to keep these chemicals out of your groundwater as well as your foods.
- Filter your tap water, whether it comes from a municipal water system or a well, to reduce your exposure to pesticides, fertilizers, and other contaminants. It is preferable to use filtered tap water rather than commercially bottled water.

TABLE 5	Shopper's Guide to Pesticides in Produce
The "Dirty Dozen": Buy These Organic	**The "Clean Fifteen": Lowest in Pesticides**
1. Peaches	1. Onions
2. Apples	2. Avocados
3. Bell peppers	3. Sweet corn
4. Celery	4. Pineapples
5. Nectarines	5. Mangoes
6. Strawberries	6. Asparagus
7. Cherries	7. Sweet peas
8. Kale	8. Kiwi
9. Lettuce	9. Cabbage
10. Grapes (imported)	10. Eggplant
11. Carrots	11. Papayas
12. Pears	12. Watermelon
	13. Broccoli
	14. Tomatoes
	15. Sweet potatoes

Data from Environmental Working Group. www.foodnews.org.

Growth Hormones and Antibiotics Are Used in Animals

Introduced in the United States food supply in 1994, **recombinant bovine growth hormone (rBGH),** also known as *recombinant bovine somatotropin (rBST),* is a genetically engineered growth hormone. It is used in beef herds to induce animals to grow more muscle tissue and less fat. It is also injected into a third of U.S. dairy cows to increase milk output. Currently, there are no labeling requirements for products containing rBGH.

Although the FDA has allowed the use of rBGH in the United States, both Canada and the European Union have banned its use because of studies showing an increased risk for mastitis (inflamed udders), infertility, and lameness in dairy cows injected with rBGH.[57] In addition, the milk of cows receiving this hormone has higher levels of insulin-like growth factor (IGF-1). This protein can pass into the bloodstream of humans who drink milk from cows who receive rBGH, and some studies have shown that an elevated level of IGF-1 in humans may increase the risk for breast and prostate cancers.[58,59] However, there are no studies directly linking increased risk for these cancers with eating products from animals injected with rBGH.

Advocates of rBGH say that its use allows farmers to use less feed for the same yield, reducing resource use by each ranch or farm. In addition, they argue that approximately 90% of the hormone in milk is destroyed during pasteurization and that the remaining percentage is destroyed during digestion in the human gastrointestinal tract.

A related concern is the use of antibiotics, not only in dairy cows but also in other animals raised for food. As just noted, dairy cows subjected to rBGH are known to have an increased tendency to develop mastitis, which is treated with antibiotics. In addition, antibiotics are routinely added to the feed of swine, in part to reduce the number of disease outbreaks in overcrowded pork-production facilities. Many researchers are concerned that cows, pigs, and other animals treated with antibiotics are becoming significant reservoirs for the development of a particularly virulent antibiotic-resistant strain of bacteria known as methicillin-resistant *Staphylococcus aureus* (MRSA).[60] Infection with MRSA can cause symptoms ranging from a "flesh-eating" skin rash to death: the CDC reports that, in 2005, MRSA was responsible for more than 18,000 deaths in the United States.[61] In a recent study conducted on hog farms in Illinois and Iowa, 100% of swine aged 9 and 12 weeks tested positive for

recombinant bovine growth hormone (rBGH) A genetically engineered hormone injected into dairy cows to enhance their milk output.

MRSA, and the prevalence among their workers was 64%.[62] MRSA appears to spread from animals to humans via contact, not consumption of animal foods; however, because the microorganism resists methicillin and other conventional antibiotics, it can rapidly spread through communities.

You can reduce your exposure to antibiotics, growth hormones, and toxic run-off from livestock feed lots by choosing organic eggs, milk, yogurt, and cheeses and by eating free-range meat from animals raised without the use of these chemicals. You can also reduce your risk by eating vegetarian and vegan meals more often.

Are Organic Foods More Healthful?

The term *organic* describes foods that are grown without the use of toxic and persistent fertilizers and pesticides, genetic engineering, or irradiation. The thought of organic food used to conjure up images of hippies and bean sprouts. Now organic food has become part of the mainstream food supply. A recent national survey indicates that approximately 3.5% of all food products sold in the United States are organic.[63] Moreover, between 1990 and 2008, sales of organic products in the United States skyrocketed from $1 billion to $23 billion.[64]

To Be Labeled Organic, Foods Must Meet Federal Standards

The National Organic Program (NOP) of the USDA came into law in October 2002. The organic industry itself had asked for national standards on organic labeling, as different U.S. states had different requirements for organic food labels and some had no rules at all. The European Union enforced a common standard for organic plant produce in 1991. Without a national standard, it was feared that European countries might seek to exclude U.S. organic exports.

The new Organic Standards established uniform definitions for all organic products. Any label or product claiming to be organic must comply with the following definitions:

- *100% organic:* products containing only organically produced ingredients, excluding water and salt
- *Organic:* products containing 95% organically produced ingredients by weight, excluding water and salt with the remaining ingredients consisting of those products not commercially available in organic form
- *Made with organic ingredients:* a product containing more than 70% organic ingredients

If a processed product contains less than 70% organically produced ingredients, then that product cannot use the term *organic* in the principal display panel, but ingredients that are organically produced can be specified on the ingredients statement on the information panel.

Products that are "100% organic" and "organic" may display the USDA seal (Figure 13) or mark of certifying agents. Any product that is labeled as organic must identify each organically produced item in the ingredient statement of the label. The name and address of the certifying agency must also be on the label.

The USDA Regulates Organic Farming

The USDA regulates organic farming standards, and every farm must be certified as organic by a government-approved certifier, who inspects the farm and verifies that the farmer is following all USDA organic standards.[65] Companies that handle or process organic food before it arrives at your local supermarket or restaurant must also be certified. Organic farming methods are strict and require farmers to find natural alternatives to many common problems, such as weeds and insects. Contrary to common belief, organic farmers can use pesticides as a final option for pest control when all other methods have failed or are known to be ineffective, but they are restricted to a limited number that have been approved for use based on their origin, environmental impact, and potential to persist as residues.[66] Organic farmers emphasize the use of renewable resources and the conservation of soil and water to

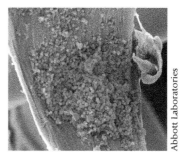

The resistant strain of bacteria responsible for methicillin-resistant *Staphylococcus aureus* (MRSA).

Figure 13 The USDA organic seal identifies foods that are at least 95% organic.

enhance environmental and nutritional quality. Once a crop is harvested, a winter crop (usually of a legume origin) is planted to help fix nitrogen in the soil and decrease erosion, which also lessens the need for fertilizers.

Organic meat, poultry, eggs, and dairy products come from animals fed only organic feed, and if the animals become ill, they are removed from the others until well again. None of these animals are given growth hormones to increase their size or ability to produce milk.

Studies Comparing Organic and Conventionally Grown Foods Are Limited

Over the past decade, several promising studies at the University of California, Davis, and other institutions indicated that some organically grown fruits and vegetables are higher in vitamins E and C and in certain antioxidant phytochemicals than their nonorganic counterparts.[67-69] However, a 2009 systematic review of 162 studies published from 1958 through 2008 found no nutritional superiority of organically produced foods over foods conventionally produced. The study's lead author concluded that there is currently no evidence to support the selection of organic foods for nutritional superiority.[70] What's more, an organic seal does not guarantee food safety: the company responsible for the *Salmonella* outbreak described at the beginning of this chapter had federal organic certification.[71] Still, as discussed earlier in the chapter, you might decide to choose organic produce if you are concerned about reducing your exposure to pesticides.

RECAP Persistent organic pollutants (POPs), including mercury and lead, contaminate many foods. Both are toxic to the nervous system. Dioxins are extremely persistent pollutants that accumulate in animal fats. Pesticides are substances used to prevent or reduce food crop losses due to weeds, insects, fungi, and other organisms, including birds and mammals. They are potential toxins. Recombinant bovine growth hormone (rBGH) is injected into meat and dairy cows to increase meat production and milk output. Concerns include possible health problems as well as increased use of antibiotics in cows receiving the hormone. Antibiotics are also used in pork production, and researchers are concerned that both cows and swine are becoming reservoirs for a virulent strain of antibiotic-resistant bacteria called MRSA. Organic Standards in 2002 established uniform definitions for all organic products sold in the United States. Although organic foods are produced without toxic or persistent pesticides, there is insufficient evidence that they are more nutritious than nonorganic foods.

Nutrition DEBATE

Genetically Modified Organisms: A Blessing or a Curse?

As we noted earlier in this chapter, genetic modification is a process in which entirely new (*transgenic*) organisms are created by splicing genes from one species into another. Supporters of this process envision an ever-expanding role for genetic modification in food production. The following are a few of the potential benefits seen as resulting from the application of this technology:

- Enhanced taste and nutritional quality of food
- Crops that grow faster, have higher yields and can be grown in inhospitable soils with increased resistance
- Increased production of high-quality meat, eggs, and milk
- Improved animal health
- Environmentally responsible outcomes—such as the use of less harmful herbicides and insecticides; the conservation of soil, water, and energy; and more efficient food processing

Despite these potential benefits, there has been significant opposition to genetic engineering including the following:

- Gene transfer from GM foods to cells of the body or to bacteria in the gastrointestinal tract.[72]
- Unintentional crossing of genes through cross-pollination. This can result in undesirable plants—such as "superweeds" that can tolerant conventional herbicides—or in foods tainted with non-food-grade ingredients. The risks of

such unintended gene crossing (called "outcrossing") were revealed when traces of a type of maize (corn) that was approved for use only in animal feed appeared in maize products for human consumption in the United States.[72]

- Loss of biodiversity of plants and animals.
- Development of new diseases that can attack plants, animals, and humans.
- Production of bacteria that are resistant to all antibiotics.
- Potential for only a few food companies and countries to control the majority of world food production, such as in the seed industry.[73]
- Creation of biological weapons and increased risk of bioterrorism.

Some people who oppose genetic engineering believe it's unnatural and unethical to alter the genes of any organism. Most opponents base their concerns on the fact that potential

Many people oppose the genetic engineering of foods for environmental, health, or economic reasons.
Oby Talbot/AP Photo

long-term risks and dangers are still unknown and may far outweigh the potential short-term benefits.

Genetically modified organisms are welcomed in some countries but outlawed in others. Six countries grow almost 100% of the world's genetically modified crops: the United States (59%), Argentina (20%), Canada (6%), Brazil (6%), China (5%), and Paraguay (2%).[74] Although the United States and Canada are among the top three, regions within these countries have succeeded in banning the production of GMOs, including several counties in California and the Canadian province of Prince Edward Island.

The European Union (EU) has strict regulations regarding GMOs, including mechanisms for tracking GMO products through production and distribution chains and monitoring of the environmental effects of GMOs. All foods produced for human consumption and all animal feed products that contain GMOs must be clearly labeled. Companies desiring to market GMOs and genetically modified foods in the EU must include a full environmental risk assessment and a safety assessment in their application.

What do you think about the cultivation and distribution of genetically modified foods? Do you have any reservations about buying and consuming genetically modified foods? Because GMOs and modified foods have been available for only a few years, it will take more time to fully understand their impact.

Chapter Review

1. False. The actual number is much larger. Each year, about 76 million Americans are sickened and about 5,000 die as a direct result of eating food contaminated with germs or their toxins.

2. False. Freezing inhibits the ability of most microscopic organisms to reproduce, but when the food is thawed, reproduction can resume.

3. True. Some studies have found higher levels of certain micronutrients and antioxidant phytochemicals in organic foods as compared to nonorganic foods. However, a recent review study did not support these findings; thus, there are not enough data to state with confidence that organic foods are consistently more nutritious than nonorganic foods.

Find the Quack

You visit your cousin Lori, who has three school-age children. You take out a pack of chewing gum and offer a piece to each of the kids. "No way!" Lori says. "You need to check with me before offering food to the kids. Most foods sold in the United States are full of harmful additives, including chewing gum!" Lori takes out a leaflet advertising a new book on food additives. It's called *Stealth Ingredients: The Dangerous Additives in Your Food.* You read the front of the leaflet. It states:

- "Additives in your food destroy your health and may even cause cancer!"
- "Many of the most harmful ingredients in packaged foods are not listed on the label."
- "Powerful food manufacturers' lobbies influence Congress to pass laws allowing food companies to add cancer-causing ingredients to your food."
- "The Food and Drug Administration does not protect you against dangerous ingredients in your food."

The leaflet then offers a solution: a new book identifying and describing every ingredient added to foods. It suggests purchasing the book and taking it to the grocery store, so that you can check the ingredients panels of foods to make sure the foods you buy are safe.

The leaflet closes with three testimonials from individuals who state that, prior to reading the book, they were very ill and now that they avoid all harmful food additives their health has returned.

"See what I mean?" Lori asks you. "I bet you wish you knew what was *really* in that chewing gum!"

1. Evaluate the leaflet's statement "Additives in your food destroy your health and may even cause cancer."

2. Comment on the statement that the FDA "does not protect you against dangerous ingredients in your food."

3. Look again at the leaflet's argument "Many of the most harmful ingredients in packaged foods are not listed on the label." Identify the flaw in the argument that purchasing the book will protect you.

4. Discuss the value of the three testimonials at the end of the leaflet.

Answers can be found on the companion website, at www.pearsonhighered.com/thompsonmanore.

Review Questions

1. Leftovers from a meal should be refrigerated
   a. immediately after serving.
   b. within 30 minutes of serving.
   c. within 2 hours of serving.
   d. within 3 hours of serving.

2. Yeasts are
   a. a type of mold used in baked goods as a stabilizer.
   b. a type of bacteria that can cause food intoxication.
   c. a type of fungus used to ferment foods.
   d. a type of mold inhibitor used as a food preservative.

3. Monosodium glutamate (MSG) is
   a. a thickening agent used in baby foods.
   b. a flavor enhancer used in a variety of foods.
   c. a mold inhibitor used on grapes and other foods.
   d. an amino acid added as a nutrient to some foods.

4. Foods that are labeled *100% organic*
   a. contain only organically produced ingredients, excluding water and salt.
   b. may display the EPA's organic seal.
   c. were produced without the use of pesticides.
   d. contain no discernible level of toxic metals.

5. The potential spread of MRSA is a public health concern because
   a. MRSA is a strain of bacteria resistant to conventional antibiotics.
   b. MRSA readily spreads from animal populations to humans.
   c. MRSA can be fatal.
   d. all of the above.

6. True or false? Heating foods to at least 160°F guarantees that they will not cause food-borne illness.

7. True or false? The CDC has established an Adverse Reaction Monitoring System (ARMS) to investigate complaints of adverse reactions to food additives.

8. True or false? In the United States, farms certified as organic are allowed to use pesticides under certain conditions.

9. True or false? Recombinant bovine growth hormone (rBGH) is used to increase the amount and quality of meat in beef herds and milk production in dairy cows.

10. True or false? Some colorings used as food additives do not need to be tested for safety.

Answers to Review Questions can be found at the back of this text, and additional essay questions and answers are located on the companion website at www.pearsonhighered.com/ thompsonmanore.

Web Resources

www.cdc.gov/travel/foodwater
Centers for Disease Control and Prevention

Before your next trip, check out this webpage for information on food safety when traveling.

www.foodsafety.gov
Foodsafety.gov

Use this website as a gateway to government food-safety information.

www.fsis.usda.gov
The USDA Food Safety and Inspection Service

This site provides information on all aspects of food safety. Click on "Publications" for links to additional information.

www.fsis.usda.gov/Fact_Sheets/ Cooking_Safely_in_the_Microwave
USDA Food Fact Sheet on Cooking Safely in the Microwave

This fact sheet provides information on the safe cooking and reheating of foods in a microwave oven.

www.cspinet.org/foodsafety
Center for Science in the Public Interest: Food Safety

Visit this website for summaries of food additives and their safety, alerts and other information, and interactive quizzes.

www.cfsan.fda.gov
The USDA Center for Food Safety and Applied Nutrition

This site contains thorough information on topics such as national food-safety programs, recent news, and food labeling.

www.extension.iastate.edu/foodsafety
Food Safety Project

The Food Safety Project compiles educational materials about food safety for consumer use. Provided on the site are links for food safety from farm to table.

www.epa.gov/pesticides
The U.S. Environmental Protection Agency: Pesticides

This site provides information about agricultural and home-use pesticides, pesticide health and safety issues, environmental effects, and government regulation.

www.ams.usda.gov
The USDA National Organic Program (NOP)

Click on "National Organic Program" to find the website describing the NOP's standards and labeling program, consumer information, and publications.

www.slowfoodusa.org
Slow Food USA

The Slow Food movement sponsors training and activities to promote a good, clean, and fair food system. Check out Slow Food on Campus, its network of chapters at colleges and universities throughout the United States.

References

1. Centers for Disease Control and Prevention (CDC). March 17, 2009. Investigation Update: Outbreak of Salmonella typhimurium Infections, 2008–2009. Available at www.cdc.gov/salmonella/typhimurium/update.html; U.S. Food and Drug Administration (FDA). FDA Urges Consumers Not to Eat Hundreds of Products Recalled Because of Contaminated Peanuts and Peanut Ingredients. FDA Hot Topics. Available at www.fda.gov/oc/opacom/hottopics/salmonellatyph/article.html.

2. Centers for Disease Control and Prevention (CDC). Salmonella Outbreak Investigations. March 3, 2010. Available at www.cdc.gov/salmonella/outbreaks.html.

3. Centers for Disease Control and Prevention (CDC), Division of Bacterial and Mycotic Diseases (DFBMD). Salmonellosis. May 21, 2008. Available at www.cdc.gov/nczved/dfbmd/disease_listing/salmonellosis_gi.html#8.

4. Doering, C. Foodborne illness costs $152 billion annually. Reuters. March 4, 2010. Available at www.reuters.com/article/idUSTRE6220NO20100304.

5. Centers for Disease Control and Prevention (CDC), Division of Bacterial and Mycotic Diseases (DFBMD). 2005. Disease Listing. Foodborne Illness. Available at http://www.cdc.gov/ncidod/dbmd/diseaseinfo/foodborneinfections_g.htm.

6. Centers for Disease Control and Prevention (CDC). CDC Report Points to Need for New Foodborne Illness Strategies. April 10, 2008. Available at www.cdc.gov/media/pressrel/2008/r080410.htm.

7. Centers for Disease Control and Prevention (CDC). April 9, 2009. Annual Report Indicates Salmonella Continues to Show Least Improvement. Available at www.cdc.gov/media/pressrel/2009/r090409.htm.

8. Harris, G. President Promises to Bolster Food Safety. March 15, 2009. The New York Times. Available at www.nytimes.com/2009/03/15/us/politics/15address.html.

9. Doering, C. Foodborne illness costs $152 billion annually. Reuters. March 4, 2010. Available at www.reuters.com/article/idUSTRE6220NO20100304.

10. Centers for Disease Control and Prevention (CDC). Foodborne Illness. January 10, 2005. Available at www.cdc.gov/ncidod/dbmd/diseaseinfo/foodborneinfections_g.htm.

11. Ibid.

12. Centers for Disease Control and Prevention (CDC), Division of Viral Diseases Norovirus: Q&A. February 23, 2010. Avilable at www.cdc.gov/ncidod/dvrd/revb/gastro/norovirus-qa.htm.

13. Norovirus Blog. January 14, 2009. Michigan Continues to Be a Hotspot for Norovirus. Available at www.noroblog.com/2009/01/articles/norovirus-outbreaks/michigan-continues-to-be-a-hotspot-for-norovirus/.

14. United States Department of Agriculture (USDA) Food Safety and Inspection Service. Parasites and Foodborne Illness. May, 2001. Available at http://origin-www.fsis.usda.gov/Fact_Sheets/Parasites_and_Foodborne_Illness/index.asp.

15. Bauman, R.W. 2009. Microbiology. San Francisco: Pearson Benjamin Cummings.

16. International Society for Infectious Diseases. Prion Disease Update 2010. March 4, 2010. Available at http://promedmail.oracle.com/pls/otn/pm?an=20100304.0709.

17. Bauman, R.W. 2009. Ibid.

18. Preidt, R. Predicted "Red Tide" Could Make Shellfish a Dangerous Dish. National Library of Medicine's Medline Plus: Health Day. February 26, 2010. Available at www.nlm.nih.gov/medlineplus/print/news/fullstory_95794.html.

19. Centers for Disease Control and Prevention (CDC), Division of Bacterial and Mycotic Diseases (DFBMD). Marine Toxins. October 12, 2005. Available at www.cdc.gov/ncidod/dbmd/diseaseinfo/marinetoxins_g.htm.

20. Ibid.

21. Pavlista, A. D. 2001. Green potatoes: The problem and solution. NebGuide. The University of Nebraska-Lincoln Cooperative Extension. Available at http://ianrpubs.unl.edu/horticulture/g1437.htm.

22. Food and Drug Administration (FDA). FDA Finalizes Report on 2006 Spinach Outbreak. March 23, 2007. FDA News. Available at www.fda.gov/bbs/topics/NEWS/2007/NEW01593.html

23. U.S. Department of Agriculture (USDA). Partnership for Food Safety Education (PFSE). Fight Bac! Safe Food Handling. 2006. www.fightbac.org/content/view/6/11/.

24. National Digestive Diseases Information Clearinghouse (NDDIC). May, 2007. Bacteria and foodborne illness. NIH Publication No. 07-4730. Available at http://digestive.niddk.nih.gov/ddiseases/pubs/bacteria/index.htm.

25. Ibid.

26. Food and Drug Administration (FDA) 2005c. Eating defensively: Food safety advice for persons with AIDS. Available at http://www.cfsan.fda.gov/∼dms/aidseat.html.

27. U.S. Department of Agriculture (USDA). Food Product Dating. February 8, 2007. Fact Sheets: Food Labeling. Available at www.fsis.usda.gov/Factsheets/Food_Product_Dating/index.asp

28. U.S. Department of Agriculture (USDA). Partnership for Food Safety Education (PFSE). Fight Bac! Safe Food Handling. 2006. Op cit.

29. Ibid.

30. Ibid.

31. Food Marketing Institute. 2003. A Consumer Guide to Food Quality and Safe Handling: Meat, Poultry, Seafood, Eggs [pamphlet]. Washington, DC: Food Marketing Institute, pp. 1–5.

32. Ibid.

33. Food and Drug Administration (FDA) 2003. Anisakis simplex and related worms. Foodborne Pathogenic Microorganisms and Natural Toxins Handbook. Available at www.cfsan.fda.gov/~mow/chap25.html.

34. Center for Science in the Public Interest (CSPI). 2006b. Tips to prevent food poisoning: CSPI's "eggspert" egg advice. Available at http://www.cspinet.org/foodsafety/eggspert_advice.html.

35. U.S. Department of Agriculture (USDA). 2003. Safe Food Handling. Barbecue Food Safety. Available at http://www.fsis.usda.gov/Fact_Sheets/Barbecue_Food_Safety/index.asp.

36. Shephard, S. 2000. Pickled, Potted and Canned: The Story of Food Preserving. London: Headline Publishing.

37. Aseptic Packaging Council. 2005. The award-winning, Earth smart packaging for a healthy lifestyle. Available at http://www.aseptic.org/main.shtml.

38. United States Food and Drug Administration (FDA). News & Events. Bisphenol A (BPA). January 2010. Available at www.fda.gov/NewsEvents/PublicHealthFocus/ucm064437.htm; Centers for Disease Control and Prevention (CDC) Fact Sheet: Bisphenol A (BPA). February 11, 2010. Available at www.cdc.gov/exposurereport/BisphenolA_FactSheet.html; Kristof, N. Chemicals in Our Food, and Bodies. November 8, 2009. New York Times. Available at www.nytimes.com/2009/11/08/opinion/08Kristof.html.

39. United States Department of Health and Human Services (USDHHS). Bisphenol A (BPA) Information for Parents. February 12, 2010. Available at www.hhs.gov/safety/bpa/.

40. Loaharanu, P. 2003. Irradiated Foods. New York: American Council on Science & Health Booklets.

41. Center for Science in the Public Interest (CSPI). 2006a. Food safety. Chemical cuisine. CSPI's guide to food additives. Available at http://www.cspinet.org/reports/chemcuisine.htm.

42. Geha, R. S., A. Beiser, C. Ren, R. Patterson, P. A. Greenberger, L. C. Grammer, A. M. Ditto, K. E. Harris, M. A. Shaughnessy, P. R. Yarnold, et al. 2000. Review of alleged reaction to monosodium

glutamate and outcome of a multicenter double-blind placebo-controlled study. *J. Nutr.* 130(4S Suppl):1058S–1062S.

43. World Health organization (WHO). 2010. Twenty Questions on Genetically Modified (GM) Foods. Available at www.who.int/foodsafety/publications/biotech/20questions/en/.

44. U.S. Department of Agriculture (USDA), Economic Research Service. 2005. Data. Adoption of Genetically Engineered Crops in the U.S. Available at http://www.ers.usda.gov/Data/BiotechCrops/.

45. McHughen, A. 2000. Pandora's Picnic Basket: The potential and hazards of genetically modified foods. Oxford: Oxford University Press, pp. 17–45.

46. President's Cancer Panel. 2010. Reducing environmental cancer risk: What we can do now: 2008-2009 annual report. Available online at: http://deainfo.nci.nih.gov/advisory/pcp/pcp.htm.

47. Schafer, K. S., and S. E. Kegley. 2002. Persistent toxic chemicals in the U.S. food supply. J. Epidemiol. *Community Health* 56:813–817.

48. Food and Drug Administration (FDA). March 2004. Update 11/23/2009. What You Need to Know About Mercury in Fish and Shellfish. Available at www.fda.gov/Food/ResourcesForYou/Consumers/ucm110591.htm.

49. Ibid.

50. U.S. Food and Drug Administration (FDA). Questions and Answers About Dioxins. 09/21/2009. www.fda.gov/Food/FoodSafety/FoodContaminantsAdulteration/ChemicalContaminants/DioxinsPCBs/ucm077524.htm.

51. Ibid.

52. Environmental Protection Agency (EPA). 2005c. Pesticides: Health and Safety: Human Health Issues. Available at www.epa.gov/pesticides/health/human.htm.

53. Environmental Protection Agency (EPA). 2005d. Pesticides: Health and Safety: Pesticides and Food: Health Problems Pesticides May Pose. Available at http://www.epa.gov/pesticides/food/risks.htm.

54. Environmental Protection Agency (EPA). 2005e. Pesticides: Health and Safety: Pesticides and Food: Why Children May Be Especially Sensitive to Pesticides. Available at http://www.epa.gov/pesticides/food/pest.htm.

55. Environmental Protection Agency (EPA). 2005a. About Pesticides. Available at http://www.epa.gov/pesticides/about/index.htm.

56. Environmental Protection Agency (EPA). 2005b. Pesticides and Food: Healthy, Sensible Food Practices. Available at http://www.epa.gov/pesticides/food/tips.htm.

57. LeSage, L. 1999. News Release. Health Canada rejects bovine growth hormone in Canada. Health Canada Online. Available at http://www.hc-sc.gc.ca/ahc-asc/media/nr-cp/1999/1999_03_e.html.

58. Hankinson, S. E., W. C. Willett, G. A. Colditz, D. J. Hunter, D. S. Michaud, B. Deroo, B. Rosner, F. E. Speizer, and M. Pollak. 1998. Circulating concentrations of insulin-like growth factor-I and risk of breast cancer. *Lancet* 351(9113):1393–1396.

59. Chan, J. M., M. J. Stampfer, E. Giovannucci, P. H. Gann, J. Ma, P. Wilkinson, C. H. Hennekens, and M. Pollak. 1998. Plasma insulin-like growth factor-I and prostate cancer risk: A prospective study. *Science* 279(5350):563–566.

60. Smith T. C., M. J. Male, A. L. Harper, J. S. Kroeger, G. P. Tinkler, et al. (2009). Methicillin-Resistant Staphylococcus aureus (MRSA) Strain ST398 Is Present in Midwestern U.S. Swine and Swine Workers. PLoS ONE 4(1): e4258. Doi: 10.1371/journal.pone.0004258.

61. Centers for Disease Control and Prevention (CDC). October 17, 2007. Invasive MRSA. Available at www.cdc.gov/ncidod/dhqp/ar_mrsa_Invasive_FS.html.

62. Smith T. C., et al. (2009). Op. cit.

63. Organic Trade Association. 2009. OTA's 2009 Organic Industry Survey. May, 2009. Available at www.ota.com/pics/documents/01a_OTAExecutiveSummary.pdf.

64. Ibid.

65. United States Department of Agriculture (USDA). Agricultural Marketing Service. National Organic Program. 02/05/2010. Understanding Organic. Available at www.ams.usda.gov/AMSv1.0/ams.fetchTemplateData.do?template=TemplateA&leftNav=NationalOrganicProgram&page=NOPUnderstandingOrganic&description=Understanding%20Organic&acct=nopgeninfo.

66. Heaton, S. 2003. Organic Farming, Food Quality and Human Health: A Review of the Evidence. Soil Association. Bristol: Briston House.

67. Asami, D. K., Y. J. Hong, D. M. Barrett, and A. E. Mitchell. 2003. Comparison of the total phenolic and ascorbic acid content of freeze-dried and air-dried marionberry, strawberry, and corn grown using conventional, organic, and sustainable agricultural practices. *J. Agric. Food Chem.* 51(5):1237–1241.

68. Carbonaro, M., M. Mattera, S. Nicoli, P. Bergamo, and M. Cappelloni. 2002. Modulation of antioxidant compounds in organic vs conventional fruit (peach, Prunus persica L., and pear, Pyrus communis L.). *J. Agric. Food Chem.* 50(19):5458–5462.

69. Grinder-Pedersen, L., S. E. Rasmussen, S. Bügel, L. O. Jørgensen, D. Vagn Gundersen, and B. Sandström. 2003. Effect of diets based on foods from conventional versus organic production on intake and excretion of flavonoids and markers of antioxidative defense in humans. *Agric. Food Chem.* 51(19):5671–5676.

70. Dangour, A. D., S. K. Dodhia, A. Hayter, E. Allen, K. Lock, and R. Uauy. 2009. Nutritional quality of organic foods: a systematic review. *American Journal of Clinical Nutrition.* July 29, 2009. Doi:10.3945/ajcn.2009.28041.

71. Severson, K. and A. Martin. 2009. It's organic, but does that mean it's safer? *New York Times.* March 4. Available at www.nytimes.com/2009/03/04/dining/04cert.html.

72. World Health organization (WHO). 2010. Twenty Questions on Genetically Modified (GM) Foods. Available at www.who.int/foodsafety/publications/biotech/20questions/en/.

73. Neuman, W. 2010. Justice Dept. Tells Farmers It Will Press Agriculture Industry on Antitrust. *New York Times.* March 12. Available at www.nytimes.com/2010/03/13/business/13seed.html.

74. James, C. 2004. Preview: Global Status of Commercialized Biotech/GM Crops: 2004. ISAAA Briefs No. 32. Ithaca, NY: ISAAA.

Answers to Review Questions

Answers to Review Questions 11-15 (essay questions) for this chapter are located on the Companion Website at **www.pearsonhighered.com/thompsonmanore**

1. **c.** within 2 hours of serving.
2. **c.** a type of fungus used to ferment foods.
3. **b.** a flavor enhancer used in a variety of foods.
4. **a.** contain only organically produced ingredients, excluding water and salt.
5. **d.** all of the above.
6. False. The appropriate temperature for cooking foods varies according to the food.
7. False. The ARMS was established by the FDA, not the CDC.
8. True.
9. True.
10. True.

Index

Page references followed by "f" indicate illustrated figures or photographs; followed by "t" indicates a table.

2

2005 Dietary Guidelines for Americans, 44, 220, 361

A

absorption
  alcohol, 13, 75, 128-129, 188, 244, 282, 300, 423
  alcohol and, 188, 244
  beta-carotene, 113, 202, 237, 417
  lipids, 70, 135, 200
  of amino acids, 167-168
  of copper, 200, 323-325
  of zinc, 200-201, 322-323
  organs of, 71
  process of, 71-74, 139, 168, 246, 275, 301, 419
  small intestine and, 77, 103
  small intestine, from, 140
  stomach and, 64
  stomach, from, 83
  summary of, 157
  vitamin K, 138, 198, 270, 300
abuse, alcohol, 79, 224, 244, 282
Acceptable daily intake (ADI), 116
Acceptable Macronutrient Distribution Range (AMDR)
  Dietary Reference Intakes, 13, 143, 192, 364
  fat intake, 142, 351, 373
Acceptable Macronutrient Distribution Range and
  beverages during exercise, 227
  calcium intake, 265
  grape juice, 65
  hand washing, 84, 405
  infant formula, 415
  nitrates and nitrites, 415
  older adults and, 363
  vitamin and mineral supplements, 203, 257
accessory organs, 62
Accutane, 250
acesulfame-K, 116-117
acetylcholine, 311
acid group, 128, 162-164
acidosis, 171
acquired immunodeficiency syndrome (AIDS), 396
Activia yogurt, 55
activity
  creatine supplements, 358
  MyPyramid, 43-44, 185, 363
  sound fitness program, 335-337
Addiction
  nicotine, 256
  symptoms, 256
adenine, 297, 365
adenosine diphosphate (ADP)
  structure of, 282, 341
adenosine triphosphate (ATP)
  ATP-CP energy system, 341
  metabolism and, 280
  vitamins and, 198-200, 346
adequate diet, 15, 32
Adequate Intake, 13-14, 92, 143, 196-197, 216, 246, 269-270, 305
Adequate Intake (AI)
  biotin, 12, 196-197, 297-298
  choline, 298
  essential fatty acids, 11, 42, 132-134, 346
  manganese, 12, 199-200, 237, 298
  pantothenic acid, 12, 196-197, 297-298
adipose cells, 137
Adipose tissue
  amount of fluid in, 214
  energy for later use, 137
adolescents
  food choices and, 43
  nutrient needs, 58

ADP (adenosine diphosphate), 341
Adverse Reaction Monitoring System, 418
advice about nutrition
  government sources, 23
Aerobic capacity, maximal (VO2max)
  target heart rate and, 364
aerobic environment
  glycolysis, 342
aflatoxin, 401
African Americans
  osteoporosis in, 287
African heritage, people with
  lactose intolerance, 55, 121
age and aging
  body fluid levels, 208
Agribusiness, 183
agricultural practices, 431
air pollution
  reducing, 93, 405
  sulfur dioxide, 417
Alcohol
  absorption of, 76, 129, 187, 244, 283, 423
  athletes and, 355
  breakdown of, 11, 165-166, 299
  breastfeeding women and, 422
  calories in, 375
  harmful effects, 245
  harmful effects of, 245
  liver and, 81, 155, 245, 371
  metabolism of, 284, 299
Alcohol abuse
  hypokalemia, 224-225
alcohol (ethanol)
  breastfeeding, 215, 422-423
  liver damage, 79, 422
  thiamin deficiency, 299
Alcohol use/abuse
  health effects of, 148
  malnutrition and, 183
Alcoholic beverages
  breast milk, 95, 215
alcoholism (alcohol dependence)
  disease of, 299
alkalosis, 171
Allergens, 171, 235
allergic reactions, 171
alpha-carotene, 245
alternative sweeteners, 92
Alzheimer's disease
  smoking and, 83, 378
Amanita phalloides, 402
amenorrhea
  female athlete triad, 355-356, 389-390
  female athletes and, 355-356
American Academy of Pediatrics (AAP)
  vitamin D supplements, 289
American College of Sports Medicine (ACSM)
  advice about nutrition, 4
American Dental Association, 121, 289
American Diabetes Association (ADA), 192
American diets
  calcium-rich foods, 45, 274
  vitamin D deficiencies, 279
American Heart Association
  omega-3 fatty acids and, 371-372
  trans fatty acids and, 157
American Journal of Clinical Nutrition
  Mediterranean diet, 48
American Psychiatric Association
  bulimia nervosa, 381-383
amine group, 162-164
amino acid pool, 165-166
Amino acids
  absorbed in the small intestine, 153
  carbon skeleton, 166
  catabolism, 364
  conditionally essential, 163

DRI for, 314
enzymes and, 170, 266
limiting, 43, 127, 168-169, 372
nonessential, 163, 302, 417
nonessential amino acids, 163, 302, 417
peptide bonds, 164
phenylalanine, 117-118, 163
physical activity and, 10, 56, 351, 371
selenium and, 253-254
shape of, 130, 166-168, 265, 306
soy products, 174, 352
supplements and, 313
synthesis of, 134, 165-166, 197, 241, 297
to glucose, 100, 173, 303
ammonia
  deamination, 172
amniotic fluid, 211
Amylase, 72-73, 102-103
amylopectin, 98
amylose, 98-99
anaerobic energy production, 362
anal canal, 80-81
anaphylactic shock, 418
anemia
  macrocytic, 197, 294
  pernicious, 197, 294
  sickle cell anemia, 306
  sports, 328, 354-356, 386-387
  sports anemia, 355
  vitamin B12 and, 309
  vitamin B6, 196-198, 300, 355-356
  vitamin C deficiency, 244
  vitamin E deficiency, 240
Anemia Lifeline, 327
Animal and Plant Health Inspection Service, 191
Anorexia nervosa
  health risks of, 385
  signs and symptoms, 384
  treatment for, 390-391
antibiotic-resistant bacteria, 426
Antibiotics
  resistance to, 419-420
antibodies
  role of proteins in, 171
anticoagulant, 240, 280
antidiuretic hormone (ADH)
  blood volume, 214, 346
  thirst mechanism, 213-214
Antigen, 171-172
antioxidant function, nutrients involved in
  nutrients that function as antioxidants, 237
Antioxidants
  food preservatives, 414
  superoxide dismutase, 237
anus, 71-72
Appert, Nicolas-François, 413
appetite
  environmental cues, 66
  high-fructose corn syrup, 218
  triggering, 64
appetite suppressants, 26, 67
aquifers, 217
ariboflavinosis, 197, 300
aroma, 64
arsenic, 204, 259, 290, 319
asbestos, 236
ascending colon, 80-81
Aseptic packaging, 414-416
asparagine, 163
aspartic acid, 117, 162-163
Aspergillus flavus, 401
Aspiration, 73-74
Asthma
  GERD, 83-85
atherosclerosis
  coronary heart disease and, 378
Athletes